Fundamentals of US Regulatory Affairs

Seventh Edition

RAPS | REGULATORY AFFAIRS
PROFESSIONALS SOCIETY

*Making better healthcare products possible*sm

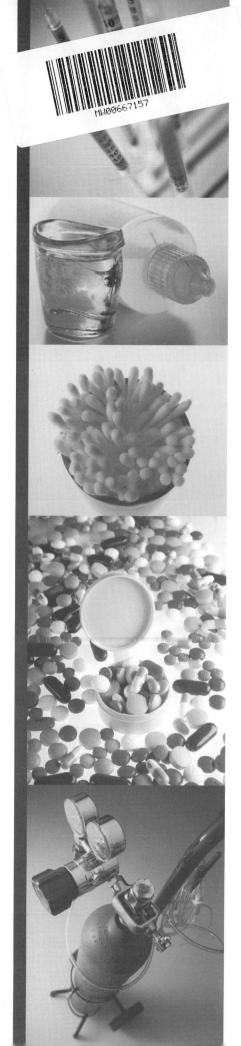

ISBN: 978-0-9829321-2-4
Every precaution is taken to ensure the accuracy of the content of this publication; however, the publisher cannot accept responsibility for the correctness of the information supplied. At the time of publication, all Internet references (URLs) in this book were valid. However, these references are subject to change without notice.

Book Design by Keane Design & Communications, Inc., keanedesign.com

Regulatory Affairs Professionals Society
5635 Fishers Lane
Suite 550
Rockville, MD 20852
USA

RAPS.org

Washington, DC ▪ Brussels ▪ Tokyo

Foreword

The Regulatory Affairs Professionals Society (RAPS) is pleased to bring you *Fundamentals of US Regulatory Affairs, Seventh Edition.*

As advances in science and technology are reflected in new regulations and guidances from the US Food and Drug Administration (FDA) and other state and federal agencies, regulatory professionals must keep pace with these requirements to ensure their knowledge is current and their employers remain in compliance, bringing safe and effective products to the marketplace. This new edition of *Fundamentals* can help.

Since its introduction in 1999, *Fundamentals of US Regulatory Affairs* has expanded to cover new product areas and new technologies. This seventh edition includes regulatory requirements in place through early 2011. For ease of use, the 33 chapters are categorized into topic-specific sections:

- **Section I:** General information—topics spanning product types, such as the history of US regulations, the role of FDA and other regulatory agencies, GxPs and quality
- **Section II:** Drug products
- **Section III:** Medical devices
- **Section IV:** Biologic products
- **Section V:** Other product classifications—chapters on combination products, orphan products, blood products, tissue products and more
- **Section VI:** FDA inspection and enforcement; healthcare fraud and abuse compliance
- **Section VII:** Regulatory intelligence sources

You will also find a comparative matrix of regulations across product lines, a glossary and an extensive index. *Fundamentals* is an excellent reference text for regulatory personnel at all levels. Experienced professionals can quickly check a fact or seek information on a subject outside their area of expertise; newcomers to the field can use it to build their knowledge and careers. It is also an essential preparatory tool for the US Regulatory Affairs Certification (RAC) exam.

Pamela A. Jones
Editor & Director of Publications

Acknowledgements

The Regulatory Affairs Professionals Society (RAPS) expresses its gratitude to the following individuals, who have shared their expertise to advance the regulatory profession by contributing to this invaluable reference tool for their colleagues.

Richard Angelo, PhD
Director, Executive Consultant
Scientific Consulting
Beckloff Associates, Inc.

Jennifer D. Burgar
Arnall Golden Gregory LLP

Chas Burr, SM, MBA, FRAPS
Graduate Program Director
Regulatory and Clinical Research Management (RCRM)
Assistant Professor
Regis College

Evelyn Cadman
Principal Consultant
Bioscience Translation & Application

Kell Cannon
Partner
3D Communications LLC

John DeLucia
VP, Regulatory Affairs, Quality Assurance, and Clinical Affairs
ICAD Inc.

Miguel de Soto-Perera, PhD
Director, Managing Consultant, Scientific Consulting
Beckloff Associates, Inc.

John DeLucia
VP, Regulatory Affairs, Quality Assurance, and Clinical Affairs
ICAD Inc.

Cindy DiBiasi
Founding Partner
3D Communications LLC

John Driscoll
Assistant Director, Regulatory Affairs Advertising and Promotion
Forest Research Institute

Dana Dunn
Vice President and COO
Aclairo Pharmaceutical Development Group Inc.

Christopher Ernst
Director, Quality Assurance
Medpace

Marcia Gaido, PhD, RAC
Associate Director, Regulatory Affairs Oncology
MedImmune

Grant S. Griffin, CCRC
Regulatory Affairs Associate
Abbott Laboratories

Susan K. Hamann, MS MT(ASCP) RAC
Regulatory Affairs Manager
Perkin Elmer

Naseem Kabir, MS, RAC
Senior Director, Regulatory Affairs International
Genzyme Corp.

Kurt R. Karst, JD
Director
Hyman, Phelps & McNamara PC

William H. Kitchens, JD
Partner
Arnall Golden Gregory LLP

Mark D. Kramer, MS, RAC
President
Regulatory Strategies Inc.

Alan Minsk
Partner & Leader, Food & Drug Practice Group
Arnall Golden Gregory LLP

Richard Morroney, CQA, RAC
Director of Quality and Regulatory Affairs
VuCOMP Inc.

Nandini Murthy, RAC
Regulatory Consultant
ENEM Consulting LLC

Hari Nagaradona, PhD
Director, Regulatory Affairs
Kendle International

Scott A. Oglesby, PhD
Director, Executive Consulting
Beckloff Associates

Maruthi Prasad Palthur
Senior Director, Technical Operations & Regulatory Affairs
Indigene Pharmaceuticals, Inc.

Linda Pollitz
Director Regulatory Affairs, Advertising & Promotion
Alkermes Inc

William C. Putnam, PhD, RAC
Director, Managing Consultant, Scientific Consulting
Beckloff Associates Inc.

Kelly Rowland
Regulatory Affairs Specialist
Elekta Inc.

Moulakshi Roychoudhary, PharmD, JD
Associate Director, Regulatory Affairs – Advertising,
Labeling, & Promotion
Biogen Idec

David J. Schifkovitz
Vice President – Regulatory Affairs, CHRD
GlaxoSmithKline Consumer Healthcare

Kurt Stahl
Consultant
Aclairo Pharmaceutical Development Group Inc.

Sue Sutton Jones
VP, RA/QA
ConMed Linvatec Corporation

Alice J. Welenc-Masters, MS
US Regulatory Affairs Associate
GlaxoSmithKline Consumer Healthcare

Martha A. Wells, MPH, RAC
VP Regulatory Affairs for Tissue and Biologics
Reglera LLC

Diane Whitworth, MLS
Principal Research Consultant
DRW Research & Information Services LLC

Michael Wienholt, RAC (US, EU)
Principal Consultant
d.b.a. Regulatory Consulting

Jeff Zinza, RAC
Regulatory Analyst
Life Technologies Corporation

Reviewers
Peggy J. Berry, MBA, RAC
Amarin Corporation

Meredith E, Brown-Tuttle, RAC
Regulatory Consultant

Chas Burr, SM, MBA, FRAPS
Regis College

Table of Contents

Appendices

Figures

Tables

History of FDA and Related Regulatory Agencies

By Richard Morroney, CQA, RAC and Nandini Murthy, RAC

Objectives

- Introduce the FDA and provide a history of the agency's evolution over more than a century and significant laws that guided FDA's growth
- Discuss the structure of FDA and its relationship with other US regulatory agencies

Laws, Regulations and Guidelines Covered in This Chapter

- *Food and Drug Act of 1906*
- *Federal Food, Drug and Cosmetic Act of 1938 (FD&C Act)*
- *Family Smoking Prevention and Tobacco Control Act of 2009*
- *Vaccine Act of 1813*
- *Federal Advisory Committee Act of 1972*
- *Federal Trade Commission Act of 1914*
- *Health Insurance Portability and Accountability Act of 1996*
- *Consumer Product Safety Act of 1972*
- *Occupational Safety and Health Act of 1970*
- *Food and Medical Administration Act of 1995*
- *Poultry Products Inspection Act of 1957*
- *Safe Drinking Water Act of 1974*

Introduction

Today, the US Food and Drug Administration (FDA) is part of the executive branch of government and falls under the jurisdiction of the US Department of Health and Human Services (DHHS). From its humble beginnings in 1862 as a laboratory that analyzed samples of food, fertilizers and agricultural substances, FDA has evolved over a century and a half, expanding its regulatory responsibility to include drugs, cosmetics and devices. Today, FDA regulates more than $1 trillion worth of consumer goods, about 25% of US consumer expenditures. This amount includes $466 billion in food sales, $275 billion in drugs, $60 billion in cosmetics and $18 billion in vitamin supplements.[1] Consistent with FDA's evolution, the agency's influence is likely to grow in the future.

FDA's Mission

FDA's current mission statement reads:
"FDA is responsible for protecting the public health by assuring the safety, efficacy, and security of human and veterinary drugs, biological products, medical devices, cosmetics, products that emit radiation and food supply. The FDA is also responsible for advancing the public health by helping to speed innovations that make medicines and foods more effective, safer, and more affordable. The FDA shares with the public accurate, science-based information they need to use medicines and foods to maintain and improve their health."

FDA's History

During the 19th century, states exercised principal control over domestically produced and distributed foods and drugs, while federal authority was restricted to imported foods and drugs. The *Vaccine Act* of 1813 was one of the first federal laws dealing with consumer protection and therapeutic substances. The Division of Chemistry, which became the Bureau of Chemistry in July 1901, began investigating the adulteration of agricultural commodities as early as 1867. Dr. Harvey W. Wiley, credited as the father of US food and drug law, and who eventually became chief chemist of the US Department of Agriculture, expanded the division's research in this area. He demonstrated his concern about chemical preservatives as adulterants in the highly publicized "poison squad" experiments, in which able-bodied volunteers consumed varying amounts of questionable food additives to determine their impact on health. Wiley also unified a variety of groups behind a federal law to prohibit the adulteration and misbranding of food and drugs, which was a rampant problem (e.g., arsenic in vinegar, sulfuric acid in pickles, woodchips in bread, alum and clay in wheat flour). Foods were also marketed with bold and unsubstantiated claims (e.g., as cures for cancer and the prevention of baldness). Upton Sinclair's description of the meatpacking industry in *The Jungle* was a precipitating force behind both a meat inspection law and a comprehensive food and drug law. On 30 June 1906, President Theodore Roosevelt signed the *Food and Drugs Act*, known simply as the *Wiley Act*.

Structure of FDA

FDA is an agency within the Department of Health and Human Services and consists of nine centers/offices:
- Office of the Commissioner (OC)
- Center for Biologics Evaluation and Research (CBER)
- Center for Devices and Radiological Health (CDRH)
- Center for Drug Evaluation and Research (CDER)
- Center for Food Safety and Applied Nutrition (CFSAN)
- Center for Tobacco Products (CTP)
- Center for Veterinary Medicine (CVM)
- National Center for Toxicological Research (NCTR)
- Office of Regulatory Affairs (ORA)

More information on FDA's organizational structure may be found at www.fda.gov/AboutFDA/CentersOffices/default.htm and www.fda.gov/AboutFDA/CentersOffices/OrganizationCharts/default.htm.

Office of the Commissioner (OC)

The Office of the Commissioner provides centralized agency-wide direction and management to support effective administration of all programs. It is responsible for the efficient and effective implementation of FDA's mission.

Among the offices reporting directly to OC are the Office of the Chief Counsel, the Office of the Chief Scientist, the Office of International Programs and the Office of Special Medical Programs.

For more information on the Office of the Commissioner, go to www.fda.gov/AboutFDA/CentersOffices/OC/default.htm.

Office of the Chief Counsel (OCC)

The Office of the Chief Counsel represents FDA in court proceedings, handling both civil and criminal enforcement cases and defending challenges to the *Food, Drug, and Cosmetic Act* (*FD&C Act*). It also provides legal advice and policy guidance for FDA programs. The office drafts or reviews all proposed and final FDA regulations, performs legal research and gives legal opinions on regulatory issues, actions and petitions. OCC also acts as a liaison to the Department of Justice (DOJ) and other federal agencies for programs administered by FDA. In addition, FDA attorneys are involved in explaining agency programs to Congress, regulated industry and the public. For more information about the Office of the Chief Counsel, visit www.fda.gov/AboutFDA/CentersOffices/OC/OfficeoftheChiefCounsel/default.htm.

Office of the Chief Scientist

The Office of the Chief Scientist provides strategic leadership, coordination and expertise to support scientific excellence, innovation and capacity. It fosters the development and use of innovative technologies and provides cross-agency scientific coordination and supports the professional development of FDA scientists in all areas through the Commissioner's Fellowship Program, continuing education and scientific interaction with academia. In today's environment, the office supports science and public health activities to effectively anticipate and respond to counter-terrorism and emerging deliberate and natural threats (e.g., chemical, biological, radiological and nuclear) to US and global health and security. Offices under the auspices of the Office of the Chief Scientist include:
- Office of Counterterrorism and Emerging Threats
- Office of Scientific Integrity
- Office of the Ombudsman
- Office of Science and Innovation
- Office of Critical Path Programs

More information about the Office of the Chief Scientist may be found at www.fda.gov/AboutFDA/CentersOffices/OC/OfficeofScientificandMedicalPrograms/default.htm

Office of International Programs

The Office of International Programs (OIP) is the focal point for all international FDA matters. It works in

Figure 1-1. Food and Drug Administration Organizational Chart

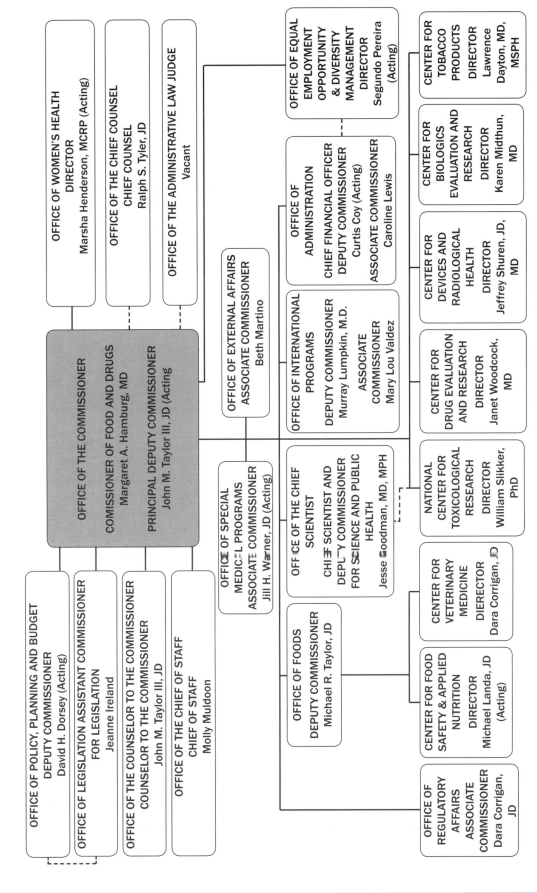

collaboration with international health and regulatory partners through ongoing communications, cooperation on health and regulatory issues, exchanges of information and documents, technical cooperation and training, personnel exchanges and certification of certain products exported to and from the US.

OIP activities include bilateral arrangements such as memoranda of understanding; formal arrangements with regulatory counterparts in other countries; participation in regional programs such as the Trilateral Cooperation (US/Canada/Mexico); multilateral organizations such as the World Health Organization and Pan American Health Organization; and taking part in harmonization and multilateral activities such as Codex Alimentarius and the International Conference on Harmonisation.

In addition, FDA has established a permanent presence in China, India, Europe and Latin America and there are ongoing efforts to establish a presence in the Middle East.

For more information about the Office of International Programs, see www.fda.gov/AboutFDA/CentersOffices/OC/OfficeofInternationalPrograms/ucm236581.htm.

Office of Special Medical Programs

The Office of Special Medical Programs serves as the agency focal point for special programs and initiatives that are cross-cutting and clinical, scientific and/or regulatory in nature.

According to the FDA website, The Office of Special Medical Programs provides for:

- coordinating internal and external review of pediatric science, safety, ethical and international issues as mandated by law and agency activities
- overseeing the implementation of the orphan products provisions of the *FD&C Act*
- executive leadership to the Office of Good Clinical Practice
- overseeing the functions of the Office of Combination Products as provided in the *FD&C Act*
- advisory committee oversight and management staff, working in close collaboration with all FDA centers to provide consistent operations and seek continuous improvements in the agency advisory committee program
- liaison with the Office of the Secretary, the DHHS Committee Management Office, all of FDA's center advisory committee support staff and other organizations/offices within FDA
- ensuring that all FDA committee management activities are consistent with the provisions of *Federal Advisory Committee Act*, departmental policies, and related regulations and statutes

The Office of Special Medical Programs includes the following offices:

- Office of Combination Products
- Office of Good Clinical Practice
- Office of Orphan Product Development
- Office of Pediatric Therapeutics

More information on the Office of Special Medical Programs can be found at www.fda.gov/AboutFDA/CentersOffices/OC/OfficeofScienceandHealthCoordination/default.htm.

Center for Drug Evaluation and Research (CDER)

CDER evaluates all new prescription and over-the-counter drugs before they are sold to ensure that they are safe and effective. The center routinely monitors television, radio and print drug ads to ensure they are truthful and balanced. CDER also plays a critical role in providing healthcare professionals and consumers with information on how to use drugs appropriately and safely. More information on CDER may be found at www.fda.gov/AboutFDA/CentersOffices/CDER/default.htm.

Center for Biologics Evaluation and Research (CBER)

CBER regulates biological products for disease prevention and treatment, including vaccines, protein-based products such as monoclonal antibodies and cytokines, and blood and blood products such as plasma, blood-derived proteins, tests used to screen blood donors and devices used to make blood products. More information on CBER, including the organizational structure, may be found at www.fda.gov/AboutFDA/CentersOffices/CBER/default.htm.

Center for Devices and Radiological Health (CDRH)

CDRH is tasked with ensuring that new medical devices are safe and effective before they are marketed. CDRH regulates medical devices and radiation-emitting products such as microwaves, TV sets, cell phones and lasers to ensure they meet radiation safety standards. Many of these devices are the first of a kind. The center also monitors devices throughout the product lifecycle, including a nationwide postmarket surveillance system. More information on CDRH, including the center's organizational structure, may be found at www.fda.gov/AboutFDA/CentersOffices/CDRH/default.htm.

Center for Veterinary Medicine (CVM)

CVM helps ensure that animal food products are safe. CVM regulates the manufacture and distribution of food additives and drugs that will be given to animals. CVM also evaluates the safety and effectiveness of drugs used

Table 1-1. CDER vs. CBER Product Oversight Responsibilities

CDER Oversight	CBER Oversight

• Small Molecule Drugs
• Therapeutic Biologics
    ○ Monoclonal antibodies
    ○ Cytokines
    ○ Growth factors
    ○ Enzymes and Interferons (including recombinant versions)
    ○ Proteins intended for therapeutic use derived from animals or microorganisms
    ○ Therapeutic immunotherapies
	• Vaccines
	• Blood products
	• Plasma expanders
	• Gene therapy
	• Products composed of human or animal cells or cell parts
	• Allergen patch tests and allergenic extracts
	• Antitoxins
	• Antivenins
	• Venoms
	• In vitro diagnostics
	• Toxoids/toxins intended for immunization

to treat companion (pet) animals. More information on CVM may be found at http://www.fda.gov/AboutFDA/CentersOffices/CVM/default.htm.

Center for Food Safety and Applied Nutrition (CFSAN)

CFSAN is responsible for the safety of almost all food consumed in the US, with the exception of meat, poultry and some egg products, which are regulated by the US Department of Agriculture (USDA). CFSAN pioneered widespread use of the Hazard Analysis and Critical Control Point (HACCP) system, which places preventive controls at the most contamination-prone points in the production process. More information on CFSAN may be found at www.fda.gov/AboutFDA/CentersOffices/CFSAN/default.htm.

National Center for Toxicological Research (NCTR)

In partnership with other FDA entities, government agencies, industry and academia, NCTR conducts research and provides advice and training necessary for science-based decision making and developing sound regulatory policy. For example, in the areas of counterterrorism and food defense, NCTR scientists collaborate with scientists from other FDA centers and several federal and state agencies to evaluate the disease-causing potential of food-borne pathogens and to develop methods for rapid detection of bacterial pathogens. NCTR researchers, in collaboration with the National Institute of Child Health and Human Development (NICHD), initiated an animal study of a drug used to treat attention deficit disorder in children to assess whether this drug causes genetic alterations in children. More information about NCTR may be found at www.fda.gov/AboutFDA/CentersOffices/NCTR/default.htm.

Center for Tobacco Products (CTP)

CTP is responsible for overseeing the implementa-

tion of the *Family Smoking Prevention and Tobacco Control Act,* which became law on 22 June 2009. FDA responsibilities under the law include establishing performance standards, performing premarket review for new and modified risk tobacco products, reviewing labeling, and establishing and enforcing advertising and promotion restrictions. More information about CTP may be found at www.fda.gov/AboutFDA/CentersOffices/AbouttheCenterforTobaccoProducts/default.htm.

Office of Regulatory Affairs (ORA)

ORA advises and assists the FDA commissioner and other key officials on regulations and compliance matters. ORA evaluates and coordinates all proposed FDA legal actions to ascertain compliance with regulatory policy and enforcement objectives. It is the lead office for all FDA field activities and executes direct line authority over all agency field operations. It provides direction and counsel to FDA field offices in implementing FDA policies and operational guidelines. The Quality System Inspection Technique (QSIT) guide, which provides guidance to agency field staff on the inspectional process used to assess a manufacturer's compliance with the Quality System Regulation, was developed by ORA and CDRH staff. ORA also directs and coordinates the agency's emergency preparedness and civil defense programs. More information may be obtained at http://www.fda.gov/AboutFDA/CentersOffices/ORA/default.htm.

Agencies With Related Responsibilities
Federal Trade Commission (FTC)

FTC enforces the *Federal Trade Commission Act,* which prohibits unfair or deceptive acts or practices in or affecting commerce. The act prohibits the dissemination of any false advertisement for the purpose of inducing the purchase of food, drugs, devices, services or cosmetics. FTC is also empowered to seek monetary redress and other relief for conduct injurious to customers.

Per a 1971 memorandum of understanding (MOU), FDA has primary jurisdiction over advertising of prescription drugs and restricted devices, and over labeling of all products it regulates. FTC has primary jurisdiction over advertising of products other than restricted devices and OTC drugs. The two agencies cooperate in law enforcement efforts. For example, FTC and FDA both sent Warning Letters to website operators who were marketing coral calcium products claiming that coral calcium was an effective treatment or cure for cancer and/or other diseases.[2] While the FTC letter stated that such unsupported claims were false and deceptive and were unlawful under the *FTC Act*, FDA warned website operators that their products were in violation of the *FD&C Act* because of disease claims and unsubstantiated structure/function claims. FDA compliance and law enforcement personnel have access to FTC's secure, online complaint database, Consumer Sentinel, which receives thousands of complaints each year. More information on FTC may be found at www.ftc.gov/.

Center for Medicare and Medicaid Services (CMS)

CMS is a federal agency within DHHS. Formerly the Health Care Financing Administration (HCFA), CMS is responsible for Medicare, Medicaid and other programs. While FDA's focus is on safety and effectiveness, CMS evaluates whether new technologies are necessary and reasonable. CMS is not bound by FDA decisions and expects the clinical utility of new technologies to be proven in order to assign coding and reimbursement. Currently the two agencies review products serially. Per a DHHS announcement on 14 January 2005, FDA and CMS have agreed to work together in specific areas. At the request of the applicant and with the concurrence of both agencies, parallel review may be conducted to minimize delays between marketing approval and reimbursement. With respect to postmarket surveillance, FDA may make greater use of existing CMS mechanisms for collection of new data through the Medicare drug benefit. More information on CMS may be found at www.cms.hhs.gov/.

CMS has jurisdiction over the *Health Insurance Portability and Accountability Act* (*HIPAA*), which was enacted by Congress in 1996 to create a national standard for protecting the privacy of patients' personal health information. The regulation requires safeguards to protect the security and confidentiality of an individual's protected health information (PHI). The general rule is that healthcare entities may not use or disclose PHI without an individual's written authorization, with some exceptions as permitted or required by law. *HIPAA* allows for civil and criminal penalties for privacy and security violations. *HIPAA* also standardized the electronic exchange of health-related administrative information, such as claims forms. Where a healthcare entity conducts clinical research

involving PHI, physician-investigators need to understand the Privacy Rule's restrictions on its use and disclosure for research purposes. More information on the impact of *HIPAA* as it relates to clinical research may be found at http://privacyruleandresearch.nih.gov/clin_research.asp.

Consumer Product Safety Commission (CPSC)

CPSC is responsible for ensuring the safety of consumer goods such as household appliances (excluding those that emit radiation), paint, child-resistant packages and baby toys. Tobacco, pesticides, motor vehicles and products subject to FDA jurisdiction are expressly exempt from regulation under the *Consumer Product Safety Act* (*CPSA*). FDA and CPSC work cooperatively for consumer protection. For example, articles employed in the preparation or holding of food that malfunction and cause contamination or spoilage (e.g., home canning equipment, pressure cookers, refrigerators, freezers and can openers) are subject to regulation as "consumer products" by CPSC under the *CPSA*. Under the *FD&C Act*, FDA may take action against manufacturers of food that has been contaminated or spoiled by such articles and shipped in interstate commerce.[3] More information on CPSC may be found at www.cpsc.gov/.

Securities and Exchange Commission (SEC)

SEC's primary mission is to protect the investing public and maintain the integrity of the securities market. FDA assists in SEC investigations of possible violations of federal securities laws. FDA also supports SEC staff in assessing the accuracy of statements by FDA-regulated firms in SEC filings, especially where such statements can have a powerful effect on stock prices. Under measures adopted in February 2004 to improve the sharing of information between the two agencies, a reporting process was established to allow any FDA employees who suspect erroneous or exaggerated public statements by a company to bring them to the attention of SEC staff as quickly and efficiently as possible. More information on SEC may be found at www.sec.gov/.

Occupational Safety and Health Administration (OSHA)

The *Occupational Safety and Health Act* (*OSH*) created OSHA at the federal level within the Department of Labor. OSHA's mission is to prevent work-related injuries, illnesses and deaths by issuing and enforcing rules (called standards) for workplace safety and health. FDA's statutory authority does not extend to the occupational safety and health responsibilities of OSHA. FDA has no workplace inspection program. However, the agencies coordinate their efforts in cases of overlapping regulatory responsibility (e.g., unshielded syringes and natural rubber latex). More information on OSHA may be found at www.osha.gov/.

Table 1-2. Selected Primary FDA Centers/Offices Involved in Sponsor Interface During the Development and Approval of Drugs and Devices

FDA Center/Office	Primary Responsibility
Office of the Commissioner • Office of Orphan Products Development (OOPD) • Office of Combination Products (OCP)	Review and adjudicate requests for orphan drug designation and review and award orphan drug grants
Center for Biologics Evaluation and Research (CBER) • Office of Biostatistics and Epidemiology • Office of Blood Research and Review • Office of Vaccines Research and Review • Office of Compliance and Biologics Quality • Office of Cellular, Tissue, and Gene Therapies	Evaluate and monitor the safety and effectiveness of biological products for disease prevention and treatment, including blood and blood products, vaccines, human gene therapy, xenotransplants, human tissues and cellular product and allergenics.

Center for Drug Evaluation and Research (CDER)
• Office of Compliance
  o Division of Compliance Risk Mgmt. and Surveillance (assigns NDC numbers)
• Office of Pharmacoepidemiology and Statistical Sciences
  o Office of Drug Safety
    ▪ Division of Drug Risk Evaluation (brand name review)
  o Office of Biostatistics (Biostats reviewers)
• Office of Clinical Pharmacology and Biopharmaceutics (Clin Pharm reviewers)
• Office of Medical Policy
  o Division of Drug Marketing, Advertising, and Communication (DDMAC)
• Office of New Drugs (includes OTC products)
• Office of Pharmaceutical Science
  o Office of Generic Drugs (OGD)
  o Office of New Drug Chemistry (CMC Reviewers and CMC Project Managers)
	Evaluate and monitor the safety and effectiveness of all prescription and over-the-counter drugs (including peptides and well-characterized proteins used for therapeutic purposes).

Center for Devices and Radiological Health (CDRH) • Office of Compliance • Office of Device Evaluation • Office of In Vitro Diagnostic Device Evaluation and Safety	Evaluate and monitor the safety and effectiveness of new medical devices for human use and assure that radiation-emitting products (e.g., microwave ovens, cell phones, x-ray machines) meet radiation safety standards.
Center for Veterinary Medicine (CVM) • Office of New Animal Drug Evaluation • Office of Surveillance and Compliance • Office of Minor Use and Minor Species	Evaluate and monitor the safety and effectiveness of new drugs for animals and the safety of animal food products.

Tax and Trade Bureau (TTB)

The *Federal Alcohol Administration Act* (*FAAA*) provides for federal regulation of beer, wine and distilled spirits. It establishes requirements for packaging used to hold alcohol over and above those imposed by FDA for foods under the *FD&C Act*. The *FAAA* is administered by the Treasury Department's Alcohol and Tobacco Tax and Trade Bureau (TTB). TTB consults with FDA regarding the approval of ingredients in alcoholic beverages and the requirements of label disclosure. Under a 1987 MOU, FDA is directed to contact TTB when it learns or is advised that an alcoholic beverage is or may be adulterated. More information on TTB may be found at www.ttb.gov.

United States Department of Agriculture (USDA)

USDA's Food Safety and Inspection Service (FSIS) has oversight over dairy, poultry, fruit and meat products, except for shell eggs, for which FDA and USDA share jurisdiction. Egg processing plants (egg washing, sorting, egg breaking and pasteurizing operations) are under USDA jurisdiction. However, FDA is responsible for egg-containing products and other egg processing not covered by USDA, e.g., restaurants, bakeries, cake mix plants, etc. The *Poultry Products Inspection Act* (*PPIA*) defines the term "poultry" as any domesticated bird. USDA has interpreted the term "poultry" to include domestic ducks, domestic geese, chickens and turkeys. FDA is responsible for all non-specified birds, including wild turkeys, wild ducks and wild geese. FDA also regulates game meats such as venison and ostrich. FDA and USDA together published guidance on quality and environmental concerns for companies producing human and animal drugs from genetically modified plants. FDA has jurisdiction over labeling of genetically modified foods and food from cloned animals. More information on USDA may be found at www.usda.gov/wps/portal/usdahome.

Department of Commerce (DOC)

FDA operates a mandatory safety program for all fish and fishery products under the provisions of the *FD&C Act*. Seafood is one of the few FDA-regulated food groups further regulated under a system of risk prevention controls known as Hazard Analysis and Critical Control Points (HACCP). Under HACCP, domestic and foreign processors are required to prepare site- and product-specific plans that analyze potential safety hazards, determine where they are likely to occur during processing, identify control points and how they will be monitored, and study how hazards are being controlled.

The National Oceanic and Atmospheric Administration (NOAA) within DOC oversees fisheries management in the US. It has its own authority for the promulgation of grade standards and for inspection and certification of fish and shellfish. NOAA Fisheries administers a voluntary, fee-for-service seafood inspection program that exceeds FDA HACCP-based requirements by providing grading, certification, label review, laboratory testing, training and consultative services. Participants may use official marks on compliant products, indicating that they are federally inspected. More information may be found at www.nmfs.noaa.gov/.

Environmental Protection Agency (EPA)

The mission of EPA is to protect human health and the environment, which includes jurisdiction over the public water supply. In the past, FDA considered drinking water to be a food. However, both agencies have determined that the passage of the *Safe Drinking Water Act* (*SDWA*) in 1974 implicitly repealed FDA's authority under the *FD&C Act* over drinking water. EPA and FDA have a 1979 Memorandum of Agreement specifying that EPA regulates and develops national standards for the safety of drinking water from municipal water supplies while FDA regulates the labeling and safety of bottled water as a consumer beverage.

Antimicrobial surface solutions applied to counter tops, table tops, food processing equipment, cutlery, dishware or cookware, to sanitize such objects after they have been washed, meet the definition of "pesticide chemical" and therefore, are subject to regulation by EPA. However, any antimicrobial surface solutions used to sanitize food packaging materials are excluded from "pesticide chemical" classification and are considered food additives subject to regulation by FDA. Materials preservatives are sometimes incorporated into food-contact articles to protect the finished product from discoloration, degradation or decomposition due to microbiological activity, rather than to prevent microbial activity. These materials are regulated as food additives by FDA. Antimicrobials impregnated into food packaging to protect either the package, or to extend the shelf life of the food are also regulated as food additives by FDA. More information on EPA may be found at www.epa.gov/.

FDA, USDA and EPA share responsibility for regulating pesticides. EPA determines the safety and effectiveness of the chemicals and establishes tolerance levels for residues on feed crops, as well as on raw and processed foods. FDA and USDA are responsible for monitoring the food supply to ensure that pesticide residues do not exceed the allowable levels in the products under their jurisdictions.

Drug Enforcement Administration (DEA)

Illegal drugs with no approved medical use, such as heroin and cocaine, are under the jurisdiction of DEA. FDA assists DEA in deciding how stringent DEA controls should be on drugs that are medically accepted but that have a strong potential for abuse. DEA establishes limits on the amount of these prescription drugs that is permitted to be manufactured each year. More information on DEA may be found at www.usdoj.gov/dea/index.htm.

Tips for Obtaining Information

Information for consumers and industry can be obtained directly from FDA. Each agency division has its own website, containing a wide variety of information including laws and regulations, administrative information regarding FDA's organizational structure and staff contact information, news and events, problem reporting, guidance documents, forms and links to other national and international regulatory agencies. There also are databases of products cleared or approved for marketing, adverse event reporting and recalls. The websites and databases are fully searchable.

A network of FDA offices exists to help small businesses. The Commissioner's Office of the Ombudsman liaises with the Small Business National Ombudsman to resolve complaints and answer questions. Product-specific centers each have their own ombudsmen. Also, each of the five regional offices has a small business representative available to answer questions and provide training. The Division of Small Manufacturers, International, and Consumer Assistance (DSMICA) provides assistance to medical device manufacturers and consumers. A detailed directory identifies staff by area of expertise, and a toll-free number will connect you directly to staff members during normal business hours. Similarly, CDER and the other product-specific centers have staff members available to answer inquiries from small business owners and help explain the agency's structure and rules.

Information pertaining to the rulemaking process can be found at www.regulations.gov. This website facilitates public participation in the federal rulemaking process by enabling the public to view and comment on federal regulatory actions. Information may also be obtained through the Regulatory Affairs Professional Society (RAPS), which provides numerous resources to industry professionals. In addition to RAPS workshops and conferences, local RAPS chapters provide educational events for industry professionals.

Summary

FDA's regulatory responsibility has evolved over 150 years from being tasked with regulating foods to include drug, cosmetics, devices, biologics and tobacco products.

FDA is responsible for protecting the public health by assuring the safety, efficacy and security of human and veterinary drugs, biological products, medical devices, cosmetics, products that emit radiation and the food supply.

During the 19th century, states exercised principal control over domestically produced and distributed foods and drugs, while federal authority was restricted to imported foods and drugs. Dr. Harvey Wiley, the father of the food and drug laws, was concerned about the use of preservative chemicals "adulterants" in food production. He organized various groups to support a federal law to prohibit the adulteration and misbranding of foods and drugs.

FDA is an agency within DHHS and consists of nine main centers/offices.

The Office of the Commissioner is responsible for the efficient and effective implementation of FDA's mission.

CDER evaluates all new prescription and over-the-counter drugs before they are sold to ensure that they are safe and effective.

CBER regulates biological products for disease prevention and treatment, including vaccines, protein-based products such as monoclonal antibodies and cytokines, and blood and blood products such as plasma, blood-derived proteins, tests used to screen blood donors and devices used to make blood products.

CDRH is tasked with ensuring that new medical devices are safe and effective before they are marketed.

CVM helps ensure that animal food additives and drug products are safe.

CFSAN is responsible for the safety of most food consumed in the US, with the exception of meat, poultry and some egg products, which are regulated by the USDA.

NCTR conducts research and provides advice and training necessary for science-based decision making and developing sound regulatory policy.

CTP is responsible for overseeing the implementation of the *Family Smoking Prevention and Tobacco Control Act*, which became law on 22 June 2009.

ORA advises and assists the FDA commissioner and other key officials on regulations and compliance matters and oversees all agency field operations.

Other agencies play a role or work with FDA in the regulation of food, drugs, cosmetics and devices. These agencies include: FTC, CMS, CPSC, SEC, OSHA, TTB, USDA, DOC, EPA and DEA.

References

1. www.nytimes.com/2008/11/02/magazine/02fda-t.html. Accessed 11 May 2011.
2. www.ftc.gov/opa/2003/06/trudeau.shtm. Accessed 11 May 2011.
3. www.fda.gov.

Recommended Reading

Grossman LA. "Food, Drugs and Droods: A Historical Consideration of Definitions and Categories in American Food and Drug Law." *Cornell Law Review*. Volume 93, pp. 1091–1148 (2008).

Burditt GM. "The History of Food Law." *Food and Drug Law Journal*, 50th Anniversary Special Edition, pp 197–201 (2009).

Chapter 1

History of Food, Drug and Cosmetic Laws

By Nandini Murthy, RAC and Richard Morroney, CQA, RAC

Objectives

- Provide an overview of the laws, regulations and regulatory agencies governing foods, drugs and medical products marketed in the US
- Discuss the historical context in which those laws were enacted
- Review the differences between laws, regulations and guidance documents
- Provide an overview of the rulemaking process

Laws, Regulations and Guidelines Covered in this Chapter

- *Pure Food and Drugs Act* of 1906
- *Federal Food, Drug, and Cosmetic Act* of 1938
- *Nutrition Labeling and Education Act* of 1990
- *Bioterrorism Act* of 2002
- *Food Allergen Labeling and Consumer Protection Act* of 2004
- *Color Additive Amendment* of 1960
- *Kefauver-Harris Amendments* of 1962
- *Controlled Substances Act of 1970*
- *Drug Price Competition and Patent Term Restoration Act* of 1984 *(Hatch-Waxman Act)*
- *Prescription Drug User Fee Act* of 1992
- *Food and Drug Administration Modernization Act* of 1997
- *Food and Drug Administration Amendments Act* of 2007
- *Medical Device Amendments* of 1976
- *Safe Medical Devices Act* of 1990
- *Medical Device User Fee and Modernization Act* of 2002
- *Durham-Humphrey Amendment* of 1951
- *Orphan Drug Act* of 1983
- *Prescription Drug Amendments* of 1992
- *FDA Export Reform and Enhancement Act* of 1996
- *Pediatric Research Equity Act* of 2003

Introduction

The history of modern food and drug law begins in the 20th century. During the 1800s, commerce in food and drugs was largely unregulated due to concerns about government interference with free trade and the inability of the individual states to control sales of products that were manufactured in other states.

This led to conditions such as those described in *The Jungle* by Upton Sinclair, published in 1906. Although it was presented as a work of fiction, the book's description of the unsanitary conditions in Chicago's meatpacking plants led to widespread public outrage and a demand for legislation.

In response, Congress passed the *Pure Food and Drugs Act* in 1906. This act prohibited interstate commerce of mislabeled and adulterated drugs and food.

Pure Food and Drugs Act of 1906

The 1906 *Pure Food and Drugs Act*, which the Bureau of Chemistry was charged to enforce, prohibited the interstate transport of unlawful food and drugs under penalty of seizure of questionable products and/or prosecution of responsible parties. The statute provided: "The term 'food,' as used herein, shall include all articles used for food, drink, confectionary, or condiment by man or other animals, whether simple, mixed or compound." The 1906 act defined "drug" as including "all medicines and preparations recognized in the United States Pharmacopoeia (USP) or National Formulary (NF) for internal or external use, and any substance or mixture of substances intended to be used for the cure, mitigation, or prevention of disease of either man or other animals." This "intended use" language, which was later also incorporated into the definition of "device," survives largely intact in the *Food, Drug, and Cosmetics Act (FD&C Act)* today.

The basis of the law rested on the regulation of product labeling rather than premarket approval. The food or drug label could not be false or misleading in any particular, and the presence and amount of 11 dangerous ingredients—including alcohol, heroin and cocaine—had to be listed. Specific variations from the applicable USP and NF standards for drugs were to be plainly stated on the label. Labels were not even required to state the weight or measure; only that any contents statement, if used, be truthful. If the manufacturer opted to list a food's weight or measure, the information had to be accurate. The law prohibited the addition of any ingredients that would substitute for the food, conceal damage, pose a health hazard or constitute a filthy or decomposed substance.

The law assumed that average consumers could avoid risks if they were made aware of same via product labeling; therefore, it relied upon consumer vigilance to assess labeling for deception or harm. Food manufacturers were not required to submit labeling for regulatory review. The Bureau of Chemistry was tasked with actively identifying violations and bringing legal action. The law enabled the government to prosecute manufacturers of illegal products but lacked affirmative requirements to guide compliance.

The Federal Food, Drug, and Cosmetic Act (FD&C Act) of 1938

The 1938 *FD&C Act* replaced the 1906 act and revised the misbranding standard for therapeutic claims in a way that helped further differentiate food labeling from drug labeling. The *Pure Food and Drugs Act*, as revised in 1912, stated that a drug was misbranded if its label contained a "false and fraudulent" statement regarding "curative or therapeutic effect." The requirement of demonstrating fraud made this a difficult standard for the US Food and Drug Administration (FDA) to satisfy. The 1938 act relaxed the standard from "false and fraudulent" to "false or misleading in any particular," a change that greatly eased FDA's burden in proving misbranding. The 1938 act also introduced premarket drug review, requiring the manufacturer of a "new drug" (defined as a drug not generally recognized as safe) to submit a New Drug Application (NDA) to FDA, setting forth the company's evidence of the drug's safety. It prohibited false therapeutic claims for drugs, while a separate law granted the Federal Trade Commission (FTC) jurisdiction over drug advertising. This act also brought cosmetics and medical devices under FDA's control and mandated legally enforceable food standards. In addition, tolerances for certain poisonous substances were addressed. The law formally authorized factory inspections and added injunctions to the enforcement tools at the agency's disposal.

The *FD&C Act* and its subsequent amendments remain the statutory framework under which FDA operates today. The *Durham-Humphrey Amendments* of 1951 clarified what constituted a prescription versus an over-the-counter drug. The *Kefauver-Harris Amendments* of 1962 mandated the establishment of efficacy as well as safety before a drug could be marketed, required FDA to assess the efficacy of all drugs introduced since 1938, instituted stricter agency control over drug trials (including a requirement that patients involved must give their informed consent), transferred regulation of prescription drug advertising from FTC to FDA, established Good Manufacturing Practice (GMP) requirements for the drug industry and granted FDA greater powers to access company production and control records to verify those practices.

Regulating Devices After the 1938 Act

While premarket approval in the 1938 *FD&C Act* did not apply to devices, for regulatory purposes, the new law equated them to drugs in every other sense. Issues facing FDA included increasing medical device quackery and a proliferation of medical technology in the post-World War II years. On the heels of a therapeutic disaster in which thousands of women were injured by the Dalkon Shield intrauterine device, Congress passed the 1976 *Medical Device Amendments*. This legislation established three classes of medical devices, each requiring a different level of regulatory scrutiny, up to premarket approval.

Regulating Foods After the 1938 Act

Significant amendments to the *FD&C Act* regarding the regulation of food include the *Nutrition Labeling and Education Act* of 1990, which requires manufacturers to provide standardized food labels and consistency in health claims and serving sizes. The *Dietary Supplement Health and*

Education Act of 1994 was another significant amendment, classifying dietary supplements as foods and establishing a framework and requirements for labeling and GMPs, among other regulatory provisions.

The events of 11 September 2001 prompted a closer look at the food industry, leading to the *Bioterrorism Act* of 2002. This law and its implementing regulations were designed to improve the ability to trace the movement of foods through international and interstate commerce, to restrict the availability of certain biological agents and toxins and to improve the security of the drinking water supply.

In 2004, concerns regarding food allergies led to the passage of the *Food Allergen Labeling and Consumer Protection Act*, which requires food labels to include specific statements regarding the presence of eight major allergens.

Regulating Cosmetics After the 1938 Act

The *Color Additive Amendment* of 1960 requires manufacturers to establish the safety of color additives in foods, drugs and cosmetics, and was the source of the designation of colors as FD&C (safe for foods, drugs and cosmetics), D&C (safe for drugs and cosmetics) or Ext. D&C (for externally applied products only).

An important point worth noting is that some cosmetics are regulated as drugs based upon their labeling. For instance, cosmetics containing sunscreens are considered drugs because they are intended to affect the body's physiological response to solar radiation.

Current Trends in Drugs and Devices—Amending the FD&C Act
The Orphan Drug Act of 1983

The 1983 *Orphan Drug Act* originally defined the term "orphan drug" as "a drug for a disease or condition which is rare." In October 1984, the term "rare" was defined in an amendment as "any rare disease or condition which (a) affects less than 200,000 persons in the U.S. or (b) affects more than 200,000 persons in the U.S. but for which there is no reasonable expectation that the cost of developing and making available in the U.S. a drug for such disease or condition will be recovered from sales in the U.S. of such drug." The act guarantees the developer of an orphan product seven years of market exclusivity following FDA's approval of the product. Incentives also include tax credits for clinical research undertaken by a sponsor to generate data required for marketing approval.

The Drug Price Competition and Patent Term Restoration Act of 1984

Because the approval process for each new product required the submission of full safety and efficacy data,

the economic pressures resulting from the lengthy review process led to the *Drug Price Competition and Patent Restoration Act* of 1984, also known as the *Hatch-Waxman Act*. This law established a process for the approval of drugs based upon comparison to an already approved product, and provided for exclusive marketing status for a period of time based upon the length of the approval process for new drugs or upon the patent status of the branded drug for generics.

This act included provisions for patent term extension, which gave certain patent holders the opportunity to extend patent terms by five years for human drug products, including antibiotics and biologics, medical devices, food additives and color additives. By giving inventors a portion of the patent term lost during federal regulatory review, Congress sought to restore some of the incentive for innovation to US domestic drug companies that was weakened as federal premarket approval requirements became more expensive and time-consuming. The *Hatch Waxman Act* authorized Abbreviated New Drug Applications (ANDAs) for generic drugs and specifically provided that FDA could require only bioavailability studies for ANDAs.

The Safe Medical Devices Act (SMDA) of 1990

The *SMDA* defined a "medical device" as "any instrument, apparatus, or other article that is used to prevent, diagnose, mitigate, or treat a disease or to affect the structure or function of the body, with the exception of drugs." It required user facilities and manufacturers to report certain adverse events to FDA, where a legally marketed medical device either had the potential to cause or contributed to a death, illness or injury. It instituted device tracking and postmarket surveillance requirements. It allowed FDA to temporarily suspend as well as withdraw approval of an application for premarket approval. The rule provided for civil penalties for violation of a requirement of the *FD&C Act* relating to devices. The act amended the *FD&C Act* to create an incentive for the development of orphan or humanitarian use devices (HUDs), defined as devices for use in the treatment or diagnosis of diseases or conditions affecting fewer than 4,000 patients in the US each year.

The Prescription Drug User Fee Act (PDUFA) of 1992

PDUFA authorized FDA to collect fees from companies that produce certain human drug and biological products and submit applications for FDA review. In addition, companies are required to pay annual fees for each manufacturing establishment and for each prescription drug product marketed. Previously, taxpayers paid for product reviews through budgets provided by Congress. In the new program, industry provides the funding in exchange for

FDA's agreement to meet drug review performance goals, which emphasize timeliness.

The Food and Drug Administration Modernization Act (FDAMA) of 1997

FDAMA provided additional authority for monitoring the progress of drug and biologic postmarketing studies. The provisions in this act required FDA to issue regulations that allowed clinical study sponsors to modify any investigational device or study protocol by submitting to FDA a "Notice of Change" five days after instituting such a change, where such changes did not significantly affect the study design or patient safety. The law codified the expedited review policy for certain medical devices, amended and clarified the humanitarian device provisions of *SMDA* and allowed FDA to recognize international or other national standards. *FDAMA* also directed FDA to consider least-burdensome means of establishing substantial equivalence for certain device marketing applications. The act repealed the mandatory tracking requirements for some high-risk devices imposed by *SMDA*, and instead established requirements and a process under which FDA may order device tracking.

The Medical Device User Fee and Modernization Act *of 2002* (MDUFMA)

MDUFMA established fees for premarket approval applications, supplements and 510(k) submissions. In return, FDA committed to strict performance goals for medical technology reviews.

The Pediatric Research Equity Act (PREA) *of 2003*

PREA gave FDA clear authority to require pediatric studies of drugs when other approaches are not sufficient to ensure that drugs are safe and effective for children. If the course of a disease and the effects of the drug treatment for that disease are "sufficiently similar in adults and pediatric patients," FDA may waive the requirement if it can be concluded that "pediatric effectiveness can be extrapolated from adequate and well-controlled studies in adults."

The *Food and Drug Administration Amendments Act (FDAAA) of 2007*

FDAAA reauthorized a number of key programs, including *PDUFA, MDUFMA* and *PREA. FDAAA* requires all clinical trials of drugs, biologics and devices—except Phase 1 clinical trials—to be registered in a clinical trial registry databank. ClinicalTrials.gov, established by the National Institutes of Health (NIH)/National Library of Medicine (NLM) in collaboration with FDA, meets *FDAAA* mandates. The results of clinical trials that serve as the basis for an efficacy claim or postmarketing studies are also required to be posted. *FDAAA* provides civil monetary penalties of as much as $10,000 for failure to comply with the registration requirements. If violations are not corrected within 30 days, additional penalties of up to $10,000 per day of violation may accrue. *FDAAA* permits FDA to require sponsors to submit direct-to-consumer (DTC) television advertisements for agency review no later than 45 days before dissemination of the advertisement, and permits FDA to impose penalties of as much as $500,000 for false and misleading DTC advertisements. In addition, civil penalties of as much as $10 million may be imposed for violations of postmarket studies, clinical trials or labeling changes required under *FDAAA*.

More information about the laws enforced by FDA can be obtained at www.fda.gov/RegulatoryInformation/Legislation/default.htm.

Other Food- and Drug-Related Laws

While the discussion above covers many of the laws that form the basis of current regulations, there are many others that affect foods, drugs and medical devices. **Table 2-1** lists some of these other laws.

Laws, Regulations and Guidance

Laws begin as legislation enacted by the US Congress. A bill is introduced by one house of Congress and is considered in committee where public hearings may be held. The bill is then amended as necessary and reintroduced into committee for debate and vote. Once approved, it becomes an act and goes through a similar process in the other house of Congress. The act is then submitted to the president. If the president signs the bill, it becomes a law. Laws establish general principles and clarify congressional intent. They can only be changed by Congress. Laws are enforced by regulations through an agency of the executive branch.

Regulations establish standards or requirements of conduct and provide details of how the law is to be followed. Regulations are both interpretive (they explain the meaning of the language of a section of the act) and substantive (they provide a specific scientific or technical basis). They are promulgated through the "rulemaking process" and have the force of law. Guidance documents and guidelines establish principles or practices that represent an agency's thinking. However, they do not go through the formal rulemaking process, and therefore do not have the force of law.

Rulemaking Process

Government agencies create regulations that are derived from statutes created through the legislative branch. Regulations define how FDA regulates products. Regulations are developed through the rulemaking process. Rulemaking is a transparent process that involves the public. By law, anyone can participate in this process.

Table 2-1 Other Laws, Regulations and Guidelines

• Federal Meat Inspection Act of 1906
• Poultry Products Inspection Act of 1957
• Egg Products Inspection Act of 1970
• Dietary Supplement Health and Education Act of 1994
• Public Health Service Act of 1944
• GMPs for the 21st Century (2004)
• Wheeler-Lea Act of 1938
• Food Additives Amendment of 1958
• Fair Packaging and Labeling Act of 1967
• Animal Drug Amendments of 1968
• Poison Prevention Packaging Act of 1970
• Infant Formula Act of 1980
• Generic Animal Drug and Patent Term Restoration Act of 1988
• Animal Medicinal Drug Use Clarification Act of 1994
• Food Quality Protection Act of 1996
• Animal Drug Availability Act of 1996
• Best Pharmaceuticals for Children Act of 2002
• Animal Drug User Fee Act of 2003
• Minor Use and Minor Species Animal Health Act of 2001
• Dietary Supplement and Nonprescription Drug Consumer Protection Act of 2006

Public comments are gathered through proposed rules or petitions. FDA carefully considers the public's comments when drafting final rules. Final rules become federal regulations upon codification in the Code of Federal Regulations. The *Administrative Procedure Act* of 1946 gave the public the right to participate in the rulemaking process by commenting on proposed rules. The public's rights were further extended through procedural rules that established a 60-day minimum public comment period for significant regulations. The enactment of the Government in the Sunshine Act of 1976 required advanced notice of rulemaking meetings, and required them to be open to the public. A regulatory agenda known as the Unified Agenda is published semi-annually and summarizes each agency's planned rulemaking activities for the following six months.

Proposed Rules

New regulations or revisions to existing regulations are announced in the *Federal Register*. A Notice of Proposed Rulemaking describes the rule and provides background information. A comment period is established that defines how long the agency will accept comments. The *Federal Register* announcement marks the beginning of the comment period.

Comment Period/FDA Action

Public comments may be submitted electronically through the regulations.gov website. Comments are logged, numbered and placed in a file upon receipt by FDA. The comments become part of the public record and are available for anyone to read on the regulations.gov website or in the FDA Dockets Management Reading Room (Room 1061, 5630 Fishers Lane, Rockville, MD). Comment periods are generally at least 60 days including weekends and holidays, and can be as long as one year. Some comment periods may be shorter than 60 days. During the comment period, FDA carefully analyzes the public's comments. Upon the expiration of the comment period, FDA may perform one of these actions:

- promulgate interim or final rules
- extend the comment period
- abandon its intention to promulgate a rule

Rule Publication and Codification

Final rules are published in the *Federal Register*. Rules in the *Federal Register* are cited by volume and page number and are codified annually in the Code of Federal Regulations. Title 21 consists of nine volumes divided into two chapters. FDA regulations are provided in Chapter 1, which are contained in the first eight volumes. DEA regulations are provided in Chapter 2 in the ninth volume.

Petitions

Agency processes may be influenced through the petition process. Requests can be made to FDA to issue, change or cancel a regulation. Petitions must contain specific information:

- action requested

- statement of grounds
- environmental impact
- official certification statement
- petitioner identifying information

FDA may request economic impact information after reviewing the petition. FDA management will decide whether to grant or deny the petition after a review period.

Summary

Food and drug law, which provides the framework for regulatory practices, is closely linked to the larger historical context of the times in which the laws were enacted. Many laws, such as the *FD&C Act*, the *Kefauver-Harris Amendments* and the *Bioterrorism Act*, were enacted in response to specific events that called attention to the need for additional authorities or controls. Based on this history, it is likely that future such events will continue to shape food and drug law and regulation.

References

1. FDA websites:
   www.fda.gov. Accessed 11 May 2011.
   www.fda.gov/AboutFDA/Transparency/Basics/default.htm. Accessed 11 May 2011.
   www.fda.gov/RegulatoryInformation/Legislation/default.htm. Accessed 11 May 2011.
2. *Fundamentals of Law and Regulation,* Food and Drug Law Institute, Washington, DC, 1997.

Overview of Drug, Biologic and Device Regulatory Pathways

By Scott A. Oglesby, PhD

Objectives

- To provide an overview of US federal regulations and processes related to the development of drugs, biologics, devices and combination products and filing of a marketing application
- To provide an overview of the scientific questions and approaches that underpin the development process
- To provide a roadmap of the facts and related decisions that define how a drug, biologic, device or combination product needs to be developed to meet US federal regulations

Laws, Regulations and Guidelines Covered in This Chapter

Regulations

- 21 CFR 511 New Animal Drugs for Investigational Use
- 21 CFR 514 New Animal Drug Applications
- 21 CFR 314.92 Drug products for which abbreviated applications may be submitted
- 21 CFR 314.93 Petition to request a change from a listed drug
- 21 CFR 314.54 Procedure for submission of an application requiring investigations for approval of a new indication for, or other change from, a listed drug
- 21 CFR 310.3 Definitions and interpretations (new drugs)
- 21 CFR 316 Orphan Drugs
- 21 CFR 312 Subpart E Drugs intended to treat life-threatening and severely debilitating illnesses
- 21 CFR 314 Subpart H Accelerated approval of new drugs for serious or life-threatening illnesses
- 21 CFR 312 Investigational New Drug Application
- 21 CFR 312.50 General responsibilities of sponsors
- 21 CFR 312.60 General responsibilities of investigators
- 21 CFR 312.33 Annual reports (IND)
- 21 CFR 312.32 IND safety reports
- 21 CFR 312.23 IND content and format
- 21 CFR 312.38 Withdrawal of an IND
- 21 CFR 312.45 Inactive status (IND)
- 21 CFR 314 Applications for FDA Approval to Market a New Drug
- 21 CFR 207 Registration of Producers of Drugs and Listing of Drugs in Commercial Distribution
- 21 CFR 190.6 Requirement for premarket notification (dietary supplements)
- 21 CFR 3.2(e) Assignment of agency component for review of premarket applications—Definitions
- 21 CFR 328–358 OTC Monographs
- 21 CFR 330.11 NDA deviations from applicable monograph (OTC drugs)
- 21 CFR 10.30 Citizen petition
- 21 CFR 862–892 Device Classifications

- 21 CFR 807 Subpart E; Premarket notification procedures
- 21 CFR 812 Investigational Device Exemptions
- 21 CFR 814 Subpart H Humanitarian use devices
- 21 CFR 56 Institutional Review Boards
- 21 CFR 50 Protection of Human Subjects
- 21 CFR 54 Financial Disclosure by Clinical Investigators
- 21 CFR 814 Premarket Approval of Medical Devices
- 21 CFR 807 Establishment Registration and Device Listing for Manufacturers and Initial Importers of Devices

Guidance Documents

- *Guidance for Industry No. 185: Target Animal Safety for Veterinary Pharmaceutical Products VICH GL43* (April 2009)
- *Guidance for Industry No. 104: Content and Format of Effectiveness and Target Animal Safety Technical Sections and Final Study Reports for Submission to the Division of Therapeutic Drugs for Non-Food Animals* (July 2001)
- *Guidance for Industry No. 3: General Principles for Evaluating the Safety of Compounds Used in Food-Producing Animals* (July 2006)
- *Guidance for Industry No. 149: Studies to Evaluate the Safety of Residues of Veterinary Drugs in Human Food: General Approach to Testing* (March 2009)
- *Guideline No. 24: Guidelines for Drug Combinations in Animals* (October 1983)
- *Guidance for Industry: Bioavailability and Bioequivalence Studies for Orally Administered Drug Products—General Considerations* (March 2003)
- *Guidance for Industry: Food-Effect Bioavailability and Fed Bioequivalence Studies* (December 2002)
- *Guidance for Industry: Bioanalytical Method Development* (May 2001)
- *Guidance for Industry: Statistical Approaches to Establishing Bioequivalence* (January 2001)
- *Guidance for Industry: 180-Day Exclusivity When Multiple ANDAs are Submitted on the Same Day* (July 2003)
- *Draft Guidance for Industry: Bioequivalence Recommendations for Specific Products* (May 2007)
- *Draft Guidance for Industry: Contents of a Complete Submission for the Evaluation of Proprietary Names* (November 2008)
- *Guidance for Industry: Formal Meetings Between the FDA and Sponsors or Applicants* (May 2009)
- *Draft Guidance for Industry: End-of Phase 2A Meetings* (September 2008)
- *Guidance for Industry: Special Protocol Assessment* (May 2002)
- *Guidance for Industry: Fast Track Drug Development Programs—Designation, Development, and Application Review* (July 2004)
- *Guidance for Industry M4: Organization of the CTD* (August 2001)
- *Guidance for Industry M4Q: The CTD—Quality* (August 2001)
- *Guidance for Industry M4S: The CTD—Safety* (August 2001)
- *Guidance for Industry M4S: The CTD—Safety Appendices* (August 2001)
- *Guidance for Industry M4E: The CTD—Efficacy* (August 2001)
- *Guidance for Industry M2 eCTD: Electronic Common Technical Document Specification* (April 2003)
- *Draft Guidance for Industry: Animal Models—Essential Elements to Address Efficacy Under the Animal Rule* (January 2009)
- *Guidance for Industry: Estimating the Maximum Safe Starting Dose in Initial Clinical Trials for Therapeutics in Adult Healthy Volunteers* (July 2005)
- *Draft Guidance: M3(R2) Nonclinical Safety Studies for the Conduct of Human Clinical Trials and Marketing Authorization for Pharmaceuticals* (July 2008)
- *Guidance for Industry: Immunotoxicology Evaluation of Investigational New Drugs* (October 2002)
- *Guidance for Industry: Nonclinical Evaluation of Pediatric Drug Products* (February 2006)
- *Guidance for Industry: Single Dose Acute Toxicity Testing for Pharmaceuticals* (August 1996)
- *Guidance for Industry: Dissolution Testing of Immediate Release Solid Oral Dosage Forms* (August 1997)
- *Guidance for Industry: CGMP for Phase 1 Investigational Drugs* (July 2008)
- *Draft Guidance for Industry: Analytical Procedures and Methods Validation Chemistry, Manufacturing, and Controls Documentation* (August 2000)
- *Guidance for Industry: Collection of Race and Ethnicity Data in Clinical Trials* (September 2005)
- *Guidance for Industry: Exposure-Response Relationships—Study Design, Data Analysis, and Regulatory Applications* (April 2003)

- *Draft Guidance for Industry: Drug-Induced Liver Injury: Premarketing Clinical Evaluation* (October 2007)
- *Guidance for Industry: S1C(R2) Dose Selection for Carcinogenicity Studies* (September 2008)
- *Draft Guidance for Industry: Drug Interaction Studies—Study Design, Data Analysis, Implications for Dosing and Labeling* (September 2006)
- *Guidance for Industry: Pharmacokinetics in Patients with Impaired Hepatic Function: Study Design, Data Analysis, and Impact on Dosing and Labeling* (May 2003)
- *Guidance for Industry: Pharmacokinetics in Patients with Impaired Renal Function: Study Design, Data Analysis, and Impact on Dosing and Labeling* (May 1998)
- *Guideline for Industry: Studies in Support of Special Populations: Geriatrics* (August 1994)
- *Draft Guidance for Industry: How to Comply with the Pediatric Research Equity Act* (September 2005)
- *Draft Guidance for Industry and Investigators – Safety Reporting Requirements for INDs and BA/BE Studies (September 2010)*
- *Draft Guidance for Industry: E2F Development Safety Update Report* (June 2008)
- *Draft Guidance for Industry and Review Staff: Target Product Profile—A Strategic Development Process Tool* (March 2007)
- *Guidance for Industry: Guideline for the Format and Content of the Nonclinical Pharmacology/Toxicology Section of an Application* (February 1987)
- *Draft Guidance for Reviewers on the Integration of Study Results to Assess Concerns about Human Reproductive and Developmental Toxicities* (November 2001)
- *Guidance for Industry and Review Staff: Recommended Approaches to Integration of Genetic Toxicology Study Results* (January 2006)
- *Draft Guidance for Industry: Statistical Aspects of the Design, Analysis, and Interpretation of Chronic Rodent Carcinogenicity Studies of Pharmaceuticals* (May 2001)
- *Guideline for the Format and Content of the Clinical and Statistical Sections of an Application* (July 1988)
- *Draft Guidance for Industry: Integrated Summary of Effectiveness* (August 2008)
- *Guidance for Industry: Premarketing Risk Assessment* (March 2005)
- *Guidance for Industry: Development and Use of Risk Minimization Action Plans* (March 2005)
- *Guidance for Industry: Good Pharmacovigilance Practices and Pharmacoepidemiologic Assessment* (March 2005)
- *Guidance for Industry: Submitting Separate Marketing Applications and Clinical Data for Purposes of Assessing User Fees* (December 2004)
- *Draft Guidance for Industry: Standards for Securing the Drug Supply Chain—Standardized Numerical Identification for Prescription Drug Packages* (January 2009)
- *Draft Guidance for Industry: Forms for Registration of Producers of Drugs and Listing of Drugs in Commercial Distribution* (April 2001)
- *Draft Guidance for Industry: Applications Covered by Section 505(b)(2)* (October 1999)
- *Guidance for Industry: Structure/Function Claims Small Entity Compliance Guide* (January 2002)
- *The New 510(k) Paradigm—Alternate Approaches to Demonstrating Substantial Equivalence in Premarket Notifications—Final Guidance* (March 1998)
- *Guidance for Industry and FDA Staff: How to Write a Request for Designation (RFD)* (August 2005)
- *Guidance for Industry: Nonclinical Safety Evaluation of Drug or Biologic Combinations* (March 2006)

Introduction

The development of drugs, biologics and devices in the modern era is a scientific process (hypothesis testing and the recognition and control of dependent and independent variables) in the context of objective and subjective interpretations of a product's potential or actual risks and benefits. The scope, interpretation and application of US federal regulations that must be met to market a drug, biologic or device have evolved over the past century (generally in a reactive fashion, see "Chapter 2 History of Food, Drug and Cosmetic Laws") and are documented in the Code of Federal Regulations (CFR). In practice, this translates into agency use of scientific review, standards, manufacturing

and other inspections, advertising controls, conditional approvals, laboratory product testing and postmarketing pharmacovigilance activities. In the last quarter century, a plethora of US Food and Drug Administration (FDA) and International Conference on Harmonisation (ICH) guidelines have been issued to assist the regulatory professional in interpreting and defining the processes needed to successfully develop drugs and devices for marketing in a regulated industry. Although not enforceable as regulations, FDA guidelines (usually draft versions are available for public comment before finalization) provide an understanding of the agency's current thinking on any given topic.

This chapter provides an overview of the development

Table 3-1. 21 CFR Parts Most Relevant to Drug and Device Development

21 CFR Parts	General Topics
1–100	Administrative Issues and Protection of Human Subjects
100s	Foods (not covered in this chapter except for dietary supplements)
200s	Labeling, CGMPs, Controlled Substances
300s	Drugs for Human Use
500s	Drugs for Animal Use
600s	Biologics
700s	Cosmetics (not covered in this chapter)
800s	Medical Devices
1000s–1400s	Contain many miscellaneous topics but 1270 Human Tissues Intended for Transplantation and 1271 Human Cells, Tissues and Tissue-Based Products are relevant

and approval process for prescription drug, biologic, device and combination products in an environment regulated by the US government. Other chapters in this book provide details regarding many of the development and approval aspects touched on in this chapter. The purpose of this chapter is to tie the various topics together to provide a development context and roadmap.

Regulatory professionals must understand where regulations originate and how they are organized and updated. The difference between a law and a regulation is sometimes misunderstood. Only Congress can enact laws ("acts" of Congress). Federal executive departments and agencies such as FDA write the regulations to implement the authority of laws. The US Code (USC, which contains 19 "titles") is the official compilation of codified laws by subject, while the CFR is the official compilation of regulations. The CFR is updated annually (in April for food and drugs—Title 21) while the *Federal Register* is the daily supplement to the CFR. Thus, these two publications should be used together to find the latest version of a regulation. The original *Federal Food, Drug, and Cosmetic Act* of 1938 (*FD&C Act*) and its many subsequent amendments constitute the basic food and drug law of the US. A current version of this act can be found at www.fda.gov/RegulatoryInformation/Legislation/FederalFoodDrugandCosmeticActFDCAct/default.htm.

The CFR is divided into 50 titles that represent broad subject areas. Each title is divided into chapters, which usually bear the name of the issuing agency. Each chapter is further subdivided into parts that cover specific regulatory areas. Large parts may be subdivided into subparts. Finally, parts are divided into sections. Thus, the order for citations is: Title, CFR, Part, Section. For drugs and devices, Title 21 (Food and Drugs), and Chapter 1 (Food and Drug Administration) are the most relevant. There are 1,499 parts in Title 21 with the most applicable summarized in **Table 3-1**.

The CFR is accessible online, and the following FDA website is a convenient CFR research point for drugs and devices: www.accessdata.fda.gov/scripts/cdrh/cfdocs/cfcfr/CFRSearch.cfm. The full CFR can be found and searched at www.access.gpo.gov/nara/cfr/cfr-table-search.html.

Although this book and the current chapter describe drug, biologic and device development and approval processes in the US, modern drug development is becoming more and more globalized. Hence, in any development program, consideration should be given to the impact of regulations in other world regions (for example, the usual requirement for a positive control in safety and efficacy trials of drugs in the EU).

Finally, this chapter touches on aspects of drug, biologic and device development to explain the relationships between different technical areas. Because chemistry, manufacturing and controls (CMC) relative to drugs and biologics involves a number of unique issues that are covered in detail in other chapters (including GMPs and Quality Systems), this aspect of drug development is not emphasized in this chapter.

Drug, Device or Combination?

FDA regulates more than 150,000 marketed drugs and medical devices. At any time, nearly 3,000 investigational new drugs are being developed. Organizationally, FDA is part of the Public Health Service (PHS) within the Department of Health and Human Services (DHHS). PHS also oversees the Centers for Disease Control and Prevention (CDC), the National Institutes of Health (NIH) and other agencies.

The workload described above is distributed across FDA's nine centers and offices with approximately 9,000 employees and 167 field offices. "Chapter 1 History of FDA and Related Regulatory Agencies" describes the primary centers and offices involved in drug and device development pathways. Since 1977, FDA centers have issued numerous guidances to increase the transparency of the development process and help move products through the process more rapidly. More recently, the Center for

Drug Evaluation and Research (CDER) has developed a system of manuals of policies and procedures (MAPPs), which are written statements issued by CDER management to prescribe policies, responsibilities or procedures for the conduct of the center's work or daily operations. "MAPP 4000.1—Developing and Issuing Manuals of Policies and Procedures" (updated most recently in 2010) describes the guidance development process. All MAPPs can be accessed at www.fda.gov/AboutFDA/CentersOffices/ CDER/ManualofPoliciesProcedures/default.htm. Several MAPPs regarding agency review processes are useful in understanding how FDA staff will use information from sponsors to make regulatory decisions, and can help sponsors prepare more reviewer-friendly documents. The Center for Biologics Evaluation and Research (CBER) has a similar system termed manuals of standard operating procedures and policies (SOPPs).

Figure 3-2 shows the decision tree regarding which regulations and FDA center or office will primarily govern development and approval of any given drug, device or combination product. Because the purpose of this flow diagram is to provide a simple overview for situations that require FDA premarket review, some complexities, such as the distinction between drugs and biologics and the development of combination products, OTC drugs and dietary supplements, are not highlighted but are addressed in the text of this chapter.

Drugs
Drugs for Veterinary Use

There has been a formal veterinary unit (currently the Center for Veterinary Medicine, CVM) at FDA since 1928.[1] The development and approval of drugs for animal use follows the same framework as for human drugs. For new drugs, the sponsor must file an Investigational New Animal Drug application (INAD, 21 CFR 511) and a New Animal Drug Application (NADA, 21 CFR 514). Under the *Generic Animal Drug and Patent Restoration Act* of 1988, generic veterinary drugs can be marketed under an approved Abbreviated New Animal Drug Application (ANADA). The Reference Listed Drugs (RLDs) for veterinary use are published in the *Green Book* (accessible at www.fda.gov/AnimalVeterinary/Products/ ApprovedAnimalDrugProducts/ucm042847.htm). CVM oversees the veterinary drug development and approval process. However biologics for animal use (vaccines, bacterins, antisera and other products of biological origin) are overseen by the US Department of Agriculture, Animal and Plant Health Inspection Service, Center for Veterinary Biologics (CVB) on the basis of the *Virus Serum and Toxin Act* of 1902. More specifics are available on the CVB website, www.aphis.usda.gov/animal_health/vet_biologics.

Although the development of drugs for animal use has many of the same components and approaches as

for human drugs, including Good Laboratory Practices (GLPs), Good Manufacturing Practices (GMPs), Good Clinical Practices (GCPs), study reports, characterization of dose-response relationships, adequate and well-controlled studies and even user fee), it does differ in a number of key aspects including:

- the ability to use known data from the development of a drug for use in humans or other animal species, as applicable
- the requirement of safety and efficacy studies for far smaller numbers of animals per group, compared to the hundreds of patients per group required for human drugs
- the relevance of species, class and breed of animals as well as geographic differences
- the distinction between drugs developed for the treatment of companion animals versus for animals (or their products) used for human food (e.g., cattle, poultry)

For the general development of drugs for veterinary use, safety aspects are covered in *Guidance for Industry No. 185: Target Animal Safety for Veterinary Pharmaceutical Products* (April 2009), as well as *Guidance for Industry No. 104: Content and Format of Effectiveness and Target Animal Safety Technical Sections and Final Study Reports for Submission to the Division of Therapeutic Drugs for Non-Food Animals* (July 2001). Although the latter guideline does address efficacy in a general fashion, a number of additional guidelines address therapeutic- and animal-specific efficacy issues.

For development of drugs for food-producing animals, two guidelines are helpful. The first, *Guidance for Industry No. 3: General Principles for Evaluating the Safety of Compounds Used in Food-Producing Animals* (July 2006), is very useful and provides links to seven additional guidelines for more in-depth coverage of specific topics. The second guideline (which should be read in conjunction with the first) is *Guidance for Industry No. 149: Studies to Evaluate the Safety of Residues of Veterinary Drugs in Human Food: General Approach to Testing* (March 2009).

Combining veterinary drugs into a single dosage form is addressed in *Guideline No. 24: Guidelines for Drug Combinations in Animals* (October 1983). Specifically, prior to approval of a drug combination, the sponsor must submit data to demonstrate that the combination provides a benefit that cannot be obtained by the use of each drug individually. Further discussion of the above topics is included in "Chapter 29 Veterinary Products."

Finally, although slightly out of place in this section, it should be noted that for devices used in veterinary medicine, FDA does not require submission of a 510(k) or formal premarket approval application. Moreover, device manufacturers that exclusively manufacture or distribute veterinary devices are not required to register their establishments and list veterinary devices. However, FDA can take appropriate regulatory action if a veterinary device is misbranded, mislabeled or adulterated. A more detailed discussion of veterinary products is provided in Chapter 29.

Generic Drugs for Human Use and the Abbreviated New Drug Application (ANDA)
Overview

In part as a result of the thalidomide tragedy, the *Kefauver-Harris Amendments* (*Drug Amendments*) to the *FD&C Act* were passed by Congress in 1962. These amendments required drug manufacturers to prove to FDA that their products were both safe and effective prior to marketing (only safety was required to be demonstrated in the original *FD&C Act*). The *Drug Amendments* also gave FDA control over prescription drug advertising and established GMPs and the requirement for informed consent of subjects in clinical trials. To comply, FDA contracted in 1966 with the National Academy of Sciences' National Research Council to study drugs that had been approved for safety only between 1938 and 1962 relative to the new requirement for demonstration of efficacy. The Drug Efficacy Study Implementation (DESI) program evaluated more than 3,000 separate products and 16,000 therapeutic claims. One of the early effects of the DESI program was the development of the ANDA. ANDAs were accepted for reviewed products that required changes in existing labeling to be in compliance.[2]

The modern era of generic drugs was born in 1984 with passage of the *Drug Price Competition and Patent Term Restoration Act* (the *Hatch-Waxman Act*), which represented a compromise between the innovator pharmaceutical industry and the generic pharmaceutical industry. This act expedited the availability of less-costly generic drugs by permitting FDA to approve abbreviated applications after the patent of the innovator drug had expired. They are termed "abbreviated" applications because they are not required to include animal safety and clinical data to establish safety and effectiveness, but for oral dosage forms must scientifically demonstrate that the product is bioequivalent to the innovator drug (Reference Listed Drug (RLD)). In the case of products (usually steriles, otics and ophthalmics) that have a high solubility-high permeability rating (A/A rated), a waiver for *in vivo* bioequivalence testing can be obtained from FDA. To be bioequivalent, the generic drug product must deliver the same amount (within a range specified by FDA) of active ingredient into a subject's bloodstream over the same amount of time as the RLD. Specifically, a generic drug product is comparable to the innovator drug product in dosage form, strength, route of administration, quality, performance characteristics and intended use. All approved products, both innovator and generic, are listed in FDA's Approved Drug Products with Therapeutic Equivalence Evaluations (the *Orange Book*), which is accessible on FDA's website (www.accessdata.fda.gov/scripts/cder/ob/default.cfm). The *Orange Book* identifies the RLD and provides information on applicable patents and their expiration dates. A product approved under the ANDA process will have the same labeling as the RLD. Approximately 70% of the total drug prescriptions dispensed in the US are generic.

The ANDA is comprised of three primary components:
- chemistry, manufacturing and controls (CMC) information
- bioequivalence data
- administrative information (including labeling and patent certification information)

ANDA requirements for CMC information and manufacture under CGMPs are not significantly different from NDA requirements. A relatively recent initiative in FDA's Office of Generic Drugs (OGD) to streamline the review process for the CMC section is submission of the ANDA Quality Overall Summary in question-based review (QbR) format (versus a more traditional non-question based summary format). The QbR questions and answers are placed in Module 2 of the Common Technical Document (CTD); therefore, QbR assumes the ANDA is submitted in the CTD format which is not mandatory but strongly suggested. OGD has also developed a standard group of summary tables (termed Model Bioequivalence Data Summary Tables) consistent with the CTD format to ensure consistent and concise data are submitted in the applicable sections of the ANDA.

The design, conduct and analysis of clinical bioequivalence studies are covered in *Guidance for Industry: Bioavailability and Bioequivalence Studies for Orally Administered Drug Products: General Considerations* (March 2003) and *Guidance for Industry: Food-Effect Bioavailability and Fed Bioequivalence Studies* (December 2002). A third guideline, *Guidance for Industry: Bioanalytical Method Development* (May 2001), covers the requirements for validation of bioanalytical methods used to evaluate blood concentrations of the active ingredient, which also applies to drugs developed through the NDA route. OGD issued *Draft Guidance for Industry: Bioequivalence Recommendations for Specific Products* in May 2007, indicating how and where OGD will release bioequivalence recommendations for specific products in the future.

Generally, two-way crossover studies (sometimes preceded by pilot studies to determine variability and group sizes) of the generic drug product versus the RLD in the fasted state are performed. If the label of the RLD indicates a food effect, a second study in the fed state (using a standardized high-fat meal) is typically required. Additional studies may be needed to demonstrate bioequivalence of different strengths if the ratio of excipients to the active pharmaceutical ingredient in each dosage strength of the generic drug is not the same. As defined by FDA, the generic is deemed bioequivalent to the RLD in any of the above studies if the 90% confidence interval for the ratio of population geometric means between the two treatments, based on log-transformed data, is contained within the equivalence limits of 80%–125% for the area under the curve (AUC) and peak serum concentration (C_{max}). A common misinterpretation of this is that levels of the active ingredient in generic drugs may vary from minus 20% to plus 25% compared to the innovator. In fact, those numbers relate to a derived statistical calculation and do not represent the actual difference in the amount of active ingredient in a patient's bloodstream, which is generally similar to the variation between different batches of the same innovator drug. For those who are statistically minded, *Guidance for Industry: Statistical Approaches to Establishing Bioequivalence* (January 2001), describes how to conduct the above analysis. If the bioequivalance studies are being conducted to support an ANDA, they do not have to be conducted under an IND, but do need to be reviewed and approved (including an informed consent form) by a duly constituted Institutional Review Board (IRB).

An ANDA must contain a statement by the applicant that one of the following patent certifications applies for the RLD:

- The patent information has not been filed (Paragraph I).
- The patent has expired (Paragraph II).
- The patent will expire on a specific date (Paragraph III) and the sponsor submitting the ANDA does not intend to market its product before that date.
- The patent is invalid or will not be infringed by the proposed drug product (Paragraph IV).

If the ANDA applicant certifies that the patent is invalid or will not be infringed (a Paragraph IV certification), the applicant is required to notify the NDA holder and patent owner. If the NDA holder brings an action for patent infringement within 45 days of this notification, FDA will not approve the ANDA for 30 months, or such shorter or longer period as a court may order, or until the date of a court decision (known as the 30-month stay). Originally, the 180-day exclusivity for generic drugs applied only to the first company to submit an ANDA with a Paragraph IV certification. However, the current approach to 180-day exclusivity (described in *Guidance to Industry: 180-Day Exclusivity When Multiple ANDAs are Submitted on the Same Day* (July 2003)) is applicable to all cases in which multiple ANDA applicants submit Paragraph IV certifications challenging the same listed patent or patents on the same first day. This provides a shared incentive for multiple companies willing to challenge a listed patent and possibly defend a patent infringement suit.

Although the development time for a generic is relatively short, ANDA review (several hundred applications each year) and approval times average approximately two years, and clearly impact the timeframe for moving generic products to the market. This suggests a proactive strategy of submitting ANDA applications well in advance of patent expiration date. A company with an approved ANDA is subject to the same postapproval reporting requirements as an NDA holder (21 CFR 314.80 Postmarketing reporting of adverse drug experiences and 21 CFR 314.81 Field alert reports and annual reports). Many of the topics above are covered in more detail in "Chapter 11 Generic Drug Submissions." The OGD website is also a good resource (www.fda.gov/AboutFDA/CentersOffices/CDER/ucm119100.htm).

Suitability Petitions

The regulations regarding ANDAs are contained in 21 CFR 314.92 and Section 505(j) of the *FD&C Act*. In addition, 21 CFR 314.92 cross-references the limits set forth in 21 CFR 314.93 for what characteristics a generic drug not identical to the RLD can possess and still potentially be submitted as an ANDA, subject to acceptance by FDA of a suitability petition. A suitability petition by the sponsor seeks permission to file an ANDA for the drug product and contains comparisons and contrasts between the generic drug and the RLD, forming the basis for approval. FDA is required to respond to the petition within 90 days. If a suitability petition is not accepted, an NDA under Section 505(b)(2) of the *FD&C Act* may be an option. Another route is a citizen petition. Details of this latter approach are beyond the scope of this chapter.

Branded and Authorized Generics

Recently, "branded" generics have become more prevalent. Branded generics are approved in the same manner as all generics, but the ANDA applicant also applies for and receives a brand (i.e., proprietary) name under the same process used for NDAs (*Draft Guidance for Industry: Contents of a Complete Submission for the Evaluation of Proprietary Names* (November 2008)). A brand name will allow the company to distinguish its generic from others if marketing activities are contemplated.

An "authorized generic" is a drug product for which there is a licensing agreement between the innovator company and a generic drug manufacturer. It allows the innovator company to obtain revenue through the generic process by licensing a manufacturer to market the RLD as a generic using a different "trade dress" while continuing to market the innovator drug under the original proprietary name. A list (updated quarterly) of authorized generics, including the original NDA applicant name, is available on the CDER OGD website (www.fda.gov/AboutFDA/CentersOffices/CDER/ucm126391.htm). The appeal of this approach is avoiding the ANDA review and approval process; instead, the generic can be added to the original

NDA as a supplement or described in the NDA annual report.

In March 2010, the *Patient Protection and Affordable Care Act* was signed into law. This act contains a subtitle called the *Biologics Price Competition and Innovation Act* of 2009 (*BPCI Act*) that amends Section 351 of *Public Health Service Act* and other statutes to create an abbreviated approval pathway for biological products shown to be highly similar (biosimilar) to, or interchangeable with, an FDA-licensed reference biological product. FDA is currently soliciting input regarding the agency's implementation of the statute and considering how to deal with biosimilars that are regulated under Section 505 of the *FD&C Act* (well-characterized proteins and peptides). The approval process for biosimilars is more mature in the EU and further details of the biosimilar development approach, issues and examples can be reviewed on the relevant EU websites.

Chapter 11 provides a more detailed discussion of the generic drug approval process.

New Chemical Entities and the New Drug Application for a Marketing Application for Human Use (Section 505(b)(1) of the FD&C Act)

Overview of the Approach to Drug Development and Approval

A "drug" is defined as a product used in diagnosing, curing, mitigating, treating or preventing a disease or affecting a structure or function of the body (21 CFR 310.3). Under the same regulation, a drug is considered a new drug if:

- There is a new drug use of any substance (e.g., active ingredient, excipient, carrier, coating etc.) that composes the drug.
- There is a new drug use of a combination of approved drugs.
- The proportion of the ingredients in combination is changed.
- There is a new intended use for the drug.
- The dosage, method or duration of administration or application is changed.

Thus, the following are subject to FDA approval:

1. a drug containing a novel chemical compound as its active ingredient (new chemical entity (NCE))
2. a drug containing an existing active ingredient that has never been approved for use as a medicine in the US
3. a drug previously approved by FDA but now proposed for a new use or indication
4. a drug previously approved by FDA but in a dosage form, route of administration or other key condition of use different from what was originally approved

The distinction between a drug and a biologic is primarily based on historical issues. As a result of the St. Louis tetanus contamination due to infected serum and smaller occurrences of contaminated smallpox vaccine and diphtheria antitoxin, Congress passed the *Virus Serum and Toxin Act* (also known as the *Biologics Control Act*) in 1902. The act authorized the Hygienic Laboratory of the Public Health and Marine Hospital Service (which eventually became PHS) to issue regulations governing all aspects of commercial production of vaccines, serums, toxins, antitoxins and similar products with the objective of ensuring their safety, purity and potency. In 1934, the Hygienic Laboratory (renamed NIH in 1930 by the *Ransdell Act*) issued a regulation stating that licenses to manufacture new biologics would not be granted without evidence that the products were effective. The *Public Health Service Act* of 1944 (*PHS Act*) saw the reorganization of PHS, with authority given to NIH to license, research and develop new biological products. Hence, one of the primary historical differences between biologics and drugs has been the inherent government research component of biologics as opposed to the testing and regulation emphasis for drugs.[3] In addition, because biologics are derived from living organisms, immunogenicity issues and how they are addressed in nonclinical and clinical studies often distinguish them from small-molecule drugs.

In 1972, the Division of Biological Standards (part of NIH and in turn part of PHS) was transferred to FDA and eventually became CBER. Although the *PHS Act* established the regulation of biologics licensure, biologics are classified as drugs under the *FD&C Act* and new biologic products require approval based upon safety and efficacy prior to marketing (through a Biologics License Application (BLA) as opposed to an NDA). Biologics are defined as substances derived from or made with the aid of living organisms. Review and approval of these products is conducted by CBER. As technology has evolved, CBER has reviewed more therapeutic proteins. To allow CBER to focus its expertise on vaccines, blood products and other, more-complex products such as gene therapy, FDA shifted the review and approval of biological therapeutics (primarily oncology products, peptides or well-characterized proteins) from CBER to CDER in 2003. Chapter 1 summarizes the types of products now regulated by the two centers.

The intake of any exogenous substance that has pharmacological actions on the body presents some level of risk. Drug development consists of characterizing the safety profile (risk) and the efficacy profile (benefit) as it relates to the body's exposure to the drug (pharmacokinetic profile). The most successful drugs are those with minimal risk and maximum benefit. To align development with continuous evaluation of risk and benefit, it is often productive to consider questions and answers that affect decisions whether to continue a drug's development to the point of submitting a

Table 3-2. Key Questions to be Addressed in a Drug Development Program

In Vitro—Animals—Adults—Children		
Safety **(Risk)**	**Pharmacokinetics** **(What the body does to the drug)**	**Pharmacodynamics/Efficacy** **(Benefit)**
How do you maximize the intellectual property aspect of the product?		
What is the known safety profile of other drugs like yours or the class of drugs in general? For a new class of drugs or mechanism of action this will not necessarily be known and hence associated with more risk.	Are there competitor drugs that have a less than ideal route of administration or pharmacokinetic profile (e.g., substrates, inhibitors or inducers of more commonly used cytochrome P [CYP] 450 isoenzyme pathways)?	What endpoints have been accepted by FDA for other drugs developed to treat the target disease, or is this a first-in-class drug?
What safety profile would provide a competitive advantage?	What pharmacokinetic (including route of administration) profile would provide a competitive advantage?	What is the potential breadth of the target indication(s)?
What do you want to say in your label? (This will drive the development of your product.)		
What are the target organs/systems for toxicity?	What exposure profiles produce target organ/system effects?	What are the target organs/systems for pharmacological effects?
What toxicity is observed acutely versus chronically?	How is the time course of the effects related to the time-concentration curves of the parent drug and its metabolites?	What is the time course and duration of pharmacological/ therapeutic effects?
Can the toxicities be monitored?	Are there potential or actual interactions with other drugs (especially those most commonly used by the target patient population)?	How do you measure the benefits?
Are the toxicities reversible?	What are the single-dose versus steady-state pharmacokinetics of the drug and its metabolites?	What happens to the therapeutic effects when you stop dosing?
What is the maximum tolerated dose and what are risks of overdose?	Is the pharmacokinetic profile linear?	What is the minimal effective dose and duration of treatment?
What are the frequency and severity of safety findings?	How variable (intra- and inter-subject) are drug concentrations (may be impacted by drug bioavailability or greater involvement of the more commonly used CYP isoenzyme systems)?	How reproducible and clinically relevant are the pharmacodynamic and/or efficacy endpoints (speaks to the validity of the endpoints)?

marketing application. The order and importance of these questions are different for each drug based upon aspects such as the product (formulation) chemical and physical characteristics, the route of administration, the target patient population, the medical need, the ability to monitor safety, the ability to predict potential benefits from pharmacodynamic measures (surrogate endpoints) and the duration of treatment needed to demonstrate efficacy.

Table 3-2 lists some of the key questions FDA expects to be addressed as a drug is developed. Generally, due to risk, cost and time, evaluations are performed in the following order:

in vitro

live animals (juvenile if applicable)

adult humans (often in healthy subjects before patients)

children (if applicable)

However, as information is gained, new hypotheses may need to be tested. Therefore, drug development often is an iterative, dynamic process that involves ongoing effective communication between all the disciplines involved.

Table 3-2 identifies key questions to be addressed in a drug development program, i.e., how a company can maximize the market share of its product and realize the maximum return on investment with the least amount of risk. The sections below describe key aspects of the drug development process and regulatory tools and approaches to help reach these goals.

FDA Interface and Development Leverage Options

The relationship between FDA and an investigational drug product sponsor can begin very early in the process (before the sponsor submits an IND to test the product in humans) and extends through the typical IND development process (often defined as Phases 1, 2 and 3) to a marketing application and postapproval commitments, safety surveillance and product lifecycle management. It is important to structure the presentation to meet FDA expectations. To succeed, it is important to learn—through experience or interaction—the relevant review division's approach to issues under its purview. The most effective interfaces between sponsors and FDA are formal meetings and Special Protocol Assessment (SPA) requests.

FDA–Sponsor Meetings

Although sponsor meetings with FDA occurred prior to 1997, it was not until the reauthorization of the 1992 *Prescription Drug User Fee Act* in 1997 (*PDUFA 2*) that a formal process for meetings (with expectations and commitments from both parties) was established. Processes for the request and classification of meetings are covered in *Guidance for Industry: Formal Meetings Between the FDA and Sponsors or Applicants* (May 2009). Different kinds of meetings are categorized as Type A, B or C with different associated timelines (see aforementioned guidance). Meetings can be requested at any time for any valid reason, but FDA will decide if there is sufficient justification for a meeting (usually dictated by the product background and draft questions submitted in a written meeting request) or if a written response to questions and/or a teleconference would suffice. Most commonly, meetings are classified as either pre-IND, End-of-Phase 2 (*Draft Guidance for Industry: End-of Phase 2A Meetings* (September 2008)) or pre-NDA. For products that have been granted accelerated approval or fast track, an End-of-Phase 1 meeting generally will be granted.

For any meeting with FDA, it is important to submit clear and meaningful draft questions and a supporting pre-meeting package that is not merely a summary of what is known about a given drug (e.g., submission of only an Investigator's Brochure). "Chapter 4 FDA Communications and Meetings" provides a more detailed discussion of the above topic.

SPA

The SPA process is described in *Guidance for Industry: Special Protocol Assessment* (May 2002). Although prior to 1997, FDA reviewed draft protocols on a case-by-case basis, the process often took several months and did not always address all the issues. As a result of *PDUFA 2*, the SPA process was established. Within 45 days of receipt, FDA will evaluate certain protocols and related issues to determine whether they meet scientific and regulatory requirements identified by the sponsor (in the form of specific questions). Three types of protocols are eligible for an SPA under the *PDUFA* goals:

1. animal carcinogenicity protocols
2. final product stability protocols
3. clinical protocols for Phase 3 trials, the data from which will form the basis for an efficacy claim (i.e., a pivotal trial) if the trials were discussed at an End-of-Phase 2/Pre-Phase 3 meeting with the review division, or in some cases, if the division is aware of the developmental context in which the protocol

is being reviewed and the questions are being posed

The clinical protocols for Phase 3 trials can relate to efficacy claims that will be part of an original NDA/BLA or an efficacy supplement to an approved NDA/BLA. Although the initial 45-day period is generally adhered to, depending upon FDA's responses to the questions, there could be several review/response cycles (that are no longer part of the timeframe) to reach a final understanding with the sponsor. If documentation of the final agreement is not provided by the FDA review division, the sponsor should request written communication from FDA acknowledging the final agreement.

In addition, sponsors have several available avenues to help focus FDA attention on the drug development program and expedite marketing application approval. These include orphan drug designation (when eligible) and, for drugs indicated for serious or life-threatening conditions, fast track development designation with opportunities for a "rolling NDA" and priority review. Sponsors may also seek accelerated NDA review based upon a surrogate endpoint or an effect on a clinical endpoint other than survival or irreversible morbidity. Details are described in 21 CFR 314.510, Subpart H Accelerated Approval of New Drugs for Serious or Life-threatening Illnesses. Confirmatory studies are likely to be required if FDA approves an NDA under Subpart H.

Orphan Drug Designation

The *Orphan Drug Act* was signed into law in 1983 and, for the first time, provided incentives for development of drugs necessary, and often lifesaving, for patients with rare diseases but with minimal prospects for commercial return on investment. The *Orphan Drug Act* is codified in 21 CFR 316.

Since 1983, Congress has amended the act several times.

- The 1984 amendment redefined "rare disease or condition" as affecting fewer than 200,000 persons in the US at a given point or for which there is no reasonable expectation of recovering development costs through US sales.
- The 1985 amendment extended the marketing exclusivity to patentable as well as unpatentable drugs and allowed federal grants for the clinical evaluation of orphan-designated drugs.
- The 1988 amendment required industry sponsors to apply for orphan designation prior to submission of a marketing application.
- The *Food and Drug Administration Modernization Act* of 1997 (*FDAMA*) included a provision that exempted designated orphan drug products from paying new drug application fees (user fees). It also allowed sponsors to seek waivers of annual postapproval establishment and product fees on a case-by-

case, year-by-year basis.

The *Orphan Drug Act* provides a number of specific incentives for sponsors:

- seven years of exclusive marketing rights for the designated indication once the drug receives FDA marketing approval
- a tax credit for up to 50% of qualified clinical research expenses incurred in developing a designated orphan product (This tax credit has a provision that allows the sponsor to carry the excess credit back one tax year if unable to use part or all of the credit because of tax liability limits, and then to carry forward any additional unused credit for up to 20 years after the year of the credit. The latter is important to start-up companies that may not make any profits until the drug is on the market. The US Internal Revenue Service administers the tax credit provisions of the *Orphan Drug Act*.)
- eligibility to apply for orphan drug grants

There is no formal application for orphan drug designation in the US; however, the European Medicines Agency (EMA) and FDA's Office of Orphan Products Development (OOPD) have developed a common application, benefitting sponsors seeking orphan drug designation in both regions. For US-only applications, the OOPD/EMA common application may be used or sponsors can produce a request consistent with the provisions of 21 CFR 316.20, which identifies the information to be included in a complete, signed and dated document. Essentially, it is a text document with appropriate literature references appended. References are provided to support the incidence statements and can increase the total size of the submission to approximately one to three volumes of paper (a volume is generally defined as between 250 and 350 pages).

An application for orphan drug designation generally includes:

- specific rare disease or condition for which designation is being requested
- sponsor contact, drug names and sources
- description of the rare disease or condition with a medically plausible rationale for any patient subset type of approach
- description of the drug and the scientific rationale for its use for the rare disease or condition
- summary of the drug's regulatory status and marketing history
- for a treatment indication, documentation that the disease or condition affects fewer than 200,000 people in the US (prevalence)
- for a prevention indication, documentation that the disease or condition affects fewer than 200,000 people in the US per year (incidence)

- alternatively, a rationale for why there is no reasonable expectation that costs of research and development for the indication can be recovered by US sales

Specifics on the submission format and other details are available on FDA's website (www.fda.gov/ForIndustry/DevelopingProductsforRareDiseasesConditions/default.htm). Once the request for designation has been received, OOPD will send a receipt letter, and a formal response will take one to three months. Upon notification of orphan drug designation, the sponsor's name and the proposed rare disease or condition will be published in the *Federal Register*.

Once an orphan drug designation has been granted by FDA, it can only be revoked if the application is found to contain false data or there is insufficient drug product to supply market needs. Notably, the designation cannot be revoked even if post-designation prevalence exceeds the original estimates. Finally, the sponsor must provide annual updates that contain a brief summary of any ongoing or completed nonclinical or clinical studies; a description of the investigational plan for the coming year; as well as any anticipated difficulties in development, testing and marketing; and a brief discussion of any changes that may affect the product's orphan drug status. Further details are covered in "Chapter 23 Regulation of Products for Small Patient Populations."

Fast Track Designation

The fast track drug development program designation process is described in *Guidance for Industry: Fast Track Drug Development Programs—Designation, Development, and Application Review* (July 2004). FDA better defined the program (see 21 CFR 312 Subpart E) as a result of *FDAMA* in 1997. The fast track program is designed to facilitate the development and expedite the review of new drugs intended to treat serious or life-threatening conditions and that demonstrate the potential to address unmet medical needs. A disease is considered serious based upon the likelihood that if left untreated, it will progress from a less-severe to a more-severe condition (e.g., AIDS, Alzheimer's disease, heart failure and cancer, but also epilepsy, depression and diabetes). FDA defines "meeting an unmet medical need" as providing a therapy where none exists or that may be superior to existing therapy by either:

- showing superior effectiveness
- avoiding serious side effects of an available treatment
- improving the diagnosis of a serious disease where early diagnosis results in an improved outcome
- decreasing a clinically significant toxicity of an accepted treatment

Depending upon the stage of drug development, data that become available should support the drug's potential to address unmet medical needs, and the development plan should be designed to assess this potential. The agency will rely on summaries of available data to determine whether the potential to address unmet medical needs has been demonstrated and will provide a designation response within 60 days of receipt of the request. When fast track designation is no longer supported by emerging data or the designated drug development program is no longer being pursued, FDA may choose to send a letter notifying the sponsor that the product is no longer classified as fast track.

A sponsor may request fast track designation at any point in the development process. A product that is in a fast track development program is eligible for heightened interest by FDA in sponsor meetings, a greater probability of priority review of the marketing application (six months versus the standard 10 months), and piecemeal submission of portions (complete CTD modules—constituting a "reviewable unit") of a marketing application (referred to as a "rolling NDA"). Note that this latter provision is unique to fast track programs, but needs to be specifically requested. Moreover, the FDA review clock for the rolling NDA does not start until the marketing application submission is complete.

ICH and FDA Guidelines and Their Relationship to the Development Process
ICH and the CTD Format

The International Conference on Harmonisation (ICH) was formed in 1990. It is a unique project that brings together the regulatory authorities of the EU, Japan and the US and experts from the pharmaceutical industry in the three regions to discuss scientific and technical aspects of product registration. ICH recommends ways to achieve greater harmonization in the interpretation and application of technical guidelines and requirements for product registration to reduce or avoid duplicating testing during the research and development of new drugs. The objectives are conservation of human, animal and material resources and elimination of unnecessary delays in global development and availability of new medicines, while safeguarding quality, safety and efficacy and protecting public health.

The ICH process has resulted in numerous guidelines in four major categories:

1. Quality—topics relating to chemical and pharmaceutical quality assurance including stability testing and impurity testing (approximately 24 guidelines)
2. Safety—topics relating to *in vitro* and *in vivo* nonclinical studies including carcinogenicity testing and genotoxicity testing (there are approximately 15 guidelines)
3. Efficacy—topics relating to clinical studies in human subjects including dose-response studies and GCPs (approximately 21 guidelines)
4. Multidisciplinary—topics covering cross-disciplinary issues or not uniquely fitting into one of the other categories, including *Medical Dictionary for Regulatory Activities* (*MedDRA*) terminology, the CTD and electronic CTD submissions (approximately 8 guidelines)

Copies of these guidelines and information on their history and status in the four-step review and consensus process are available at www.ich.org/products/guidelines. html. The majority of these guidelines have been accepted by FDA as reflecting current agency thinking (as documented in *Federal Register* announcements).

Two important aspects of the ICH endeavor are the CTD concept and *MedDRA*. The CTD is divided into five modules as shown in **Figure 3-1,** with a hierarchical structure with the most detail at the base leading to higher and higher level summaries and integration. *Guidance for Industry M4: Organization of the CTD* (2001) provides further details.

Module 1 is region-specific (US, EU, Japan). Modules 2, 3, 4 and 5 are intended to be common for all regions. For US submissions, Module 1 will contain various FDA forms, draft labeling, Risk Evaluation and Mitigation Strategies (REMS) plans, key FDA correspondence (e.g., FDA meeting minutes), patent information and the Investigator's Brochure (IB) (important if the CTD format is used at the IND stage). Module 2 contains CTD summaries of the three technical areas:

*   Module 3 Quality (see *Guidance for Industry M4Q: The CTD—Quality* (August 2001)) and corresponding summary in Module 2.3
*   Module 4 Nonclinical/Safety (see *Guidance for Industry M4S: The CTD—Safety* (August 2001) and *Guidance for Industry M4S: The CTD—Safety Appendices* (August 2001)) and corresponding summaries in Module 2.4 Nonclinical Overview and 2.6 Nonclinical Written and Tabulated Summaries
*   Module 5 Clinical (see *Guidance for Industry M4E: The CTD—Efficacy* (August 2001)) and corresponding summaries in Module 2.5 Clinical Overview and 2.7 Clinical Summary

Module 2 also has several sections, the goal of which is to provide a concise context for the reviewer and integrate key risk/benefit data. The above-cited guidelines contain not only information on their respective modules, but also what should be included in the related portions of Module 2. If submitting electronically, *Guidance for Industry M2 eCTD: Electronic Common Technical Document Specification* (April 2003) is a key starting point.

MedDRA, the currently accepted international medical

Figure 3-1 CTD Organization

terminology dictionary developed by ICH, is designed to support the classification, retrieval, presentation and communication of medical information throughout the regulatory cycle for drugs and medical devices. It is particularly important in the electronic transmission of adverse event reporting and the coding of clinical trial data. Further details are available at www.meddramsso.com/public_subscribe_meddra.asp. and in associated ICH *MedDRA* specific guidelines. *MedDRA* replaces the older *Coding Symbols for a Thesaurus of Adverse Reaction Terms* (COSTART) dictionary.

Guidance Documents

Collectively, CDER and CBER have issued more than 800 guidelines since 1977. These range from general topics addressing a number of the issues outlined in **Table 3-4** to drug-specific issues. They are not regulations, but do represent FDA's current thinking on a given topic. However, some guidelines are relatively old, so the definition of "current thinking" often needs to be validated by recent experience with the agency in the area covered by the guidance. Because they are guidance documents, they should not be blindly followed, but consideration should be given to their intent and applicability to a given development issue.

The Initial IND and the IND Amendment Process

Before initiating a clinical trial in the US (other than bioequivalence studies to support an ANDA), the drug product sponsor must submit nonclinical, CMC and previous human experience data (if applicable) to FDA in a notice of claimed investigational exemption for a new drug in the form of an Investigational New Drug Application (IND). The IND application requests permission to initiate clinical trials. IND regulations are detailed in 21 CFR 312.

The IND application is not a request for approval, rather, it is a request for exemption from federal law. Federal law requires that prior to transporting or distributing a drug in interstate commerce, an NDA or BLA must be approved by FDA. Because in most cases the drug product must be shipped to investigative sites across state lines to perform clinical trials, the sponsor must receive an exemption from this legal requirement.

After receipt of the initial IND application, FDA will send the sponsor a letter with the assigned IND number (note that an IND number with a "P" preface can be obtained at a pre-IND meeting, and the final IND number is the same minus this preface). The letter will indicate that the proposed clinical trial cannot begin until 30 calendar days after receipt of the IND. This 30-day safety review period gives FDA an opportunity to determine whether the data in the IND application support the safety of subjects in the proposed clinical trial. Following review, rather than providing formal approval, the agency will take action on the application as follows. If the proposed study is judged not to be reasonably safe for human subjects, FDA is required to inform the sponsor within 30 calendar days of receipt of the IND application that it may not begin the clinical trial (clinical hold). If the sponsor is not contacted by FDA within 30 days, approval to initiate clinical trials is implicit. In the latter case, it is advisable to contact the FDA project manager assigned to your IND to develop a relationship and to confirm the results of the review.

For the initial IND (the same is true for NDAs), FDA assigns a review team led by a regulatory project manager (RPM) that includes a medical reviewer and pharmacology/toxicology reviewer from the review division. Generally, a CMC reviewer from the Office of New Drug Chemistry is assigned. Depending upon the proposed study, a clinical pharmacologist from the Office of Clinical Pharmacology and a statistician from the Office of Biostatistics may be assigned as well. The team will generally meet the week that the 30-day review period ends and, with the division director, decide whether the proposed study may proceed. In some cases, the RPM may contact the sponsor to request additional information or to propose that the study may be initiated if certain amendments are made to the study protocol. In the latter case, or in the case of clinical hold, FDA will eventually issue a letter containing the details of any requested modifications to the protocol or supporting data.

If a pre-IND meeting was held with FDA, the assigned P-IND number becomes the IND number (the "P" is removed) and the initial submission is given a serial number (SN) 0000. Form FDA 1571 must accompany any submission (except a pre-IND meeting request) to the IND (termed an IND amendment) and each submission is given the next consecutive SN by the sponsor. This form is completed and signed by the sponsor or authorized representative to acknowledge sponsor responsibilities as codified in 21 CFR 312.50. Form FDA 1571 contains sponsor and drug product information and an indication of what the submission contains. Any initial IND submission must contain a clinical study protocol and at least one (if a multicenter study) completed Form FDA 1572. This form contains study site details and IRB name and address, as well as a signoff by the investigator acknowledging legal responsibilities as indicated on the form and in 21 CFR 312.60. The investigator's curriculum vitae, documenting qualifications to conduct the proposed study, is submitted with the Form FDA 1572. There is no 30-day review period for IND amendments.

Where previous clinical studies have not been conducted for an NCE, the initial IND is a major milestone because it summarizes the data that support moving a drug from in vitro and animal testing into evaluation in humans. There are a number of guidances (some in draft stage) on the content and issues relating to either first-in-human or IND clinical trials. These include:

- *Draft Guidance for Industry: Animal Models— Essential Elements to Address Efficacy Under the Animal Rule* (January 2009)
- *Guidance for Industry: Estimating the Maximum Safe Starting Dose in Initial Clinical Trials for Therapeutics in Adult Healthy Volunteers* (July 2005)
- *Draft Guidance: M3(R2) Nonclinical Safety Studies for the Conduct of Human Clinical Trials and Marketing Authorization for Pharmaceuticals* (July 2008)
- *Guidance for Industry: Immunotoxicology Evaluation of Investigational New Drugs* (October 2002)
- *Guidance for Industry: Nonclinical Evaluation of Pediatric Drug Products* (February 2006)
- *Guidance for Industry: Single Dose Acute Toxicity Testing for Pharmaceuticals* (August 1996)
- *Guidance for Industry: Dissolution Testing of Immediate Release Solid Oral Dosage Forms* (August 1997)
- *Guidance for Industry: CGMP for Phase 1 Investigational Drugs* (July 2008)
- *Draft Guidance for Industry: Analytical Procedures and Methods Validation Chemistry, Manufacturing, and Controls Documentation* (August 2000)
- *Guidance for Industry: Collection of Race and Ethnicity Data in Clinical Trials* (September 2005)
- *Guidance for Industry: Exposure-Response Relationships—Study Design, Data Analysis, and Regulatory Applications* (April 2003)
- *Draft Guidance for Industry: Drug-Induced Liver Injury: Premarketing Clinical Evaluation* (October 2007)
- *Guidance for Industry: S1C(R2) Dose Selection for Carcinogenicity Studies* (September 2008)
- *Draft Guidance for Industry: Drug Interaction Studies—Study Design, Data Analysis, Implications for Dosing and Labeling* (September 2006)
- *Guidance for Industry: Pharmacokinetics in Patients with Impaired Hepatic Function: Study Design, Data Analysis, and Impact on Dosing and Labeling* (May 2003)
- *Guidance for Industry: Pharmacokinetics in Patients with Impaired Renal Function: Study Design, Data Analysis, and Impact on Dosing and Labeling* (May 1998)
- *Guideline for Industry: Studies in Support of Special Populations: Geriatrics* (August 1994)
- *Draft Guidance for Industry: How to Comply with the Pediatric Research Equity Act* (September 2005)

In addition, there are a number of other FDA guidelines specific to certain therapeutic indications that should be consulted where relevant.

The content and format of an initial IND are described in 21 CFR 312.23. Traditionally, the content follows the items listed in Section 12 of Form FDA 1571 and includes an

Table 3-3. IND Safety Reports Reporting Timeframes

SAE Outcome	Deadline for Reporting
Fatal or life-threatening	7 calendar days, by phone or facsimile, followed by a written report within 8 additional calendar days
All other outcomes	15 calendar days, in writing

IB, clinical protocol, CMC information, nonclinical pharmacology and toxicology information, and previous human experience information (the latter only if relevant). Although an initial IND can still be submitted in paper format (three copies of the submission are required), using the CTD format for the initial IND submission is becoming more common and is accepted by FDA. The advantage of this approach, especially when done electronically, is that it begins building a CTD for an eventual marketing application that is progressively updated during the course of drug development under the IND. The disadvantages are that the CTD structure in some areas (especially Module 1 and 2) does not easily fit the information available at an initial IND stage, and Section 12 of Form FDA 1571 (application contents) does not currently directly correlate with the CTD structure. The initial IND in CTD format can also be submitted electronically in the eCTD format (with the same considerations as for an electronically submitted NDA). However, once an IND is submitted electronically, all future IND submissions also must be submitted electronically.

For active INDs (an IND can be withdrawn (21 CFR 312.38) or considered inactive (21CFR 312.45)), sponsors are required to submit expedited safety reports for serious, unexpected adverse reactions to the IND (IND Safety Reports) as per the definitions provided in 21 CFR 312.32. A serious adverse event (SAE) is any untoward medical occurrence that results in death, is life-threatening, requires subject hospitalization or prolongation of existing hospitalization, results in persistent or significant disability/incapacity, or is a congenital anomaly/birth defect. Submission of IND safety reports to FDA is time sensitive. The date that the sponsor is notified of the SAE by the study site is considered Day 1, and all reporting timeframes are tied to this notification. **Table 3-3** summarizes these requirements. *Draft Guidance for Industry and Investigators—Safety Reporting Requirements for INDs and BA/BE Studies* (September 2010) provides further details and covers SAE reporting requirements for bioavailability (BA) and bioequivalence (BE) studies.

IND sponsors are required to submit annual reports to the IND within 60 days of the anniversary of the date the IND went into effect (21 CFR 312.33). The annual report focuses on safety signals (deaths or other SAEs, dropouts due to adverse events, and new nonclinical safety findings) and includes an outline of the development plan for the coming year. *Draft Guidance for Industry: E2F Development Safety Update Report* (June 2008) describes a new approach for annual safety reporting and is expected to replace the IND annual report with a comprehensive, harmonized safety summary that represents a common standard for the ICH regions.

Finally, FDA requires clinical trials to be registered with the Clinical Trials Data Bank (maintained by NIH's National Library of Medicine). This initiative began in 2001 with the posting of clinical studies for serious or life-threatening diseases and, under the *Food and Drug Administration Amendments Act* of 2007 (*FDAAA*), was expanded to include all controlled clinical trials in patients (i.e., other than Phase 1 studies). The Clinical Trials Data Bank can be accessed at www.clinicaltrials.gov. To date, the database has registered hundreds of thousands of trials in virtually every country in the world and can be a good resource for clinical study design information.

NDA and Risk/Benefit
General Considerations

The culmination of a drug or biologic development program is the preparation and submission of a marketing application (NDA or BLA). This is accomplished either through studies conducted by (or with a right of reference from) the sponsor (505(b)(1) approach) or by reference to FDA's finding of safety and effectiveness for a previously approved product (Section 505(b)(2) approach). Through frequent interactions with FDA during the development program, including a pre-NDA meeting (usually held no later than three months prior to the target filing date), sponsor and agency expectations should be reasonably well aligned. One tool suggested by FDA for late-stage discussions is the Target Product Profile (see *Draft Guidance for Industry: Target Product Profile—A Strategic Development Process Tool* (March 2007)). The marketing application should contain sufficient data for FDA to decide whether the drug's benefits outweigh its risks in the context of the sponsor's proposed label.

There are a number of key FDA guidances (some in draft stage) regarding the content and approaches to data organization in marketing applications. These include:

- *Guidance for Industry: Guideline for the Format and Content of the Nonclinical Pharmacology/Toxicology Section of an Application* (February 1987)
- *Draft Guidance for Reviewers on the Integration of Study Results to Assess Concerns about Human Reproductive and Developmental Toxicities* (November 2001)
- *Guidance for Industry and Review Staff: Recommended Approaches to Integration of Genetic Toxicology Study Results* (January 2006)
- *Draft Guidance for Industry: Statistical Aspects of the*

Design, Analysis, and Interpretation of Chronic Rodent Carcinogenicity Studies of Pharmaceuticals (May 2001)
- *Guideline for the Format and Content of the Clinical and Statistical Sections of an Application* (July 1988)
- *Draft Guidance for Industry: Integrated Summary of Effectiveness* (August 2008)
- *Guidance for Industry: Premarketing Risk Assessment* (March 2005)

An NDA number for an application in paper format can be requested by contacting the Central Document Room at CDER by telephone. A number may be assigned directly over the phone upon provision of the review division name, sponsor's name, drug name, indication and your name and phone number. For electronic applications, there are specific instructions available on FDA's website for requesting a pre-assigned eCTD application number via secure email (www.fda.gov/Drugs/DevelopmentApprovalProcess/FormsSubmissionRequirements/ElectronicSubmissions/UCM085361).

Package Insert

Federal regulations pertaining to marketing applications are contained in 21 CFR 314. In addition to the study reports supporting the drug's safety and efficacy and the associated summaries, the core of the NDA is the draft package insert (or prescribing information, also referred to as simply the "label") which, since 2005, is required to be in structured product label (SPL) format in an XML (Extensible Markup Language) backbone in order to meet FDA filing requirements. SPL is a model-derived standard adopted for exchange of FDA-regulated product information in the content of the labeling, coded information from the content of the labeling (data elements) and a "wrapper" for electronic listing elements. In addition, most review divisions will request a copy of the label in Microsoft Word to be able to communicate in the label negotiation process using the track changes function. This should be confirmed either in the pre-NDA meeting or with the FDA project manager assigned to the NDA prior to filing. When a final label is agreed to, the sponsor will submit a revised copy of the label to the NDA in SPL format. Moreover, since 2006, new NDAs must follow the format required by the Physician Labeling Rule (PLR), which is made up of three parts: highlights (one page), contents and full prescribing information. The PLR format identifies and dates recent major changes to the prescribing information and includes the date of initial US approval for the active ingredient. Further information (including links to specific FDA guidelines on the content of different sections of the label) is available at www.fda.gov/Drugs/GuidanceComplianceRegulatoryInformation/LawsActsandRules/ucm084159.htm.

Electronic Submission

Since January 2008, sponsors submitting NDAs electronically have been required to use the eCTD format. Waivers are available for those who would like to submit electronically but are unable to do so in eCTD format. For further information, FDA maintains a useful Electronic Regulatory Submissions and Review website at www.fda.gov/Drugs/DevelopmentApprovalProcess/FormsSubmissionRequirements/ElectronicSubmissions/UCM085361. For an NDA, the content and format are dictated by the CTD format described above.

REMS

Evaluation of a product's risk potential has always been a difficult aspect of FDA drug approval. Generally, it is difficult to extrapolate from data derived from a few thousand patients exposed to the drug under relatively well-controlled conditions to millions of patients with much less oversight. FDA's mandate to mitigate potential risks of drugs throughout their development and marketing lifecycle led to the issuance of three draft guidances in 2004 (*Guidance for Industry: Premarketing Risk Assessment, Guidance for Industry: Development and Use of Risk Minimization Action Plans* and *Guidance for Industry: Good Pharmacovigilance Practices and Pharmacoepidemiologic Assessment*). For drugs in development, FDA wanted to know how a sponsor planned to mitigate actual and potential risks (Risk MAP) if a marketing application was approved and how risk would be monitored postapproval. However, the agency did not have the statutory authority to require these assessments. This was rectified as part of *FDAAA,* which gave FDA the authority to require sponsors to submit a risk evaluation and mitigation strategy (REMS) plan prior to approval. A REMS may be as simple as inclusion of a medication guide with the package insert or as complex as a patient and pharmacist training program (additional elements to assure safe use). The REMS includes, at a minimum, a postapproval evaluation by the sponsor at 18 months, three years and seven years. However, given the newness of this requirement, only recently has more granularity on FDA expectations for these evaluations become available.

Proprietary Name

If not previously submitted, a request for review of the sponsor's proposed proprietary name(s) should be made to the review division under the IND (*Draft Guidance for Industry: Contents of a Complete Submission for the Evaluation of Proprietary Names* (November 2008)) or as a separate supplemental submission following submission of the initial NDA. Although the guidance states that this request may be submitted as early as at the end of Phase 2, FDA has begun to delay designating a proprietary name until close to the approval date. The review division will forward the proprietary name request to the Office of

Postmarketing Drug Risk Assessment, Division of Drug Risk Evaluation, which will perform the primary review in consultation with the Division of Drug Marketing, Advertising, and Communication (DDMAC).

User Fees

Under the original *PDUFA* of 1992 (and subsequent amendments), user fees were levied on each "human drug application," including applications for:

- approval of a new drug submitted under section 505(b)(1) after 1 September 1992
- approval of a new drug submitted pursuant to section 505(b)(2) after 30 September 1992 for certain molecular entities or indications for use
- licensure of certain biological products under section 351 of the *PHS Act* submitted after 1 September 1992

PDUFA specifies different user fees for original applications depending upon whether they are accompanied by clinical data on safety and/or efficacy (other than BA or BE studies). The act also levies fees on supplements to human drug applications that require clinical data. Under the fee schedules provided in the act, original applications without clinical data and supplements that require clinical data are assessed approximately one-half the fee of original applications. Further details are provided in *Guidance for Industry: Submitting Separate Marketing Applications and Clinical Data for Purposes of Assessing User Fees* (December 2004). The user fee for a full submission has increased every year since it was implemented and is currently well over $ 1 million. FDA also levies annual establishment and product fees. Further information on these fees can be found at www.fda.gov/Drugs/DevelopmentApprovalProcess/SmallBusinessAssistance/ucm069943.htm. The Office of Regulatory Policy within CDER is responsible for all the above fees.

PAI

One of FDA's objectives in the NDA review process is to determine whether the methods used in manufacturing the drug and the controls used to maintain its quality are adequate to preserve the drug's identity, strength, quality and purity. In conjunction with this evaluation, FDA field inspectors conduct a CGMP preapproval inspection (PAI) of the drug product manufacturing site if it has not recently been inspected by FDA with a favorable outcome. A PAI can occur as early as 90 days after an NDA submission. An adequate PAI is generally required for NDA approval.

Periapproval Activities

There are a number of periapproval activities that should be part of the overall submission and approval plan. A safety update is required to be submitted as an amendment to the NDA within 120 days. In addition, approximately one month prior to the FDA action date, the FDA RPM will contact the sponsor and begin label negotiations. At this time (if not previously done), the sponsor should submit a request for a National Drug Code (NDC) assignment (*Draft Guidance for Industry: Standards for Securing the Drug Supply Chain—Standardized Numerical Identification for Prescription Drug Packages* (January 2009)). Historically, FDA has provided these NDC numbers months before approval of the application, but recently has limited this to the periapproval timeframe due to drug piracy concerns. Thus, the drug label, packaging artwork and labels and promotional material cannot be finalized until very close to the approval date.

In 1972, Congress passed the *Federal Advisory Committee Act*, which prescribed the formal use of Advisory Committees throughout the federal government. With the increasing complexity of risk benefit decisions, FDA has increasingly used Advisory Committees to provide independent advice that will contribute to the quality of the agency's regulatory decision making and lend credibility to the product review process in cases where additional input is desired by FDA. Chapter 5 provides a detailed description of FDA Advisory Committees and the timing of these in the periapproval process when FDA requests such a meeting.

Establishment Listing

Under 21 CFR 207, FDA requires establishments (e.g., manufacturers, repackers and relabelers) upon first engaging in the manufacture, preparation, propagation, compounding or processing of human drugs, veterinary drugs and biological products, with certain exceptions, to register their establishments and submit listing information for all drugs and biological products in commercial distribution. Registrants are also required to submit, on or before 31 December each year, updates in registration information for their establishments. Form FDA 2656 is used for registration of the drug establishment (and also the labeler code assignment) and Form FDA 2657 is used for drug product listing purposes. In 2008, FDA began a pilot program to allow submission of the above information in an electronic format and, since 1 June 2009, all submissions are required to be completely electronic and in XML format, unless a waiver is granted. Further information is available in *Draft Guidance for Industry: Forms for Registration of Producers of Drugs and Listing of Drugs in Commercial Distribution* (April 2001) and at www.fda.gov/Drugs/GuidanceComplianceRegulatoryInformation/DrugRegistrationandListing/ucm084014.htm.

Patent Restoration

The passage of the *Hatch-Waxman Act* in 1984 represented a compromise between the innovator pharmaceutical industry and the generic pharmaceutical industry. It allowed the innovator pharmaceutical companies to apply for up to five years of additional patent protection for new drugs to make up for time lost while their products were going through the development and regulatory review process. The drug (animal or human), medical device, biologic or food or color additive must be the first commercial marketing or use of the product under the provision of the law for which regulatory review occurred. FDA assists the Patent and Trademark Office (PTO) in determining a product's eligibility for patent extension, but PTO is ultimately responsible for determining the period of patent extension. Similarly, up to three years of exclusivity is granted for a change in an approved drug product where approval requires new clinical investigations other than BA studies (e.g., new indication, strength, dosage form or route of administration). The following website provides further details on the patent term restoration program, www.fda.gov/Drugs/DevelopmentApprovalProcess/SmallBusinessAssistance/ucm069959.htm. Six months of pediatric exclusivity (FDA's incentive to conduct more studies of the use of the drug in pediatric populations) also can be requested; see www.fda.gov/Drugs/DevelopmentApprovalProcess/DevelopmentResources/UCM049867.htm for additional details.

NDA Amendments

Finally, an NDA amendment is submitted to change or add information to an unapproved NDA or NDA supplement. With the exception of the required 120-day safety update, sponsors should try to avoid initiating NDA amendments because they will potentially reset the review clock (especially if submitted in the final three months of the review period).

The 505(b)(2) NDA
Overview

The "paper" NDA approach was created after the 1962 passage of the *Drug Amendments* to the *FD&C Act*. It created a means by which duplicates (now known as generic drugs) of post-1962 drugs could be approved because the DESI program and the ANDA did not apply to drugs approved after 1962. The paper NDA policy allowed applicants to use published literature to satisfy the requirements for full reports of safety and effectiveness. The *Hatch-Waxman Act* eliminated the paper NDA policy because it provided a mechanism to approve duplicates of post-1962 drugs, including situations where the applicant did not have the right of reference to the original NDA submitted and approved under Section 505(b)(1) of the *FD&C Act*.

The 505(b)(2) NDA is a submission type that shares characteristics of both traditional NDAs and ANDAs and is named after the section of the *FD&C Act* that describes it. **Figure 3-2** outlines how this type of NDA potentially fits into the overall development and approval scheme for

a drug. As with an NDA, a 505(b)(2) application is submitted under Section 505(b)(1) and is considered a complete application. Like a traditional NDA, it is approved under Section 505(c) of the act. Like an ANDA, a 505(b)(2) application may refer to FDA's finding of safety and effectiveness for a previously approved product, and its approval is subject to patent exclusivity limitations. The applicant may also rely on published literature. *Draft Guidance for Industry: Applications Covered by Section 505(b)(2)* (October 1999) provides additional details. The regulations for this type of application are codified in 21 CFR 314.54.

Bridging and Expansion Issues and Approaches

The most common uses of the 505(b)(2) route are for:
- change in drug product dosage form (including route of administration), formulation, strength and/or dosing regimen, including changes that were not accepted by OGD in a Suitability Petition
- change in active ingredient (different salt, acid or base)
- new combination product in which the active ingredients have been previously approved individually
- change from a prescription indication to an over-the-counter (OTC) indication
- indication that has not been previously approved for the active moiety
- NCE that is a prodrug or active metabolite of a drug approved in the US

If the applicant is the original NDA holder or has right of reference to that NDA from the holder, the above changes become supplements to the original NDA as outlined in **Figure 3-2**.

The data most commonly required in a 505(b)(2) approach provide a bridge between the data forming the basis for approval of the referenced NDA (and agreed to by FDA in the approved drug product label) and the different or additional claims in the 505(b)(2) NDA label. For active ingredient modifications, bridging centers on changes in impurity profiles and/or bioavailability and subsequent exposure. For drug product modifications, bridging centers on differences in the exposure profile. In both cases, a bridging toxicology program usually includes multiple-dose toxicology studies (between 14 and 90 days), with toxicokinetics in appropriate species, as well as mutagenicity and genotoxicity studies. The bridging program generally should not be initiated until agreement is reached with FDA in a formal meeting and the IND is in effect.

The above types of changes will also require additional bridging clinical pharmacokinetic studies. The product should be at least as bioavailable as the RLD unless it has some other advantage such as a smaller peak/trough exposure ratio. Moreover, the pattern of release of the proposed product, although different, should be at least as favorable

Figure 3-2. **Decision Tree for Drug and Device Delopment and Approval for Situations that Require FDA Premarket Review**

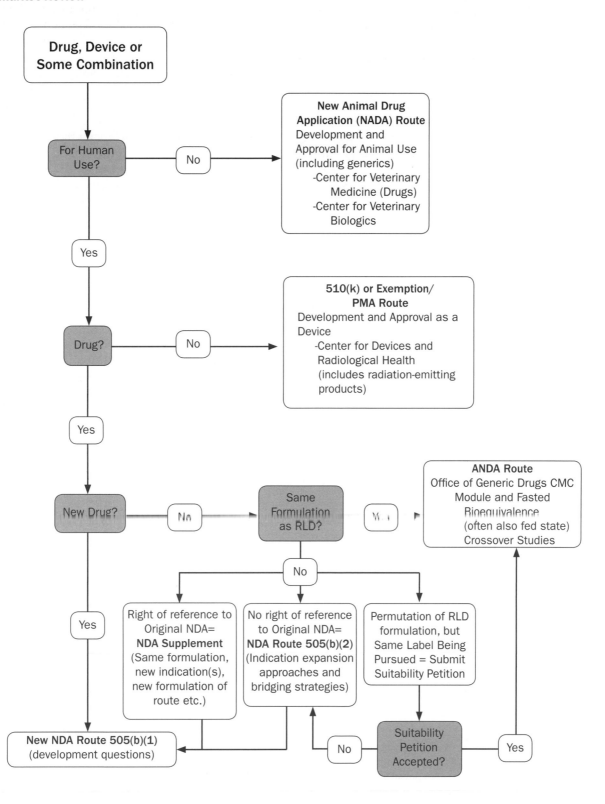

(ANDA, Abbreviated New Drug Application; CMC, Chemistry, Manufacturing, and Controls; NDA, New Drug Application; PMA, Premarket Approval; RLD, Reference Listed Drug (per *Orange Book*))

as that of the RLD. Clinical studies conducted for a 505(b)(2) application generally should be performed under an IND. A 505(b)(2) application may itself be granted three years of exclusivity if one or more of the clinical investigations, other than BA/BE studies, was essential to approval and was conducted for or sponsored by the applicant. A 505(b)(2) application may also be granted five years of exclusivity if it is for an NCE.

Between 1996 and 2004, 126 Section 505(b)(2) applications were filed,[4] and this continues to be a productive approach for moving older drugs into new technology platforms and/or better characterized and understood therapeutic areas. Tuttle[5] provides a concise description of how the regulatory professional can research this development approach.

Dietary Supplements and Natural Health Products

A dietary supplement is a product taken by mouth that contains a "dietary ingredient" intended to supplement the diet. These dietary ingredients may be vitamins, minerals, herbs or other botanicals, amino acids or substances such as enzymes, organ tissues, glandulars and metabolites.

Until 1994, dietary supplements were subject to the same regulatory requirements as other foods. Based upon the belief in a positive relationship between sound dietary practices and health, Congress passed the *Dietary Supplement Health and Education Act (DSHEA)* in 1994, which amended the *FD&C Act* to create a new regulatory framework for the safety and labeling of dietary supplements (yet still under the regulatory umbrella of foods). Provisions of *DSHEA* define dietary supplements and dietary ingredients, and describe the proper use of statements of nutritional support. *DSHEA* also set forth new labeling requirements and required manufacturers of dietary supplements to notify FDA of new dietary ingredients (after 1994; 21 CFR 190.6) prior to marketing. Interestingly, it also authorized FDA to prescribe GMPs for the industry. A final rule on this latter aspect was not forthcoming until 2007. The *Final Rule on CGMPs in Manufacturing, Packaging, Labeling, or Holding Operations for Dietary Supplements* established dietary supplement CGMPs for all domestic and foreign companies that manufacture, package, label or hold these supplements, including those involved with testing, quality control, packaging and labeling and distribution in the US. The dietary supplement CGMPs bear a stronger resemblance to drug CGMPs than to the rather general food CGMPs; however, dietary supplement CGMPs do not require process validation, which is mandated for drug CGMPs.

Dietary supplements do not require premarket approval by FDA. The manufacturer is responsible for ensuring that a dietary supplement is safe before it is marketed. *DSHEA* places the burden on FDA to prove that a marketed dietary supplement is unsafe prior to any action to remove the product from the market. Because of this requirement

and the fact that FDA received numerous reports of safety concerns for a number of products,[6] Congress passed the *Dietary Supplement and Nonprescription Drug Consumer Protection Act* in 2006. It mandates the same type of adverse event reporting for dietary supplements as for prescription drugs.

Dietary supplement claims allowed under *DSHEA* include:

- claims of benefits related to nutrient deficiencies (if the prevalence of the disease in the US is disclosed)
- claims describing the role of the dietary supplement's effects on structure or function in humans (e.g., "calcium builds strong bones")
- claims describing the mechanism of effects on structure or function (e.g., "fiber maintains bowel regularity")
- claims of general well being

Manufacturers cannot make an express or implied claim that a product will diagnose, mitigate, treat, cure or prevent a specific disease or class of diseases. Examples of prohibited statements include: "protects against the development of cancer" or "reduces the pain and stiffness associated with arthritis." Examples of allowable structure/function claims include: "helps promote urinary tract health," "helps maintain cardiovascular function," or "promotes relaxation." Further details can be found in *Guidance for Industry: Structure/Function Claims Small Entity Compliance Guide* (2002). Also see "Chapter 27 Dietary Supplements and Homeopathic Products."

Over-the-Counter (OTC) Drugs

An OTC product is a drug product marketed for use by the consumer without the intervention of a healthcare professional. There are more than 80 therapeutic categories of OTC drugs, and more than 100,000 OTC drug products are marketed in the US, encompassing approximately 800 active ingredients. Oversight of OTC drugs is performed by the CDER's Office of Nonprescription Drugs.

The distinction between drugs that do and do not require a physician prescription dates back to the 1951 *Durham-Humphrey Amendment* to the 1938 *FD&C Act*.[7] FDA applied the principle of retrospective review to OTC drugs starting in 1972. The OTC review by panels of experts focused on active ingredients (initially, approximately 1,000 different moieties). The agency published the results as a series of monographs in 21 CFR 328–358, specifying the active ingredient(s), restrictions on formulations and labeling by therapeutic category for those drugs deemed appropriate for OTC use.

If the standards of the relevant monograph are met, marketing preclearance of an OTC is not required. An NDA 505(b)(2) can be used to request approval of an OTC drug that deviates in any respect from a monograph that has become final (21 CFR 330.11). However, a citizen petition (see 21 CFR 10.30) is an alternate route that bypasses the requirement of *PDUFA* user fees.

"Prescription-to-OTC switch" refers to over-the-counter marketing of a former prescription drug product for the same indication, strength, dose, duration of use, dosage form, population and route of administration. An efficacy supplement to an approved NDA for a prescription product should be submitted if the sponsor plans to switch a drug product covered under an NDA to OTC status in its entirety without a change in the previously approved dosage form or route of administration. An NDA under Section 505(b)(1) should be submitted if the sponsor is proposing to convert some, but not all, of the approved prescription indications to OTC marketing status. An original NDA ((505)(b)(1) or 505(b)(2)) needs to be submitted if the sponsor plans to market a new product whose active substance, indication or dosage form has never previously been marketed OTC.

FDA has approved the switch of a number of drugs from prescription to OTC status under NDAs:

- antidiarrheals (loperamide)
- topical antifungals (clotrimazole, terbinafine)
- antihistamines (clemastine fumarate)
- vaginal antifungals (clotrimazole, miconazole nitrate)
- analgesics (ketoprofen, naproxen sodium)
- acid reducers (cimetidine, famotidine)
- hair growth treatments (minoxidil)
- smoking cessation drugs (nicotine polacrilex)

In allowing these drugs to be sold OTC, FDA considered safety and effectiveness, risk/benefit ratio and whether clear and understandable labeling could be written to enable consumers to safely self-medicate. In 21 CFR 201.66, the agency established standardized content and format for OTC drug product labeling. In addition, manufacturers commonly are required to conduct studies to determine whether consumers understand the proposed OTC labeling and can use the products in a safe and effective manner.[8] OTC product labeling has always contained usage and safety information for consumers. With the introduction of the "Drug Facts" label regulation in 1999, the information became more uniform and easier to read and understand. Patterned after the Nutrition Facts food label, the Drug Facts label uses simple language and an easy-to-read format to help people compare and select OTC medicines and follow dosage instructions. The following information must appear in the indicated order:

- product's active ingredients, including the amount in each dosage unit
- purpose of the product
- product uses (indications)
- specific warnings, including when the product

should not be used under any circumstances, and when it is appropriate to consult with a doctor or pharmacist; this section also describes possible side effects and substances or activities to avoid

- dosage instructions—when, how and how often to take the product
- inactive ingredients, to help consumers avoid ingredients that could cause an allergic reaction

See "Chapter 13 Over-the-Counter Drugs" for more information.

Medical Devices
Overview and Medical Device Classification

A "device" is defined by FDA as an instrument, apparatus, implement, machine, contrivance, implant, in vitro reagent or other similar or related article, including a component part, or accessory which is:

- recognized in the official *National Formulary* or the *United States Pharmacopoeia* or any supplement to them
- intended for use in the diagnosis of disease or other conditions, or in the cure, mitigation, treatment or prevention of disease, in man or other animals
- intended to affect the structure or any function of the body of man or other animals, and which does not achieve any of its primary intended purposes through chemical action within or on the body of man or other animals and which is not dependent upon being metabolized for the achievement of any of its primary intended purposes

Devices first became subject to regulation under the *FD&C Act* (which also defined medical devices for the first time). As a result of the increasing hazards that could result from new, more-complicated devices that were being introduced in the 1960s and 1970s (e.g., pacemakers, kidney dialysis machines, replacement heart valves), Congress passed the *Medical Device Amendments* in 1976 and heralded the modern age of device regulation. These amendments included the following major provisions:

- redefined medical devices to make them more distinct from drugs and expanded the definition to include diagnostics for conditions other than disease
- established safety and efficacy requirements for devices
- established premarket review by FDA
- established the medical device classification system
- created two routes to market (premarket notification and premarket approval) and established Investigational Device Exemptions (IDEs)

Table 3-4. Summary of Device Classification System

Class	Required Controls			Exemptions	Examples
	General	Special	Premarket Approval		
I	X			Exempt = subject to limitations on exemptions covered under 21 CFR xxx.9, where xxx refers to Parts 862–892. Class I devices are usually exempt.	elastic bandages, examination gloves, hand-held surgical instruments
II	X	X		Nonexempt = 510(k) required for marketing	powered wheelchairs, infusion pumps, surgical drapes
III	X	X	X	Exempt if it is a preamendment device (i.e., on the market prior to the passage of the Medical Device Amendments in 1976, or substantially equivalent to such a device) and PMAs have not been called for. In that case, a 510(k) will be the route to market	heart valves, silicone gel-filled breast implants, implanted cerebellar stimulators

A second milestone in device regulation was the passage of the *Safe Medical Device Act* (*SMDA*) in 1990. This act included the following major provisions:

- extended adverse device incident reporting to user facilities including hospitals, ambulatory surgical facilities and nursing homes (This was a landmark event because FDA had never extended its jurisdiction so broadly. When a user facility receives information regarding a death caused by a device, it must report it to FDA and the manufacturer. If a user facility receives information about a serious injury or illness caused by a device, it must report it to the manufacturer. A user facility must also submit to FDA an annual summary of its reports to the agency.)
- required device tracking requirements for high-risk devices
- defined substantial equivalence
- required that submitters of 510(k)s receive clearance by FDA prior to marketing
- gave FDA the authority to regulate combination products
- defined the humanitarian device exemption
- gave FDA recall authority

These regulatory milestones gave rise to most of the modern components of the regulations used by FDA's Center for Devices and Radiological Health (CDRH) to fulfill its responsibilities for regulating firms that manufacture, repackage, relabel and/or import medical devices sold in the US.

Because medical devices vary widely in complexity and risks or benefits, they do not all require the same degree of regulation. Thus, FDA places medical devices into one of three regulatory classes based upon the level of control necessary to assure safety and effectiveness. Device classification depends upon intended use as well as indications for use. In addition, classification is based upon the risk the device poses to the patient and/or the user. Class I includes devices with the lowest risk and Class III includes those with the greatest risk. The class to which a device is assigned determines the type of premarketing submission/application required for marketing. **Table 3-4** summarizes this system.

General controls for all classes include:

1. establishment registration of companies required to register under 21 CFR 807.20, such as manufacturers, distributors, repackagers and relabelers; foreign establishments, however, are not required to register with FDA
2. medical device listing with FDA
3. manufacturing devices in accordance with GMP in 21 CFR 820
4. labeling devices in accordance with labeling regulations in 21 CFR 801 or 809
5. submission of a premarket notification (510(k)) (unless exempt) before marketing a device

Special controls may include special labeling requirements, mandatory performance standards and postmarket surveillance.

Premarket approval is the required process of scientific review to ensure the safety and effectiveness of Class III devices, the most stringent regulatory category. Class III devices are those for which insufficient information exists to assure safety and effectiveness solely through general or special controls. They usually support or sustain human life, are of substantial importance in preventing impairment of human health or present a potential, unreasonable risk of illness or injury.

FDA has established classifications for approximately 1,700 different generic types of devices and grouped them into 16 medical specialties, referred to as "panels."

Classification of a device can be obtained through the CFR or the CDRH database.

CBER reviews marketing and investigational device submissions (510(k)s, PMAs and IDEs) for medical devices associated with blood collection and processing procedures, as well as those associated with cellular therapies and vaccines. Although these products are reviewed by CBER, the medical device laws and regulations still apply.

It is important for the regulatory professional to ensure that a general product definition is available for new devices. Responses to the following questions will help to guide this effort:

1. What will the device do? (intended use)
2. For what clinical conditions or patient population will the device be used? (indications for use)
3. How does the device work? (principles of operation)
4. What are the features of the product? For example, is it electronic versus mechanical, controlled by software or other mechanism, invasive or noninvasive, implanted versus not, sterile versus nonsterile, disposable versus reusable? (product characteristics)
5. What are the risks inherent in the use of the device? (risks)

A designation similar to that for an orphan drug provides an incentive for the development of devices for use in the treatment or diagnosis of diseases affecting small populations. A Humanitarian Use Device (HUD) is intended to benefit patients by treating or diagnosing a disease or condition that affects or is manifested in fewer than 4,000 individuals in the US per year. A request for HUD designation (21 CFR 807) needs to be submitted to FDA; if so designated, the device is eligible for a humanitarian device exemption (HDE). An HDE submission is similar in both form and content to a premarket approval (PMA) application, but is exempt from the effectiveness requirements of a PMA.

An approved HDE authorizes marketing of the HUD. However, an HUD may only be used in facilities that have established a local IRB to supervise clinical testing of devices and after the IRB has approved the use of the device to treat or diagnose the specific disease. The device labeling must state that it is a humanitarian use device and that, although authorized by federal law, its effectiveness for the specific indication has not been demonstrated.

The CDRH website has a number of useful, searchable databases including one for device classifications, one for 510(k)s, a similar one for PMAs, and one for registrations and listings. There is also Device Advice (www.fda.gov/MedicalDevices/DeviceRegulationandGuidance/default.htm), which is very helpful, and a relatively new CDRH Learn site (www.fda.gov/MedicalDevices/ResourcesforYou/Industry/ucm126230.htm) that provides both visual and audio components. Finally, Chapters 15, 16, 17 and 18 of this book are devoted to devices and provide more detailed coverage.

Premarket Notification 510(k) and Exemptions

A sponsor wishing to market a Class I, II or III device intended for human use in the US, for which a PMA is not required, must submit a 510(k) exemption to FDA unless the device is exempt from those requirements and does not exceed the limitations of exemptions in the CFR device classifications as detailed below.

FD&C Act Section 513(d)(2)(A) authorizes FDA to exempt certain generic types of Class I devices from the premarket notification (510(k)) requirement. FDA has exempted more than 800 generic types of Class I devices and 60 Class II devices from the requirement. It is important to confirm the exempt status and any limitations that apply with 21 CFR 862–892, the CDRH Product Code Classification Database or subsequent *Federal Register* announcements on Class I or II exemptions. The 510(k) exemption has certain limitations, which are so noted in ".9" of each chapter of the regulation.

There is no 510(k) form; however, 21 CFR 807 Subpart E describes requirements for a 510(k) submission. This premarket submission to FDA demonstrates that the device to be marketed is as safe and effective as (i.e., substantially equivalent to) a legally marketed predicate device that is not subject to PMA. A predicate device can be:

1. a preamendment device (a currently marketed device that was on the market prior to 1976)
2. a device reclassified from Class III to Class II or I
3. a device found to be substantially equivalent to a device in the one of the above two categories

A device is substantially equivalent if, in comparison to a predicate, it:

- has the same intended and the same technological characteristics as the predicate

or

- has the same intended use as the predicate and different technological characteristics and the information submitted to FDA
  - o does not raise new questions of safety and effectiveness
  - o demonstrates that the device is at least as safe and effective as the legally marketed device

A claim of substantial equivalence does not mean that the new device and the predicate device must be identical. Substantial equivalence is established with respect to intended use, design, energy used or delivered, materials, performance, safety, effectiveness, biocompatibility, standards and other applicable characteristics (e.g., sterility).

FDA determines substantial equivalence, usually within 90 days. If the device is determined to be substantially equivalent, it can be marketed in the US when the submitter receives a letter from the agency (and the sponsor has complied with the general controls provisions). If FDA determines that a device is not substantially equivalent, the applicant may:

- resubmit another 510(k) with new data
- request a Class I or II designation through the *de novo* process
- file a reclassification petition
- submit a PMA

A 510(k)'s content and complexity can vary significantly depending upon the amount of information needed to establish substantial equivalence to the predicate. A typical 510(k) is between 15 and 100 pages. There are three subtypes of 510(k)s: a traditional 510(k), described in 21 CFR 807; a special 510 (k); and an abbreviated 510(k) The latter two are described in *The New 510(k) Paradigm—Alternate Approaches to Demonstrating Substantial Equivalence in Premarket Notifications: Final Guidance* (March 1998).

Investigational Device Exemption (IDE) and Premarket Approval (PMA) Process

An IDE (21 CFR 812) allows the investigational device to be used in a clinical study to collect safety and effectiveness data required to support a PMA application or a Premarket Notification (510(k)) submission to FDA. Clinical studies are most often conducted to support a PMA. Only a small percentage of 510(k)s require clinical data to support the application. Investigational use also includes clinical evaluation of certain modifications or new intended uses of legally marketed devices. All clinical evaluations of investigational devices, unless exempt, must have an approved IDE before the study is initiated. The IDE is similar in content and organization to an IND. The sponsor may begin clinical trials 30 days after FDA receives the IDE, unless the agency objects.

Clinical evaluation of devices that have not been cleared for marketing requires:

- an IDE approved by an IRB; if the study involves a significant risk device, the IDE must also be approved by FDA
- informed consent from all patients
- labeling for investigational use only
- study monitoring
- records and reports

An approved IDE permits a device to be shipped lawfully for the purpose of conducting investigations without complying with other requirements of the *FD&C Act* that apply to devices in commercial distribution. Sponsors need not submit a PMA or Premarket Notification 510(k), register their establishment or list the device while it is under investigation. IDE sponsors are also exempt from the

Quality System Regulation (QSR) except for the requirements for design control.

In an industry of 15,000 manufacturers, where half have fewer than 10 employees, the planning and conduct of a clinical study can take a significant proportion of resources. For significant risk devices, where trials can be relatively complex and expensive, following the types of processes used for industry-sponsored drug trials is advisable to protect the validity of the company's investment. This should include the use of clinical study protocols, informed consent forms that meet FDA regulations (21 CFR 50) and are reviewed by duly constituted IRBs (21 CFR 56), source documents at the investigational sites, clinical study reports and well-written investigator agreements that include not only financial aspects (see 21 CFR 54), but also compliance with the study protocol and IDE responsibilities.

Premarket approval is FDA's review process to evaluate the safety and effectiveness of Class III medical devices. Due to the level of risk associated with Class III devices, FDA has determined that general and special controls alone are insufficient to assure their safety and effectiveness. Therefore, these devices require a PMA application (21 CFR 814).

A PMA is the most stringent type of device marketing application required by FDA. The applicant must receive FDA approval of its PMA application prior to marketing the device. Approval is based upon a determination by FDA that the PMA contains sufficient valid scientific evidence to assure that the device is safe and effective for its intended use(s). An approved PMA is, in effect, a private license granting the applicant (or owner) permission to market the device. The PMA owner, however, can authorize use of its data by another.

The PMA application is similar in content and organization to a traditional (non-CTD format) NDA application, although with much less clinical data required. FDA has observed problems with study designs, study conduct, data analyses, presentations and conclusions. Sponsors should always consult all applicable FDA guidance documents, industry standards and recommended practices. Numerous device-specific FDA guidance documents are available. Although FDA has 180 days to review the PMA, in reality this usually takes longer, due to the frequent involvement of an Advisory Committee.

Establishment Registration and Medical Device Listing

Establishments involved in the production and distribution of medical devices intended for marketing or leasing (commercial distribution) in the US are required to register with FDA. This process is known as establishment registration. Registration provides FDA with the location of medical device manufacturing facilities and importers. An establishment is defined as any place of business under one management at one physical location at which a device is manufactured, assembled or otherwise processed for commercial distribution. The "owner/operator" is defined as the corporation, subsidiary, affiliated company, partnership or proprietor directly responsible for the activities of the registering establishment. The owner/operator is responsible for registering the establishment.

The regulations for establishment registration are provided in 21 CFR 807. As of 1 October 2007, all establishment registrations and listings must be submitted electronically using FDA's Unified Registration and Listing System (FURLS), unless a waiver has been granted. Congress also authorized FDA to implement a user fee for certain types of establishment registrations processed after 30 September 2007 (for 2011 this fee is $2,179). Registration of an establishment is not an approval of the establishment or its products by FDA. That is, it does not provide FDA clearance to market. Unless exempt, premarketing clearance or approval is required before a device can be placed into commercial distribution in the US.

Most medical device establishments required to register with FDA must also identify the devices they have in commercial distribution, including those produced exclusively for export. This process is known as medical device listing and is a means of keeping FDA advised of the generic category(s) of devices an establishment is manufacturing or marketing. The regulations for medical device listing are also provided in 21 CFR 807.

Quality Systems for Manufacturing

The CGMP requirements set forth in the QSR require domestic or foreign manufacturers to have a quality system for the design, manufacture, packaging, labeling, storage, installation and servicing of finished medical devices intended for commercial distribution in the US. The regulation requires:

- various specifications and controls to be established for devices
- devices to be designed under a quality system to meet these specifications
- devices to be manufactured under a quality system
- finished devices to meet these specifications
- devices to be correctly installed, checked and serviced
- quality data to be analyzed to identify and correct quality problems
- complaints to be processed

FDA monitors device problem data and inspects the operations and records of device developers and manufacturers to determine compliance with the GMP requirements in the QSR.

The QSR is contained in 21 CFR 820. It covers quality management and organization, device design, buildings, equipment, purchasing and handling of components, production and process controls, packaging and labeling control, device evaluation, distribution, installation, complaint handling, servicing and records.

Combination Drug-Device and Drug-Drug Products

Combination products (i.e., drug-device, drug-biologic and device-biologic products, formally defined in 21 CFR 3.2(e)) have been regulated for decades. Prior to 1990, FDA regulated such products on a case-by-case basis. Generally, the sponsor and FDA negotiated an ad hoc regulatory approach without explicit statutory guidance. As combination products multiplied and increased in complexity, the ad hoc approach was no longer satisfactory, and in 1990, Congress enacted the *SMDA*. This provision required the agency to designate a center (CDER, CBER or CDRH) with primary jurisdiction based upon the product's primary mode of action. FDA issued intercenter agreements between the three centers in 1991; however, there were still a number of problems with this approach.[9]

As part of the *Medical Device User Fee and Modernization Act* of 2002 (*MDUFMA*), Congress established the Office of Combination Products (OCP) within FDA's Office of the Commissioner to ensure prompt assignment of combination products to FDA centers and oversee coordination of the development and approval processes.

By submitting a Request for Designation (RFD), a company may obtain a formal agency determination of a combination product's primary mode of action and assignment of the lead center for the product's premarket review and regulation. OCP will make a determination within 60 days of receipt of the RFD. *Guidance for Industry and FDA Staff: How to Write a Request for Designation* (August 2005) provides more specifics. "Chapter 23 Combination Products" also provides additional details.

In recent years, in part as pharmaceutical companies strive to reduce the inherent risks of drug development, drug-drug combinations have become increasingly common. Combination drug products are convenient and can improve dosing compliance, especially in polypharmacy scenarios. Moreover, by combining drugs with different mechanisms of action, lower doses can be used, which may decrease adverse effects (e.g., diuretics combined with angiotensin-converting enzyme (ACE) inhibitors, angiotensin receptor blockers or beta-adrenergic blockers for the treatment of hypertension, or some antiretroviral agents combining up to three drugs in one dosage form).

The type of development program for drug-drug combinations will depend upon whether one, both or neither component of a two-drug (or greater) combination product has been previously approved. From a nonclinical perspective, FDA has issued *Guidance for Industry: Nonclinical Safety Evaluation of Drug or Biologic Combinations* (March

2006). Similar principles would apply to the clinical portion of the development program. However, in both cases, proposed development approaches should be discussed with FDA in the early stages.

Summary

The development of drugs and devices is a scientific process in the context of objective and subjective interpretations of a product's potential or actual risks and benefits. The scope, interpretation and application of US federal regulations that must be met to market a drug or device have evolved over the past century and are documented in the CFR. This translates into agency use of scientific review, standards, manufacturing and other inspections, advertising controls, conditional approvals, laboratory product testing and postmarketing pharmacovigilance activities. Over the last 25 years, a plethora of FDA and ICH guidelines have been issued to assist in interpreting and defining the processes needed to successfully develop drugs, biologics and devices for marketing in a regulated industry.

FDA is part of the PHS within DHHS and comprises nine centers/offices.

There has been a formal veterinary unit at FDA since 1928. CVM oversees the veterinary drug development and approval process. However biologics for animal use (vaccines, bacterins, antisera and other products of biological origin) are overseen by the US Department of Agriculture, Animal and Plant Health Inspection Service, CVB.

The modern era of generic drugs was born with passage of the *Hatch-Waxman Act*. This act expedited the availability of less-costly generic drugs by permitting FDA to approve abbreviated applications after the patent of the innovator drug had expired. These abbreviated applications generally are not required to include animal safety and clinical data to establish safety and effectiveness. Specifically, a generic drug product is comparable to the innovator drug product in dosage form, strength, route of administration, quality, performance characteristics and intended use.

A "drug" is defined as a product used in diagnosing, curing, mitigating, treating or preventing a disease or affecting a structure or function of the body. A "biologic" is defined as a substance derived from or made with the aid of living organisms. Drug development consists of characterizing the safety profile (risk) and the efficacy profile (benefit) as it relates to the body's exposure to the drug (pharmacokinetic profile). The most successful drugs are those with minimal risk and maximum benefit.

The relationship between FDA and an investigational drug product sponsor can begin very early in the process (before the sponsor submits an IND) and extends through the typical IND development process (often defined as Phases 1, 2 and 3) to a marketing application and postapproval commitments, safety surveillance and product lifecycle management. Meetings with FDA are an important component of the IND process. Meetings can be requested at any time for any valid reason, but FDA will decide whether there is sufficient justification for a meeting (usually dictated by the product background and draft questions submitted in a written meeting request) or if a written response to questions and/or a teleconference would suffice.

Sponsors can submit a request for a Special Protocol Assessment (SPA). Within 45 days of receipt, FDA will evaluate certain protocols and related issues to determine whether they meet scientific and regulatory requirements identified by the sponsor. Three types of protocols are eligible for an SPA under the *PDUFA* goals—animal carcinogenicity protocols, final product stability protocols and clinical protocols for Phase 3 trials whose data will form the basis for an efficacy claim (i.e., a pivotal trial).

The *Orphan Drug Act*, for the first time, provided incentives for development of drugs necessary, and often lifesaving, for patients with rare diseases (defined as a US prevalence of less than 200,000 patients) but with minimal prospects for commercial return on investment.

The fast track program is designed to facilitate the development and expedite the review of new drugs intended to treat serious or life-threatening conditions and that demonstrate the potential to address unmet medical needs. A disease is considered serious based upon the likelihood that if left untreated, it will progress from a less-severe to a more severe condition. FDA defines "meeting an unmet medical need" as providing a therapy where none exists or that may be superior to existing therapy by meeting a number of conditions. A sponsor may request fast track designation at any point in the development process. A product in a fast track development program is eligible for heightened interest by FDA in sponsor meetings, a greater probability of priority review of the marketing application and piecemeal submission of portions (complete CTD modules) of a marketing application ("rolling NDA").

ICH was formed in 1990. It brings together the regulatory authorities of the EU, Japan and the US and experts from the pharmaceutical industry in the three regions to discuss scientific and technical aspects of product registration. ICH recommends ways to achieve greater harmonization in the interpretation and application of technical guidelines and requirements for product registration to reduce or avoid duplicating testing during the research and development of new drugs.

The ICH process has resulted in numerous guidelines in four major categories—quality, safety, efficacy and multidisciplinary. Two important aspects of the ICH endeavor are the CTD concept and *MedDRA*.

Before initiating a clinical trial in the US (other than bioequivalence studies to support an ANDA), the sponsor must submit nonclinical, CMC and previous human experience data (if applicable) to FDA in the form of an IND. The IND application requests permission to initiate clinical trials. It is not a request for approval; rather, it is a request for exemption from federal law requiring an approved NDA or BLA prior to transporting or distributing a drug in interstate commerce. For an NCE, the initial IND is a major milestone because it summarizes the data that support moving a drug from *in vitro* and animal testing into evaluation in humans. Sponsors are able to initiate their proposed clinical trial if they have not received any communication from the FDA within 30 days of FDA receipt of the initial IND application.

The culmination of a drug or biologic development program is the preparation and submission of a marketing application (NDA or BLA). This is accomplished either through studies conducted by (or with a right of reference from) the sponsor (505(b)(1) approach) or by reference to FDA's finding of safety and effectiveness for a previously approved product (Section 505(b)(2) approach). Through frequent interactions with FDA during the development program, including a pre-NDA meeting, sponsor and agency expectations should be reasonably well aligned. Items to be considered when preparing a marketing application include package inserts (labeling), electronic submissions, Risk Evaluation and Mitigation Strategies (REMS), proprietary names, user fees, preapproval inspections (PAIs), establishment listings, patent restoration, other periapproval activities and NDA amendments and supplements.

A dietary supplement is a product taken by mouth that contains a "dietary ingredient" intended to supplement the diet. *DSHEA* created a new regulatory framework for the safety and labeling of dietary supplements (yet still under the regulatory umbrella of foods). Provisions of *DSHEA* define dietary supplements and dietary ingredients, and describe the proper use of statements of nutritional support. *DSHEA* set forth new labeling requirements and required manufacturers of dietary supplements to notify FDA of new dietary ingredients prior to marketing. It also authorized FDA to prescribe GMPs for the industry. Dietary supplements do not require premarket approval by FDA. The manufacturer is responsible for ensuring that a dietary supplement is safe before it is marketed. *DSHEA* places the burden on FDA to prove that a marketed dietary supplement is unsafe (including noncompliance with CGMPs) prior to any action to remove the product from the market.

An OTC product is a drug product marketed for use by the consumer without the intervention of a healthcare professional. There are more than 80 therapeutic categories of OTC drugs, and more than 100,000 OTC drug products are marketed in the US, encompassing approximately 800 active ingredients. Oversight of OTC drugs is performed by CDER's Office of Nonprescription Drugs. In allowing drugs to be sold OTC, FDA considers safety and effectiveness, risk/benefit ratio and whether clear and understandable labeling can be written to enable consumers to safely self-medicate.

A "device" is defined as an instrument, apparatus, implement, machine, contrivance, implant, in vitro reagent or other similar or related article, including a component part or accessory that meets a number of conditions.

FDA places medical devices into one of three regulatory classes based upon the level of control necessary to assure safety and effectiveness. Device classification depends upon intended use as well as indications for use, and the risk the device poses to the patient and/or user. Class I includes devices with the lowest risk and Class III includes those with the greatest risk. The class to which a device is assigned determines the type of premarketing submission/application required for marketing.

A sponsor wishing to market a Class I, II or III device intended for human use, for which a PMA is not required, must submit a 510(k) exemption to FDA unless the device is exempt from those requirements and does not exceed the limitations of exemptions in the CFR device classifications. A 510(k)'s content and complexity can vary significantly depending upon the amount of information needed to establish substantial equivalence to the proposed predicate.

Premarket approval is the required process of scientific review to ensure the safety and effectiveness of Class III devices. Class III devices are those for which insufficient information exists to assure safety and effectiveness solely through general or special controls. They usually support or sustain human life, are of substantial importance in preventing impairment of human health or present a potential, unreasonable risk of illness or injury. An IDE allows the investigational device to be used in a clinical study to collect safety and effectiveness data required to support a PMA application or a Premarket Notification (510(k)) submission.

Establishments involved in the production and distribution of medical devices intended for commercial distribution in the US are required to register with FDA (establishment registration). In addition, the QSR requires domestic or foreign manufacturers to have a quality system for the design, manufacture, packaging, labeling, storage, installation and servicing of finished medical devices intended for commercial distribution in the US.

Combination products are defined as drug-device, drug-biologic and device-biologic products. As part of *MDUFMA*, Congress established OCP to ensure prompt assignment of combination products to FDA centers and oversee coordination of the development and approval processes. By submitting an RFD, a company may obtain a formal agency determination of a combination product's primary mode of action and assignment of the lead center for the product's premarket review and regulation.

References

1. www.fda.gov/AboutFDA/WhatWeDo/History/ FOrgsHistory/CVM/default.htm
2. Ibid.
3. www.fda.gov/AboutFDA/WhatWeDo/History/ FOrgsHistory/CBER/ucm135758.htm
4. Tuttle ME. "Researching the 505(b)(2) Application." *Regulatory Affairs Focus*, May 2004; pp. 12–14.
5. Ibid.
6. Jiang T and Zhang S. "Stringent Laws and Regulations for Dietary Supplements." *Drug Information Journal*, Vol. 43; No. 1. pp. 75–81. (2009)
7. Op cit 1.
8. Hellbusch SJ. "Involving the End User in the Development of Label Wording." *Regulatory Affairs Focus*, May 2004, pp. 48–51.
9. Kahan JS and Shapiro JK. "FDA's Regulation of Combination Products: The Road Ahead." *Regulatory Compliance Newsletter*. November 2003, pp. 37–40.

FDA Communications and Meetings

By Cindy DiBiasi and Kell Cannon

Objectives

◆ Describe FDA communication mechanisms

◆ Differentiate between public administrative proceedings

◆ Provide guidance for conducting product application meetings with FDA

◆ Provide solid understanding of the role of advisory committees within FDA

Laws, Regulations and Guidance Documents Covered in This Chapter

◆ 21 CFR 10 Administrative Practices and Procedures

◆ 21 CFR 12 Formal Evidentiary Public Hearing

◆ 21 CFR 13 Public Hearing Before a Public Board of Inquiry

◆ 21 CFR 14 Public Hearing Before a Public Advisory Committee

◆ 21 CFR 15 Public Hearing Before the Commissioner

◆ 21 CFR 16 Regulatory Hearing Before the Food and Drug Administration

◆ 21 CFR 312 Investigational New Drug Application

◆ 21 CFR 812 Investigational Device Exemptions

■ *Guidance for Industry: Formal Meetings Between the FDA and Sponsors or Applicants* (May 2009)

◆ *Guidance for the Public, FDA Advisory Committee Members, and FDA Staff on Procedures for Determining Conflict of Interest and Eligibility for Participation in FDA Advisory Committee* (August 2008)

◆ *Draft Guidance for the Public, FDA Advisory Committee Members, and FDA Staff: Public Availability of Advisory Committee Members' Financial Interest Information and Waivers* (March 2010)

◆ *Guidance for FDA Advisory Committee Members and FDA Staff: Voting Procedures for Advisory Committee Meetings* (August 2008)

◆ *Guidance for Industry: Advisory Committee Meetings—Preparation and Public Availability of Information Given to Advisory Committee Members* (August 2008)

Introduction

Communications between the US Food and Drug Administration (FDA) and the industry it regulates are key components in fostering understanding of the drug development and regulation process, and in successfully implementing and enforcing the *Federal Food, Drug, and Cosmetic Act* of 1938 (*FD&C Act*).

Understanding the various types of meetings, their purposes, formats and timelines is vital in order for regulatory professionals to obtain their desired objectives in the most effective and efficient way.

There are numerous opportunities and roles for two-way communications between FDA and industry. Communications from FDA can provide companies with critical insights into what the agency expects regarding specific requirements and pathways to development. Industry communications to FDA on proposed regulations and guidance can offer the agency insight on the impact of specific regulations on companies. In some cases, it may also give industry the opportunity to explain alternate mechanisms to achieve their regulatory objectives. At other times, communications can function as mechanisms of dispute resolution.

Types of FDA Communications

When communicating with FDA, whether through written communications, phone conferences or face-to-face meetings, it is imperative for the regulatory professional to select the appropriate vehicle.

There are four types of regulatory interactions that apply to drugs, biologics and devices. These include:
- regulatory communications
- product application meetings
- administrative meetings or communications
- public administrative proceedings

FDA regulations and guidance provide for a number of different types of application and administrative meetings. It is recognized that well-executed application meetings have the potential to provide the following benefits to both sponsors and FDA:
- design testing and development plans that will expedite review and approval
- save money and time
- allow a more collaborative approach
- minimize surprises[1]

FDA has issued guidance for sponsors describing when and how to request the various types of administrative meetings. Procedures for these meetings vary among FDA product centers, so it is important for the regulatory professional to become familiar with the guidance documents issued by each center.

Regulatory Communications

Regulatory communications originate from FDA and occur, as needed, without a set schedule. In these communications, the agency provides general advice and policies to the industry, without engaging in dialogue with a specific sponsor. Regulatory communications may take three forms:
- regulations—binding requirements
- guidance documents or guidances—recommendations that are nonbinding
- responses to citizen petitions, which serve as FDA's formal position on an issue

Background on Types of Regulatory Communications

Title 21, Part 10 of the Code of Federal Regulations (CFR) governs the practices and procedures for communicating FDA regulations, guidances and recommendations. With limited exception, regulations are published in the *Federal Register* and are available for public comment. Proposed regulations are generally subject to a 60-day comment period, which may be shortened or extended

for good cause. After consideration of the administrative record, FDA will terminate the proceeding, issue a new proposal or promulgate a final regulation.

Guidance documents describe FDA's interpretation of or policy on a regulatory issue.[2] Guidance documents can be prepared for FDA staff, sponsors or the public. FDA regulations called Good Guidance Practices govern the preparation, dissemination and use of guidance documents. FDA may also disseminate recommendations in the *Federal Register* about matters that are authorized by, but do not involve, direct regulatory action under law.

A citizen petition is a formal written request to FDA asking the agency to take or refrain from taking an administrative action. According to regulation, FDA must respond to the petitioner within 180 days of receipt. Citizen petitions are filed in the docket management system and assigned a docket number. Subsequent submissions or comments on the petition must include the docket number and become part of the docket file. Under FDA regulation, a citizen petition should contain the following:
- action requested
- statement of grounds
- environmental impact
- economic impact
- a certification by the submitter

Citizen petitions can address a wide variety of topics, such as requesting that FDA classify and regulate a product as one under FDA jurisdiction, amend an over-the-counter (OTC) drug monograph, initiate rulemaking regarding a particular topic, or amend a specific regulation. Suitability petitions are a specific type of citizen petition used to file an abbreviated application for a new human or animal drug whose active ingredients, route of administration, dosage form or strength differ from that of the approved drug. According to statute, FDA will approve or deny a suitability petition within 90 days of the submission date. An advisory opinion represents FDA's formal position on a matter. An interested person may request an advisory opinion on a matter of general applicability. The regulations provide FDA with great latitude in determining whether to grant a request for an advisory opinion. FDA statements of policy, such as the preamble to a final rule or the *Compliance Policy Guides* manual, also constitute advisory opinions.

Product Application Meetings

The second type of regulatory interaction is a product application meeting. Product application meetings occur during critical points in the regulatory process to establish or confirm a company's development plan, and increase the likelihood that the sponsor will have the appropriate data for approval.

There are several types of product application meetings—those focusing on pharmaceutical and biologics applications

Figure 4-1. Timeline for Key Application Meetings (NDA, BLA and PMA Submissions)

NDA and BLA Submissions

PMA Submissions

(NDA and BLA submissions, respectively) and those focused on medical devices (PMA submissions).

Application meetings are initiated by the sponsor and are private, two-way communications (either by phone or in person) between FDA and the sponsor. These meetings follow a systematic approach, leading to eventual submission of an application for approval. For context, **Figure 4-1** shows two schematics of key application meetings and their relative timing in the development and submission timeline.

Background on Product Application Meetings for Pharmaceutical and Biologics

Application meetings focused on the development and review of products in human drug applications are further categorized into three meeting types: A, B and C. **Table 4-1** lists meeting descriptions and timing.

Type A Meetings

Type A meetings are those immediately necessary for an otherwise stalled drug development program to proceed. Type A meetings are generally reserved for dispute resolution or discussion of clinical holds when responses to hold issues have been submitted, and Special Protocol Assessment meetings. FDA guidance advises contacting the review division of the Center for Drug Evaluation and

Research (CDER) or the Center for Biologics Evaluation and Research (CBER) prior to submitting a Type A meeting request.[3] According to agency guidance, these meetings should be scheduled within 30 days of FDA's receipt of a written request for a meeting.

Type B Meetings

Type B meetings represent pivotal development meetings that occur prior to progression to the next registration stage. According to FDA guidance, the agency will schedule Type B meetings within 60 days of receipt of a written request for a meeting.

There are several categories of Type B meetings, including:

- Pre-Investigational New Drug (IND) meetings (21 CFR 312.82)
- End-of-Phase 1 meetings (21 CFR 312.82)
- End-of-Phase 2/Pre-Phase 3 meetings (21 CFR 312.47)
- Pre-NDA/Biologic License Application (BLA) meetings (21 CFR 312.47)

Each sponsor or applicant should typically request only one of each of these Type B meetings for each potential application.

Table 4-1. Description of FDA Product Application Meetings and Timing

	Type A Meeting	Type B Meeting	Type C Meeting
Meeting description	Dispute resolution Clinical holds Special Protocol Assessment (SPA)	Pre-IND EOP1 EOP2 Pre-NDA / Pre-BLA	Any other meeting not identified as a Type A or B meeting
Confirmation of scheduling following sponsor request	14 days from time of request	21 days from time of request	21 days from time of request
Timing window for meeting to occur	30 days from time of request	60 days from time of request	75 days from time of request
Briefing information and relevant questions for discussion due to FDA	2 weeks prior to meeting	4 weeks prior to meeting	4 weeks prior to meeting

Type C Meetings

Type C meetings include any meeting other than a Type A or B meeting between FDA and a sponsor regarding the development and review of a product in a human drug application. According to FDA guidance, the agency will schedule Type C meetings within 75 days of receipt of a written request.

In the meeting request, FDA guidance recommends the sponsor include the:

1. product name
2. application number, if applicable
3. chemical name and structure
4. proposed indication(s) or context of product development
5. type of meeting requested (i.e., Type A, B or C)
6. brief statement of the meeting purpose and objectives
7. proposed agenda and draft list of specific questions grouped by discipline, including a brief explanation of context and purpose for each question to enable the agency to understand the meeting focus
8. list of individuals (including titles) who will attend the meeting on behalf of the sponsor's organization
9. list of agency staff, by title or discipline, requested by the sponsor to participate in the meeting
10. suggested dates and times for the meeting
11. format of the meeting (i.e., face-to-face, teleconference or videoconference)[4]

Following the meeting, FDA will prepare official meeting minutes summarizing meeting outcomes, agreements, unresolved issues and action items.[5] Within 30 days of the formal meeting, FDA should issue the official minutes to the sponsor.

Background on Medical Device Application Meetings

In addition to the pharmaceutical and biologics application meetings, there are five types of meetings available to sponsors of medical device applications submitted to the Center for Devices and Radiological Health (CDRH). They are:

- agreement
- determination
- Pre-Investigational Device Exemption (Pre-IDE)
- Pre-PMA
- PMA day 100

Reforms to the medical device regulatory process in 1997 led to the establishment of the agreement and determination meetings with the passage of the *Food and Drug Administration Modernization Act* (*FDAMA*).

The purpose of the agreement meeting is to reach concurrence on the key parameters of the investigational plan. Sponsors who intend to perform a clinical study of any class of device will be given an opportunity to discuss the investigational plan with FDA to reach agreement on the plan before applying for an Investigational Device Exemption (IDE). Agreements reached in the meeting are documented in writing, shared with the sponsor and made part of the administrative record. The written agreement is binding on the agency and may be changed only with the written agreement of the sponsor or when there is a substantial scientific issue essential to determining the device's safety or effectiveness.

Determination meetings are limited to PMAs or product development protocol (PDP) applications. The purpose of the meeting is to determine the type of valid scientific evidence needed to demonstrate that a device is effective for its intended use. Discussions at these meetings will include the types of clinical studies (e.g., concurrent randomized controls, concurrent nonrandomized controls, historical controls) or other types of evidence that will support effectiveness, and the least-burdensome way of evaluating effectiveness. The determination is based upon data supplied by the sponsor, which include information about the device, its intended use, relevant performance information and a proposed plan for evaluation of the product. Within 30 days of the determination meeting, the agency will convey a memorandum, signed by the division director, to the applicant documenting the determination. The determination is legally binding unless it could be contrary to public health.

Although *FDAMA* established formal medical device collaboration meetings, Pre-IDE meetings are more frequently used to discuss issues or topics pertaining to medical device product applications.[6] Contrary to its name, a Pre-IDE meeting does not need to occur prior to filing an IDE, and is available for medical devices that do not require an IDE.[7]

A submission made under the Pre-IDE process is not an official IDE application as described in 21 CFR 812. The purpose of the Pre-IDE meeting is to expedite the regulatory process and minimize delays in device development. The meeting may involve discussion about:

- analytical protocols
- clinical protocols
- proposed study design
- statistical plan
- bench/animal testing to support initiation of the clinical investigation
- preliminary guidance on significant/nonsignificant risk of the device
- feasibility study protocols
- preliminary guidance on regulatory pathway
- primary and secondary endpoints

For PMA applicants, the Pre-PMA and day-100 meeting provide additional avenues for an efficient application review process. Pre-PMA meetings are intended to help guide the PMA submission, and include topics such as the strength of a particular clinical data set or the formatting of the application.[8] Prior to requesting a Pre-PMA meeting, it is a good idea to contact the respective CDRH review division, as little formal guidance is available for these meetings.

The PMA day-100 meeting provides an opportunity to discuss the application's review status and obtain additional information, if any, required to complete the PMA review. Upon written request, FDA is required to meet with the applicant no later than 100 days following the receipt of a filed PMA application. To assist the applicant in preparing for this meeting, FDA is to inform the applicant in writing of any identified deficiencies and what information is required to correct those deficiencies. FDA must also promptly notify the applicant if the agency identifies additional deficiencies or any additional information required to complete the review.

Administrative Meetings or Communications

A third type of regulatory interaction is administrative meetings or communications. These are additional ad hoc, private, two-way communications (either by phone, email or in person) between FDA and outside parties regarding matters within FDA jurisdiction.[9] These meetings can occur between FDA and a pharmaceutical company, a medical association or an advocacy group. They can be initiated by either the sponsor or FDA. Additionally, individuals outside the federal government may request a private meeting with an FDA representative.

When guiding a product through the FDA application process, a sponsor may identify scientific issues that warrant discussion with the agency. Administrative meetings or communications take place with the purpose of addressing scientific issues that warrant discussion with the agency. In response to sponsor questions, FDA will provide nonbinding advice.

Similar to application meetings, requests for administrative meetings will have a specific timeline for deliverables based on their urgency, categorized as either a Type A or Type C meeting, as referenced for product application meetings.

Public Administrative Proceedings

The last type of FDA meeting is the public administrative proceeding. These are face-to-face scheduled meetings, which the public has a right to attend,[10] and are intended to create transparency and disclosure. These proceedings occur as specified by regulations, when ordered by the FDA commissioner or when requested by the sponsor or affected public parties and approved by the FDA commissioner.

Public administrative proceedings take one of four forms:

- formal evidentiary hearing
- public board of inquiry
- hearing before the commissioner
- Advisory Committee meeting

With the exception of Advisory Committee meetings that might occur prior to the *Prescription Drug User Fee Act* (*PDUFA*) action date,[11] public administrative proceedings occur as needed, without a set schedule or an established timeline.

Provided the public is informed of the time, place and matters under discussion, FDA, at its discretion, may hold a public meeting. Certain laws or regulations also provide opportunities to affected parties to request a public administrative proceeding. Additionally, individuals outside the federal government may request a private meeting with an FDA representative.

A formal evidentiary hearing is the administrative

equivalent of a civil court hearing and involves comparable preparation and procedural controls.[12] This type of hearing occurs when specifically provided by law, mandated by Congress or when ordered by the FDA commissioner, in order to discuss public health concerns on a product, or review proposed guidances such as Risk Evaluation and Mitigation Strategies (REMS).

A public hearing before a board of inquiry is called at the discretion of the FDA commissioner when specifically authorized by regulation or as an alternative to a formal evidentiary public hearing.[13] The purpose of this hearing is to review medical, scientific and technical issues.[14] The proceedings are conducted as a scientific inquiry and, therefore, are not comparable to a legal trial.[15]

A public hearing before the commissioner occurs when the FDA commissioner determines that it is in the public interest to permit persons to present information and views at a public hearing on matters pending before the agency. These meetings are intended to solicit general views and information from interested parties on a particular topic. Direct-to-consumer (DTC) advertising and risk communication are two examples of areas where FDA has determined that public input would be of assistance with regard to policy development.

A public regulatory hearing, under 21 CFR 16, is called at the discretion of the FDA commissioner when considering regulatory action or when provided by law or regulation. For example, the statutory provision pertaining to the withdrawal of a PMA approval affords an opportunity for a regulatory hearing. The regulations relating to the disqualification of an Institutional Review Board is an example of a regulatory provision that affords an opportunity for a regulatory hearing.

A public hearing before an Advisory Committee is a meeting, on a matter of importance that comes before FDA, to review the issues involved and to provide advice and recommendations to the commissioner. Advisory Committees are made up of panels of independent experts and are convened by FDA to help the agency ensure the safety and effectiveness of foods, drugs, biologics and medical devices. Most frequently, FDA utilizes committees for advice on product approvals and labeling conditions, scientific issues and research projects.[16]

Medical device classifications; safety and efficacy of a New Drug Application (NDA) or Biologics License Application (BLA); recommendations regarding common therapeutic class toxicities; preferred clinical design guidance; review of a Premarket Approval (PMA) application; and the establishment, amendment or revocation of a performance standard, are all examples of subjects that might be covered at Advisory Committee meetings.

The *Food and Drug Administration Amendments Act* of 2007 (*FDAAA*) now explicitly mandates that FDA must either convene an Advisory Committee panel for all new molecular entities or provide a written explanation as to why one is not necessary.[17]

In addition to the new regulations, there has also been an increased public focus on the transparency of Advisory Committees and the potential for conflicts of interest of Advisory Committee members.[18] As a result, FDA released improved policies and procedures governing transparency and public disclosure related to its advisory committees. In August 2008, the agency issued the following four final guidance documents on these two topics:

- *Guidance for the Public, FDA Advisory Committee Members, and FDA Staff on Procedures for Determining Conflict of Interest and Eligibility for Participation in FDA Advisory Committee*
- *Guidance for the Public, FDA Advisory Committee Members, and FDA Staff: Public Availability of Advisory Committee Members' Financial Interest Information and Waivers*
- *Guidance for FDA Advisory Committee Members and FDA Staff: Voting Procedures for Advisory Committee Meetings*
- *Guidance for Industry: Advisory Committee Meetings—Preparation and Public Availability of Information Given to Advisory Committee Members*

FDA has 49[19] Advisory Committees organized by the different centers within the agency (drugs, devices, biologics and food), and by specialty. Each committee is subject to a two-year renewal, unless otherwise stated in its charter. Advisory Committees may be ad hoc or standing panels. They may be technical advisory committees, which focus on product-related regulatory decisions, or policy advisory committees, which deal with general policy issues. As part of the meeting process, FDA provides its Advisory Committees with specific questions to guide their discussion, and usually requests a vote from the committee. While the committee's vote is a nonbinding recommendation to FDA, it is heavily considered by the agency.

Format of Advisory Committee Meetings

Advisory Committee meetings for new product approvals are typically convened for a half-day or full-day. Issues of high interest sometimes require a two-day meeting. A typical advisory committee meeting includes a 45- to 90-minute presentation by the drug, biologic or device "sponsor;" a presentation by FDA; a public comment period; a question and answer (Q&A) and deliberation session and, ultimately, a committee vote.

Transparency of Advisory Committee Meetings

The committees also serve an important function for consumers by providing an open public forum for discussion on all manner of topics and a mechanism for consumers to stay abreast of product development and new technologies. Advisory Committee meetings are open to the public.[20] It is also important to note that materials provided to an Advisory Committee must be made available to the public.[21] Any individual or company presenting at an Advisory Committee meeting must understand that if any of the information declared as proprietary has been shared in a public forum such as a scientific meeting, filed under patent, published, given to a customer, provided to financial analysts and stockholders or otherwise distributed upon request, it is not exempt from disclosure.[22]

Summary

Collaborative meetings between FDA and the industry it regulates have become an important part of the product application process. These interactions, if managed properly, can provide vital information to companies as well as important insights to FDA about the impact of regulatory policies on industry.

Communications between FDA, FDA Advisory Committees, and industry take on various forms, all of which have different objectives. Guidance documents represent FDA interpretation on issues, and advisory opinions represent the agency's formal position on regulatory matters and policy.

A critical responsibility of the regulatory professional is the proper selection of the appropriate meeting type and ensuring the organization is well prepared in order to facilitate a productive FDA meeting.[23]

While all of the types of communications and meetings outlined in this chapter are of varying complexity and scope, they all require preparation. Chapter 5 will present general preparation guidelines for all meetings, and will detail the preparation process for the most complicated of these—public Advisory Committee meetings.

References

1. "Understanding the Pre-IDE Program: FDA Perspective." Presentation by Elisa D. Harvey, DVM, PhD, Director IDE and HDE Programs, Office of Device Evaluation. AdvaMed 15th Annual Device Submissions Workshop, 25 May 2005. Slide 4.
2. 21 CFR 10.115(b)
3. FDA. *Guidance for Industry: Formal Meetings between the FDA and Sponsors or Applicants* (May 2009). Page 3. Available at www.fda.gov/downloads/Drugs/GuidanceComplianceRegulatoryInformation/Guidances/UCM153222.pdf. Accessed 11 May 2011.
4. Ibid pages 4–5.
5. Ibid page 10.
6. FDA. "FY 2004 Performance Report to the President and the Congress for the Medical Device User Fee and Modernization Act" which states "the more formal types of meetings (agreement meetings, determination meetings, 100-day meetings) are not used as frequently by premarket applicants." Available at www.fda.gov/AboutFDA/ReportsManualsForms/Reports/UserFeeReports/MDUFMA/ucm114858.htm. Accessed 11 May 2011.
7. FDA. IDE Guidance #D99-1. *Pre-IDE Program: Issues and Answers* (March 1999). Available at www.fda.gov/MedicalDevices/DeviceRegulationandGuidance/GuidanceDocuments/ucm126600.htm. Accessed 11 May 2011.
8. FDA. *Early Collaboration Meetings under the FDA Modernization Act (FDAMA); Final Guidance for Industry and for CDRH Staff* (February 2001). Page 3.
9. 21 CFR 10.65(a)
10. 21 CFR 10.203
11. *PDUFA* action due date (or user fee goal date) is the date by which an action is due on a marketing application under the timeframes negotiated as a result of the *Prescription Drug User Fee Act* of 1992 (*PDUFA*) and subsequent legislation amending that act. (SOPP 8401.3: *Filing Action: Communication Options*, www.fda.gov).
12. FDA. *Guidance for Industry on Medical Device Appeals and Complaints: A Guidance on Dispute Resolution* (February 1998). Page 8. Available at www.fda.gov/downloads/MedicalDevices/DeviceRegulationandGuidance/GuidanceDocuments/ucm094523.htm. Accessed 11 May 2011.
13. Ibid.
14. Ibid.
15. Ibid.
16. *21 CFR—Food and Drugs Chapter 1—Food and Drug Administration Department of Health and Human Services. Subchapter A—General. Part 14, Public Hearing Before a Public Advisory Committee.*
17. Section 918 of *Food and Drug Administration Amendments Act* of 2007 (P.L. 110-85, in effect March 2008)
18. *Food and Drug Administration Amendments Act* of 2007 (*FDAAA*).
19. Biologics (n=5), Drugs (n=16), Food (n=1), Devices (n=18), Pediatrics (n=1), Radiation-emitting Products (n=2), Risk Communication (n=1), Science Board (n=1), Toxicology (n=2), Veterinary (n=1), Tobacco (n=1).
20. Op cit 17.
21. Op cit 18.
22. 21 CFR 14.27
23. *The FDA Advisory Committee Survival Manual:*

A Step-by-Step Guide to Preparing for a Successful Meeting. Published by 3D Communications (2008). Available at: http://www.3dcommunications.us/ FDAsurvivalguide.html. Accessed 11 May 2011.

24. Ibid.

Preparing for Key FDA Meetings and Advisory Committee Meetings

By Cindy DiBiasi

Objectives
- Provide general recommendations for preparing for FDA meetings
- Detail the extensive preparation process for Advisory Committee presentations

Guidance Documents Covered in This Chapter
- *Guidance for Industry: Formal Meetings Between the FDA and Sponsors or Applicants* (May 2009)
- *Guidance for the Public, FDA Advisory Committee Members, and FDA Staff on Procedures for Determining Conflict of Interest and Eligibility for Participation in FDA Advisory Committee* (August 2008)
- *Guidance for the Public, FDA Advisory Committee Members, and FDA Staff: Public Availability of Advisory Committee Members' Financial Interest Information and Waivers* (March 2010)
- *Guidance for FDA Advisory Committee Members and FDA Staff: Voting Procedures for Advisory Committee Meetings* (August 2008)
- *Guidance for Industry: Advisory Committee Meetings—Preparation and Public Availability of Information Given to Advisory Committee Members* (August 2008)
- *Guidance for the Public, FDA Advisory Committee Members, and FDA Staff: The Open Public Hearing at FDA Advisory Committee Meetings* (December 2010)

Introduction

The various types of meetings with the US Food and Drug Administration (FDA) outlined in Chapter 4 require different levels of preparation by the company, ranging from regulatory communications, which require less preparation, to highly publicized Advisory Committee meetings, requiring intensive preparation.

All meetings should begin with a goal of maximizing the opportunities provided by FDA interactions. Establishing an open and forthright relationship with the FDA division and demonstrating credibility for your product or issue are paramount in every interaction.

This chapter highlights the general steps that companies should consider in preparing for all FDA meetings, and outlines the more detailed and comprehensive process of preparing for an Advisory Committee meeting.

General Preparation for FDA Meetings

Regardless of the type of meeting, the category of product for which a company may be requesting approval, or any issues playing out in the external environment, there is one commonality for all FDA meetings—the need to tell a clear story and to set the data or issue in context. Just as FDA has a process for determining whether a drug or device should be approved, a company needs a process to keep its team on track and prepare in the most efficient and effective way. A good process will incorporate the following objectives: the development of a strategy to best attain company goals; an understanding of the various FDA audiences; a prioritization of data and other information; preparing speakers to articulate the information and effectively answer questions; and testing and measurement of progress with well-organized practice and rehearsals.

Prior to all meetings with FDA, whether in person or by telephone, companies should consider the following 10 steps:

1. Know your audience.

- Conduct research on FDA personnel who will be in attendance at the meeting. Learn about their experiences, biases and backgrounds in order to better anticipate their opinions.

2. Know the issues.

- Review recent relevant precedents and actions by the FDA division responsible for evaluating the product; understand published or implied FDA guidances and consider explicitly incorporating them into the sponsor's strategy or presentation.

3. Set a goal for each FDA conversation or meeting.

- Determine the meeting objective or purpose, whether it is to obtain FDA guidance, present the development program or obtain FDA agreement.
- Determine the issues and questions that will be addressed and who will attend on behalf of the company and the agency.
- Stay focused on the goal during each meeting. Seek specific answers and commitments from FDA to achieve that goal.
- Strive for agreement on main issues. Try to get clarity, direction and, if possible, commitment on these issues.

4. Know your position.

- Conduct a high-level messaging session before filing a new drug or device application for consistency across all communications. In this session:
  - o Analyze key data with a public forum and media in mind.
  - o Brainstorm and identify potential issues among all stakeholders.
  - o Develop high-level messages to provide the basis for conversations with FDA.
- Make sure the team clearly understands and is aligned with the company's position and knows how to articulate it.

5. Provide pertinent materials for each meeting in a timely way to allow FDA to adequately analyze the information.

- Do not overwhelm FDA with thousands of pages of background information; streamline the information, and focus it on the issues and goal of each meeting. Include a preliminary proposed agenda, focused questions and a background package or briefing document that includes the sponsor's position, an outline of the product data and the sponsor's development recommendation.

6. Anticipate concerns and interests, and be prepared to sufficiently answer likely FDA questions.

- Understand potential risks from a difference in data interpretation or recommended data requests and proactively prepare acceptable contingency scenarios that could resolve them.
- In addition to FDA concerns, proactively address resolutions to any issues regarding therapeutic area, class perception and public concern.

7. Be organized.

- Manage the meeting time carefully to ensure adequate discussion and clear understanding of answers and recommendations within the allotted meeting time.
- Bring the appropriate people to the meeting to discuss the sponsor's questions and provide any necessary clarification to FDA.

8. Listen carefully to what FDA is actually saying.

- During in-person meetings, pay attention to body language, internal dynamics and offhand remarks. During phone meetings, listen to voice tone.
- Immediately correct any misinterpretations or misconceptions FDA may have.

9. Record feedback.

- Strive for clear agreement on critical decisions and make sure they are documented in the FDA meeting minutes.
- Keep an ongoing list of all issues raised by FDA officials during the meetings and conference calls. Record how many times specific issues are raised to gauge their importance. Remember to note who at the agency is raising them.
- Explicitly document when FDA mutes the phone. This usually indicates either an important question they want to refine or internal disagreement, and may help you determine what issues are still causing dissent or confusion internally at the agency. Consider additional data or programs that could clarify or resolve these issues.
- Save the last five minutes of the meeting to summarize the discussion and obtain agreement on action steps.

10. Foster a flexible, collaborative and nonadversarial relationship.

- Keep the lines of communication open—even if FDA's message is negative.
- Do not take a divergent point of view personally. Always retain composure if FDA takes the opposite position.

- Listen to FDA's requests, and provide answers where possible. Look for opportunities to resolve issues before they become obstacles to approval.
- Be respectful, but not meek.
- Be prepared to calibrate the communications strategy in light of shifting issues, an evolving environment and changes within the FDA review team.
- Anticipate potential data requirements beyond those being articulated by FDA in case the agency shifts direction or changes its mind.

Overview of Advisory Committee Meetings

Because the *Food and Drug Administration Amendments Act* of 2007 (*FDAAA*) mandates that Advisory Committees be convened for all new molecular entities, or requires FDA to provide a written explanation as to why there will not be a meeting, sponsors of a new drug or device must plan for the likelihood that an Advisory Committee will be part of their regulatory processes. However, sponsors often do not know whether their products will have to face a committee hearing until a few months before the actual event. Thus, strategic planning for a potential meeting must be an integral part of any product's development process.

An Advisory Committee meeting to review a new drug or device application is unlike most other FDA meetings. It is not only a scientific discussion of the data and issues surrounding a drug or devices, it is also a high-profile regulatory, financial and legal event—a very public day in court for the sponsor and its product.

Advisory Committee meetings are typically attended by rival pharmaceutical or device companies, the media and key stakeholders, including patient and advocacy groups. The voting members on an Advisory Committee are not a typical scientific audience. Due to concerns with regard to conflicts of interest, FDA is often prohibited from including on the panel any experts who may have collaborated on the study or may have contributed to the development of the product. This means the panel's clinicians, academicians and statisticians, while experts in their respective fields, may know little more about the specific issues than what they read in the FDA and sponsor briefing books and will hear at the meeting. Sponsors need to be aware of this and be careful not to assume in-depth, product-specific knowledge on the part of the committee members. (See Chapter 4 for more detailed information on the purpose and format of Advisory Committee meetings.)

Preparing for an Advisory Committee Meeting

A three-step approach to preparing for an Advisory Committee includes analysis, content development and testing of the strategy and materials.

The analysis step includes: understanding the audience (FDA division heads, medical reviewers and Advisory Committee members); evaluating the data and science; analyzing the external environment and assembling the preparation team. The content development step is comprised of creating a communications strategy and materials including the core presentation, slides, briefing materials and advocacy outreach. The testing step includes rehearsals, expert feedback and, ultimately, adjustment of the strategy and materials.

Selecting the Team

Most sponsors underestimate the amount of time it will take to sufficiently prepare for an FDA Advisory Committee meeting. Thus, it is critical to select the right team, assign members to the right roles, and set ground rules and realistic expectations. A key starting point on team selection is identifying a senior person in research and development or regulatory to champion the project and to ensure that Advisory Committee preparation is the presentation team's top priority. The ideal team should include representatives from a variety of areas: regulatory, medical, clinical, toxicology, statistics, pharmacovigilance and marketing. Each brings individual expertise and a unique perspective that can help secure a positive recommendation from the committee and attain the target label. Orchestrating the team, considering and weighing its input, and selecting the proper role for each team member is as much an art as it is a science.

The size of an Advisory Committee preparation team will vary according to the company and its resources. Frequently, an overlap of responsibilities will exist among sub-teams, with some people performing more than one role. Although there are many ways to organize a team, a typical breakdown of roles and responsibilities follows:

- Presentation team: core presenters and back-up presenters
- Data/slide triage team: people who compile and organize data and slides
- Briefing book team: main author and data triage team members
- Internal/external scientific advisors: content experts and responders for question and answer development
- Regulatory team: regulatory executives who manage communication and scheduling with FDA throughout the Advisory Committee process
- Communications team: presentation support team of writers, editors, presentation coaches, marketing, brand, public relations executives and media trainers
- Slide development and slide logistics team
- Logistics team: project manager, meeting organizers, schedulers and administrative support

Figure 5-1. Major Milestone Timeline

Once the team has been selected, it is important to brief members on what to expect during the preparation process and at the hearing. Team members should be briefed on everything from how the slide process will work and what the room layout will be, to how the Advisory Committee hearing schedule will flow, and anticipated media interest.

Organizational tools such as a major milestone timeline (**Figure 5-1**) and a project management chart (**Figure 5-2**) are highly effective ways to brief the team and keep it on track. These tools provide an overview of the process, the tasks, the assignments and the schedule, and provide a realistic view of the time commitment required by the team members and how their roles are critical to achieving the goal.

Researching and Analyzing the Advisory Committee Members

Each Advisory Committee member has his or her own individual style and concerns, which can affect what questions are asked during the meeting, how they are asked, and how members ultimately vote. Knowing who is on the committee, their backgrounds and how they may influence one another is critical, as it helps frame a relevant presentation, predict questions and prepare answers.

To analyze Advisory Committee members, the team may:

- Study past votes and discussions around issues similar to the sponsor's. Companies can gain a wealth of information by reviewing transcripts of previous meetings from the FDA's website (www. fda.gov) or viewing videos of meetings on FDA Live (www.fdalive.com). Panel members often ask similar questions at different Advisory Committee hearings, so it is highly instructive to learn what they have asked in the past and, of equal importance, to

Figure 5-2. Sample Project Management Chart

ID	Task Name	Start	Finish
1	**Strategic Definition of Key Focus**	**2/7**	**2/21**
2	Define team members (roles/responsibilities)	2/11	2/12
3	Initiate Team Charter	2/12	2/12
4	Identify potential AC meeting	2/7	2/12
5	Team Assembled Timeline, resource, comms plan	2/13	2/19
6	Approval of timeline, resource, comms plan	2/21	2/22
7	Work initiated following plan approval	2/25	2/25
8	**Regulatory Background Review**	**2/13**	**3/4**
9	Summary of AC member background compiled	2/15	2/21
10	Summary of correspondence, meeting minutes, issues, etc.	2/25	2/29
11	**Identification of Relevant Advisory Commitee Meetings**	**2/13**	**3/4**
12	obtain copies of stranscripts and/or video	2/13	3/4
13	obtain copies of briefing pkgs	2/13	3/4
14	Host Adcomm review session with Core Team	3/6	3/6
15	**Key Messages Outlined**	**2/28**	**3/7**
16	Identify key messages	2/28	3/5
17	Submit Key Messages to PDC for approval	3/6	3/6
18	Team Finalizes Key Clinical messages	3/6	3/7
19	**Key Issues Identified**	**3/6**	**3/26**
20	Identify key issues (Draft list)	3/6	3/12
21	Team Review of Key Issues	3/13	3/13
22	Subimte Key Issues to PDC for input	3/13	3/14
23	Draft outline of responses to issues with team input	3/17	3/21
24	Team approval of outline responses to key issues	3/24	3/24
25	Submit outline (issues response) to PDC	3/25	3/25
26	Team review of outline (issues response)	3/25	3/25
27	**Slide Production Key Presentations**	**3/6**	**4/25**
28	Develop outline of Primary Presentation	3/6	3/12
29	Team approves Draft Outline of core	3/13	3/13
30	Management approval of outline of core	3/14	3/17
31	Primary Presentation	3/18	4/25

1/27, 2/3, 2/10, 2/17, 2/24, 3/2, 3/9, 3/16, 3/23, 3/30, 4/6, 4/13, 4/20, 4/27

Gantt chart annotations: 3D, PL/T; 3D, PL/T; Core Team; Core Team; PDC 2/25; Clinical QC; Clinical QC; Regulatory; Regulatory 3/6; Clinical Team; Clinical Team; Clinical Lead 3/13; Team Leader; Clinical Lead; Core Team 3/25; Clinical Lead; Clinical Team; Team Leader analyze their comments.

- Analyze their interests and positions on specific issues, including scientific studies they have authored, associations with which they are affiliated, practice guideline committees on which they serve, public comments in presentations and media interviews on specific issues.
- Identify the relationships among committee members including what association, university and company affiliations they may have in common.
- See the committee in action. Reviewing old Advisory Committee tapes and taking the team on a "field trip" to an Advisory Committee meeting are invaluable ways to analyze what types of questions are being asked, how they are being asked, and give the team the full flavor and experience of the event.

Leveraging Advocacy

Because FDA and Advisory Committee members are influenced by the public and political environment, sponsors must consider these external influences in the planning process. Sponsors should have a well-thought-out plan to communicate with key stakeholders—from patient advocacy groups and healthcare associations to key opinion leaders and policy groups.

Third-party advocates, key opinion leaders and medical experts can fill a variety of valuable roles in supporting the sponsor's goals. Assuming all ties with the sponsor are clearly revealed, they can publish articles on the data or the need for the product, speak at medical symposia, answer highly technical or specific questions from the Advisory Committee during the hearing, testify during the public comment period, and speak to the media.

It is important to note that engaging key opinion leaders and groups has never been more complicated, so any compensation must come with no strings attached. All financial relationships should be appropriately disclosed. In today's environment, transparency is extremely important.

Some key steps in creating an effective advocacy program are:

- identifying the most influential patient and consumer groups and healthcare associations and ranking them in terms of leadership and influence
- assessing opinions of medical experts in the field, as well as the position statements of medical societies
- listening to what financial analysts are saying about the product and how they are characterizing its impact on the company

Finally, it is important to prioritize the information and factor it into the communications strategy and core messages for all communications, including the Advisory

Committee presentation, the briefing book, the Q&A book and media outreach. As part of this process, it is also important to brief advocacy groups and, when appropriate, enlist their support.

Preparing the Briefing Materials, Core Presentation, and Q&A Book

There is no substitute for good data. But good data alone are not always sufficient to secure a positive recommendation at an Advisory Committee meeting. A well-constructed scientific story that provides context for that data is the backbone of a sponsor's briefing book and presentation.

To ensure consistency of messages across all materials, no content should be developed until a strategic messaging session is conducted. The messaging should drive the direction of the briefing book, the presentation script, the slides and answers to key questions. This process should begin as soon as the sponsor has selected and organized its team and is analyzing the environment, the audiences and its issues.

The primary steps in creating, prioritizing and harmonizing content are:

- Conduct a brainstorming session with key people from the sponsor's team. Set a goal for the content. What is it you really want to communicate to your audience about your product? Focus on the high-level messages that will serve as the foundation of the presentation to the Advisory Committee. These messages should be based on the medical need of the product, the strength of the data and the benefit the product provides.
- Discuss and prioritize the data, outlining all relevant studies for easy reference and outline key metrics of each study (e.g., meaningful endpoints, results, sample size, demographics), and rank the studies to determine which to emphasize during the presentation.
- Incorporate the data into a message matrix to serve as a guide to outline and develop the presentations and the questions and answers (Q&A), and prioritize the messages by rating what is most important by considering the strengths of the product and science, the issues FDA officials have highlighted and the areas of interest from Advisory Committee members.
- Finally, assign individual "owners" to issues by topic, assigning responsibility and accountability to specific team members for gathering data, drafting the first set of answers to questions, and developing supporting documentation in the form of charts, graphs or tables for slides.

Once the key messages and data for the briefing materials and presentation have been determined, it is time to construct the flow of the presentation and the briefing book.

Although the content and flow of both of these will vary depending upon the product and the issues, there are some general guidelines to follow.

For both the presentation and the briefing book, follow the rules of clear writing and logical organization. Headline main points. Be succinct, and write in short sentences. Summarize key messages at the beginning and end of the documents.

Writing the Briefing Book

Because the Advisory Committee members will get briefing books from both FDA and the sponsor, it is best to keep the book short, concise and well-organized, so it can be easily read and understood. Aim for approximately 100 to 150 pages in length, depending upon the extent of the clinical program.

For the purposes of efficiency, consistency and clarity, be sure to base the briefing book on the clinical section of the New Drug Application (NDA), Biologics License Application (BLA) or Premarket Approval Application (PMA), focusing on information directly related to the issues being considered by the committee. Edit out information and data not directly related to these issues. Consider how the product will fit within current treatment patterns in order to address treatment issues, barriers or beliefs. Never include new data in the book that have not been submitted in the NDA, BLA or PMA, and have therefore not been reviewed by FDA. Finally, avoid any statements or suggestions that can be viewed as misleading or promotional, or that can be misconstrued as a recommendation of off-label product use.

Structure the book in an organized way by dividing it into distinct sections, beginning with a clear executive summary that provides an overview of the main points of the book and makes the best case for the product or issue. Summarize and synthesize the data within each section.

Make certain that all presenters know the contents of the briefing book and can answer questions that arise from the book as well as the presentation.

Scripting the Core Presentation

Sponsors typically have between 45 and 90 minutes to deliver the core presentation. As a result, every word counts. The core presentation is the sponsor's opportunity to make its strongest case to a "jury" deciding its fate. Because this is not a typical scientific presentation but rather a persuasive argument with a singular goal, controlling the story around the data is critical. The science does not speak for itself; not everyone will interpret the same data in the same way; therefore, context and clear explanation are essential components of success.

While sponsors routinely develop core presentations from pre-developed slides, outlining and scripting the presentation before creating core slides will allow the messages to drive the presentation rather than data without context. Scripting every word of the presentation is also a must, as this will ensure the precision and clarity of the message and reduce the chances of "surprises" surfacing during the presentation.

As previously mentioned, the most effective and efficient way to develop a core presentation is to start with the goal and high-level messages from the brainstorming session. From those messages, create an outline to develop a story flow for the overall presentation, and then for each individual presentation. Look for opportunities to weave in and reinforce the main messages of the overall presentation for consistency.

Because the core is delivered as the spoken versus the written word, it is important that the script be written for the ear and not the eye. That means using short sentences and an active voice that can easily be delivered by the presenter and understood by the audience the first time. The goal of the presentation is that everyone listening understands the data in the same way.

Writing the Q&A Book

The same rules apply when developing answers to questions. Answers should be clearly headlined so the responses and messages are clear and direct. In addition, the questions and answers should be ordered in a well-organized book, so responders learn the answers and identify the appropriate slides. The book should serve as a practice tool as well as a map for the day of the hearing. This dynamic document will change as information is incorporated from new studies, agency feedback and external sources such as stakeholders and the media. The Q&A book should be organized by topic, and identify not only the question and answer, but also the appropriate responder and what, if any, slides support the point.

Developing and Managing Slides

Once the script is written, and as answers to questions are being crafted, slides should be developed to visually reinforce the information. The purpose of a slide is to support the presenter's message—not confuse it. As a result, slides should follow the same rules of clear communication. Choose a simple, clear slide template with mid-to-dark blue backgrounds, and a simple sans-serif font to reduce eye strain. For graph slides, make sure the x- and y-axes are thick and vibrant enough to be seen in the back of a large meeting room and are clearly labeled with easy-to-find legends. For text slides, the fewer words the better. The goal of any slide is to pass the "glance test," so the audience immediately understands the slide's message. It is better to have multiple slides that "build" and explain a point than to crowd too much information on one slide. Too much information on one slide can lead committee members to focus on different information and confuse the message.

With slides, as with writing, less is more.

To help in both the development and management of slides, a specific process should be followed and a team assigned. This team has several important functions. One function is to compile and organize data and slides for each component of the core presentation. A second function is to gather data and prepare backup slides for the questions the Advisory Committee members may ask. A third function is to quickly and calmly locate a requested backup slide for responders during the Q&A sessions. A fourth function is to help a presenter answer a question by prompting the presenter with an appropriately chosen slide on the preview monitor.

It is common for sponsors to have several thousand backup slides for the Q&A portion of the Advisory Committee meeting. Ideally, a slide should be displayed within a few seconds of the question being asked. For this to occur, it is best for sponsors to use an automated slide recall process. This system should allow responders to preview a slide on a monitor that only they can see, and then, in real time, decide whether to show that slide or call for another.

The intricate and important process of developing and locating the right slide at the right moment starts with the data triage team. The backup slides are typically organized by topic matter (e.g., safety, efficacy, unmet need, postmarketing surveillance). Each team member is responsible for at least one of these areas and is an expert.

Conducting Perfect Practice Through Rehearsals

As the content is being developed, it also needs to be tested. Sponsor teams frequently wait too long in the process to begin testing. This is a lost opportunity because testing through practice is the best way to refine content. In addition to internal team rehearsals, sponsors should also run several realistic rehearsals with external experts role-playing the Advisory Committee members.

A mock Advisory Committee hearing is a rehearsal "on steroids," and is where the sponsor's team gets its first taste of what it is like to present to a potentially critical audience and answer questions under pressure. If done correctly, it will provide a reality check for the sponsor. The more realistic the mock panel, the better prepared the presenters and other responders will be for the actual hearing.

The key to a realistic mock panel is convening one that mirrors the actual Advisory Committee as closely as possible. This increases the opportunity for mock members to examine, interpret and challenge the data in the same way as Advisory Committee members. This is one area in which effective profiles of committee members provide benefits. The mock Advisory Committee hearing should be constructed like a dress rehearsal. The room should be set up in the same formation as it will be on the day of the hearing.

Mock members should stay in role to provide presenters with a realistic run-through. The sponsor should provide briefing books to the mock Advisory Committee members prior to the rehearsal so they will go into the meeting with the same information as the actual committee. This book should be a near-complete draft of the final briefing book that will be submitted. The panel should critique the value of the book and the consistency of information provided with the presentations.

Following the rehearsal, the mock panelists should provide a tough, insightful critique and give honest feedback about the presenters as well as the presentation. This feedback should be used to adjust and enhance strategy, core messages and responses for the Q&A session.

The sponsor's internal team should schedule a debrief immediately following each mock hearing, and document what worked well and what can de done differently in preparation for the next mock hearing.

Maximizing the Final Days before the Advisory Committee Meeting

In the few days leading up to the meeting, sponsor teams should set up rehearsals on or near the FDA meeting site, near Washington, DC. Forty-eight hours before the meeting, FDA will release final names of the Advisory Committee members, as well as the specific questions they will pose to the committee. This is the time to readjust strategy, if necessary, edit the final presentation and refine Q&A responses.

A logistics plan should be in place to help facilitate and control communications among team members during the meeting. Given the pressure and time constraints of Advisory Committee day, discipline in communications is critical. Only vital issues should be discussed, and that discussion should be fast, focused and confidential.

Whatever system is chosen, it must be thought through in advance and communicated to everyone involved. This includes everything from ensuring the availability of enough meeting rooms with working computers, printers, copiers and faxes, to ensuring the presence of a solid security system to guard against breaches. Whether a company hires a professional meeting planning company or security firm, or handles these tasks internally, organization and security are crucial components to ensuring that the meeting runs smoothly.

Summary

With Advisory Committee meetings becoming more like adversarial proceedings than presentations of scientific data, companies must prepare as they would for a big court case that has major implications on everything from the company's stock price to its reputation. Clear and persuasive communication is the key to success in this challenging environment.

Strategic communications planning is critical and must begin early in the product's lifecycle. Companies must honestly assess and analyze their products and be open to criticism and perceptions, right or wrong, that exist in the external environment. It is imperative to understand the concerns of the various audiences, and to be proactive and persuasive in addressing their issues through an effective communication plan. By applying these principles zealously to the Advisory Committee meeting preparation process, companies can hope to achieve their goal of a positive Advisory Committee recommendation and, ultimately, FDA approval of their product.

Reference and Recommended Reading

The FDA Advisory Committee Survival Manual: A Step-by-Step Guide to Preparing for a Successful Meeting. © 3D Communications (2008). Available at: www.3dcommunications.us/FDAsurvivalguide.html. Accessed 11 May 2011.

Chapter 5

Good Laboratory Practice Regulations

Updated by Kurt Stahl and Dana Dunn, MS

Objectives

- Review the history and purpose of GLP regulations
- Learn the key GLP regulation components
- Examine the implications of noncompliance with GLP regulations

Regulations and Guidance Documents Covered in This Chapter

- Section 701(a) of the *Federal Food, Drug, and Cosmetic Act* of 1938
- 21 CFR 58, Good Laboratory Practice for nonclinical laboratory studies, Final Rule (1987)
- Organization for Economic Cooperation and Development, *Principles of Good Laboratory Practice* (Revised 1997)
- Japanese Ministry of Health, Labour and Welfare, *Good Laboratory Practice Standards,* Ordinance No. 21 (Revised 2008)
- 40 CFR 792, *Toxic Substances Control Act,* Good Laboratory Practice Standards (29 December 1983)
- 40 CFR 160, *Federal Insecticide, Fungicide, and Rodenticide Act,* Good Laboratory Practice Standards (2 May 1984)
- US Department of Health and Human Services, Food and Drug Administration, Office of Regulatory Affairs, Comparison Chart of FDA and EPA Good Laboratory Practice (GLP) Regulations and the OECD Principles of GLP (June 2004)
- US Food and Drug Administration, Office of Regulatory Affairs, *Bioresearch Monitoring Good Laboratory Practice Compliance Program Guidance 7348.808 (Nonclinical Laboratories)* (21 February 2001)
- Food and Drug Administration Compliance Program Guidance Manual, Program 7348.808A, *Good Laboratory Practice Program (Nonclinical Laboratories) EPA Data Audit Inspections,* (25 August 2000)

Introduction

The US Food and Drug Administration (FDA) requires manufacturers of human drugs, biopharmaceuticals and biological products, animal drugs, medical devices, electronic products and food additives to demonstrate the safety of their products prior to use in humans or, in the case of animal drugs, prior to use in the indicated species. Compliance with Title 21 of the Code of Federal Regulations (CFR) Part 58, the Good Laboratory Practice (GLP) regulation, is intended to assure the quality and integrity of the safety data used to support applications for research or marketing permits for FDA-regulated products. Compliance with GLPs allows for accurate reconstruction

of the conduct of a nonclinical study based on quality recordkeeping and reporting. GLP regulations are promulgated by the FDA commissioner under the general authority of the *Federal Food, Drug, and Cosmetic Act* of 1938 (*FD&C Act*).

The US Environmental Protection Agency (EPA) requires manufacturers of chemical substances and mixtures and pesticide products to conduct studies to evaluate their health effects, environmental effects and chemical fate. Compliance with EPA's *Toxic Substances Control Act* (*TSCA*) Good Laboratory Practice Standards regulation, 40 CFR 792, and the *Federal Insecticide, Fungicide, and Rodenticide Act* (*FIFRA*) Good Laboratory Practice

Standards regulation, 40 CFR 160, is intended to assure data quality for the testing of chemical substances and mixtures and pesticides, respectively.

The Organization for Economic Cooperation and Development (OECD), which includes member countries throughout North America, Europe and Asia, developed a set of principles very similar to FDA GLP regulations. Like FDA GLPs, the OECD regulations are applicable to nonclinical safety studies for pharmaceutical products, animal drugs and food additives, but also are applicable to studies to evaluate the safety of pesticides and industrial chemicals. The Japanese Ministry of Health, Labour and Welfare (MHLW) has also issued regulations similar to the FDA GLPs. Studies conducted in compliance with OECD and MHLW GLPs are generally accepted by FDA under mutual recognition agreements.

FDA, EPA and MHLW GLPs are regulations and are required by law, whereas the OECD GLP principles are voluntary procedures that must be adopted as a regulation within each member country.[1]

FDA's Office of Regulatory Affairs (ORA) issued a "Comparison Chart of FDA and EPA Good Laboratory Practice (GLP) Regulations and the OECD Principles of GLP" in June 2004. The comparison chart provides a listing of the similarities and differences among the three GLP regulations.[2]

GLPs, whether put forth by FDA, EPA or OECD, "were designed to ensure data quality and to reduce fraud by requiring that specific documentation be kept regarding several key areas that include laboratory staff, facilities and operations, equipment, test and control articles, protocol, conduct of the study, quality assurance and archiving of data, records and specimens."[3]

Most drug and biologic developers will not need to refer to the EPA GLPs and because the focus of this book is on US regulations, the remainder of this chapter is devoted to a discussion of the FDA GLP regulation as set forth in 21 CFR 58. However, it is not uncommon for non-clinical studies to be conducted in accordance with FDA, OECD and MHLW GLP regulations, depending upon the intended market for the product, so familiarity with the OECD and MHLW GLPs may be helpful.

Definition and Scope of 21 CFR 58

21 CFR 58 "prescribes good laboratory practices for conducting nonclinical laboratory studies that support or are intended to support applications for research or marketing permits for products regulated by the Food and Drug Administration, including food and color additives, animal food additives, human and animal drugs, medical devices for human use, biological products, and electronic products. Compliance with this part is intended to assure the quality and integrity of the safety data filed pursuant to sections 406, 408, 409, 502, 503, 505, 506, 510, 512–516, 518–520, 721, and 801 of the *Federal Food, Drug, and Cosmetic Act* and sections 351 and 354-360F of the *Public Health Service Act*."[4]

A "nonclinical laboratory study means *in vivo* or *in vitro* experiments in which test articles are studied prospectively in test systems under laboratory conditions to determine their safety. The term does not include studies utilizing human subjects or clinical studies or field trials in animals. The term does not include basic exploratory studies carried out to determine whether a test article has any potential utility or to determine the physical or chemical characteristics of a test article."[5]

Studies that are expected to be in compliance with GLPs include, but are not limited to:

- acute, subchronic and chronic toxicology studies
- carcinogenicity and genotoxicity (*in vitro* and *in vivo*) studies
- developmental and reproductive toxicology studies
- dermal/eye/venous/muscle irritation studies
- safety pharmacology studies (core battery)
- bioanalytical studies of samples from dose groups of study animals
- studies to validate the analytical methods to be used for samples from GLP studies (e.g., bioanalysis and test article formulation analysis)

Laboratories that analyze samples generated from GLP studies, such as clinical chemistry, histology and pathology, are subject to GLP regulations.

Examples of studies that are not subject to GLPs include, but are not limited to:

- basic research
- proof of concept studies
- exploratory pharmacokinetic studies (absorption, distribution, metabolism and elimination)
- dose-range finding studies
- primary pharmacodynamic studies
- analytical quality control testing for clinical and commercial products
- stability testing of clinical and commercial products
- studies using human subjects
- field trials in animals

Analytical/quality control laboratories that test raw materials and in-process samples; perform release testing for active pharmaceutical ingredients, drug products and medical devices; and perform stability testing are not subject to GLP regulations. These laboratories are subject to Good Manufacturing Practice regulations.

There are no specific FDA regulations or guidances for laboratories that perform testing of clinical samples from human clinical trials. GLPs state that nonclinical laboratory studies do not include studies utilizing human subjects or clinical studies. *Clinical Laboratory Improvement*

Amendments (*CLIA*) regulations are not applicable to research laboratories that test human specimens and do not report patient-specific results for the diagnosis, prevention or treatment of any disease or impairment of, or the assessment of the health of individual patients.[6]

GLPs and *CLIA* share similar goals in terms of assuring the quality and integrity of data produced during laboratory testing. Because there are no specific regulations or guidances for the testing of human clinical samples, many organizations—i.e., clinical trial sponsors—use the GLP and/or *CLIA* regulations as audit standards when assessing the quality of the laboratories used to test human clinical samples. The College of American Pathologists (CAP) serves as an accreditation organization under *CLIA* and has published its own guidelines for GLPs for testing of human samples.[7] The CAP guidelines have some similarity to FDA GLPs, but are focused more on laboratory process quality rather than study quality as a whole.

History of FDA GLPs

Throughout the 1960s and 1970s, the use of chemicals became more prevalent in the US. The fear of negative health effects caused by the widespread use of chemicals was shared by the public and the government. As a result, there was an increase in the number of federal laws applicable to chemical and pharmaceutical companies and an increase in the amount of product testing required. In 1969, FDA developed a plan to inspect laboratories that conducted animal research. The plan included directed inspections of facilities whose submitted studies contained inconsistencies or had questionable data integrity, where there was simultaneous performance of a large number of complex studies or where a tip had been received alleging scientific misconduct. The results of the initial investigations showed significant data quality problems and a lack of industry standards in animal toxicology testing.[8]

In 1975, FDA conducted a facility inspection of G.D. Searle and Company of Skokie, IL. Searle manufactured several pharmaceutical products and had submitted toxicology data to FDA in support of product applications. The inspection found questionable test data due to sloppy work; untrained personnel; and poor data collection, analyses, review and reporting practices.[9] In another case, numerous instances of scientific misconduct were found when FDA inspected Industrial Bio-Test Laboratories (IBT), a contract testing laboratory located in Northbrook, IL in 1976. Some of the findings noted by FDA were fabrication of data, replacement of dead study animals with healthy ones that had not received drug treatment, changes in the interpretation of histopathology slides, and changes in report conclusions to make them look more favorable.[10]

In 1976, as a result of numerous scientific integrity and data quality problems found when inspecting toxicology laboratories, FDA proposed GLP regulations. The final regulations were published in 1978 and became law in 1979. Proposed changes to the GLPs were published in 1984, revisions were made and the GLP regulations, final rule, were published in 1987. FDA published a request for comments on proposed revisions to the current regulations in 2010, discussed later in this chapter.

FDA GLP Subparts and Sections

To predict safety prior to use in humans or therapeutic use in animals, nonclinical studies are required for FDA-regulated products such as human and animal drugs, biopharmaceuticals, biological products, food and color additives, animal food additives, medical devices for human use and electronic products. The data obtained from the GLP nonclinical studies and submitted to FDA are used to make decisions on the product's overall toxicity profile, including the dose level at which there were no observed adverse effects, the potential adverse effects and risks associated with clinical studies involving humans or animals, the product's teratogenic and/or carcinogenic potential, and the dose level, frequency and duration of use that can be approved.[11]

Strict adherence to scientific principles, data integrity and quality assurance provide the foundation for the GLP regulations. As mentioned above, the GLPs are codified in 21 CFR 58. The GLP regulations specify the minimum standards for the conduct and reporting of nonclinical laboratory studies that are to be used in support of a marketing application in the US. The GLPs are organized into subparts A through K with subparts H and I reserved. The subparts and their sections are noted in **Table 6-1**.

Key Elements of FDA GLPs

Key elements of the GLPs that merit discussion include:

Subpart A:
§58.3 Definitions

It is important to read and understand the definitions used in 21 CFR 58. A thorough understanding of the definitions is critical to correct interpretation of and compliance with the regulations in this section.

§58.10 Applicability to Studies Performed under Grants and Contracts

When electing to use a contract research organization (CRO) or a contractor to perform all or part of a nonclinical laboratory study intended to be submitted to FDA in support of an application or marketing permit, the sponsor is responsible for notifying the CRO/contractor that the study must be conducted in compliance with GLPs. The study protocol should include a statement

Table 6-1. 21 CFR 58

Subpart	Section
Subpart A - General Provisions	§58.1 Scope
	§58.3 Definitions
	§58.10 Applicability to studies performed under grants and contracts
	§58.15 Inspection of a testing facility
Subpart B - Organization and Personnel	§58.29 Personnel
	§58.31 Testing facility management
	§58.33 Study director
	§58.35 Quality assurance unit
Subpart C - Facilities	§58.41 General
	§58.43 Animal care facilities
	§58.45 Animal supply facilities
	§58.47 Facilities for handling test and control articles
	§58.49 Laboratory operation areas
	§58.51 Specimen and data storage facilities
Subpart D - Equipment	§58.61 Equipment design
	§58.63 Maintenance and calibration of equipment
Subpart E - Testing Facilities Operation	§58.81 Standard operating procedures
	§58.83 Reagents and solutions
	§58.90 Animal care
Subpart F - Test and Control Articles	§58.105 Test and control article characterization
	§58.107 Test and control article handling
	§58.113 Mixtures of articles with carriers
Subpart G - Protocol for and Conduct of a Nonclinical Laboratory Study	§58.120 Protocol
	§58.130 Conduct of a nonclinical laboratory study
Subpart J - Records and Reports	§58.185 Reporting of nonclinical laboratory study results
	§58.190 Storage and retrieval of records and data
	§58.195 Retention of records
Subpart K - Disqualification of Testing Facilities	§58.200 Purpose
	§58.202 Grounds for disqualification
	§58.204 Notice of and opportunity for hearing on proposed disqualification
	§58.206 Final order on disqualification
	§58.210 Actions upon disqualification
	§58.213 Public disclosure of information regarding disqualification
	§58.215 Alternative or additional actions to disqualification
	§58.217 Suspension or termination of a testing facility by a sponsor
	§58.219 Reinstatement of a disqualified testing facility

about the regulatory standards under which the study will be conducted.

Though not specifically stated, there is an expectation that the sponsor will ensure the GLP capabilities of the contracted facility prior to initiation of work. The sponsor usually evaluates the facility's regulatory inspection history and/or performs a GLP prequalification audit. This is important because a facility may claim GLP compliance without a full understanding of the intricacies of 21 CFR 58. A sponsor should be wary of a facility, in the US or abroad, that claims GLP compliance but has never been inspected by FDA or contributed data to a submission reviewed by FDA.

Subpart B:
§58.29 Personnel

An adequate number of personnel, appropriately qualified by education, training, experience or a combination thereof are required by the regulations. Job qualifications are defined by laboratory management and not the regulations; however, the sponsor should ensure that appropriately qualified personnel are available to conduct the study. Maintenance of a comprehensive training file for each individual is required to document these qualifications.

§58.31, 58.33, 58.35 Testing Facility Management, Study Director, and Quality Assurance Unit (QAU), respectively

The GLP regulations are very specific regarding the responsibilities of these three functions. Testing facility management is responsible for approving all test facility standard operating procedures (SOPs). Facility management is responsible for designating a study director prior to the initiation of the study and promptly replacing the study director, if necessary, during the conduct of the study. Facility management must assure that test and control articles and mixtures thereof have been appropriately tested for identity, purity, stability or other defining characteristics. Facility management also has the authority to provide resources and implement changes necessary to comply with GLP requirements and, if necessary, to ensure corrective actions are taken to address audit findings.

The study director is the single point of control for a nonclinical study. The study director has overall responsibility for the study's design, conduct and reporting, including compliance with the study protocol and GLP regulations. The study director must ensure that all circumstances that could affect the study's integrity are documented and assessed for impact and that corrective actions are taken as necessary. This should include evaluation of unexpected events occurring at other test sites that contribute data to the study.

The study director is usually at the testing facility where the test article is administered to the test system. It has become common practice to conduct nonclinical studies across multiple test sites with an individual (usually called a contributing scientist or principal investigator) identified to oversee the work conducted at each facility. It is important that this individual not be referred to as a study director because he or she does not have the same responsibilities or authority for the overall study.

QAU is responsible for ensuring that studies are conducted in accordance with the study protocol and GLPs. QAU must remain independent from the study and must not report to the director conducting the study.

QAU personnel maintain a master schedule of GLP studies and copies of the study protocol and amendments, and ensure that no deviations from approved procedures and study protocols are made without proper authorization and documentation. QAU personnel inspect facilities on a schedule defined by an SOP to ensure GLP compliance within the facility. These inspections include equipment

maintenance, training records, etc. The findings from these inspections are sent to facility management for remedial actions. QAU personnel inspect studies at intervals appropriate to assure integrity, provide inspection findings and prepare final reports, which include a statement specifying the dates of the inspection, to the study director and facility management.

Subpart D:
§58.61 and §58.63 Equipment Design and Maintenance and Calibration of Equipment

The GLP regulations do not have a section specific to the requirements for computer systems and they do not contain the term "computerized system," but a review of the *Bioresearch Monitoring Good Laboratory Practice Compliance Program 7348.808*, Appendix A, shows that computer systems and computer operations are included in an FDA inspection of a GLP test facility. If computerized systems are used to generate, measure, assess and store data, appropriate procedures and controls must be established and followed to ensure the quality and integrity of the study.

As revised in 2002, 21 CRF 11, Electronic Records; Electronic Signatures, established FDA's "criteria under which the agency considers electronic records, electronic signatures, and handwritten signatures executed to electronic records to be trustworthy, reliable, and generally equivalent to paper records and handwritten signatures executed on paper." While Part 11 is separate from the GLPs, the two are closely linked when computerized systems are used during GLP-compliant studies. The current trend among nonclinical CROs is the use of computerized systems for all recordkeeping, and FDA expects these systems will be compliant with 21 CFR 11.

Subpart E:
§58.81 Standard Operating Procedures

SOPs are an integral part of the conduct and recreation of GLP studies. SOPs are intended to ensure that laboratory procedures and processes are consistently performed by all individuals throughout the facility. Accordingly, SOPs should be readily available to all laboratory staff and a mandatory review of SOPs should be performed and documented. Test facility management is responsible for periodically reviewing and updating SOPs as needed.

In general, the study protocol outlines "what" is to be done during a nonclinical study, but SOPs describe "how" those procedures are to be performed. For example, the protocol would instruct you to administer an intravenous injection, but the SOP would tell you what size needle and syringe to use, the appropriate vein for the injection, the proper method of restraint for the animal, etc. A comprehensive set of SOPs should address all aspects of study conduct from pre-initiation work through archiving data and specimens after study completion. SOPs should also describe the processes in place to address each requirement outlined in 21 CFR 58.

All deviations from SOPs that occur during a study should be documented, authorized by the study director, and assessed for impact on study integrity. Specific instructions given in the study protocol supersede SOPs and in this case it should not be considered a deviation if SOPs are not followed.

Subpart F:
§58.105, 58.107, 58.113 Test and Control Article Characterization and Handling and Mixtures of Articles with Carriers

"Test article" means any food additive, color additive, drug, biopharmaceutical, biological product, medical device or electronic product intended for human use. "Control article" means any article other than the test article that is intended to serve as a control in the study; it typically establishes a basis for comparison with the test article.

GLPs require that characterization, stability testing, sample retention and inventory for the test and control articles be performed and documented. Characterization and stability testing may be performed by the test facility conducting the study, by the sponsor or by a laboratory contracted by the sponsor. Responsibility for the testing should be stated in the study protocol. Stability testing of the test and control articles and mixtures thereof can be performed prior to initiation or concomitantly with conduct of the study. It is important to demonstrate stability under both the conditions of storage and the conditions of use during the study. Stability of the mixture of a test article with a carrier (vehicle) must be established for a range of concentrations that bracket those used during the study.

Proper handling of the test and control articles is essential to the quality and integrity of the nonclinical study. Section 58.107 requires sponsors to establish procedures for the proper storage, distribution, identification and receipt/distribution of the articles.

Although the term "chain of custody" is not used in the GLP regulations, there is an expectation that documentation showing all movements and locations of the test and control articles from the time of sponsor shipment to final disposition will be generated and maintained.

Subpart G:
§58.120 and §58.130 Protocol for and Conduct of a Nonclinical Laboratory Study

Each GLP study is conducted according to a formal plan, i.e., study protocol. There can be only one protocol for each study. A document that describes subcontracted work conducted by a contributing scientist in support of a GLP study should not be titled as a protocol. The GLP regulations provide a list of items to be included, as applicable, in the study protocol. The order of the items presented in the study protocol may vary provided that all relevant items are included. The study director must sign the study protocol prior to the generation of any study-specific data. The sponsor is not required to sign the protocol, but the date of the sponsor's approval must be documented within.

During the execution of the study protocol, changes to the protocol may be needed. Planned changes from the protocol, i.e., changes before they occur, are made by issuing protocol amendments, which are approved by the individuals who approved the initial study protocol. Following approval, all relevant parties should be notified of a protocol amendment.

Study deviations—those specific to the study protocol or to SOPs applicable to the conduct of the study—may occur during the course of the study. These unplanned events must be documented and assessed for study impact by the study director and reviewed by QAU.

Quality data and the ability to accurately recreate a study are major goals of the GLPs. To this end, Section 58.130(e) is very specific about the handling of raw data. Data generated by hand are to be recorded "directly, promptly, and legibly in ink." Each entry must be accompanied by the date and the signature or initials of the recorder. Changes to data must not obscure the original entry and must be accompanied by an explanation or justification and the signature or initials of the person making the change. Prompt recording of data is important so changes made to an entry at a later date must include strong supporting documentation and justification. The same general processes apply to data generated electronically and are also related to the requirements set forth in 21 CFR 11, Electronic Records; Electronic Signatures.

Subpart J:
§58.185 Reporting of Nonclinical Study Results

The GLP regulations provide a list of required elements to be included in the final study report. A final report should be prepared for each study conducted. The date the study director signs the final report is the study completion date.

Instructions defined in Compliance Program 7348.808 specify that FDA inspectors are to verify that study reports contain all the required elements. If a subcontractor was used, the name and address of the subcontractor's facilities and the portion of the study that the subcontractor executed must be included. There must be a description of any computer program changes. The dated signature of the study director is required and, if any changes or additions were made to the final report after the study director's signature, it must include a statement and signature that the changes/additions were made in accordance with the requirements of Section 58.185.

The study director is responsible for documenting in the final study report all circumstances that may affect the study's quality and integrity. This should include, at a minimum, descriptions of deviations from the study protocol.

Although the GLP regulations do not specifically require the final report to contain a statement of GLP compliance, it is common practice for the study director to include such a statement. Sponsors generally find this preferable because they are ultimately required to make such a statement, when applicable, by 21 CFR 312.23(a)(8)(b)(iii), Investigational New Application, and 314.50 (d)(2)(v), Application for FDA Approval to Market a New Drug. Both regulations state that "for each nonclinical laboratory study subject to the good laboratory practice regulations under Part 58, a statement that the study was conducted in compliance with the good laboratory practice regulations in Part 58, or, if the study was not conducted in compliance with those regulations, a brief statement of the reason for the noncompliance" must be submitted. For studies conducted across multiple sites, each contributing scientist is expected to provide a statement to the study director that attests to the GLP compliance of the work conducted at his or her facility. This, along with QAU inspection reports, allows the study director to make an accurate statement of GLP compliance for all aspects of the study.

Full compliance with GLPs for studies subject to the regulation is always preferable, but FDA indicated in its Questions and Answers document that nonclinical laboratory safety studies with areas of noncompliance may be acceptable, provided the noncompliance did not compromise the study's quality and integrity.[12]

§58.190 Storage and Retrieval of Records and Data

The GLPs are specific with regard to the establishment of an archive for the storage of raw data documentation, protocols, specimens and interim and final reports from completed studies. The regulations also require that an individual be assigned responsibility for the archives. At the conclusion of the study, i.e., after the study director has signed the final study report, all the raw data, protocols, amendments, analytical data and specimens are transferred to a secure storage area. The records and data are maintained under appropriate conditions in accordance with the record retention requirements specified in Section 58.195.

Proposed Changes to Current FDA GLPs

In December 2010, FDA issued a public request for comments on proposed revisions to the GLPs.[13] Since the final regulations were published in 1978, there have been changes in the complexity and logistics of conducting nonclinical studies, most notably in the conduct of studies across multiple test sites. FDA established a working group in 2007 to evaluate the adequacy of the current GLPs relative to modern nonclinical studies and they concluded that

changes to certain aspects of the regulations may be needed. Areas identified for potential revision include addressing multi-site studies, expanding sponsor responsibilities, monitoring QAU inspection findings, test and control article information, and implementation of GLP quality systems at nonclinical laboratories. A timeline for implementing the changes has not been set.

FDA Inspection of GLP Laboratories and the Consequences of Noncompliance

All laboratories operating within the US that perform nonclinical laboratory studies are subject to inspection by FDA. The agency also conducts GLP inspections of laboratories outside the US, but only after it has requested and received consent from the laboratory.

FDA has established a Bioresearch Monitoring Program (BIMO) to address both domestic and international inspections of nonclinical testing laboratories operating under US GLPs. FDA and ORA issued *Compliance Program Guidance 7348*.808,[14] which represents FDA's current thinking on the inspection of GLP facilities and studies. The guidance provides insight into how nonclinical testing laboratory inspections are conducted and likely focal areas for the inspection.

A review of FDA archived Warning Letters from 1996 through 2010 showed the most frequently cited GLP violations involved the failure of QAU and study directors to fulfill their responsibilities. Lack of a QAU and inadequate qualification of QAU personnel were also cited in the Warning Letters. Other selected GLP violations cited included: failure to follow the study protocol, inadequate final report, failure to establish SOPs adequate to ensure the quality and integrity of the data, failure of the test facility management to fulfill their responsibilities and failure to archive study records and data.

While most of the requirements established in the GLPs are clearly described, FDA inspectors' interpretations of the regulations can evolve over time. A recent example applies to preparation of final study reports that include sub-reports from contributing scientists.[15] Per Section 58.185(a)(12), a final report shall include, "the signed and dated reports of each of the individual scientists or other professionals involved in the study." It is common practice among CROs to prepare a draft final report using unsigned contributor reports and then submit it for review by the sponsor and QAU. However, FDA has recently cited at least three CROs for preparing draft final reports using unsigned contributor reports, noting that, as a result, the report "lacked accountability and confirmation that the contributing scientists' raw data was accurate."[16] In addition, allowing the sponsor to review and edit the final report before it is signed by the study director implies that "bias in data interpretation and reporting cannot be ruled out."

The consequences of noncompliance with GLP regulations can be severe. Deficiencies, such as those found during the inspections of IBT and Searle, made it impossible to either prove or disprove the safety of the products; consequently, numerous studies were declared invalid. Noncompliance with GLPs can result in research applications being placed on clinical hold and marketing permits being delayed or refused.

The measures FDA can take against a nonclinical test facility can range from the issuance of FDA inspectional observations (Form FDA 483), to Warning Letters, to consent agreements, to disqualification of a testing facility for conducting nonclinical laboratory studies.

If noncompliance with GLPs results in disqualification of the testing laboratory, any nonclinical laboratory study conducted by the laboratory that is submitted to FDA in an application for research or a marketing permit before or after the laboratory is disqualified may be presumed to be unacceptable and the application may be deemed unacceptable.

Summary

GLP compliance is expected for studies that support or are intended to support FDA-regulated applications including INDs, NDAs, IDEs, PMAs, etc. Compliance with GLPs ensures the quality, integrity, accuracy and reproducibility of data submitted for review by FDA. GLPs set minimum requirements for facility management, study personnel, study conduct, standardization of procedures, reporting, record retention and quality control systems.

References

1. Swidersky P. "Quality Assurance and Good Lab Practice, Examining the FDA's & OECD's GLPs." *Contract Pharma.* 76–83, May 2007.
2. US Department of Health and Human Services, Food and Drug Administration, Office of Regulatory Affairs, Comparison Chart of FDA and EPA Good Laboratory Practice (GLP) Regulations and the OECD Principles of GLP (Issue date: June 2004).
3. Op cit 1.
4. US Department of Health and Human Serivces, Food and Drug Administration, Code of Federal Regulations, Title 21 Part 58, Good Laboratory Practice for Nonclinical Laboratory Studies, Final Rule, 1987.
5. Ibid.
6. *Clinical Laboratories Improvement Amendments (CLIA),* 42 CFR Part 493.3.
7. Centers for Disease Control and Prevention. "Good Laboratory Practices for Waived Testing Sites." *Morbidity and Mortality Weekly Report.* 54(No. RR-13), November 2005.
8. Baldeshwiler A. "History of FDA Good Laboratory Practices." *Qual Assur J.* 7: 157–161 (2003).
9. Weisskopf C. "Here's another fine mess you've gotten us into." *Washington State University, Agrichemical and Environmental News.* May 1998.
10. Marshall E. "The murky world of toxicity testing." *Science.* 220:1130–1132 (1983).
11. US Department of Health and Human Services, Food and Drug Administration, Office of Regulatory Affairs, *Compliance Program Guidance 7348.808, Bioresearch Monitoring, Good Laboratory Practice, Compliance Program Guidance 7348.808 (Nonclinical Laboratories)* (Issued 21 February 2001).
12. US Department of Health and Human Services, Food and Drug Administration. Bioresearch Monitoring Staff (HFC-30), *Guidance for Industry, Good Laboratory Practices Questions and Answers.* June 1981, revised December 1999 and September 2000.
13. "Good Laboratory Practice for Nonclinical Laboratory Studies; Advanced Notice of Proposed Rulemaking," *Federal Register* 75 (21 December 2010), pp. 80011–80013.
14. US Department of Health and Human Services. Food and Drug Administration, Office of Regulatory Affairs, *Compliance Program Guidance 7348.808, Bioresearch Monitoring, Good Laboratory Practice, Compliance Program Guidance 7348.808 (Nonclinical Laboratories)* (Issued 21 February 2001).
15. Snyder S. "Regulatory Shockwaves: An FDA Ruling Stuns the Industry." *Contract Pharma.* October 2010. Web. http://www.contractpharma.com/articles/2010/10/preclinical-outsourcing. Accessed 26 April 2011.
16. US Department of Health and Human Services, Food and Drug Administration, Inspections, Compliance, Enforcement, and Criminal Investigations, *Warning Letter (to SNBL USA, Ltd.).* Issued 9 August 2010. Web. http://www.fda.gov/ICECI/EnforcementActions/WarningLetters/ucm222775.htm. Accessed 26 April 2011.

Recommended Reading

Cataneo R. "Good Laboratory Practice for Nonclinical Laboratory Studies: A Review." *Regulatory Focus* July 2008: 31–35.
US Department of Health and Human Services, Food and Drug Administration, Bioresearch Monitoring Staff (HFC-30), GLP Regulations (Management Briefings) Post Conference Report, Rockville, MD. August 1979: 5–12.
US Department of Health and Human Services, Food and Drug Administration, Bioresearch Monitoring Staff (HFC-30), *Guidance for Industry, Good Laboratory Practices Questions and Answers.* June 1981, revised December 1999 and September 2000.
US Department of Health and Human Services, Food

and Drug Administration, Office of Regulatory Affairs, *Compliance Program Guidance 7348.808, Bioresearch Monitoring, Good Laboratory Practice, Compliance Program Guidance 7348.808 (Nonclinical Laboratories)* (Issued 21 February 2001).

US Department of Health and Human Services, Food and Drug Administration, Bioresearch Monitoring. *Good Laboratory Practices Regulation* (Issued 4 September 1987).

Chapter 6

Clinical Trials: GCPs, Regulations and Compliance

Updated by Grant S. Griffin, CCRC

Objectives

- Provide an overview of GCPs for drugs and devices
- Provide an overview of clinical trial monitoring responsibilities
- Provide differences between *HIPAA*: FDA's Common Rule and HHS Privacy Rule
- Provide an overview of drug and device regulations
- Distinguish clinical trial requirements at the state and federal levels
- Provide regulatory compliance guidance

Laws, Regulations and Guidelines covered in this chapter

- 21 CFR 11 Electronic Records; Electronic Signatures
- 21 CFR 50 Protection of Human Subjects (Informed Consent)
- 21 CFR 54 Financial Disclosure by Clinical Investigators
- 21 CFR 56 Institutional Review Boards
- 21 CFR 312 Investigational New Drug Application
- 21 CFR 812 Investigational Device Exemptions
- 45 CFR 46 Protection of Human Subjects
- 45 CFR 164 Security and Privacy
- *Guidance for Industry: Investigator Responsibilities—Protecting the Rights, Safety and Welfare of Study Subjects* (October 2009)
- *Financial Relationships and Interests in Research Involving Human Subjects: Guidance for Human Subject Protection* (May 2004)
- *Guidance for Industry and Clinical Investigators: The Use of Clinical Holds Following Clinical Investigator Misconduct* (September 2004)
- *Guidance for Industry: Financial Disclosure by Clinical Investigators* (March 2001)
- *Guidance for Industry: Guideline for the Monitoring of Clinical Investigations* (January 1988)
- *Guidance for Industry on Using a Centralized IRB Process in Multicenter Clinical Trial* (March 2006)
- *Draft Guidance for Institutional Review Boards, Clinical Investigators, and Sponsors; Exception from Informed Consent Requirements for Emergency Research* (July 2006)
- *Guidance for Clinical Investigators, Sponsors, and IRBs: Adverse Event Reporting—Improving Human Subject Protection* (January 2009)
- *Guidance for Clinical Investigators, Institutional Review Boards and Sponsors: Process for Handling Referrals to FDA under 21 CFR 50.54, Additional Safeguards for Children in Clinical Investigations* (December 2006)
- *Information Sheet Guidance for Sponsors, Clinical Investigators, and Institutional Review Boards on Frequently Asked Questions--Statement of Investigator (Form FDA 1572)* (July 2008)
- *Guidance for Industry: Collection of Race and Ethnicity Data in Clinical Trials* (September 2005)

- *Guidance for Industry: Guideline for the Study and Evaluation of Gender Differences in the Clinical Evaluation of Drugs* (July 2003)
- *Guidance for Industry: Development and Use of Risk Minimization Action Plans* (March 2005)
- *Guidance for Industry: Good Pharmacovigilance Practices and Pharmacoepidemiologic Assessment* (March 2005)
- *Guidance for Industry: Premarketing Risk Assessment* (March 2005)
- *Guidance for Industry: End-of-Phase 2A Meetings* (September 2008)
- *Guidance for Industry: IND Meetings for Human Drugs and Biologics Chemistry, Manufacturing, and Controls Information* (May 2001)
- ICH, *Development Safety Update Report E2F (Draft)* (June 2008)
- ICH, *Structure and Content of Clinical Study Reports E3* (November 1995)
- ICH, *Ethnic Factors in the Acceptability of Foreign Clinical Data E5(R1)* (February 1998)
- ICH, *Guideline for Good Clinical Practice E6(R1)* (May 1996)
- ICH, *Choice of Control Group and Related Issues in Clinical Trials E10* (July 2000)
- ICH, *Guidance on Nonclinical Safety Studies for the Conduct of Human Clinical Trials and Marketing Authorization for Pharmaceuticals M3(R2)* (November 1995)
- ICH, *Pharmaceutical Development Q8(R1)* (November 2005)
- ICH, *Quality Risk Management Q9* (November 2005)
- ICH, *Dose Selection for Carcinogenicity Studies of Pharmaceuticals S1C(R2)* (March 2008)
- *Guidance on Engagement of Institutions in Human Subjects Research* (October 2008)
- *Guidance on Institutional Review Board Review of Clinical Trial Websites* (October 2005)
- Human Subject Regulations Decision Charts (September 2004)
- Informed Consent Checklist
- *Informed Consent Requirements for In Vitro Medical Device Clinical Investigations Conducted Under FDA's Interim Final Rule at 21 CFR 50.23(e)* (June 2006)
- Informed Consent—Legally Effective and Prospectively Obtained
- OHRP 45 CFR 46 Frequently Asked Questions (FAQs)
- OHRP FWA Frequently Asked Questions (FAQs)
- OHRP Informed Consent Frequently Asked Questions
- OHRP Investigator Responsibility Frequently Asked Questions
- OHRP IRB Registration Frequently Asked Questions (FAQs)
- Summary of Basic Protections for Human Subjects
- Tips On Informed Consent
- *Draft Guidance for Sponsors, Industry, Researchers, Investigators, and Food and Drug Administration Staff: Certifications to Accompany Drug, Biological Product, and Device Applications/Submissions: Compliance With Section 402(j) of the Public Health Service Act, Added by Title VIII of the Food and Drug Administration Amendments Act of 2007* (Revised March 2009)
- "Memorandum of Understanding Between the National Cancer Institute and the Food and Drug Administration on Janns Study Data Repository"
- *Guidance for Industry: Acceptance of Foreign Clinical Studies* (March 2001)
- *Guidance on New Law (Public Law 110-85) Enacted to Expand the Scope of ClinicalTrials.gov: Registration* (November 2007)
- *Guidance: Financial Disclosure by Clinical Investigators* (March 2001)
- *Final Guidance Document: Financial Relationships and Interests in Research Involving Human Subjects: Guidance for Human Subject Protection* (May 2004)
- *Guidance for Clinical Trial Sponsors: Establishment and Operation of Clinical Trial Data Monitoring Committees* (March 2006)
- *Guidance: Drug Safety Information—FDA's Communication to the Public* (March 2007)
- "Protecting Personal Health Information in Research: Understanding the HIPAA Privacy Rule" (Revised July 2004)
- "Research Repositories, Databases, and the HIPAA Privacy Rule" (Revised July 2004)
- "Institutional Review Boards and the HIPAA Privacy Rule" (Revised July 2004)
- *Guidance for Industry: IRB Review of Stand-Alone HIPAA Authorizations Under FDA Regulations* (October 2003)
- "Pre-IDE Program: Issues and Answers #D99-1 (Blue Book Memo)" (March 1999)
- *Changes or Modifications During the Conduct of a Clinical Investigation; Final Guidance for Industry and CDRH Staff* (May 2001)

- *Information Sheet Guidance for IRBs, Clinical Investigators, and Sponsors: Significant Risk and Nonsignificant Risk Medical Device Studies* (January 2006)
- *Early Collaboration Meetings Under the FDA Modernization Act (FDAMA); Final Guidance for Industry and CDRH Staff* (February 2001)
- "Goals and Initiatives for the IDE Program, #D95-1 (Blue Book Memo)" (July 1995)
- *Guidance for FDA Staff: Regulating In Vitro Diagnostic Device (IVD) Studies*—Frequently Asked Questions (June 2010)
- *Guidance for Industry and FDA Staff: Premarket Assessment of Pediatric Medical Devices* (May 2004)
- *Guidance for Industry: E11 Clinical Investigation of Medicinal Products in the Pediatric Population* (December 2000)

Introduction

Good Clinical Practices (GCPs) are international ethical and scientific quality standards used for designing, conducting, monitoring, auditing, analyzing, recording and reporting clinical trials involving the participation of human subjects. Compliance with these standards provides assurance to the public that the study subjects' rights, safety and well-being are protected and consistent with the ethical principles originating in the Declaration of Helsinki. Compliance also ensures that the data obtained from the clinical trial will be credible.[1]

GCPs have two primary objectives:
- protect human subjects during a clinical trial
- protect patients who might receive an approved product in the future

Clinical Trial Conduct and GCPs

GCPs in the US are captured in the *Federal Food, Drug, and Cosmetic Act* of 1938 (*FD&C Act*), Title 21 of the Code of Federal Regulations (CFR) and guidances at the state and federal levels. Areas covered by these laws, regulations and guidances include Institutional Review Boards (IRBs) and the informed consent process; obligations of investigators, sponsors and monitors; and contract research organizations (CROs).[2]

The submission of an Investigational New Drug (IND) application is required prior to conducting a human clinical trial in the US for an unapproved new drug or a new use of a marketed drug product. 21 CFR 50 and 312 define and list clinical trial personnel who must follow GCPs. Key personnel include the following:
- Sponsor—a person who initiates a clinical investigation but who does not actually conduct the investigation
- Contract research organization (CRO)—a person, corporation or agency acting as an independent contractor for the sponsor and who assumes one or more of the sponsor's obligations
- Sponsor-investigator—an individual who both initiates and actually conducts, alone or with others, a clinical investigation

An 18-month pilot phase of the European Medicines Agency (EMA)-FDA GCP Initiative began on 1 September 2009, based on ICH *E6: Guideline for Good Clinical Practice*, the EU *Clinical Trial Directive* (2001/20/EC) for EMA, and 21 CFR 11, 50, 54, 56, 58, 312 and 314 for FDA. The initiative is concentrated on GCP inspections of clinical investigator trial sites, sponsors and CROs, and laboratories and central technical facilities.

Additional regulatory guidance is available from US Department of Health and Human Services (DHHS) regulations and 45 CFR 46 Protection of Human Subjects. These provide the regulatory basis for the policies that protect individuals in investigative clinical trials conducted under DHHS.

The following government agencies provide resources on ethical considerations in biomedical research in the US:
- DHHS Office of Research Integrity
- National Institutes of Health (NIH) Office for Human Research Protections
- Office of Human Subjects Research and Department of Clinical Bioethics
- National Human Genome Research Institute (NHGRI)

Clinical Trial Responsibilities
Sponsor Obligations[3,4]

The sponsor's primary responsibility is to focus on the clinical study's ethical, scientific and regulatory obligations. The sponsor's single most important obligation is to protect each study subject's rights, safety and welfare. Other sponsor obligations include:
- Ensure the proposed clinical trial is adequately supported by nonclinical and clinical information on the investigational product.
- Provide a clear, scientifically sound protocol.
- Ensure all clinical trial study personnel are adequately qualified and trained.
- Ensure the protocol is approved by the IRB or Independent Ethics Committee (IEC).
- Ensure all decisions made on behalf of study subjects are made by a qualified physician.
- Ensure all clinical study tasks are performed by qualified personnel.
- Ensure all clinical trial information is recorded.
- Ensure all informed consents are obtained and freely given.
- Ensure the confidentiality of records is protected.
- Ensure the investigational product are prepared

Table 7-1. Common Rule vs. Privacy Rule

Common Rule:* FDA's Requirements	Privacy Rule: HHS Requirements
Both DHHS and FDA Protection of Human Subject Regulations are concerned with risk-associated participation in research. This includes, but is not limited to, the risks associated with the investigational products, risks of experimental procedures or procedures performed for research purposes and the confidentiality risks associated with the research.	The Privacy Rule is concerned with the risks to the subject's privacy associated with the use and disclosure of the subject's protected health information (PHI).
The scope of the FDA Protection of Human Subject Regulations applies only to research over which FDA has jurisdiction, primarily research involving investigational products. The scope of the DHHS Protection of Human Subject Regulations applies only to research conducted or supported by DHHS, or instances in which the researcher has voluntarily agreed to follow the DHHS Protection of Human Subject Regulations.	The Privacy Rule applies to a covered entity's use or disclosure of PHI for any research purposes, regardless of funding or agency that has regulatory authority over the research.
As required by both DHHS and FDA Protection of Human Subject Regulations, an individual's ICF is consent to participate in the research study as a whole, not simply a consent for the research use or disclosure of PHI.	Under the Privacy Rule, a patient's authorization is for the use and the disclosure of PHI, which can include use or disclosure for research purposes.
Neither DHHS' nor FDA's Protection of Human Subject Regulations expressly requires that the Privacy Rule Authorization be reviewed or approved by the IRB. However, under DHHS regulation 45 CFR 46.117(a) and FDA regulation 21 CFR 50.27(a), IRB review and approval are required for any documents that contain the required informed consent document for human research.	The Privacy Rule does not require the IRB to review or approve authorizations for research or other disclosures. It only requires that the authorization comply with the Privacy Rule section 144.508.
DHHS and FDA and FDA Protection of Human Subject Regulations (45 CFR46.107 and 21 CFR 56.107), respectively require that the IRB consist of five members. At least one member's primary concern must be in the scientific area, one in the nonscientific area, and one without institution affiliation.	Under the Privacy Rule, the number of members that constitutes the Privacy Board is not specified (section 164.512(i)). However, the members must have varying backgrounds and the appropriate professional competency necessary to review the research protocol as it pertains to the individual's privacy rights. At least one member should lack affiliation with the covered entity.

*   Information extracted from *HIPAA Privacy for Researchers: Guidance from the National Institutes of Health*, chapters on Clinical Research and *HIPAA* Privacy Rule and Institutional Review Boards and *HIPAA* Privacy Rule.

under current Good Manufacturing Practices (CGMPs).
- Ensure quality systems are in place and have been implemented.
- Report unanticipated adverse events.

Although the sponsor may transfer some or all of its obligations to a CRO, it maintains responsibility for ensuring all aspects of the study comply with current regulations.

Institutional Review Board (IRB) Obligations[5,6]

The purpose of an IRB, IEC, Ethics Committee Independent Research Committee (IRC) or Research Ethics Board (REB) is to protect the rights and welfare of human subjects involved in a clinical trial. 21 CFR 56 codifies

these regulations. US law requires each clinical study site to obtain approval from an IRB prior to commencement of the trial. If the trial includes sites outside the US in support of a US product application, the sponsor must comply with that country's regulations as they apply to the ethical review of clinical trial protocols. IRB review is not required for clinical studies that began prior to 27 July 1981, emergency use of an investigational new drug (emergency use must be reported to the IRB within five working days) or consumer acceptance studies for taste and food quality.

Other IRB responsibilities under US law include the following:
- Ensure risks to subjects are minimized and reasonable in relation to anticipated benefits.
- Ensure patient selection is as equitable as possible relative to demographics and the clinical trial's purpose.

- Review the protocol, informed consent form (ICF) and Investigator's Brochure (IB).
- Ensure a pediatric clinical trial is conducted according to current regulations.
- Provide initial and continuing review of the ongoing clinical trial at different intervals.
- Request more information, if required.
- Approve, disapprove and/or terminate a trial.

Investigator Obligations[7,8]

An investigator's primary responsibility is to ensure the rights, safety and welfare of study subjects. Other duties are:

- Follow the protocol and its specific procedures.
- Ensure the trial's proper conduct at the sites under his or her authority, in compliance with the signed agreement, the investigational plan, the protocol, and all applicable FDA and other government regulations.
- Prepare timely and accurate reports to the IRB, sponsor, medical monitor and FDA, if applicable.
- Maintain accurate records.
- Control the investigational new drug product.
- Ensure that patients sign the ICF before study procedures begin.
- Maintain appropriate and scheduled communication with the study sponsor, medical monitor and IRB.

Health Insurance Portability and Accountability Act (HIPAA) Privacy Rule

The *Health Insurance Portability and Accountability Act* of 1996, also known as the Privacy Rule, established the minimum federal requirements for protecting the privacy of individually identifiable health information. The Privacy Rule specifies conditions under which covered entities can permit research access to and use of protected health information (PHI) when necessary to conduct research.[9] PHI is defined as any information about health status, provision of healthcare or payment for healthcare that can be linked to an individual. This is interpreted rather broadly as any part of a patient's medical record or payment history. Some examples of PHI are names, addresses, dates of birth, phone numbers, fax numbers, email addresses and Social Security numbers.

Much biomedical and behavioral research conducted in the US is governed by the Federal Policy for the Protection of Human Subjects (also known as the Common Rule), which is codified in 45 CFR 46, Subpart A, and 21 CFR 50 and 56.[10]

A patient's authorization under the Privacy Rule is for the use and disclosure of protected health information for research purposes. In contrast, an individual's informed consent, as required by the Common Rule and FDA's human subjects regulations, is consent to participate in the research study as a whole, not simply consent for the research use or disclosure of protected health information.[11]

There are important differences between the Privacy Rule's requirements for individual authorization, and the Common Rule and FDA's requirements for informed consent. However, the Privacy Rule's authorization elements are compatible with the Common Rule's informed consent elements. Accordingly, the Privacy Rule permits the use of a single, combined form that may accommodate both sets of requirements. For example, the Privacy Rule allows the research authorization to state that it will be valid until the conclusion of the study, or to state that the authorization will not have an expiration date or event. This is compatible with the Common Rule's requirement for an explanation of the expected duration of the research subject's participation in the study. It is important to note that where the Privacy Rule, the Common Rule and/or FDA's Protection of Human Subject Regulations are applied, each pertinent regulation must be followed. The Privacy Rule regulates only the content and conditions of the documentation that covered entities must obtain before using or disclosing PHI for research purposes.[12,13]

GCPs for Device Trials

Although GCPs are applicable to both investigational new drugs and investigational devices, differences exist between trial conduct for drugs and devices that are not addressed in the International Conference on Harmonisation (ICH) E6 guideline on GCPs. For example, Form FDA 1572 Statement of Investigator is not required for a device clinical trial. However, the sponsor should provide the elements listed under 21 CFR 812.43(c) to the investigator. The Principal Investigator (PI) should sign this Investigator Agreement prior to commencing a device clinical trial.

In 2011, the International Organization for Standardization (ISO) issued a revised standard, ISO *International Standard 14155:2011, Clinical Investigation of Medical Devices for Human Subjects—Good Clinical Practices,* which is specific to device clinical trial investigations.[14]

Clinical Trial Regulations

Regulations are designed to ensure that clinical trial subjects are protected from harm, that subjects' rights are protected and that the trial's scientific integrity is assured (i.e., that it is designed, conducted and analyzed using sound scientific principles). Compliance with regulations is essential to achieve these aims, which require:

- a strong, effective and efficient regulatory framework
- willingness of investigators to participate and comply
- adequate site/research infrastructure
- willingness of patients to participate and comply

Table 7-2. Clinical Trial Regulations Comparison Between Investigational New Drugs and Investigational Devices

Regulation	Drugs	Devices
Investigational New Drug/Device Application	21 CFR 312	21 CFR 812
IND/IDE Application Process	21 CFR 312.23	21 CFR 812.20, 812.25 and 812.27
Form FDA 1571 (Investigational New Drug Application)	21 CFR 312.23(a)(1)	
Form FDA 1572 (Statement of Investigator)	21 CFR 312.53(c)	21 CFR 812.43(c) (Form FDA 1572 not required for devices)
Foreign Clinical Trials not conducted under an IND	21 CFR 312.120	
Legal Representation (Transfer of Obligations)	21 CFR 312.52	
Labeling	21 CFR 312.6	21 CFR 812.5
Responsibilities of Sponsors and Investigators	21 CFR 312 Subpart D	21 CFR 812 Subparts C and E
Record and Reports	21 CFR 312.57, 21 CFR 312.58, 21 CFR 312.62, 21 CFR 312.64, 21 CFR 312.68	21 CFR 812.140 21 CFR 812.150
Safety Reporting	21 CFR 312.32	21 CFR 803
Bioavailability and Bioequivalence Requirements	21 CFR 320	
Quality System Regulations		21 CFR 820

Numerous federal statutory and regulatory requirements control the conduct of clinical trials. These requirements include regulations on clinical trial misconduct, PHI privacy, fraud and abuse.

Federal Clinical Trial Requirements Regulations

Either an IND or an Investigational Device Exemption (IDE) is required to conduct clinical research in the US. **Table 7-2** compares clinical trial regulations for drugs and devices. **Table 7-3** specifies clinical trial regulations for drugs and devices.

State Clinical Trial Regulations

Compliance with individual state clinical trial regulations is one of the most difficult compliance issues for a sponsor, since state requirements may differ from federal regulations. Some states have regulations that are broader in scope than those of the federal government. In addition, federal regulations may not preempt state regulations for clinical research. For the most part, federal regulations rely upon state laws for informed consent. Compliance with federal regulations does not ensure compliance with state regulations.[15]

For multi-center trials, more than one state's regulations may apply. The study location usually determines which laws apply. However, such a determination becomes more complicated in instances where management of the study occurs in one location while investigative sites operate in other states. For example, a New York hospital may enroll patients in a study. Once the hospital discharges the patients to their homes in the nearby states of New Jersey, and Connecticut, where their family doctors are collecting data, the laws of New York, New Jersey and Connecticut may apply.[16]

Most states defer to federal regulations for federally funded programs. However, those states with stricter laws may contend that their laws should apply. State laws do not apply to clinical trials conducted solely in a federal institution. For a privately funded study, state regulations will apply when federal laws do not. State regulations differ from federal in that they do not distinguish among funding sources.[17]

Sponsors pursuing clinical research should seek specific legal advice from each respective state's applicable regulatory agency prior to conducting clinical research in that state. For a list of clinical trial regulations by state, refer to States That Require Health Plans to Cover Patient Care Costs in Clinical Trials (www.cancer.gov/clinicaltrials/ctlaws-home and www.ncsl.org/programs/health/clinicaltrials.htm) and Clinical Trials: State Laws Regarding Insurance Coverage (www.cancer.org/docroot/ETO/content/ETO_6_2x_State_Laws_Regarding_Clinical_Trials.asp).

Table 7-3. Clinical Trial Regulations Applicable to Investigational New Drugs and Investigational Devices

Regulation	Source
Electronic Records; Electronic Signatures	21 CFR 11
Protection of Human Subjects (Informed Consent)	21 CFR 50
Financial Disclosure by Clinical Investigators	21 CFR 54
Institutional Review Boards	21 CFR 56
Form FDA 3674 (Certification)	*Food and Drug Administration Amendments Act* of 2007
Data Protection Rules Applicable to Clinical Trials (*HIPAA*)	1. *Privacy Act*, 5 U.S.C. § 552a (1974): 2. *Health Insurance Portability and Accountability Act* (1996) (HIPAA Privacy Rule: Standards for Privacy of Individually Identifiable Health Information, Final Rule, 45 CFR parts 160 and 164 (2002) and HIPAA Security Rule, 45 CFR parts 160, 162, and 164)
Pediatric Clinical Trials	21 CFR 50, Subpart D—Additional Safeguards for Children in Clinical Investigations

State Clinical Trial Insurance Requirements

Approximately half of the state legislatures have passed clinical trial legislation and/or instituted special agreements requiring health plans to pay the cost of routine medical care for study subjects. Usually, the trial sponsor covers the costs of tests, procedures, drugs, extra doctor visits and any research directly related to the study itself for enrolled subjects. Some health plans do not cover the cost of "routine patient care" for a study subject in instances in which he or she would receive the medical care even if not participating in a clinical trial.[18,19]

Potential study subjects are sometimes reluctant to participate in clinical trials because they fear denial of their healthcare coverage. This also limits PIs from enrolling study subjects who meet all inclusion criteria. Enactment of state regulations that require health insurance companies to provide coverage for clinical trials benefits both potential study subjects, by providing them with an alternative form of treatment that would otherwise not be available, and investigators, by providing access to a larger pool of possible study subjects.

Table 7-4 contains the most current information available at the time of publication about laws and special agreements that require insurance plans to cover a patient's clinical trial expenses. The laws and special agreements vary from state to state. Contact the respective state's insurance department for additional and updated information.

Clinical Trial Regulatory Compliance

Most noncompliance in clinical trial research is due to clinical trial or protocol misconduct. The investigator, the sponsor, the institution and the IRB are all responsible for ensuring the protection of subjects' rights. Institutions are accountable for the actions of individual investigators and IRBs. On a broader scale, institutional noncompliance is a systemic failure of the institution to implement practices and procedures contained in its certification of compliance with DHHS regulations, or "assurance." Although the investigator is the most frequent source of noncompliance, all of the aforementioned parties have responsibilities and the sponsor is ultimately accountable for ensuring that subjects' rights, safety and welfare are protected.[20,21]

Regulatory authorities use inspections and regulatory audits to ensure that clinical trial sponsors are compliant with human subject regulations. The clinical trial site, the governing IRB and/or the sponsor's site are all subject to regulatory audits. Other avenues used to ensure regulatory compliance are routine site visits, and internal, client or sponsor audits.

Under FDA's mandate are specific regulations to ensure compliance. However, other agencies of DHHS, such as NIH, support research, and do not have FDA's enforcement authority. Unlike DHHS regulations (45 CFR 46), FDA regulations provide specific administrative actions and sanctions for noncompliance (21 CFR 56.120–24).

FDA has a dedicated program within its Office of Regulatory Affairs called Bioresearch Monitoring (BIMO), which is a comprehensive program of on-site inspections and data audits designed to monitor all aspects of the conduct and reporting of FDA-regulated research. BIMO compliance program policy guides (e.g., Compliance Program 7348.811, Clinical Investigator) provide guidance to assist industry in complying with regulations that pertain to conducting clinical trials.[22,23]

Regulatory compliance under DHHS regulations is governed by 45 CFR 46.123(a). This regulation requires the institution where the clinical trial is being conducted to report serious or continuing noncompliance with the regulations (45 CFR 46.103(b)(5)) to the IRB, appropriate institutional officials and the agency, and that it establishes procedures to report this information. Under 21 CFR 56.108(b), FDA requires the IRB itself to notify

Table 7-4. List of Clinical Trial State Legislation and Insurance Legislation

State	Clinical Trial Legislation[1]	Clinical Trial Legislation Comments	Clinical Trial Insurance Legislation[2]	Clinical Trial Insurance Legislation Coverage
Alabama	No			
Alaska	Yes		Yes	A clinical trial related to cancer, including leukemia, lymphoma, and bone marrow stem cell disorders, and approved by an IRB compliant with federal law and one of the following: DHHS, NIH or its institutes or centers, FDA, Department of Defense, Department of Veterans Affairs or a nongovernmental research agency abiding by current NIH guidelines.
Arizona	Yes	There is a specific general provision for prisoners.	Yes	Patient costs associated with participation in Phase 1–4 clinical trials.
Arkansas	No			
California		California has very explicit requirements that are not set forth in federal regulations. Informed consent is determined by state case law, statutes and regulations. Under California law, failure to comply with the state's informed consent requirements can lead to federal sanctions. There are general provisions in the legislation for experimental drugs, experimental subjects' bill of rights, informed consent requirements, and specific general provisions for minors, prisoners (e.g., behavioral and biomedical research) and the developmentally disabled/ mentally handicapped.	Yes	Routine patient care costs associated with Phase 1–4 cancer clinical trials.
Colorado	Yes	There are specific general provisions for minors and the developmentally disabled/ mentally handicapped.		
Connecticut	Yes	There is a specific general provision for nursing home/long-term care facility residents.	Yes	Routine patient care costs associated with cancer clinical trials.
Delaware	Yes	There are specific general provisions for minors, the developmentally disabled/ mentally handicapped and nursing home/long-term care facility residents.	Yes	Routine patient care. costs for covered persons engaging in clinical trials for the treatment of life-threatening diseases under specified conditions.
District of Columbia	Yes	There is a specific general provision for the developmentally disabled/mentally handicapped.		

State	Clinical Trial Legislation[1]	Clinical Trial Legislation Comments	Clinical Trial Insurance Legislation[2]	Clinical Trial Insurance Legislation Coverage
Florida	Yes	There is a general provision for healthcare facility and specific general provisions for minors and the developmentally disabled/mentally handicapped.		
Georgia	Yes	There is a specific general provision for nursing home/long-term care facility residents.	Yes	Routine patient costs incurred in Phase 2 and 3 of prescription drug clinical trial programs for the treatment of children's cancer.
Georgia			**Special Agreement** (2002) Georgia Cancer Coalition	Routine patient care costs associated with Phase 1–4 cancer clinical trials.
Hawaii	No			
Idaho	No			
Illinois	Yes	There is a general provision in the legislation for any patient who is the subject of a research program or an experimental procedure, and specific general provisions for fetal research, the developmentally disabled/mentally handicapped and nursing home/long-term care facility residents.	Yes	Routine patient care if the individual participates in an approved Phase 2–4 cancer research trial.
Indiana	Yes	There is a specific general provision for fetal research.		
Iowa	Yes		Yes	Specified cancer clinical trials.
Kansas	No			
Kentucky	Yes	There is a specific general provision for fetal research.		
Louisiana	Yes	There are specific general provisions for fetal research and *in vitro* procedures.	Yes	Patient costs incurred in Phase 2–4 cancer clinical trials.
Maine	Yes	There are specific general provisions for the developmentally disabled/mentally handicapped.	Yes	Routine patient care costs associated with clinical trials.
Maryland	Yes	There is a specific general provision for nursing home/long-term care facility residents.	Yes	Patient costs for Phase 1–4 cancer treatment, supportive care, early detection and prevention trials. Phase 2–4 for other life-threatening conditions, with Phase 1 considered on a case-by-case basis.
Massachusetts	Yes	There are specific general provisions for fetal research (e.g., living fetus and dead fetus), the developmentally disabled/mentally handicapped and the mentally ill and for nursing home/long-term care facility residents.	Yes	Patient care services associated with all phases of qualified cancer clinical trials.

State	Clinical Trial Legislation[1]	Clinical Trial Legislation Comments	Clinical Trial Insurance Legislation[2]	Clinical Trial Insurance Legislation Coverage
Michigan	Yes	There is a specific general provision for pregnant women and for fetal research.	***Special Agreement*** (2002) Michigan Consensus Agreement	Routine patient care costs associated with Phase 2 and 3 cancer clinical trials. Coverage for Phase 1 clinical trials are under consideration.
Minnesota	Yes	There are specific general provisions for fetal research, the developmentally disabled/ mentally handicapped, the mentally ill and nursing home/ long-term care facility residents.		
Mississippi	No			
Missouri	Yes	There are specific general provisions for fetal research, the mentally ill and for nursing home/long-term care facility residents.	Yes	Routine patient care costs as the result of Phase 2, 3 or 4 clinical trials for the prevention, early detection, or treatment of cancer.
Montana	Yes	There are specific general provisions for the developmentally disabled/ mentally handicapped, and the mentally ill.		
Nebraska	Yes	There is a specific general provision for fetal research.		
Nevada	No		Yes	Patient costs associated with Phase 1 clinical trials for the treatment of cancer, and Phase 2, 3 or 4 clinical trials for the treatment of cancer or chronic fatigue syndrome.
New Hampshire	Yes	There are general provisions in the legislation for hospitals, home healthcare and the right to information.	Yes	Medically necessary routine patient care costs incurred as a result of a treatment in a Phase 1–4 cancer clinical trial for a life-threatening disease.
New Jersey	Yes	There are specific general provisions for minors, the developmentally disabled/ mentally handicapped, the mentally ill and nursing home/ long-term care facility residents.	***Special Agreement*** (1999) New Jersey Consensus Agreement	Routine patient care costs associated with all phases of cancer clinical trials.
New Mexico	Yes	There are specific general provisions for pregnant women, fetal research (e.g., fetus and live born infant) and *in vitro* procedures.	Yes	Routine patient care costs incurred as result of Phase 2–4 cancer clinical trials.
New Mexico			Yes	Routine patient care costs incurred as result of Phase 1–4 cancer clinical trials.
New York	Yes	There are general provisions in the legislation for informed consent and the conduct of human research, and specific provisions for minors and the mentally ill.		

State	Clinical Trial Legislation[1]	Clinical Trial Legislation Comments	Clinical Trial Insurance Legislation[2]	Clinical Trial Insurance Legislation Coverage
North Carolina	Yes	There is a specific general provision for nursing home/long-term care facility residents.	Yes	Medically necessary costs of healthcare services associated with Phase 2–4 covered clinical trials.
North Dakota	Yes	There are specific general provisions for pregnant women, fetal research (e.g., live fetus and dead fetus), the developmentally disabled/mentally handicapped and the mentally ill.		
Ohio	Yes	There is a specific general provision for nursing home/long-term care facility residents.	*Special Agreement* (1999) Ohio Med Plan	Routine patient care costs associated with Phase 2 and 3 cancer treatment clinical trials.
Oklahoma	Yes	There is a specific general provision for fetal research.		
Oregon	Yes	There is a specific general provision for nursing home/long-term care facility residents.		
Pennsylvania	Yes	There is a specific general provision for fetal research (e.g., unborn or live child and dead child).		
Rhode Island	Yes	There is a specific general provision for the developmentally disabled/mentally handicapped.	Yes	Coverage for new cancer therapies if treatment is provided under Phase 2–4 cancer clinical trials.
South Carolina	Yes	There is a specific general provision for nursing home/long-term care facility residents.		
South Dakota	Yes	There are specific general provisions for minors, fetal research, the developmentally disabled/mentally handicapped and the mentally ill.		
Tennessee	No		Yes	Routine patient care costs related to Phase 1–4 cancer clinical trials.
Texas	Yes	There is a specific general provision for nursing home/long-term care facility residents.		
Utah	No			

State	Clinical Trial Legislation[1]	Clinical Trial Legislation Comments	Clinical Trial Insurance Legislation[2]	Clinical Trial Insurance Legislation Coverage
Vermont	No	There is legislation that provides for clinical trial insurance coverage for approved cancer clinical trials conducted under the auspices of the following cancer care providers: • The Vermont Cancer Center at Fletcher Allen Health Care. • The Norris Cotton Cancer Center at Dartmouth-Hitchcock Medical Center. If no suitable trial is available at the above locations, the law covers approved cancer clinical trials administered by a hospital and its affiliated, qualified, cancer care providers in or outside the state of Vermont.	Yes	Routine patient care costs related to Phase 1–4 cancer clinical trials.
Virginia	Yes	Virginia statutes apply to all studies regardless of the funding source or purpose. There are general provisions in the legislation for informed consent, alteration or waiver of informed consent and the applicability of federal policies. There are specific general provisions for minors, prisoners, the developmentally disabled/mentally handicapped and the mentally ill.	Yes	Patient costs incurred during participation in Phase 2–4 cancer clinical trials. Coverage provided on a case-by-case basis for Phase 1.
Washington	Yes	There is a specific general provision for nursing home/long-term care facility residents.		
West Virginia	No		Yes	Patient costs associated with participation in Phase 2–4 clinical trials for treatment of life-threatening conditions or the prevention, early detection and treatment of cancer.
Wisconsin	Yes	There are specific general provisions for the developmentally disabled/mentally handicapped and the mentally ill.	Yes	Routine patient care costs incurred during participation in all phases of a cancer clinical trial. No policy, plan or contract may exclude coverage for the cost of any routine patient care that is administered to an insured patient in a cancer clinical trial satisfying the required criteria for clinical trials under paragraph (c) and that would be covered under the policy, plan or contract if the insured were not enrolled in a cancer clinical trial.

State	Clinical Trial Legislation[1]	Clinical Trial Legislation Comments	Clinical Trial Insurance Legislation[2]	Clinical Trial Insurance Legislation Coverage
Wyoming	Yes	There is a specific general provision for minors.	Yes	Routine patient care for a patient enrolled in a Phase 2, 3 or 4 clinical trial for cancer treatment, as approved by one of the following: ▪ National Institutes of Health (NIH) ▪ US Food and Drug Administration ▪ US Department of Defense ▪ US Department of Veterans Affairs ▪ A qualified research entity that meets the NIH criteria for grant eligibility

1. Rozovsky FA and Adams RK. *Clinical Trials and Human Research, A Practical Guide to Regulatory Compliance*, John Wiley & Sons, 2005
2. States That Require Health Plans to Cover Patient Care Costs in Clinical Trials (www.cancer.gov/clinicaltrials/ctlaws-home and www.ncsl.org/programs/health/clinicaltrials.htm.
    Clinical Trials: State Laws Regarding Insurance Coverage: www.cancer.org/docroot/ETO/content/ETO_6_2x_State_Laws_Regarding_Clinical_Trials.asp.

the agency of instances of noncompliance if such reporting would not otherwise occur (*Federal Register*, Vol. 74, No. 10 (15 January 2009)).

Financial Disclosure

Current regulations for drugs and devices (21 CFR 54, 312 and 812) require that anyone submitting a marketing application to FDA must also submit lists of participating clinical investigators who conducted clinical trials and certify and/or disclose certain financial arrangements. The sponsor must assure that it did not make financial arrangements with the investigator that will affect the study's outcome. It must disclose any financial arrangements and steps taken to minimize the potential for bias. Examples of applicable financial arrangements include:[24]

- the value of compensation to the investigator, if it is significant enough that it may be construed as affecting study results
- an investigator's proprietary interest in the tested product
- any investigator equity interest in the sponsor of a covered study (e.g., an investigator must disclose if he or she owns stocks in the sponsoring company)
- any investigator equity interest in a publicly held company that exceeds $50,000
- all other significant payments that have a cumulative monetary value of $25,000 or more made by the study sponsor to the investigator or the investigator's institution to support the investigator's activities, exclusive of the costs of conducting the clinical study or other clinical studies

If FDA suspects that a clinical investigator's financial interest has compromised a clinical study's scientific quality or integrity, it may conduct an audit or request the sponsor to submit more data and/or conduct additional independent studies.

Pharmacovigilance in Clinical Trials

Sponsors are required to review all information pertaining to the safety of an investigational new drug from any domestic or foreign source. An IRB is also required to continue to review the study at set intervals to assure the protection of human subjects' rights and welfare. To this end, it is critical to inform the IRB of any unanticipated issues associated with the study drug that pose a risk to study subjects. Therefore, adverse event information must be communicated among investigators, sponsors and IRBs as follows:[25]

- Sponsors are specifically required to notify all participating investigators (and FDA) in a written IND safety report of "any adverse experience associated with the use of the drug that is both serious and unexpected" and "any finding from tests in laboratory animals that suggests a significant risk for human subjects."
- Sponsors are required to "keep each participating investigator informed of new observations discovered by or reported to the sponsor on the drug, particularly with respect to adverse effects and safe use."
- Investigators are required to promptly report "to the sponsor any adverse effect that may reasonably be regarded as caused by, or probably caused by, the drug. If the adverse effect is alarming, the investigator shall report the adverse effect immediately."

- Investigators are required to report promptly "to the IRB… all unanticipated problems involving risks to human subjects or others," including adverse events that should be considered unanticipated problems.

Differences exist between the reporting obligations for IND and IDE studies to a reviewing IRB. *Guidance for Clinical Investigators, Sponsors, and IRBs: Adverse Event Reporting to IRBs—Improving Human Subject Protection* provides additional information.

Data Monitoring Committee (DMC)

As noted above, safety monitoring is required for all clinical trials. However, not all clinical trials require monitoring by a formal data monitoring committee (DMC). A DMC is a group of individuals with relevant expertise who regularly review accumulating data from one or more ongoing clinical trials. The DMC advises the sponsor regarding the ongoing safety of enrolled and prospective study subjects and the continuing validity and scientific merit of the trial.[26]

Clinical Trial Noncompliance

Compliance with GCPs during a clinical trial ensures that human subjects' rights and safety are not compromised; that the number of personnel managing the clinical trial is sufficient; that the clinical trial staff is adequately trained; that the clinical trial will be monitored properly; that all clinical trial data are accurately documented; and that the protocol is followed.[27] Following are examples of noncompliance with regulations and/or GCPs during the conduct of a clinical trial.[28,29]

Common Clinical Trial Monitoring Noncompliance Issues

- falsified data
- plagiarism and falsifying study results
- false or misleading protocols
- failure to report unanticipated adverse events
- implementing changes to the protocol or ICF without IRB approval
- commencing significant changes to a protocol without first submitting for FDA approval
- enrolling a study subject who does not meet the inclusion criteria
- failure to withdraw study subjects who no longer meet inclusion criteria or who meet one or more exclusion criteria
- failure to make timely reports to the IRB
- research conducted without IRB review

Common Investigator Noncompliance Issues

- unreported changes in protocols
- misuse or nonuse of the ICF
- failure to submit protocols to the IRB in a timely fashion

Common IRB Noncompliance Issues

- inadequate research protocol review
- failure to ensure that the ICF and process provide sufficient information to allow prospective subjects to make an informed decision as to whether to participate in the research
- failure to ensure that the research design includes adequate data monitoring and any additional safeguards necessary to protect the welfare of particularly vulnerable subjects
- failure to conduct continuing review of research at intervals appropriate to the degree of risk
- failure to maintain adequate records of IRB business
- insufficient information to make determinations required for approval of research
- inadequate review at convened meetings
- inadequate continuing review
- contingent approval of research with substantive changes and no additional review by the convened IRB
- failure to conduct continuing review at least once annually
- meeting convened without quorum due to the absence of a nonscientist
- meeting convened without quorum due to the lack of a majority
- members with conflicting interest participated in IRB review of research

Common Institution Noncompliance Issues

- failure to ensure that the IRB has the required number of members and functions in accordance with the regulations
- failure to ensure that the IRB receives appropriate institutional support and staffing
- failure to ensure that investigators meet their obligations to the IRB

Regulatory Compliance Sanctions

DHHS regulations do not specify administrative actions for noncompliance other than the following:[30,31]

- Failure to comply with regulations can result in termination or suspension of support for agency projects.
- Demonstrated inability to carry out IRB responsibilities in accordance with DHHS regulations can

be cause for suspension or withdrawal of approval of an institution's assurance.

- Systemic failure to abide by the terms and conditions of an institution's assurance will result in withdrawal of approval of the assurance.

Failure to comply with regulations in an FDA-regulated trial can result in the assessment of both civil and criminal penalties for clinical trial misconduct. Examples of regulatory actions that may occur are:

- suspension of a clinical trial until resolution of the reason(s) for misconduct
- cancellation of clinical trial approval
- rejection of an IND or IDE application due to incomplete, inadequate or fraudulent documentation
- rejection of any publication that uses data from the noncompliant clinical trial
- disqualification of a clinical investigator from receiving investigational drugs, biologics and devices when the investigator has repeatedly or deliberately violated agency regulations or has submitted false information to the sponsor in a required report[32]

The *Food and Drug Administration Amendments Act* of 2007 (*FDAAA*), added new prohibited acts under section 301(jj) of the *FD&C Act*. Penalties may be incurred if a sponsor does any of the following:[20]

- fails to submit a certification (Form FDA 3674)
- knowingly submits a false certification
- fails to submit required clinical trial information
- submits clinical trial information that is false or misleading[33]

Clinical Trial Databases

To date, the public database operated by NIH includes registration of virtually all drug clinical trials conducted in the US.[34]

The *Food and Drug Administration Modernization Act* of 1997 (*FDAMA*) required sponsors of certain key pharmaceutical and biologics clinical trials, specifically those testing the efficacy of drugs and biologics for serious or life-threatening conditions, to submit limited data to the NIH's clinical trials data bank, www.clinicaltrials.gov. Title VIII of *FDAAA* requires that additional information be submitted to the data bank, including expanded information on clinical trials and their results, and requires the registration of applicable clinical trials. This is to ensure that the public is informed and has access to information about certain clinical trials and trial results.[35,36]

One new provision requires that a certification (Form FDA 3674) accompany certain human drug, biological product and device applications and submissions to FDA.

One purpose of the certification is to require the sponsor to confirm that it has complied with all applicable *FDAAA* requirements.[19]

Title VIII of *FDAAA* extends the existing national registry in three phases. First, the registry is expanding to cover all trials of drugs and biologics except preliminary, or Phase 1 trials, and the number of registration fields that sponsors must submit is increasing. Medical devices are also included. Second, basic results from trials of approved products are required to be posted to the registry. Third, in the future, FDA may use its rulemaking powers to expand the registry to include trial results for unapproved products, as well as extra data elements. Mandatory data fields to be submitted when a study begins include the following:[37]

- primary purpose and condition being studied
- intervention name and type, including the name of the product being studied
- study design, type and phase
- study start date and expected completion date
- criteria for subject recruitment and planned numbers
- primary and secondary outcome measures
- name of sponsor and/or investigators
- study locations and contact details

This information must be registered within 21 days of enrolling the first patient.

This is the first federal legislation to mandate that device companies disclose clinical trial information and to require both drug and device companies to disclose clinical trial results through a publicly available database.[38]

FDAAA also created new disclosure requirements that may have a significant impact on drug and device sponsors. Sponsors need to be aware that these requirements may expose them to greater liability under the *False Claims Act* (31 U.S.C. § 3729), *HIPAA*, Securities and Exchange Commission (SEC) rules, FDA product labeling and advertising rules and product liability claims. Sponsors need to be familiar with these requirements and the way that they affect proprietary information, inventions, publication, insurance coverage and agreements with institutions.[39]

Pharmacovigilance Reporting

Clinical trial sponsors will be required to submit annual development safety update reports (DSURs) under a guideline proposed by FDA to match one issued previously by ICH.

The ICH *Draft Consensus Guideline: Development Safety Update Report (E2F)* is intended to become the common standard for annual clinical trial safety reporting among the ICH regions, replacing existing reports, including the US IND Annual Report and the EU Annual Safety Report.[40,41] This comprehensive, annual review will provide an additional level of assurance of protection for clinical trial subjects. Regulatory agencies in the three ICH regions will harmonize the format, content and timing of annual safety reports. Thus, all three ICH regions will receive the same information at the same time, thereby reducing the number of reports generated.[42,43]

The main objective of a DSUR is to present an annual review and evaluation of pertinent safety information collected during the reporting period:[44,45]

- summary of current understanding and management of identified and potential risks
- description of new safety issues that could have an impact on the protection of clinical trial subjects
- examination of whether the information obtained by the sponsor during the reporting period is in accordance with previous knowledge of the product's safety
- update of the clinical investigation/development program's status

While the DSUR should focus on data from interventional trials, sponsors are advised to include other findings that affect subject safety (e.g., findings from nonclinical studies, related clinical trials conducted by the sponsor's development partners and non-interventional or compassionate-use studies).[46,47]

IRB Registration

FDA issued a final rule on 29 January 2009 requiring IRBs to register through a system maintained by DHHS. IRBs will be required to provide the following information during the registration process:

- contact information (e.g., addresses and telephone numbers)
- number of active protocols involving FDA-regulated products reviewed during the preceding 12 months
- description of the types of FDA-regulated products involved in the protocols reviewed

This new regulation is intended to improve FDA's oversight of IRBs, thus making it easier for the agency to inspect and convey information to IRBs. This regulation was effective on 14 July 2009. All IRBs had to comply with the initial registration requirement and make required revisions to their registrations by 14 September 2009. The final rule is accessible at: http://edocket.access.gpo.gov/2009/E9-682.htm.

Summary

Knowledge of Good Clinical Practices ensures that not only the rights, welfare and safety of a person participating in clinical research are protected, but also that the trial is conducted in accordance with current regulations and guidances. Conformance to GCPs is pivotal to the consumer's assurance that data derived during clinical research

is scientifically valid.

The US has one statute, the *FD&C Act*, that governs new drug and device applications in all 50 states. However, each individual state has its own applicable regulations, in addition to federal law and regulations. These state regulations cover requirements for insurance, pediatric populations, fetal research and the developmentally disabled. A summary chart of these requirements is included in this chapter.

Clinical trial regulatory compliance includes many different areas, e.g., regulatory submissions (IND and IRB submissions), financial disclosure, pharmacovigilance, privacy and data protection. This chapter covers the most common compliance and noncompliance issues routinely seen or encountered during clinical trial conduct.

References

1. FDA Office of Good Clinical Practice. Available at www.fda.gov/oc/gcp/default.htm. Accessed 28 April 2011.
2. Dunn CM and Chadwick GL. *Protecting Study Volunteers in Research: A Manual for Investigative Sites.* CenterWatch (2004).
3. FDA Information Sheet Guidances for Institutional Review Boards, Clinical Investigators, and Sponsors. Available at www.fda.gov/oc/ohrt/irbs/default.htm. Accessed 28 April 2011.
4. Hurley FL and West D. "The Logistics of Conducting Clinical Studies." *Medical Device & Diagnostic Industry* (1996). Availble at http://www.mddionline.com/article/logistics-conducting-clinical-studies. Accessed 28 April 2011.
5. Op cit 3.
6. Op cit 4.
7. Op cit 3.
8. Op cit 4.
9. *HIPAA Privacy for Researchers: Guidance from the National Institutes of Health, Book 5B.* Clinical Research Resources LLC (2006-8).
10. Ibid.
11. "Do the HIPAA Privacy Rule's requirements for Authorization and the Common Rule's requirements for informed consent differ?" Available at www.hhs.gov/hipaafaq/permitted/research/313.html. Accessed 28 April 2011.
12. Ibid.
13. "By establishing new waiver criteria and Authorization requirements, hasn't the HIPAA Privacy Rule, in effect, modified the Common Rule?" Available at www.hhs.gov/hipaafaq/permitted/research/308.html. Accessed 28 April 2011.
14. Tocchi M. "Good Clinical Practice for Device Trials." *Regulatory Focus*, Vol. 14 (1) pp 32–36 (2009).

15. Rozovsky FA and Adams RK. *Clinical Trials and Human Research, A Practical Guide to Regulatory Compliance*, John Wiley & Sons (2005).
16. Ibid.
17. Ibid.
18. States That Require Health Plans to Cover Patient Care Costs in Clinical Trials. Available at www.cancer.gov/clinicaltrials/ctlaws-home and www.ncsl.org/programs/health/clinicaltrials.htm. Accessed 28 April 2011.
19. Clinical Trials: State Laws Regarding Insurance Coverage. Available at www.cancer.org/docroot/ETO/content/ETO_6_2x_State_Laws_Regarding_Clinical_Trials.asp. Accessed 28 April 2011.
20. Op cit 15.
21. Institutional Review Board Guidebook. Available at http://grants2.nih.gov/grants/guide/notice-files/not93-209.html. Accessed 28 April 2011.
22. US Department of Health and Human Services. Public Health Service. Food and Drug Administration. *Compliance Program Guidance Manual: "Chapter 48—Bioresearch Monitoring—Human Drugs—Institutional Review Board" (November 1988).*
23. FDA Compliance Program 7348.811. Available at http://www.fda.gov/downloads/ICECI/EnforcementActions/BioresearchMonitoring/ucm133773.pdf. Accessed 28 April 2011.
24. *Guidance: Financial Disclosure by Clinical Investigators* (March 2001). Available at http://www.fda.gov/RegulatoryInformation/Guidances/ucm126832.htm. Accessed 28 April 2011.
25. *Guidance for Clinical Investigators, Sponsors, and IRBs: Adverse Event Reporting to IRBs—Improving Human Subject Protection* (January 2009). Available at http://www.fda.gov/downloads/RegulatoryInformation/Guidances/UCM126572.pdf. Accessed 28 April 2011.
26. *Guidance for Clinical Trial Sponsors: Establishment and Operation of Clinical Trial Data Monitoring Committees* (March 2006). Available at www.fda.gov/OHRMS/DOCKETS/98fr/01d-0489-gdl0003.pdf. Accessed 28 April 2011.
27. Dunn CM and Chadwick GL. *Protecting Study Volunteers in Research: A Manual for Investigative Sites.* CenterWatch (2004).
28. Op cit 21.
29. *OHRP Compliance Oversight Activities: Determinations of Noncompliance* (February 2009). Available at http://www.hhs.gov/ohrp/compliance/findings/findings.pdf. Accessed 28 April 2011.
30. Op cit 15.
31. Op cit 21.
32. "Sponsors Beware: FDAAA Creates Compliance Challenges for Drug and Medical Device Clinical Trials." Available at: http://mosessinger.com/articles/files/Bloomberg%20Law%20Reports%20Health%20Law%20March%202008.pdf. Accessed 28 April 2011.
33. Disqualified/Restricted/Restrictions Removed/Assurance Lists for Clinical Investigators. Available at www.fda.gov/ora/compliance_ref/bimo/dis_res_assur.htm. Accessed 28 April 2011.
34. "Drug Trial Registration Requirements Expanded in US." Worldwide Update, Trial Registries, *The Regulatory Affairs Journal Pharma.* Vol. 19, Issue 1, p. 67 (January 2008).
35. Ibid.
36. "Annual Clinical Trial Safety Reports Proposed by FDA." FDAnews Drug Daily Bulletin, Vol. 5, No. 156 (11 August 2008). Available at www.fdanews.com/newsletter/article?issueId=11847&articleId=109316. Accessed 28 April 2011
37. Op cit 34.
38. Ibid.
39. Op cit 32.
40. Op cit 36.
41. ICH *Draft Consensus Guideline: Development Safety Update Report (E2F).* Available at http://www.pmda.go.jp/ich/e/Step3_e2f_08_09_12_e.pdf. Accessed 28 April 2011.
42. Op cit 36.
43. Op cit 41.
44. Op cit 36.
45. Op cit 41.
46. Op cit 36.
47. Op cit 41.

Recommended Reading

2011 edition of the International Compilation of Human Subject Protections. Available at http://www.hhs.gov/ohrp/international/intlcompilation/hspcompilation-v20101130.pdf. Accessed 28 April 2011.

Barnes MB, Kulynych J, et al. *HIPAA and Human Subjects Research: A Question-and-Answer Reference Guide.* Barnett International (March 2003).

Bioethics Resources on the Internet, available at http://bioethics.od.nih.gov/. Accessed 28 April 2011.

Bankowski Z, Levine RJ, eds. XXVIth CIOMS Conference." Ethics and research on human subjects: international guidelines." Geneva: CIOMS, 1993: ix + 291.

FDA Good Clinical Practice 2010 Reference Guide April 1, 2010–March 31, 2011, Book 1B. Clinical Research Resource LLC. 2010.

World Health Organization. *Guidelines for Good Clinical Practice (GCP) for Trials on Pharmaceutical Products.*

WHO Technical Report Series. Geneva: WHO, 1995: vol 850. Available at http://whqlibdoc.who.int/trs/WHO_TRS_850.pdf. Accessed 28 April 2011.

World Health Organization. *International Ethical Guidelines For Biomedical Research Involving Human Subjects*. Geneva: CIOMS, 2002. Available at http://www.cioms.ch/publications/layout_guide2002.pdf. Accessed 28 April 2011.

ISO International Standard 14155:2011, *Clinical Investigation of Medical Devices for Human Subjects—Good Clinical Practice*.

Mathieu MP (editor). *Good Clinical Practice: A Question & Answer Reference Guide*. Parexel International Corporation (May 2010).

Introduction to the Drug Approval Process and Clinical Research Dictionary, Book 8. Clinical Research Resource LLC *April 1, 2010–March 31, 2011*.

Medical Research Council. *MRC Guidelines for Good Clinical Practice In Clinical Trials*. MRC Clinical Trials Series.

National Institutes of Health (NIH) Office for Human Research Protections (http://ohsr.od.nih.gov/). Accessed 28 April 2011.

US Department of Health and Human Services. Office for Civil Rights—HIPAA (http://www.hhs.gov/ocr/privacy/). Accessed 28 April 2011.

Office for Human Research Protections (OHRP) Policy Guidances (by topic) (www.hhs.gov/ohrp/policy/index.html). Accessed 28 April 2011.

Penslar RL and Porter JP. *IRB Guidebook*. Office for Human Research Protections (OHRP). Available at http://www.hhs.gov/ohrp/archive/irb/irb_guidebook.htm. Accessed 28 April 2011.

Regulations and Guidance on the Protection of Human Subjects: Clinical Investigator, IRB and Sponsor Responsibilities, April 1, 2010–March 31, 2011, Book 3A. Clinical Research Resource LLC (2010).

Selected Documents on International Ethical Conduct, Federalwide Assurances, and OHRP Compliance in Academic Research, April 1, 2010–March 31, 2011, Book 3B. Clinical Research Resource LLC (2010).

Woodin KE and Schneider JC. *The CRA's Guide to Monitoring Clinical Research*. Thomson CenterWatch (2003).

International Compilation of Human Subject Protections: 2011 Edition. Available at http://www.hhs.gov/ohrp/international/intlcompilation/hspcompilation-v20101130.pdf. Accessed 28 April 2011.

BIMO webpage. Available at www.fda.gov/ora/compliance_ref/bimo/. Accessed 28 April 2011.

"FDA Information Sheet Guidances for Institutional Review Boards, Clinical Investigators, and Sponsors." Available at www.fda.gov/oc/ohrt/irbs/default.htm. Accessed 28 April 2011.

FDA Office of Good Clinical Practice. Available at www.fda.gov/oc/gcp/default.htm. Accessed 28 April 2011.

National Association of Insurance Commissioners State Insurance Department website: www.naic.org/state_web_map.htm. Accessed 28 April 2011.

National Cancer Institute State Cancer Legislative Database Program. Available at www.scld-nci.net/index.cfml. Accessed 28 April 2011.

National Cancer Institute: States That Require Health Plans to Cover Patient Care Costs in Clinical Trials. Available at www.cancer.gov/clinicaltrials/developments/laws-about-clinical-trial-costs. Accessed 28 April 2011.

National Conference of State Legislatures Clinical Trials: What are States Doing? September 2007 Update. Available at www.ncsl.org/programs/health/clinicaltrials.htm. Accessed 28 April 2011.

"Regulations Requiring Manufacturers to Assess the Safety and Effectiveness of New Drugs and Biological Products in Pediatric Patients" (FR Doc. 98-31902; OC 98142, Docket No. 97N-0165; Pages 66631-66672). Available at www.fda.gov/ohrms/dockets/98fr/120298c.pdf. Accessed 28 April 2011.

"Regulatory and Compliance Information for Clinical Investigators." Available at http://www.fda.gov/Drugs/DevelopmentApprovalProcess/SmallBusinessAssistance/default.htm. Accessed 28 April 2011.

The National Cancer Institute (NCI) website provides information to patients on insurance coverage and reimbursement during clinical trials. Available at www.cancer.gov/clinicaltrials/learning/insurance-coverage. Accessed 28 April 2011.

Serio JC et al. *State-by-State Clinical Trial Requirements Reference Guide*. Barnett International (November 2006).

Current Good Manufacturing Practice and Quality System Design

By Christopher Ernst

Objectives

- Understand basic Good Manufacturing Practice (GMP) requirements and provide compliance recommendations
- Describe concepts of clean design and importance of process validation
- Outline basic elements of sanitary equipment design for key manufacturing components
- Discuss aspects of effective cleaning and sanitization programs
- Provide required elements of an effective corrective and preventive action (CAPA) system
- Understand basic quality system concepts and quality system regulations
- Gain an overview of the most significant GMP regulations and guidance documents that affect drug and device development and manufacturing
- Review FDA structure, recent compliance and inspectional observations
- Understand the difference between drug quality systems and medical device quality systems
- Understand basic concepts regarding microbiological risk within the manufacturing environment

Regulation and Guidance Document Index

- 21 CFR 820 Quality System Regulation subpart H Medical Devices
- *Guide to Inspections of Pharmaceutical Quality Control Laboratories* (July 1993)
- *Guidance for Industry: Quality Systems Approach to Pharmaceutical Current Good Manufacturing Practice Regulations* (September 2006)
- *Guide to Inspections of Sterile Drug Substance Manufacturers* (July 1994)
- *Guide to Inspections of Dosage Form Drug Manufacturers* (October 1993)
- *Guide to Inspections of Medical Device Manufacturers* (December 1997)
- *CDER 2007 Update Compliance Oversight*
- ONDC's New Risk-Based Pharmaceutical Quality Assessment System (July 2005)
- *Guidance for Industry: Investigating Out-of-Specification Test Results for Pharmaceutical Production* (October 2006)
- *Guidance for Industry: Manufacturing, Processing, or Holding Active Pharmaceutical Ingredients* (March 1998)
- *Guidance for Industry: Part 11, Electronic Records; Electronic Signatures—Scope and Application* (August 2003)
- *Guidance for Industry: PAT—A Framework for Innovative Pharmaceutical Development, Manufacturing, and Quality Assurance* (September 2004)
- *Guidance for Industry: Process Validation: General Principles and Practices* (January 2011)
- *Guidance for Industry: Q8(R2) Pharmaceutical Development* (November 2009)
- *Guidance for Industry: Q9 Quality Risk Management* (June 2006)
- *Guidance for Industry: Q10 Pharmaceutical Quality System* (April 2009)
- 21 CFR 210 Current Good Manufacturing Practice in manufacturing, processing, packaging, or holding of drugs; General
- 21 CFR 211 Current Good Manufacturing Practice for finished pharmaceuticals

- *Guidance for Industry: Sterile Drug Products Produced by Aseptic Processing—Current Good Manufacturing Practice* (September 2004)
- *Guidance for Industry: Q7A Good Manufacturing Practice Guidance for Active Pharmaceutical Ingredients* (August 2001)
- *Guidance for Industry: Current Good Manufacturing Practice for Phase 1 Investigational Drugs* (July 2008)
- *Guidance for Industry: Formal Dispute Resolution: Scientific and Technical Issues Related to Pharmaceutical CGMP* (January 2006)
- *Questions and Answers on Current Good Manufacturing Practice (CGMP) for Drugs* (August 2004)
- *Pharmaceutical cGMPs for the 21st Century—A Risk-Based Approach* (September 2004)
- *Human Factors Implications of the New GMP Rule Overall Requirements of the New Quality System Regulation* (July 2008)
- *Draft Guidance for Industry: Powder Blends and Finished Dosage Units—Stratified In-Process Dosage Unit Sampling and Assessment* (October 2003)
- *Guidance for Industry: Guideline for the Monitoring of Clinical Investigations* (January 1998)
- *Expiration Dating of Unit-Dose Repackaged Drugs: Compliance Policy Guide* (May 2005)
- *Guidance for Industry: Computerized Systems Used in Clinical Trials* (May 2007)
- *Draft Guidance for Industry: Analytical Procedures and Methods Validation—Chemistry, Manufacturing, and Controls Documentation* (August 2000)

Introduction

The US Food and Drug Administration (FDA) is an administrative agency in the US government within the Department of Health and Human Services (DHHS). Through federal regulations, FDA regulates the following product areas:

- safe, whole and sanitary foods
- safe and effective medicines, biologics and medical devices
- safe consumer and medical radiation products
- safe and effective animal drugs
- safe cosmetics
- truthful and informative labels

FDA has nine centers that cover these product areas. The Center for Drug Evaluation and Research (CDER) oversees the research, development, manufacture and marketing of drugs. Specifically, CDER regulates:

- prescription drugs
- generic drugs
- over-the-counter (OTC) drugs, which includes certain personal care products that make a therapeutic claim such as medicated shampoo, topical creams, etc.

CDER regulates these activities through statutes and laws enacted by Congress. In this case, the applicable statute is the *Federal Food, Drug & Cosmetic Act* (*FD&C Act*) of 1938. Regulations are then issued by governmental departments or agencies to carry out the intent of the statutes. The applicable regulations that govern the *FD&C Act* are outlined in the Code of Federal Regulations (CFR) Title 21. Guidance documents are issued by governmental departments or agencies to provide industry guidance and agency current thinking on how to comply with and interpret applicable regulations. Guidances are not law, but merely suggestions; however, they are often interpreted by industry as laws. Examples include guidance documents, information sheets and white papers. In general, federal regulations encompass a broad range of applications and require interpretation by the user to develop the processes most appropriate for an intended application.

The regulations set forth in CFR Title 21 parts 210 and 211 contain the minimum current Good Manufacturing Practice (CGMP) for methods to be used in, and the facilities or controls to be used for, the manufacture, processing, packing or holding of a drug to assure that such drug meets the requirements of the act as to safety, and has the identity and strength and meets the quality and purity characteristics that is purports or is represented to possess.

The philosophy for both CGMP regulations and the modern quality systems is:

> "Quality should be built into the product, and testing alone cannot be relied on to ensure product quality."

Testing to show that a product meets specifications is part of GMP, but GMP involves much more than just testing. GMP takes the approach of regulating the manufacturing and laboratory testing environment itself. An extremely important part of GMP is the documentation of every aspect of the process, activities and operations involved with the manufacture of drugs and medical devices. Additionally, GMP requires all manufacturing and testing equipment to be qualified as suitable for use, and all operational methodologies and procedures utilized in the manufacturing process to be validated to demonstrate that they perform as intended.

GMP is global and therefore influenced by international bodies, such as the International Conference on Harmonisation (ICH) International Standards Organization (ISO), and mutual recognition agreements between countries. In 2003, FDA created a CGMP harmonization analysis working group to analyze internal and external CGMP requirements, including those related to quality systems. Based on the working group's analysis, the agency decided to take an incremental approach to modifying 21 CFR 210 and 211 while pursuing international harmonization. The goals of the revision will be to encourage timely detection of and response to emerging defects; to provide further clarity and modernize the regulations; and to harmonize various aspects of 21 CFR 210 and 211 with international agency regulations.

GMP requirements for nonbiological drug products can be found in *FD&C Act* Section 501(a)(2)(b). The GMP regulations are in place to ensure that drugs are safe and meet quality and purity requirements. It is important to note that the drug GMP regulation, 21 CFR 211, specifically applies to "finished pharmaceuticals." This includes clinical supply dosage forms (including placebos) and commercially marketed final dosage forms. Active pharmaceutical ingredients (APIs) are subject to the general GMP legal concept. ICH Q7A describes FDA's current requirements for drug substances.

GMP requirements for biological drug products are defined in 21 CFR, Parts 210 and 211, and the biologics regulations, 21 CFR Parts 600-680. Establishments must comply with their Biologics License Application (BLA) commitments and applicable standards, in addition to GMP.

A generic drug is identical or "bioequivalent" to a brand-name drug in dosage form, safety, strength, route of administration, quality, performance characteristics and intended use. Patent laws prohibit competition with the innovator product for a period of time. Through analytical testing, the chemical composition of the generic is determined to be the same as the branded product. Because many of the research goals of *in vivo* testing were completed previously during innovator product development (i.e., safety, therapeutic effectiveness, effective dose, etc.), the generic drug company is required to only verify "bioequivalence." Bioequivalence is often completed through smaller scale clinical research studies than those required initially for innovator drug products. Patient samples and the subsequent pharmacokinetic (PK) assessments are used to verify equivalence to the branded product. Consequently, generic drugs are chemically identical to their branded counterparts, but typically are able to be sold at substantial discounts compared to the branded price as a result of these reduced research and development costs.

The requirements for medical devices are found in *FD&C Act* Section 501(h), and are further referenced in 520(f)(1). The requirements were amended in 1976 by the *Medical Device Amendments*. The device GMP was first promulgated in 1978 and was revised and renamed the Quality System Regulation (QSR) in 1996. Human factors techniques and data should be an integral consideration in all medical device design control components. Each manufacturer must establish and maintain procedures to ensure that design requirements relating to a device are appropriate and address the device's intended use, including the needs of users and patients. Each manufacturer must establish and maintain procedures for verifying the design input. Design validation must ensure that devices conform to defined user needs and intended uses, and must include testing of production units under actual or simulated use conditions. Design validation must include risk analysis and use error.

Combination products are recent advancements that utilize the capabilities of two or more different product types to provide more effective healthcare products. They are defined in 21 CFR 3.2(e) and are composed of two or more regulated products, such as drug-device, device-biologic or biologic-drug products. In 2004, FDA published *Draft Guidance for Industry and FDA: Current Good Manufacturing Practice for Combination Products*, on the applicability of GMP to combination products. In the 23 September 2009 *Federal Register*, FDA proposed to codify an approach similar to the one taken in the draft guidance, by establishing new 21 CFR Part 4, Subpart A. The proposed rule embodies the legal framework that, in FDA's view, drugs, devices and biological products do not lose their individual regulatory identities when they become constituent parts of a combination product. In other words, a drug-device combination product is both a drug and a device, and both sets of CGMP requirements (21 CFR 210 and 211 for drugs and 21 CFR 820 for devices) apply to the combination product itself. However, the proposed rule recognizes that Parts 210 and 211 and Part 820 are similar in most respects. In this context, for single entity and co-packaged combination products, the rule provides a "streamlined approach" as an alternative to fully implementing and complying with both sets of CGMP requirements. Under this streamlined approach, a manufacturer could choose to operate under and comply with either Parts 210 and 211 or Part 820, rather than both, provided that additional specific aspects of the other cGMP framework are also incorporated. For more information, see Chapter 22 Combination Products.

FDA's *Guidance for Industry: Current Good Manufacturing Practice for Phase 1 Investigational Drugs* (July 2008) has replaced the guidance issued in 1991, entitled *Preparation of Investigational New Drug Products* (please note that the 1991 guidance still applies for investigational new drug products for Phase 2 and 3). The 2008 guidance states the requirements for manufacture of Phase 1 clinical materials. The guidance redefines CGMP requirements for Phase 1 clinical trial materials as: well-defined and written procedures; adequately controlled equipment and manufacturing environment; and accurately and consistently recorded data. Manufacturers of Phase 1 investigational drugs should consider carefully how to best ensure the implementation of standards, practices and procedures that conform to CGMP for their specific product and manufacturing operations.

The *FD&C Act* specifically declares that a drug or device is deemed to be adulterated unless it is manufactured in accordance with "Current Good Manufacturing Practice," which indicates that GMPs are constantly changing to meet industry standards.

A robust quality system can provide the necessary framework for implementing quality by design, continuous improvement and risk management in the drug manufacturing process. The CGMP regulations are harmonized to the extent possible with other widely used quality management systems, including ISO 9000, non-US pharmaceutical quality management requirements, and FDA's own QSR.

There are many different, equally acceptable ways to document that a pharmaceutical has been manufactured in compliance with all FDA regulations and guidances. The underlying principle, whether the documentation system is paper-based or electronic, is that all data must be able to be traced back to the source and verified. The statement that most aptly sums up pharmaceutical manufacturing compliance is, "If it wasn't documented, it wasn't done."

This chapter provides a brief overview of the regulations involved in ensuring a drug product or medical device complies with CGMPs, and provides some insight on industry-accepted practical interpretation of these regulations.

Six Key Quality Systems for Drug GMP Quality System

In August 2002, FDA initiated a new approach to drug product quality regulation similar to the device QSR, based on science and risk, that incorporates an integrated quality system. The new approach was adopted to ensure FDA's regulatory review and inspection polices are up to date scientifically and to encourage adoption of new technological advances. The 2002 initiative was summarized in the more recent *Guidance for Industry: Quality Systems Approach to Pharmaceutical CGMP Regulations* (September 2006). The guidance is intended to help manufacturers implementing modern quality systems and risk management approaches meet the requirements of the agency's CGMP regulations. The guidance describes a comprehensive quality system model, highlighting the model's consistency with CGMP regulatory requirements for manufacturing human and veterinary drugs, including biological drug products. The guidance also explains how manufacturers implementing such quality systems can fully comply with 21 CFR 210 and 211. The typical quality system contains six key systems and three critical elements. The six key systems are:

- quality system
- facilities and equipment system
- materials system
- production system
- packaging and labeling system
- laboratory control system

The three critical elements are:
- standard operating procedures (SOPs)
- training
- records

Following this design, FDA employs a six-point inspection model with which industry should become familiar, especially since the eventual preapproval inspection (PAI) of any innovator or generic product being considered for marketing will follow this model. Perhaps just as important as following this six-point inspection model is understanding the philosophy behind it. FDA views the six areas below as related entities, each with a quality component. In other words, the expectation is that quality is built into each area.

The quality unit includes the quality control component (QC), which monitors overall compliance with CGMPs and internal procedures and specifications, through its review and approval duties (e.g., change control, reprocessing, batch release, records review, laboratory evaluations, validation protocols, reports, etc.). Also included in the quality unit is the quality assurance component (QA), which provides compliance oversight primarily through conducting auditing functions, such as internal system audits, process audits and supplier audits. The QA group would be responsible for product specifications, SOPs, establishment of policy, evaluation of all product defects and returned and salvaged drug products, corrective and preventive action (CAPA) and other trending and metrics evaluations.

For a system to be effective there should be a distinction between routine quality control functions and the oversight responsibilities of the quality assurance group. Often the terms QA and QC are used interchangeably; however, they are in fact two distinct functions with equal responsibilities within an effective quality system. The QA department sets the standard, and QC monitors compliance to that standard, e.g., product specification, SOP, etc. Organizations employ a variety of approaches, which can include a combined QA/QC department, or separate dedicated units for QC and QA or building QC responsibilities into the operational functions. The organizational architecture (organizational charts, job descriptions, job specifications, etc.) should clearly delineate the responsibilities of the quality group(s). The structure should establish autonomy between operational departments and quality groups to prevent conflict of interest and/or fear of retaliation or retribution when performing essential functions on either side. Generally, QC functions are more resource dependent and, if not structured properly, will detract from the ability of the organization to effectively implement QA functions.

Investigation of out-of-specification (OOS) results, deviations and failures in both production and the analytical laboratory is a critical GMP compliance element. Often these investigation outcomes are reviewed during regulatory inspection. It is important to justify retest work and acceptance of retest values as opposed to original data generated. Unless there is a valid reason to replace the original value, it must be included in the data set. Without valid reasoning, "testing into compliance" can be inferred and the data (and subsequent decisions made with them, i.e., justification to release) are unable to be defended. Investigation of technical complaints and adverse reactions is mandated in the drug and device GMPs and is critical to assure the final product's safety and efficacy.

Internal and supplier audits for drug products are not required by specific GMPs in 21 CFR 211; however, CGMPs require these activities for compliance. The medical device QSR, 21 CFR 820, requires an internal quality audit, which enables the organization to achieve total quality management. Most companies dread internal audits and put them last on their "to do" list. However, the internal audit process need not be painful or difficult to implement. It is best to start with the 21 CFR 210 and 211 regulations and develop an audit checklist for each area. Once the checklist is complete, it should not change much, which allows for trending over time and demonstration of a state of control within established metrics. The audit process can be conducted periodically in smaller segments so as not to overwhelm the organization. A very simple yet effective audit is a spot check of the production line, i.e., line clearance completion, availability of current product specifications, use of proper personal protective equipment (PPE), equipment approval and availability of cleaning and sanitization records, etc. It is often effective to establish "peer group" audit teams with staff members from other disciplines who can assist in conducting the internal audits. The QA department maintains the lead auditor role. For example, when manufacturing is being audited, the audit team should consist of representatives from disciplines such as QA, formulation and analytical. The formulation and analytical personnel will gain greater insight into the manufacturing process while offering their own unique perspectives. Effective and regular internal audits are a key component of the organization's continuous improvement process.

Device Quality System Regulation

In the device QSR, FDA defines "quality system" as the organizational structure, responsibilities, procedures, processes and resources for implementing quality management. All domestic or foreign manufacturers must have a quality system in place for the design, manufacture, packaging, labeling, storage, installation and servicing of finished medical devices intended for commercial distribution in the US. The QSR helps assure that medical devices are safe and effective for their intended use. The QSR is found in 21 CFR 820.

The QSR applies to quality management and organization, device design, buildings, equipment, purchase and handling of components, production and process controls, packaging and labeling control, device evaluation, distribution, installation, complaint handling, servicing and records. The QSR requires that various specifications and controls be established for devices; that devices be designed under a quality system to meet these specifications; that devices be manufactured under a quality system; that finished devices meet these specifications; that devices be correctly installed, checked and serviced; that quality data be analyzed to identify and correct quality problems; and that complaints be processed.

The key items differentiating the QSR from drug GMPs are management responsibility, quality plan, corrective/preventative action, design controls and purchasing control. The additional requirements for devices are:

- Each device manufacturer must maintain a design history file, a device master record and a device history record for each device type.
- Every company must have quality plans and quality system records that define its quality practices.
- Device manufacturers are required to establish purchasing controls and institute post-distribution device failure investigations and corrective/preventive actions for defects or recurring technical problems.

The QSR does not apply to manufacturers of finished device components or parts.

The CAPA process is a required element specified by 21 CFR 820.100 for medical devices. A firm is required to establish (define, document and implement) CAPA processes, even if they have not experienced a CAPA event. Depending on the organization, the number and complexity of the established procedures may vary. Review of the CAPA system and supporting documentation is a basic component of each regulatory inspection of medical device manufacturers. A CAPA system evaluates data supplied from a variety of internal and external data sources to monitor the quality of products, problems, processes or people. The basic elements of the CAPA process include data analysis, investigation of root cause, identifying actions, verifying/validating effectiveness of action taken, and providing processes for documenting the event. Typical outputs of a CAPA investigation require implementation of change, dissemination of information and management review.

The procedure should clearly define the sources of data, how frequently they will be analyzed, and the statistical processes utilized. Examples of data sources include rework, employee feedback, returned goods and audit observations. Typical statistical analyses include Pareto charts, trend analysis, run charts, control charts, etc. Some common errors in effective implementation of the CAPA system that lead to inspectional observations are: not considering all data sources in analysis, e.g., forgetting service or complaint calls or product nonconformances; and vague data sources, e.g., the organization is unable to explain to an inspector how data from the source was collected or analyzed. The CAPA program should be administered by the QA department rather than the sales team.

Effectively analyzing data is a very important part of ensuring all pharmaceutical systems are operating in a state of control. An annual evaluation of batch trends is required under 21 CFR 211.180(e). However, an annual evaluation is not sufficient to spot potential problem areas early enough to implement a correction. The CAPA system will define frequency of evaluation of data. FDA requires that appropriate statistical methodology be employed where necessary to detect recurring quality problems. The organization should avoid misuse of statistics in an effort to minimize rather than address an identified problem.

The CAPA system offers an avenue for continuous improvement. The following definitions are utilized by FDA to describe corrections and actions:

- "Nonconformity" is non-fulfillment of a specified requirement.
- "(Field) Correction" is repair, rework or adjustment related to the disposition of an existing nonconformity.
- "Corrective Action" is action taken to eliminate the causes of an existing nonconformity, defect or other undesirable situation to prevent recurrence.
- "Preventive Action" is action taken to eliminate the cause of a potential nonconformity, defect or other undesirable situation in order to prevent occurrence.

Facilities and Equipment System

Under a quality system, technical experts are responsible for defining specific facility and equipment requirements. A GMP-compliant facility must be of suitable size to perform the required operations, with temperature and humidity controls, adequate lighting and appropriate sewage and sanitation facilities. Areas within the facility should be designated as "clean" and "dirty" areas. Procedures should be in place to specify PPE (hair nets, beard nets, coats, glasses, etc.) required in each area to prevent contamination of the operations by human interaction. One effective technique is to clearly display signage including pictures in the gowning area showing PPE that is being worn properly and improperly by staff to demonstrate the concepts. In facilities that intend to have CGMP and non-CGMP operations, additional care must be taken to clearly designate areas of the facility with a physical separation, equipment and staff to each operation, or ensure effective crossover in instances of resource utilization/optimization and changeover. It is not effective to simply use a paint stripe or tape line to delineate two sections, GMP and non-GMP, on the manufacturing floor. Operating to a single standard—either GMP or non-GMP—eliminates this concern.

Materials of construction should be carefully considered with respect to the intended use. Generally, smooth non-porous surfaces, including floors, walls and ceilings, with coping between floors-walls and walls-ceilings, are preferred in aseptic manufacturing environments.

Direction of air handling equipment and fans should be reviewed to ensure it will not introduce microbiological or particulate contamination into the manufacturing process. In some instances, isolated rooms and dedicated air handling equipment are required. Generally, fans and air diffusers should flow from clean to dirty areas, i.e., in a direction away from product contact surfaces. All bay doors, man doors, etc. should contain screens when open to prevent particulate contamination and flying insects/birds from entering the manufacturing areas. Aisleways around equipment should be designed to reduce air turbulence and exhaust discharge around production lines, especially near product contact surfaces, when removing finished product or resupplying components to the line with motorized equipment.

There must be designated areas for quarantined, released and rejected materials. Clearly visible signage should be used to ensure proper disposition of materials by employees. In modern systems, bar codes or other electronic labeling can facilitate this process. Materials are tracked within the system by the code. When an attempt is made to pull a supply from a lot of material, the code is scanned, and if the lot is not available for use, the system will block the action.

Warehouse storage facilities must be temperature-controlled, clean and free from pest infestations; separate areas must be maintained for on-test, off-test and rejected raw materials, components and final products.

Distribution records must be maintained as part of GMP compliance to aid recall activities. Environmental control and alert and action limits must be established, monitored and trended for contaminants (particulate and microbiological). The environment must be controlled and monitored to prevent product cross-contamination and contamination by harmful microorganisms or extraneous matter (filth). Support systems are critical and must be properly constructed, maintained and monitored. Equipment must be qualified, calibrated, clearly labeled, cleaned and maintained to prevent contamination and mix-ups.

Microbiological risk awareness is something that should be considered in every manufacturing environment, regardless of the material being manufactured. Microorganisms, in addition to causing illness in humans and animals, have the potential for other deleterious effects on finished products such as:

- discoloration
- production of malodors
- production of gas that can cause packages to bulge or burst
- breakdown in viscosity or elasticity
- otherwise unable to perform as intended

Microorganisms in the manufacturing environment can prove to be formidable opponents. When introduced into a finished product, the resulting product is considered adulterated according to GMP regulations, and both the product and manufacturer are subject to the applicable restrictions and enforcement actions for adulterated product. Below are a few of the challenges presented by microorganisms.

- Microorganisms have two main modes of introduction into a product—by contact or airborne. Therefore, many of the processes implemented in a CGMP environment can directly influence and reduce associated microbiological risk, including sanitization of product contact surfaces, use of PPE, effective housekeeping procedures to reduce dust and sampling programs for raw materials, components, water, etc.
- Microorganisms can develop resistance to product preservative systems and certain sanitizers. Similar to antibiotic resistance, microorganisms can develop resistance over time through exposure within the manufacturing environment to diluted product levels in puddles, rinse water, etc. Once the resistance is developed, a product formulation change is often required to eliminate the micro organisms. One microorganism known to exhibit such resistance was *Pseudomonas cepacia*, later renamed to *Burkholderia cepacia*. This organism alone was responsible for a majority of microbiological FDA recalls and product returns in the 1990s and early 2000s.
- Microorganisms have the ability to reproduce very quickly by binary fission. This simple cellular division means they can quickly overwhelm a product preservative system or production environment. In lower numbers it may not seem possible, as two cells become four, four become eight, etc.; however, in the log phase of growth and rapid enumeration you could have 100 million cells that become 200 million then 400 million, and can quickly overwhelm a product or process.
- Microorganisms are invisible and therefore fall into the "out of sight out of mind" category. No well-intentioned housekeeping staff, compounding or production staff can spot microbiological contamination on a product surface to take action. No line would run with visible filth on contact surfaces, but how do you spot microbiological contamination? A robust GMP program will provide training on microbiological risk awareness and the importance of such items as the use of PPE, keeping tank lids and component hoppers closed, cleaning up spills and puddles, etc. A proactive approach is required to control microorganisms.
- Classic test methods for microorganisms take 48–72 hours for an aerobic plate count and 72–120 hours for a yeast or mold count. Compare this to a routine QC analysis for color, viscosity or pH that could be completed within an hour. Often, the manufacturing and packaging processes are complete by the time results are available. This time-lag significantly increases the risk of product loss if CGMP or sanitary manufacturing practices are not effectively implemented. There are rapid identification methods available that detect the adenosine triphosphate present in cells through a chemiluminescent reaction when viewed under ultraviolet light. However, there are limitations with such methods. They have low selectivity for microorganisms relative to biological product so in instances where natural products are manufactured or natural raw materials are utilized, the ATP in those cells will also give a positive reaction (but this can be used to validate effective cleaning processes). They also do not work well with matrix effects of finished products. In classic microbiological methods, the sample is placed into a dilution fluid that buffers the matrix and neutralizes any preservative system in the product to permit detection of microorganisms. This can be problematic in rapid identification methods. Often, rapid methods are qualitative in nature (presence or absence) as opposed to quantitative, which may further limit applicability in certain applications.

The microorganisms that make up the largest group of human pathogens are the gram negative rods. The term "gram negative" refers to the reaction displayed by the cell wall when viewed under a microscope, during the gram staining process. Within the group of gram negative organisms are two main divisions which include the Enteric (literally "from the gut") and Nonenteric organisms. Typical Enteric species include familiar organisms such as *E. coli* spp., *Salmonella* spp. and *Shigella* spp. and are found in raw foods, including meats and dairy products, as well as human and animal waste. Typical Nonenteric species include the *Pseudomonas* spp. (literally, "false feet") and species such as *Pseudomonas cepacia*,

Pseudomonas aeruginosa, etc., commonly found in wet environments. The Pseudomonad organisms are non-spore forming, meaning they do not form a resting body, and have a thin cell wall that will quickly desiccate in a dry environment. Therefore, they thrive in moist areas within the manufacturing equipment in a typical facility housing water systems, compressed air systems, heat exchangers, pumps, HVAC drain pans, valves, tanks, filling equipment, etc. Initial design, validation and routine preventive maintenance of these systems becomes critical to lowering overall microbiological risk within the CGMP facility and is an opportunity for the organization to build in quality appropriate to the intended use.

Typical areas of risk in the design of equipment include:

- Heat exchangers are commonly used for super-heating or cooling steps in the compounding process. They are often used for premix applications such as preparing emulsions, opacifiers, waxes, pomades, gelatins, etc. The two most common types are "tube and shell" and "plate frame" heat exchangers. Regardless of the type, the basic premise is that the product stream is circulated within an inner core that is surrounded by an external heating or cooling solution such as glycol. The contamination risk is the potential for a break in the barrier between the cooling fluid and the product.

- Air compressors are commonly used for a variety of applications from manufacturing to maintenance. Many components within the production line including belts, cappers, fillers, label machines, milling machines, sieves/sifts, pumps, etc. are pneumatically driven by air pressure supplied by the system. Typically the compressor system design will contain hydrocarbon scrubbers, particulate filters and moisture traps along the system that should be found adjacent to each use point. Additionally, the system will contain a dryer that lowers the system's dew point to eliminate the condensate that forms in the line during the process of condensing the air to create pressure and is worse in pipes that travel through hot and cold areas of the facility. However, should any of the components in the system become clogged or otherwise not function as intended, serious microbiological risk can be introduced. If the system contains condensate water, this will become contaminated with microorganisms that could spray a fine aerosol of bacteria into or over the product at each use point. Compressed air should not be used as a component of the cleaning and sanitization process to dry equipment or parts. In addition to the aerosol risk, spraying the compressed air disturbs dust and other settled debris, including microorganisms, which then settle on the previously cleaned surfaces.

Organic solvents such as 70% isopropyl alcohol (IPA) solution are a better option, when able to be used safely, for rapid drying of equipment.

- Pumps are an integral part of the manufacturing process and are frequently used for ancillary support such as water systems, pre-mix operations, cleaning and sanitization processes and, primarily, for circulation and recirculation of product supply, etc. Pumps are of two main types: centrifugal and positive displacement. The design and orientation of the unit, i.e., vertical pump head is nonsanitary vs. horizontal pump head that is sanitary, will impact the degree of clean design. Centrifugal pumps essentially push material to the output by generating centrifugal force. They are often smaller and, consequently, portable; however, they generally have lower flow rates and are infrequently used in manufacturing. The primary designs of centrifugal pumps are radial, mixed and axillary radial flow. Positive displacement pumps move material to the output by displacement action. They are generally larger and, therefore, not portable and are more expensive. The displacement action is achieved by two design types: reciprocating via piston-plunger action or diaphragm action, and rotary via single- or multi-rotor action. The type of pump should be selected based on flow rates required, material temperature, pressure requirements, batch size, dispensing accuracy and sanitary design requirements. Replacing pumps within a validated process would require revalidation and approval via the change control system as they are key process components.

- Water systems are major components of the facility. As indicated, they can pose a significant microbiological risk if not properly maintained. Additionally, they can affect product quality if chemical and physical attributes such as total or dissolved solids, pH, conductivity, etc. are not within specification. Water has two opportunities to negatively affect product attributes as it is often used as a major raw material component and in the cleaning and sanitization process. Frequently, plants establish various grades of water for varying purposes. Water specifications for manufacturing purposes are outlined in the *US Pharmacopeia*. Systems capable of delivering purified water versus sterile water for injection (WFI) would require very different design considerations. The type of treatment system employed would vary depending upon the quality and purity of the local ground water supply. This ranges from raw water to city potable water (generally chlorinated) and well water. Each of these systems will also vary in chemical composition based upon geographic region. A basic first step in system design and planning is to conduct a complete water analysis to determine supply attributes. Based on the results, certain system components can be properly sized and or excluded as necessary, e.g., a water softener system to remove hardness ions of calcium and magnesium, may or may not be needed. As a design is considered, overall water quality and capacity/flow rate will be key factors. This will determine whether a system to "generate on demand" will be sufficient or if water storage will be necessary, which will require a more complex system design. The system design will determine the most effective methods of cleaning and sanitization such as UV, ozone, thermal, etc. Generally, three main system types are utilized based upon water grade and capacity: vapor compressed distillation, reverse osmosis and resin exchange. In some instances, combination systems are required. Technical experts should be consulted for development of piping diagrams, to ensure pipe angles in turns, Ts, valves, etc. are adequate in relation to system component sizes, e.g., tanks, pipe diameter, pump size, etc.

- Tanks should be of suitable size and materials of construction to sufficiently contain all materials with adequate room for mixing. Design aspects to consider include materials of construction (e.g, polycarbonate, fiber or 316 stainless steel), types of mixers (e.g., internal or external, paddle, side sweeps, etc.), type of outlet and position, thermal requirements and need for jacket, recirculation capabilities, pressure rating, etc. Tanks intended for clean design should be of 316 stainless steel construction, with sterile valves on the inlet and outlet and a conical bottom to permit complete draining. Flat bottom tanks or fiber-bonded, plastic tanks are not appropriate for aseptic applications. Cleaning and sanitization protocols for tanks should be clearly specified. Often large tanks are sanitized via clean-in-place (CIP) through the use of spray balls. This technique should be validated and routine maintenance is required to ensure the ball does not become clogged or is missing applying sanitizer to all interior surfaces. In some instances, tanks are entered and cleaned, with the appropriate confined space entry training and safety equipment in place.
- Valves are included throughout the manufacturing environment. In facility design, the type and materials of construction selected should be consistent with intended use. Generally there are many styles of valves including ball, mixproof, leak protection, diaphragm, check, flush bottom and butterfly. Each is best suited for certain applications. For example,

ball valves are essentially a ball bearing with a hole in the middle that rotates. When the valve is in the open position material is able to flow, and the ball is rotated perpendicular to the product stream to close. In the closed position, material is retained in the ball "dead leg" and is stored for potentially long periods of time. When the valve is opened, the retained material is delivered into the flow, which can potentially contaminate the entire system with microorganisms. Ball valves are best used in unsanitary manufacturing applications or on the exit (discharge to waste) side of tanks, pumps or other equipment. Ball valves, if used, must be sanitized via clean-out-of-place (COP) procedures. The butterfly valve is a sanitary designed valve. This essentially consists of a flat plate that rotates on a pivot point in the center. There is no trapped material on rotation of the plate. This valve type can be sanitized under CIP.

- For design materials of ancillary equipment components, including pipes, clamps, gaskets and O-rings, welds, etc., it is best to "sweat the details" during the design phase. Small differences in these areas can significantly affect the overall clean design of the system, reducing associated microbiological risk, increasing operational effectiveness, reducing down time, leading to longer product life under repeat sanitization, etc. over time. Selection of 316 stainless steel components over plastic, etc. changes the ability of the system to be easily cleaned and sanitized to eliminate harbor points for microorganisms, etc. by reducing porosity of surfaces. Variation in installation techniques will also contribute to a clean design. For example, welds of 316 SS pipe should be orbital welds with complete system passivation prior to system commissioning. Traditional top welding techniques can leave uneven pit marks on the interior of the weld that will be problematic later on.

Effective cleaning and sanitization procedures are essential to batch-to-batch reproducibility within CGMP manufacturing. Processes should be established for all types of equipment design and configurations and include housekeeping standards for each area of the facility. Proper signage should be displayed that shows the location of "clean" and "dirty" parts, equipment and utensils. All staff, including rotations/shifts, who could potentially be performing the procedure, must receive adequate training prior to executing a cleaning and sanitization (C&S) event. Often, complete execution of the process may involve multiple functions such as maintenance and sanitization teams when equipment disassembly is required. C&S processes should be fully documented in sufficient detail to permit consistent application of the process, including solution preparation instructions, final strength, contact times, etc.

There are two main approaches to C&S of equipment: CIP and COP. Each is specific to the design of the equipment being cleaned and sanitized. CIP refers to C&S procedures that are performed with the equipment fully assembled and in place. This requires draining of product supply from equipment and/or removal of product and visible filth followed by circulation of cleaning and sanitization solutions. This can be effective in equipment of sanitary design that allows for complete removal of all materials without disassembly. When CIP is the primary method of C&S, periodic disassembly of sections of the equipment for visual inspection to verify effectiveness of the process is suggested. The COP process requires complete disassembly of the equipment for proper cleaning and effective sanitization. Often the equipment is removed from the production area and taken to a separate designated area for disassembly and C&S. In these cases, longer downtime can be expected, which is another important consideration in the design phase when building quality into the process.

The distinction should be understood between cleaning and sanitization, which are often used interchangeably but are in fact two distinct processes. Cleaning involves removal of all dirt, debris and other organic or inorganic matter from equipment surfaces. The two main methods utilized for cleaning processes are: chemical agents, e.g., detergent solutions, and mechanical action, e.g., brushes or pipe pigging.

Sanitization is the step that removes microorganisms, including bacteria, yeast and molds, viruses, etc., from the equipment surface. The degree at which these are removed may vary from sanitized, which indicates significant reduction in microorganisms (with a baseline level remaining) to sterilized, which indicates complete removal of microorganisms from the surface. The degree of sanitization or sterilization required is dependent upon the intended use of the system. Generally, sanitization is completed by a variety of methods that include chemical agents, e.g., ozone, bleach solutions or 70% IPA, or thermal processes, e.g., circulation of hot water or autoclaving—a sterilization process that uses heat and pressure.

Sanitization cannot begin until effective cleaning has been completed. The sanitizer efficiency is significantly reduced or ineffective on a dirty surface. Most chemical sanitizers are oxidizers that are quickly consumed by organic material on the surface. Thermal sanitization efficiency is reduced as residues insulate the surface being sanitized, thereby increasing contact times (beyond those established in validation) and protecting bacteria from the lethal effects. Generally, cleaning and sanitization procedures should be completed using, and solutions prepared from, purified water grade or above. City water should not be used, as it contains dissolved solids, particulates, chlorine and microorganisms that can interfere with or reduce the overall effectiveness of the process.

The concentration/time relationship is critical when developing the procedure and resulting validation protocols. As concentration increases, the required contact time of the sanitizer with the equipment surface will decrease. This concept can allow efficient procedures to be established that reduce line downtime, thereby increasing productivity and profitability. The appropriate procedure is established based on materials of construction and corrosiveness to equipment, employee safety considerations and procedure effectiveness based on analytical results, etc.

The procedures should be validated in combination with process validations or as standalone procedures. Validation protocols should include verification of both cleaning and sanitization aspects of the process. The protocol should verify: removal of all residues of prior product, removal of C&S agents from the equipment surfaces in final rinse, exact sanitizer concentrations and contact times with allowable variance, and flow rates and speeds for pumps and valves within the system. It should also confirm the degree of sanitization/sterilization obtained by microbiological swab or contact samples. Protocols should include an adequate number of process replicates, with equipment and staff variations, to ensure repeatability/reproducibility. An effective sampling design should be established that covers the entire system being sanitized. Thermographic cameras, infrared sensors or maximum registering heat tapes are effective for documenting maximum temperatures achieved across a system when conducting thermal validation protocols.

Preparations of chemical sanitizers should be verified by analytical testing during validation. This would include initial concentration, as well as concentration over the duration of the contact time within the equipment during the sanitization cycle. If sanitizers are intended to be stored, validation should include stability data to determine appropriate storage times. Alternately, procedures should require chemical sanitizers to be made fresh at the point of use.

Materials System

The material system includes measurement and activities to control finished products, components, containers and closures. It includes validation of computerized inventory control processes, drug storage, distribution controls and records. There must be written procedures for the receipt, storage, testing and approval or disapproval of raw materials, components, product and containers and closures.

Production System

In a modern quality system manufacturing environment, significant product characteristics should be defined from design to delivery, and control should be exercised over all changes. In addition, quality and manufacturing processes and procedures—and changes to them—must be defined, approved and controlled. It is important to establish responsibility for designing and changing products. Documenting processes, associated controls and changes to these processes helps ensure that sources of variability are identified.

Batch numbering is a key to maintaining proper traceability. Each lot or batch number must be unique and represent the lot's complete history. Batch and equipment use records must show the ingredients, equipment, containers and labeling used and the personnel involved with batch production. Raw materials must be controlled and traceable to products in which they are used. Documentation should support a full "trace back" investigation in case a batch record needs to be completely investigated to determine the root cause of a nonconformance of a product quality attribute (microbiological, chemical or physical).

Verification steps and sign-off are required for critical process steps. All batch-related documents must undergo final review and quality unit approval before products are released.

Packaging and Labeling System

FDA recommends that, as part of the design process and before commercial production, the controls for all processes within the packaging and labeling system be planned and documented with written procedures. Distinct labels with discriminating features for different products, such as a product marketed with different strengths, should be included in the procedure to prevent mislabeling, which could result in product recalls. Approval processes for label format and text should be in place with provisions for variations such as translation and back translation as required for the generation of multilingual labels..

Distribution of approved labels to the manufacturing unit should be controlled, and access to approved labels restricted. A basic process control to have in place in a CGMP environment is a label reconciliation process. Labels should be released to the production line in the exact number required for the run. Labels damaged or destroyed during the run should be accounted for. At the conclusion of the run, a reconciliation is performed between labels issued, applied and returned (including those damaged) to ensure 100% accountability for the quantity issued. A line clearance checklist should include removal of all labels, cartons, neck hangers and other packaging, etc. from a run prior to initiating the next run.

Laboratory Control System

Laboratory controls, including analytical methods validation and laboratory equipment qualification, must be in place. Scientifically sound stability programs must be implemented for each product to support labeled expiration dating.

Important components of effective laboratory control are an adequately designed sampling program and well-trained staff members to collect the samples. Appropriate statistical models should be considered to determine the best sample scheme for a given situation. Traditionally, a $\sqrt{N}+1$ model is used and applies in most situations. In a post-validated system operating in a state of control, a reduced sampling plan could be established that reduces time and cost and improves overall operational efficiency.

Proper training of staff members, generally within the QC unit, who are collecting samples, is critical to ensure the sample is in fact representative of the entire lot. A sample that misrepresents the batch, water system condition, etc., can lead to costly or inaccurate decisions being made regarding the final disposition of the material, e.g., rework, scrap, initiate a C&S and/or line downtime. Staff members collecting microbiological samples require additional training, PPE, sterile sample collection tools and containers, etc., to both ensure aseptic sample collection and protect the bulk material being sampled from contamination during the sampling process.

Procedures should be in place to describe the conditions under which a resample will be collected and/or a retest result is generated or accepted. Unless a valid reason can be identified that would permit resampling or retesting, these should not occur. All data generated must be provided for review, and a written procedure should provide criteria for excluding a result as an "outlier" from a data set. Failure to consider all data or an ineffective OOS/out-of-limits investigation process that determines the root cause of the nonconformance can generate misleading data or the perception of the data "testing into compliance."

The Three Critical Elements for Drug GMP
Standard Operating Procedures (SOPs)

SOPs describe how a company complies with the drug or device regulations and are critical to GMP compliance. They help ensure a consistent operation that reduces variation in finished products and help to ensure compliant practices by all employees. They are also communication tools that can be used for training purposes or to demonstrate to an auditor or inspector the process being performed. Effective SOPs are a great management tool and help build accountability across the organization. Typically, a regulatory inspection will involve an independent review of the organization's SOPs, followed by a series of interviews with key staff members, and then a review of supporting production records and documentation to verify knowledge and compliance to the SOPs reviewed.

There should be a process that clearly defines administration of the SOP infrastructure, typically referred to as the "SOP on SOPs." The procedure will define frequency of review; version control; training requirements; document format and required sections; process for updates and change control; retirement and archive of prior versions;

process for management review and approval, etc. The SOP program is traditionally administered by the QA department; however, to be most effective, the content and processes described by each SOP should be developed by the operational groups responsible for performing the procedure. Each SOP should describe a process "actually," not theoretically, as it is being performed within the facility. Documents that simply repeat regulatory requirements but do not reflect the organization's actual practice tend to be difficult to implement, are more open to interpretation by the user, have reduced effectiveness, and are inadequate to demonstrate compliance with supporting documentation.

In addition to an effective system for SOP management, each organization should have a process for managing all other controlled documents, i.e., technical specifications, policies, forms, templates, test methods, etc. Anyone should be able to pick up any document, including a batch record, etc., and learn its version, when it was revised and why.

Each CGMP program requires a robust change control system. Change control exists to prevent unintended consequences to product quality. A proper change control program incorporates systems (document sign-offs) and a committee that oversees all changes likely to affect product quality. All changes are carefully documented in a systematic manner and documentation is stored where it is easily accessible and available for review. Changes could include those to: documentation, i.e., SOPs, technical specifications or test methods; equipment, such as pumps; testing equipment; supplier vendors; a process such as mix time or speed; or to product design or packaging. Each change, if not controlled, has the potential to negatively affect the final product. All changes should be properly evaluated and approved prior to implementation. Unauthorized changes must be strictly prohibited in the CGMP environment.

Training

Each person engaged in the manufacture, processing, packaging or holding of a drug product shall have the appropriate experience, education and training, or a combination thereof, to enable that person to perform the assigned functions. Training could be documented via curriculum vitae, degrees or licenses or internal or external training certificates. Training should encompass general requirements such as SOPs or policies, regulatory training and project specific aspects as applicable, i.e., on the exact instrument or test method, product compounding specification or production line to which the employee is assigned. Employee GMP training by qualified individuals is required on a continuing basis and with sufficient frequency, as defined by the organization, to ensure employees remain familiar with CGMP requirements applicable to their jobs.

All training must be sufficiently documented to include the topic presented or abstract, name of presenter, date(s)

conducted and list of attendees in a format (electronic or print) that is able to be easily retrieved upon request. Training should be adequate to cover any variations in normal routine operations that may have been included in the process validation, e.g., multiple shifts; temporary, part-time or contract workers; variations in equipment components or configurations (changes in pumps or filling equipment); or changes to product supply (tank versus tote, etc.) as applicable.

Records

All GMP activities must be documented in detail. This would also include ancillary support documents such as training records, SOP history files, equipment calibration and maintenance records, cleaning and sanitization logs, etc. All control records—including production, labeling and packaging records—are to be retained for at least one year after the batch expiration date or for certain OTC products exempt from expiration dating, for three years after batch distribution, whichever is longer. Since this time can be variable, firms often establish a standard document retention period such as 15 years. Distribution records must show where products were shipped and a process must be in place to facilitate a recall if necessary.

Documents must be properly secured and archived so as to prevent their accidental loss or destruction for the duration of the required retention period, i.e., protected from damage by fire, water, heat, rodent infestations, etc. Design aspects with regard to record storage should be considered within the facility, such as fire retardant cabinets, shelving to prevent storage directly on the floor, protection from excessive heat and direct sunlight, adequate physical security, no overhead water pipes, etc. If an adequate storage location cannot be established or designed within the facility, there are several vendors with facilities specifically designed for storage of paper records and electronic media according to regulatory requirements. When an offsite location is used, the vendor should be qualified by the QA department to verify the facility has the adequate record retention controls in place.

The record retention system employed by the organization, which includes the combination of format and physical location, should permit easy retrieval upon request by an auditor or regulatory inspector. Records may be retained in the original format or as copies of the original by reduction to electronic media such as microfilm, microfiche, electronic tape, CD, etc. If an electronic source is used, a suitable reader of the electronic format must be available for the duration of the retention period. Appropriate written procedures for disaster recovery as well as routine system backup, restore and archive should be in place for all computerized systems.

Verification, Qualification and Validation

Verification, qualification and validation activities are

extremely important compliance elements. Both drug and device GMPs require that all operational methodologies and procedures utilized in manufacturing and testing be validated to demonstrate that they can function as intended. Validation activities also include aspects related to batch production such as cleaning and sanitization of production equipment, water systems, etc. Validation activities must be conducted in accordance with approved protocols and follow appropriate guidance.

Process validation is essential in ensuring that product quality, safety and effectiveness are designed and built into, rather than tested into the final product. Establishing batch-to-batch output uniformity is an example of process validation. It is important to develop a written validation protocol that establishes a sufficient number of replicate process runs to demonstrate reproducibility and provide an accurate variability measure across successive runs. Worst-case conditions posing the greatest chance of process or product failure compared to ideal conditions should be included. Factors to include could be variation in raw material suppliers, staff variation in multi-shift operations, changes to equipment components, e.g., pumps, product supply, etc. Design control and process verification are critical elements of the device QSR.

One of the cornerstone guidance documents for process validation for human and veterinary drugs and biologics is *Guidance for Industry Process Validation: General Principles and Practices* (January 2011), which defines process validation in three stages:

- Stage 1—Process Design: The commercial process is defined during this stage based on knowledge gained through development and scale-up activities.
- Stage 2—Process Qualification: During this stage, the process design is confirmed as being capable of reproducible commercial manufacturing.
- Stage 3—Continued Process Verification: Ongoing assurance is gained that the process remains in a state of control during routine production. An ongoing program to collect and analyze product and process data that relate to product quality must be established (21 CFR 211.180(e)). The data collected should be meaningful and be able to reflect true changes in the process that might affect product quality. An example would be in-process test results. In-process tests results should be monitored closely to detect any trends that could indicate the process may not be as controlled as it should be.

This guidance emphasizes an interdisciplinary team approach in which experts from process engineering, industrial pharmacy, analytical chemistry, microbiology, statistics, manufacturing and quality assurance come together to form the team. Approval of senior management is a requirement of a successful validation program.

The team should consider all factors required for the final system or process being validated in the process design stage. A good motto is "Begin with the End in Mind." For example, a system of plastic piping, diaphragm style pumps, ball valves and polycarbonate tanks may be more cost effective initially than a system of stainless steel pipe, positive displacement pumps, butterfly style valves and stainless steel tanks, however, each will perform differently over time and each has a different intended use. Decisions made solely based upon component cost could quickly be offset by increased sanitization times, increased maintenance times and less up time and, worst case scenario, cost of recall, loss of market share, risk to patient safety or consumer health, or loss of brand recognition.

Each method used to analyze a drug or biological product must have associated validation to support the documentation of drug substance and drug/biological product identity, strength, quality, purity and potency. The primary FDA guidance, *Draft Guidance for Industry: Analytical Procedures and Methods Validation—Chemistry, Manufacturing, and Controls Documentation* (August 2000), is intended to assist applicants in assembling information, submitting samples and presenting data to support analytical methodologies.

Analytical methods for generic or innovator drug compounds frequently are found in the *United States Pharmacopeia* (*USP*) or in the published literature, and can serve as a starting point for method validation. If the analytical method used is directly from *USP*, only requalification of the method used on site in the particular laboratory is required, not revalidation. Validation of analytical methods typically starts in the formulation/product development stage. The formulation and analytical groups work as a closely-knit team since even slight changes in formulation can necessitate changes to the analytical method. Typically, several formulations are developed, tested against pre-set specifications and stability tested. Any formulations that do not meet the stability requirements are either reformulated or eliminated from the formulation development plan. As with all CGMP processes, in a robust system, method requalification and validation should be carefully documented.

Summary

For repeatable manufacturing results that meet specification, the process model in **Figure 8-1** is recommended.

The following list is a general outline of GMP concepts that are among the most important. This outline is not intended to be all-inclusive, but provides some critical points.

Figure 8-1 Process Model for Meeting GMP Requirements

Key GMP Concepts Presented

- GMPs are applicable to preparation of innovator and generic drug products and medical devices administered to humans and animals.
- GMPs are required for both marketed product and clinical supplies, including placebos.
- The fundamental GMP concept is that product quality cannot be "tested into" a product, but must be designed and built into the facility and equipment design and production process through well-defined, written procedures; adequately controlled equipment and manufacturing environment; and accurately and consistently recorded data from manufacturing (including testing).
- GMPs are constantly changing. Current Good Manufacturing Practice represents the "customary practice" or "state-of-the-art" practice used by most companies to ensure that drugs and devices are safe and effective.
- Many international factors influence GMP. The most important are ICH guidelines, ISO requirements and mutual recognition agreements with other countries.
- *Guidance for Industry: Quality Systems Approach to Pharmaceutical CGMP Regulations* (September 2006) describes a comprehensive quality system model. The quality system is very similar to the device QSR system. The typical quality system contains six key systems and three critical elements.
- Product quality must be reviewed annually and a product Annual Report must be compiled, however a robust CAPA process to more frequently evaluate product trends is expected for drugs and biologics and required for medical devices, and is generally more effective.
- Change control and document control concepts are not specifically listed in GMP regulations but are critical to GMP compliance.
- Key differences between device GMPs and drug GMPs are management responsibility, quality plan, corrective/preventive action, design controls and purchasing control. Design control is a key element of the device quality system.
- The QSR is intended to ensure that finished devices will be safe and effective and in compliance with the *FD&C Act*. The regulation does not apply to manufacturers of finished device components or parts.
- GMP compliance is a critical element of new drug and device development, and this compliance is verified during FDA's preapproval inspection prior to marketing a new drug or device. Generic drugs (which reduce drug costs to the consumer) are evaluated for "bioequivalence" through testing designed to assess equivalence.
- A focal point of GMP inspections has been the separation of the quality assurance and manufacturing or production functions, while establishing clear responsibilities for decisions affecting the product.
- Validation is an important component of GMP compliance. GMPs require all operational methodologies and procedures utilized in manufacturing and testing to be validated to demonstrate that they can perform their function(s).
- Process validation is the key to ensuring that a product's quality, safety and effectiveness are designed and built into, rather than tested into the final product. Process validation is required by both drug and medical device GMPs. Demonstrating batch-to-batch output uniformity is an example of processes validation.
- Quality risk management is a valuable component of an effective quality system. *ICH Q9: Quality Risk Management* (June 2005) provides general guidance on the quality risk management principles that can enable more-effective and consistent risk-based decisions regarding the quality of drug substances and drug products across the product lifecycle. The level of effort, formality and documentation of the quality risk management process should be commensurate with the level of risk and be based upon scientific knowledge.

Prescription Drug Submissions

By Naseem Kabir, MS, RAC

Objectives
- Understand the classification of prescription drugs
- Understand an overview of the goals and types of NDAs, as well as the NDA process, content and format (including the CTD)
- Become familiar with pre-NDA, NDA and post-NDA activities
- Become familiar with CDER's review process of the NDA
- Understand the mechanisms to expedite drug development and approval

Laws, Regulations and Guidelines Covered in This Chapter
- *Federal Food, Drug, and Cosmetic Act* of 1938
- *Food and Drug Administration Modernization Act* of 1997
- *Prescription Drug Marketing Act* of 1987
- *Prescription Drug User Fee Act* of 1992
- *Federal Advisory Committee Act* of 1972
- *Drug Price Competition and Patent Term Restoration Act* of 1984 (*Hatch-Waxman Act*)
- *Guidance for Industry: Providing Clinical Evidence for Effectiveness for Human Drugs and Biological Products* (May 1998)
- *Guidance for Industry on the Disclosure of Materials Provided to Advisory Committees in Connection with Open Advisory Committee Meetings Convened by the Center for Drug Evaluation and Research Beginning on January 1, 2000* (November 1999)
- *Guidance for Industry: Reports on the Status of Postmarketing Study Commitments—Implementation of Section 130 of the Food and Drug Administration Modernization Act of 1997* (February 2006)
- *Guidance for Industry: Postmarketing Studies and Clinical Trials — Implementation of Section 505(o)(3) of the Federal Food, Drug, and Cosmetic Act (April 2011)*
- *Guidance for Review Staff and Industry: Good Review Management Principles and Practices for PDUFA Products* (April 2005)
- *Guidance for Industry: Fixed Dose Combinations, Co-Packaged Drug Products, and Single-Entity Versions of Previously Approved Antiretrovirals for the Treatment of HIV* (October 2006)
- *Guidance for Industry: Fast Track Drug Development Programs—Designation, Development, and Application Review* (January 2006)
- *Draft Guidance for Industry: Accelerated Approval Products—Submission of Promotional Materials* (March 1999)
- *Guidance for Industry: Formal Meetings with Sponsors and Applicants for PDUFA Products* (May 2009)
- *Draft Guidance for Industry: Applications Covered by Section 505(b)(2)* (October 1999)
- 21 CFR 314 Applications for FDA approval to market a new drug.
- Manual of Policies and Procedures 6020.3: Review Classification Policy: Priority (P) and Standard (S)

Introduction

Drugs are regulated under the *Federal Food, Drug, and Cosmetic Act* of 1938 (*FD&C Act*) and its subsequent amendments. Under this act, the US Congress gave the Food and Drug Administration (FDA) authority and responsibility to oversee public health by regulating and enforcing (among other things):

- human and veterinary drugs and vaccines, blood and other biologics and medical devices intended for human use to assure they are safe and effective, are manufactured in accordance with specified quality standards and their labeling enables safe use
- food, dietary supplements and cosmetics so they are safe and labeled adequately

Additionally, FDA has other responsibilities such as protecting the public from electronic product radiation, regulating tobacco products and disseminating science-based information to the public on the products that it regulates.

This chapter provides a broad understanding of FDA's regulations and the regulatory process for obtaining marketing approval for prescription drug products.

A drug is broadly defined as:

- any product (or any component of such product) that is intended for use in the diagnosis, cure, mitigation, treatment or prevention of disease in man
- a product (other than food), or a component of a product, that affects the structure or function of the human body
- a product that is recognized in the *United States Pharmacopoeia* (*USP*), *Homoeopathic Pharmacopoeia of the United States* (*HPUS*) or the *National Formulary* (*NF*) and their supplements

A "new" drug is generally any drug that contains an ingredient or combination of ingredients, for which the safety and effectiveness under the labeled conditions for use is not previously known. However, a new drug may also be a drug that has a known safety and effectiveness profile under the labeled conditions for use, but has not been in use to a material extent or for a material time under those conditions. Generally, such drugs can only be obtained through a prescription from a healthcare provider. Thus, a prescription drug is any drug that has been approved or licensed for distribution by FDA and requires a healthcare practitioner's authorization before it can be obtained. Prescription drugs are differentiated from over-the-counter (OTC) drugs that may be obtained without a prescription. Prescription drugs are also called Rx-only drugs or "legend" drugs because they bear a legend prohibiting sale without a prescription. Prescription drugs are accompanied by a detailed package insert (PI) that contains specific drug information. The content of the PI is regulated by FDA as it informs both the prescriber and the patient about the drug's intended effects, its mechanism of action, information about side effects, information on how to take the drug and what to do in case of overdose, and warnings and precautions about using the drug.

Physicians may legally prescribe approved drugs for uses other than those approved by FDA; this is known as off-label use. However, drug companies may not promote or advertise drugs for off-label uses.

The *FD&C Act* also prohibits the introduction into interstate commerce of a prescription drug unless the drug's manufacturer has submitted a New Drug Application (NDA) to FDA and obtained agency approval. The NDA must contain "substantial evidence" from adequate and well-controlled investigations, including clinical investigations, conducted by qualified experts. These investigations should demonstrate that the drug is safe and effective under conditions for use described in the labeling and that it can be manufactured consistently, in a manner that will preserve its identity, strength, quality and purity.

Manufacturers often strategize how many pivotal (generally Phase 3) clinical trials are needed to provide substantial evidence for a drug's effectiveness. The most widely applied interpretation is that two separate, adequate and well-controlled trials (one investigation confirming the results obtained from a prior/concurrent investigation) are needed to establish effectiveness. However, under certain circumstances, FDA may find data from one well-controlled clinical investigation to be adequate to provide the evidence of effectiveness required to support approval of an NDA.

Aside from effectiveness, the NDA must provide evidence that the prescription drug is reasonably safe when used under the conditions described in the labeling. Although a new drug's safety is assiduously studied through clinical trials (which often enroll several thousand patients), the reality is that the variables in a clinical trial are specified and controlled and the results relate only to the populations studied within the trial. Therefore, side effects and adverse drug reactions (ADRs) that are reported to occur less frequently in the trial population become more apparent and sometimes more frequent or severe only after a drug enters the market and is used by millions of people who likely have different demographic profiles than the clinical trial populations. Nevertheless, evidence from clinical trials is critical in identifying ADRs associated with the drug and establishing its risk/benefit profile. The risk/benefit profile evaluates all known data for the drug and attempts to provide answers to such key questions as: does the drug do more good than harm and, if so, how much more good? If the drug has a potential for harm, how probable and how serious is the harm? So, while clinical trials do not tell the whole story of the drug's effects in all populations and all situations, they provide a good indication of the drug's safety that can be extrapolated from the populations studied to larger populations.

Drug safety continues to receive widespread negative press. As a result, Congress gave FDA greater enforcement authority under the *Food and Drug Administration Amendments Act of 2007 (FDAAA)* and mandated FDA to establish an active, integrated, electronic surveillance system for monitoring the safety of drugs and other medical products continuously and in real-time. FDA is working toward this mandate and in May 2008 launched the "FDA Sentinel Initiative" to strengthen the agency's ability to track how drugs and other healthcare products perform once they go on the market. While the Sentinel System will be developed and implemented in stages, ultimately it will help monitor healthcare products throughout the entire lifecycle. It will allow FDA to effectively communicate the risks associated with the product to the public, thus better achieving its mission of protecting and promoting public health.

Regulatory Strategy

Compiling an NDA is a highly complex activity that requires much preparation and early and effective communications with FDA. A clear and well laid-out strategy is essential for navigating the prescription drug submission regulatory process and for ultimately obtaining a timely and smooth approval for the drug product from FDA. FDA is, in turn, committed to and responsible for bringing healthcare products, particularly innovative healthcare products, to the market as expeditiously as possible. In order to achieve this common objective, there are several pathways and tools that should be carefully considered when formulating the regulatory strategy. A sound regulatory strategy should lay out the plan of action for the NDA process, linking the different activities and drug development phases, assessing the challenges along the way and formulating appropriate risk mitigation activities, all with the ultimate goal of obtaining FDA approval for the desired indications within the desired timeframe. NDA sponsors should develop the regulatory strategy years before the actual NDA submission and as early as Phase 1 of the drug development clinical studies. The strategy is often expanded during Phase 2 or Phase 3 of clinical drug development to a global strategy so that approval for the drug is obtained in the major commercial markets followed by the fastest possible reimbursement approvals from governments and payors.

Target Product Profile (TPP)

A TPP is a voluntary document that a drug sponsor, if it chooses to, may submit to FDA early in the drug development phase. It describes the eventual labeling claims and promotional concepts that the sponsor targets upon approval of the NDA. The hope is that by sharing the TPP voluntarily and as early as the pre-Investigational New Drug (IND) phase, the sponsor will initiate and facilitate effective communications with the FDA review staff regarding the drug development program. The TPP would serve as the basis for dialogue with FDA so the agency clearly understands at the outset the sponsor's end goals, what studies are being planned in order to achieve the end goals, and what substantial evidence will be generated from those studies to demonstrate the drug's safety and efficacy and to support label claims. Thus the TPP is intended to minimize the risk of late-stage drug development failures, increase the probability that optimal safety and efficacy data are available in a timely manner, improve labeling content, and possibly decrease the total time involved with drug development. A TPP does not represent a commitment or obligation on the part of either the sponsor or FDA to the drug's development strategy or eventual drug approval.

Drug Development Tools (DDT)

Another critical component of regulatory strategy lies in the use of drug development tools such as biological markers (biomarkers) and patient reported outcomes (PRO). A biomarker is a characteristic that can be objectively measured and assessed as an indicator of normal biologic processes, pathogenic processes or biological responses to a therapeutic intervention. Thus, a change to a biomarker following treatment with the drug product can predict or identify safety problems related to the drug or reveal a pharmacological activity expected to predict an eventual benefit from treatment. Biomarkers may reduce uncertainty in drug development and evaluation by providing quantitative predictions about drug performance.

A PRO is an instrument that captures the outcomes of drug intervention during a clinical trial from the patient's perspective (e.g., change in pain or depression from before the therapy compared over time after therapy). The PRO uses a questionnaire that is self-administered by the patient or through interviews by other parties that report on patient perspectives. The questionnaires measure "characteristics" (or constructs) that should have a sound theoretical basis and be relevant to the patient group in which they are to be used. Questionnaires can be designed to provide data in any disease population and cover a broad aspect of the construct measured, or can be developed specifically to measure those aspects of outcome that are of importance for people with a particular medical condition. In any case, a PRO tool should be thoroughly tested using appropriate methodology and validated in order to justify its use. Results from properly validated PRO instruments can be used to support drug approval and labeling claims. Examples of characteristics that PRO questionnaires can assess include symptoms and other aspects of well-being, functionality (disability) and quality of life (QoL)

In addition to PRO tools, FDA will also consider qualification of other DDTs to support labeling claims, such as clinician rating scales and caregiver rating scales, where a respondent is requested to assign a rating to a concept using a process similar to that used for PROs.

Sponsors should interact with FDA early in the drug development process to ensure there is consensus with the agency on the type and amount of data needed to support the qualification of a DDT. With proper qualification, analytically valid measurements using the DDT can be relied upon to have a specific use and interpretable meaning in drug development. Once a DDT is qualified for a specific context of use, industry can use the DDT for the qualified purpose during drug development, and reviewers from FDA's Center for Drug Evaluation and Research (CDER) can be confident in applying the DDT for the qualified use without the need to reconfirm the DDT's utility.

Fast Track

When developing regulatory strategy, an NDA sponsor should also consider taking advantage of the various programs offered by FDA to support the development of innovative drug products. Such programs include the orphan drug program (see "Chapter 23 Regulation of Products for Small Patient Populations) and the fast track program.

Section 112 of the *Food and Drug Administration Modernization Act* of 1997 (*FDAMA*) amended the *FD&C Act* (Section 506) and is generally regarded as the act's fast track provision. It directs FDA to facilitate the development and expedite the review of new drugs intended to treat serious or life-threatening conditions and those that demonstrate the potential to address unmet medical needs. A drug can be said to address an unmet medical need if there is no available treatment for the disease or condition, or if the only available treatments for the condition are approved under the Subpart H accelerated approval regulations (21 CFR. 314.500 and 601.40), either on the basis of an effect on a surrogate endpoint or with restrictions on distribution. Other existing FDA programs can also facilitate development and review of products for serious and life-threatening conditions such as the procedures described in the 1988 interim rule "Procedures for Drugs Intended to Treat Life-Threatening and Severely Debilitating Illnesses" (21 CFR 312.80–312.88 (Subpart E)), in which FDA formalized certain procedures to facilitate the development of promising therapies. It is important to distinguish between fast track designation itself and the specific programs that are available to a sponsor in a fast track drug development program. With the exception of the submission of portions of an NDA before submission of the entire application (rolling NDA), many of the programs described below have been established in regulations under authority separate from *FDAMA* Section 506. Therefore, products that are not in fast track drug development programs may also be able to take advantage of these programs. Fast track programs are different from expanded access programs for investigational drugs (such as Treatment INDs, see 21 CFR 312.34). Although both types of programs are intended to expedite access to drugs for patients with serious and life-threatening conditions with no therapeutic alternatives, fast track programs expedite the market availability of approved drugs, while expanded access programs facilitate access to investigational drugs (i.e., prior to the drug being approved by FDA).

Sponsors should submit requests for fast track designation to FDA in writing. Supporting documentation should clearly demonstrate that the criteria necessary for designation have been met and that the sponsor has a stage-appropriate clinical development plan in place. Fast track designation applies to both the product and the specific indication for which it is being studied.

The request for fast track designation can be submitted simultaneously with the IND, or at any time thereafter prior to receiving NDA marketing approval. To maximize the use of the fast track incentives, it is best to include the designation request in the original IND submission or as soon as possible thereafter. Note that the request for fast track designation can only be granted by FDA upon the submission of an IND.

FDA will respond to a request for fast track designation within 60 calendar days of receipt. If FDA determines that fast track criteria have been met, the review division will issue a designation letter that will state that fast track designation is granted for development of the product for use in treating the specific serious or life-threatening condition. The letter will also request that sponsors design and perform studies that can show whether the product fulfills unmet medical needs. FDA can also issue a non-designation letter either because the fast track request package was incomplete or because the drug development program failed to meet the criteria for fast track designation. The non-designation letter will explain the reasons for the agency's decision. FDA will respond to a subsequent request for fast track designation after a non-designation determination within 60 calendar days of receiving the new request.

Sponsors must continue to meet the fast track criteria throughout product development to retain the designation. The sponsor should expect the appropriateness of continuing the fast track designation for the drug development program to be discussed and evaluated at different times during the drug development process, including at the End-of-Phase 2 meeting and the Pre-NDA meeting. If FDA determines that a product is no longer eligible, it will notify the sponsor that the product is no longer part of the fast track drug development program. Sponsors can appeal FDA's decision through the dispute resolution process (21 CFR 10.75, 312.48 and 314.103).

Products with fast track designation are eligible to participate in specific programs, which are outlined below. Many of these programs existed prior to the enactment of fast track legislation. As such, products that do not have fast track designation but meet the criteria for participation in the individual programs may participate in those programs even if not under the fast track umbrella.

Additional Meetings and Written Correspondence

FDA will consider granting requests for additional meetings (such as Pre-IND meetings, End-of-Phase 1 meetings) for important drug development programs. Such meetings may be crucial to ensure efficient drug development, e.g., they allow timely forums for both the sponsor and FDA to discuss and reach agreement on critical issues and major questions or issues pertaining to the development of that particular drug (See Chapter 4 for more information on how to request, conduct and follow up on meetings with FDA).

Standard vs Priority Review

Under the *Prescription Drug User Fee Act* (*PDUFA*), FDA has specific goals for NDA review timelines: standard review and priority review. Under current *PDUFA* goals, FDA has committed to reviewing approximately 90% of original NDA submissions within 10 months (i.e., standard review) for drugs that offer minor improvement over existing marketed therapies. FDA grants priority review designation to drugs that offer major advances in treatment, or provide

a treatment where no adequate therapy exists (i.e., both to drugs that are used to treat serious diseases and to drugs for less serious illnesses). Under priority review, FDA has committed to reviewing approximately 90% of original NDA submissions within six months. FDA is able to review such submissions faster by directing additional FDA resources to drugs that have the potential to provide significant advances in treatment in at least one of the following instances:

- provide evidence of increased effectiveness in treatment, prevention or diagnosis of disease
- eliminate or substantially reduce a treatment-limiting drug reaction
- provide documented evidence of enhanced patient compliance to treatment schedule and dose
- provide evidence of safety and effectiveness in a new subpopulation, such as children

The sponsor must submit a request for priority review to FDA, providing adequate evidence that its drug product meets one of the criteria listed above. While fast track products are generally eligible for priority review, as they are intended to treat serious or life-threatening conditions and address unmet medical needs, having a fast track designation does not automatically convey a priority review; the applicant should request the priority review with appropriate justification in the cover letter of the NDA. (Note that the Center for Biologics Evaluation and Review (CBER) and CDER have somewhat different criteria for priority review classification. CBER grants priority review for drugs that provide a significant improvement in the safety or effectiveness of the treatment, diagnosis or prevention of a serious or life-threatening disease. CDER grants priority review for drugs that provide a significant improvement compared to marketed products in the treatment, diagnosis or prevention of a disease, i.e., eligibility is not limited to drugs for a serious or life-threatening disease.) A fast track product would ordinarily meet either center's criteria for priority review. However, an NDA or Biologics License Application (BLA) sponsor need not seek fast track designation to be eligible for priority review.

FDA determines within 45 days whether a priority or standard review designation will be assigned. If priority review is granted, the sponsor must still provide the same amount of scientific and medical evidence as an NDA under standard review classification in order for FDA to approve the drug.

Rolling NDA

Under this program, CDER can accept portions of an NDA for review prior to receipt of the complete application. The applicant must first obtain FDA's agreement to accept the rolling NDA. FDA generally will agree to the request if the product continues to meet the criteria for fast track designation. This is usually discussed at the Pre-NDA meeting and followed up by a written request in the form of an IND amendment for formal FDA agreement. The request must include a schedule of when each section of the NDA is planned to be completed and submitted, and when the entire NDA will be completed and submitted. Normally, the time elapsed between the first and final piece of the submission should be no more than six months. When utilizing this route, FDA generally prefers to receive a full and complete module rather than single documents or smaller sections. Each portion submitted must be complete and ready for review at the time it is submitted. Provided there are no changes to the module after it has been submitted, it is not necessary to resubmit it when filing the remaining portions or the final portion. FDA's acceptance of a portion of an application does not mean that the portion will be reviewed prior to the receipt of a complete application. If FDA has available resources, FDA staff may begin the review process as the sections arrive and may correspond with the applicant if questions arise or to request additional information.

Important considerations for filing a rolling submission are:

- If *PDUFA* fees are required, they will need to be paid at the time the first portion of the NDA is submitted.
- The FDA review clock begins when the sponsor completes the final piece of the NDA and informs FDA that it is complete.

Subpart H—Accelerated Approval (Drugs)

In 1992, FDA promulgated regulations that accelerate the approval of new drugs for serious or life-threatening illnesses for which there are no existing therapies (Subpart H, Accelerated Approval Regulations, 21 CFR. 314.500). These regulations allow FDA to approve a new drug on the basis of a surrogate endpoint or a clinical endpoint other than survival or irreversible morbidity, and the product may be approved with restrictions to assure safe use. Approval based upon a surrogate endpoint is granted in instances when the surrogate is reasonably likely to predict clinical benefit. The effect on the surrogate endpoint or on a clinical endpoint other than survival or irreversible morbidity must be demonstrated through adequate and well-controlled trials. Approval of the NDA through this route means the drug's clinical benefit must subsequently be demonstrated through postmarketing studies, and these will be communicated to the sponsor as postmarketing commitments. Data from these studies must support the drug's clinical benefit, otherwise FDA can withdraw the approval. Additionally, all promotional materials, including promotional labeling and advertisements intended for dissemination within the first 120 days following marketing approval, must be submitted to FDA. Promotional materials intended for dissemination after the 120-day postapproval period must be submitted at least 30 days prior to the intended date of initial dissemination of those materials.

Risk Evaluation and Mitigation Strategy (REMS)

Title IX, Subtitle A, Section 901 of *FDAAA* amended the *FD&C Act* by creating Section 505-1, which authorizes FDA to require sponsors of certain NDAs to submit a proposed REMS if the agency determines that one is necessary to ensure that the benefits of a drug outweigh its risks. A sponsor may also voluntarily submit a proposed REMS without having been required to do so by FDA. FDA can request the REMS at the time of the initial submission of the original NDA or at any time after its approval (usually, if FDA becomes aware of new safety information and determines that a REMS is necessary). Once the sponsor of an approved NDA is notified by FDA that a REMS is necessary, the holder must submit a proposed REMS within 120 days.

The content of the proposed REMS should adequately describe its proposed goals and the specific elements proposed for inclusion in the approved REMS for the drug product. Examples of REMS elements described in the guidance document include proposed healthcare provider communication and education materials, medication guide (per 21 CFR, part 208), patient package insert if it will help prevent serious risks, enrollment forms, prescriber and patient agreements, etc. A REMS may include any or all of the REMS elements. The proposed REMS should also contain a thorough explanation of the rationale for, and supporting information about, the content of the proposed REMS, as well as a timetable by which each of the elements will be implemented. At minimum, the REMS should include a timetable for submission of the assessments by 18 months, three years and seven years after the REMS is approved by FDA.

"Elements to Ensure Safe Use" (ETASU) may be required if a drug has been shown to be effective but is associated with a serious adverse event. In such a case, the drug can be approved only if, or would be withdrawn unless, such elements are included in the REMS to mitigate the specific serious risks listed in the labeling of the product. ETASU may be required for approved products when an assessment and medication guide, patient package insert or communication plan are not sufficient to mitigate these risks. An example of an ETASU would be a system or process to ensure that certain laboratory test result outcomes are obtained before a drug may be dispensed.

The sponsor must reach agreement with FDA on the elements of a REMS submission and the timelines for implementation. FDA will determine which elements of REMS are necessary to ensure that the benefits of the drug outweigh its risks and will determine approvability of the REMS. FDA must also approve REMS that are voluntarily submitted. An approved REMS that is submitted voluntarily is subject to the same requirements and enforcement as a required REMS. FDA will notify applicants who voluntarily submit a proposed REMS whether the REMS will be required. If FDA determines that a REMS is not required, an applicant may undertake voluntary risk management measures that would be performed outside of a REMS.

Once FDA approves the REMS, it will serve as the basis for inspection and enforcement. A drug will be considered to be misbranded if its sponsor fails to comply with a requirement of the approved REMS. A sponsor that violates a REMS requirement is also subject to civil monetary penalties of up to $250,000 per violation, not to exceed $1 million in a single proceeding. These penalties increase if the violation continues more than 30 days after FDA notifies the sponsor of the violation. The penalties double for the second 30-day period, and continue to double for subsequent 30-day periods, up to $1 million per period and $10 million per proceeding. In addition, the sponsor may not introduce into interstate commerce an approved drug that is noncompliant with the conditions of an approved REMS.

Pre-NDA Activities

Many activities need to be completed prior to NDA submission, including proprietary name submission and review, establishment registration, labeler code assignment and a Pre-NDA meeting.

Proprietary Name Submission and Review

One of the most important activities during drug development is creating a proprietary name for the product. The proprietary name is the product's critical identifier and companies expend vast resources to create the perfect proprietary name.

The sponsor must submit for FDA review proposed proprietary names as part of the NDA. The request for proprietary name approval must be submitted no later than when the NDA is submitted, although sponsors have the option of submitting a proprietary name request prior to NDA submission (perhaps as early as the End-of-Phase 2 meeting with FDA) under the IND application. However, to ensure that FDA resources are not wasted in evaluating proposed proprietary names for products that do not make it to the NDA phase or for which proposed indications are not yet sufficiently clear to form the basis to evaluate a name for potential medication errors, FDA does not evaluate proprietary names until products have completed Phase 2 trials.

The proprietary name submission package should include the primary choice for the proprietary name, as well as an alternate name, intended pronunciation of the proprietary name, name derivation, intended proprietary name modifier meanings and the name's pharmacologic/therapeutic category.

An FDA review of proprietary names includes an evaluation of both the proposed names' safety and promotional aspects. The safety review focuses primarily on preventing medication errors and evaluating other products that may have similar dosage regimens, similar names when said aloud and overlapping strengths. The promotional review is to determine whether the name implies superiority, attempts to minimize risk or overstates efficacy.

For a proposed proprietary name submitted during the IND phase, FDA reviews the complete submission and communicates a decision about the name within 180 days of the receipt of the submission. The agency reviews a complete submission for a proposed proprietary name submitted with an NDA and communicates a decision about the name within 90 days of the receipt of the submission. Proprietary names accepted during a pre-review will be re-reviewed 90 days before the action date to ensure they are still acceptable.

Establishment Registration and National Drug Code

A company that manufactures human drugs, certain biological products and animal drugs must register the manufacturing facility before FDA can approve an NDA. In addition, a company that owns, operates or engages in the manufacture, processing, preparation, propagation or compounding of a drug is required to submit a list of every drug in commercial distribution (21 CFR 207). Form FDA 2656 must be completed for Drug Establishment Registration while FDA Form 2657 is completed for Drug Product Listing (note that the listing number is the same as that assigned pursuant to the National Drug Code (NDC)). The NDC is a system designed to provide drugs in the US with a specific 11-digit number that describes the product. The first segment is assigned by FDA and identifies the vendor (or labeler) involved with the drug's manufacture, packaging or distribution. The second segment conveys the product codes and comprises the generic entity, strength and dosage form. The third segment, or package code, indicates the package size. The second and third segments of a given product's code are assigned by the manufacturer.

FDA inputs the full NDC number and information submitted as part of the listing process into a database known as the Drug Registration and Listing System (DRLS). Several times a year, FDA extracts some of the information from the DRLS database (currently, properly listed marketed prescription drug products and insulin) and publishes that information in the NDC Directory. FDA relies upon establishment registration and drug listing information to administer many of its programs, such as postmarketing surveillance (including scheduling and planning inspections), bioterrorism, drug shortages and availability, management of drug recalls and user fee assessments.

Pre-NDA Meeting

Sponsors can request meetings with FDA at various stages during the drug development process. A Pre-NDA meeting, considered a Type B meeting (see Chapter 4), is highly recommended prior to NDA submission. It generally is advisable to hold such a meeting four to six months prior to the anticipated submission date. A request for a Pre-NDA meeting should be submitted 60 days prior to the desired date. A briefing package for a Pre-NDA meeting should be submitted for review by FDA attendees at least four weeks prior to the scheduled meeting. For additional information on meetings with FDA, refer to *Guidance for Industry: Formal Meetings with Sponsors and Applicants for PDUFA Products.*

The Pre-NDA meeting allows the sponsor to present data that will be submitted in the application and to provide additional assurance that the sponsor is submitting all the necessary NDA information required by the agency in order to reach a decision on the NDA's approvability.

The NDA
NDA Goals

The goals of the NDA are to provide enough information to permit FDA reviewers to reach key decisions on whether the drug is safe and effective when used for the indications described in the labeling; whether the drug's benefits outweigh its risks; whether the proposed labeling is appropriate; and whether the drug's manufacturing methods and the controls used to maintain drug quality are adequate to preserve its identity, strength, quality and purity. More recently, as multiple drugs are approved for the same disease or condition—and they do not appear to be of significant advantage over existing drugs—FDA has begun to ask manufacturers to justify the newer drug's clinical utility and to demonstrate that it, in fact, has an edge over existing therapies (such as better safety, better efficacy, better patient compliance, ease of administration, etc.), although this is not an official requirement for approval.

NDA Content & Format

An NDA must provide all information pertaining to the drug's development. The quantity of information can vary from one NDA to another; however, the NDA structure is consistent. For example, it specifically calls for inclusion of any patent information pertaining to the drug substance and the drug product, including the type of patent, patent owner, patent expiration date(s) and information on whether the patent has been previously submitted.

In addition, per 21 CFR 314.50, an NDA must include chemistry, manufacturing and controls (CMC), nonclinical and clinical data, financial and clinical trial transparency certification and other information. The CMC section should describe the composition, manufacture and specifications of both the drug substance and the drug product,

as well as fairly detailed descriptions of all manufacturing controls and stability data. The nonclinical pharmacology and toxicology section should describe any animal and *in vitro* drug studies that help to define the drug's pharmacologic properties and address toxicity related to its administration. The clinical section should include a description of all clinical investigations completed in support of the drug's efficacy and safety, as well as the study protocols and copies of case report forms for each patient who died during a clinical study or did not complete a study because of an adverse event, regardless of the incident's relationship to the study drug.

Copies of the proposed drug product labeling—including the package insert, vial labels, cartons and medication guides—should be provided in the application. FDA requires that labeling be submitted electronically in a format that the agency can review and process. The content of labeling, labeling supplements and amendments must utilize the structured product labeling (SPL) format with an extensible markup language (XML) backbone. SPL has several advantages: the exchange of information between computer systems, automation of text comparison by section, and exchange of information needed for other submissions (i.e., cross-referencing). SPL allows labeling content to be searched, moved between systems and combined with other data sources and lends itself to the support of electronic healthcare initiatives.

The CTD Format

As outlined above, a tremendous amount of information is submitted in support of a marketing application. Generally, much the same information is broadly required in every country where a manufacturer plans to market the drug. Because the information is so similar—and to allow manufacturers to proceed more quickly with the submission and approval process—the International Conference for Harmonisation (ICH) developed the Common Technical Document (CTD) format, intended to harmonize the format requirements for the submission and registration of pharmaceuticals in the US, EU and Japan.

Per the CTD format, an application should be broken up into five modules (**Figure 9-1**). Module 1 contains documents specific to the region where the file is being submitted and Modules 2–5 are intended to be common across all regions. Module 1 (regional information) can include application forms, financial certification and disclosure statements, references to drug master files, proposed labeling and applicable patent information. Module 2 is comprised of summary documents of each of the other modules, including a quality overall summary, nonclinical and clinical overviews, nonclinical written and tabulated summaries and a clinical summary. Module 3 presents comprehensive CMC information about the drug or biologic. Module 4 contains nonclinical study reports and

Figure 9-1 CTD Triangle

related information, including relevant literature references. Module 5 contains clinical protocols, clinical study reports, case report forms, integrated safety and efficacy summaries and relevant literature references, including FDA meeting minutes and references cited in the Clinical Overview section.

The eCTD Format

Historically, submissions to FDA have been in paper format. Paper submissions not only require many resources for both the sponsor and FDA, but also require a tremendous amount of storage space. This did not go unnoticed and FDA attempted to address this issue by creating standards that permit electronic submissions. The value of electronic submissions is well recognized, but FDA has not yet mandated their use.

The current standard for electronic submissions is the electronic Common Technical Document (eCTD). Companies have been submitting NDAs in eCTD format for several years. The format of the paper CTD and eCTD submission are different. With an eCTD submission, each document is separate (granular) and named according to ICH specifications. Each submission has its own eCTD backbone file, which allows FDA to receive, archive and review the submission. Once an application is submitted in electronic format, all subsequent submissions to the application are also

submitted electronically and should include eCTD backbone files. Without these backbone files, FDA will be unable to process subsequent submissions. FDA also recommends that electronic file cover letters include a description of the submission's approximate size (e.g., 4 gigabytes), the type and number of electronic media used (e.g., two DVDs), a regulatory and technical point of contact and a statement that the submission is virus free, with a description of the software used to virus-check the file.

At any time, a sponsor can decide to convert its paper application to an electronic filing. Should a sponsor decide to do so, it is not necessary to provide all previous submissions in electronic format with eCTD backbone files; instead the electronic filing may begin with the planned submission. For ease of conversion, the Comprehensive Table of Contents Headings and Hierarchy[2] maps the NDA to the eCTD format. When converting and cross-referencing to past submissions, the applicant should be sure to include specific information, such as the date of the previous submission, document name, page numbers, volume numbers and approval dates, or may consider including any items critical for review of the current submission within the electronic format submission so the reviewer can find it more easily.

Types of NDAs

There are three types of drug applications: traditional NDA (*FD&C Act* Section 505(b)(1)), 505(b)(2) NDA (*FD&C Act* Section 505(b)(2)) and Abbreviated NDA (ANDA) (*FD&C Act* Section 606(j)).

Traditional NDA or 505(b)(1)

A 505(b)(1) application is a complete NDA that contains all the studies conducted by the sponsor necessary to demonstrate a drug's safe and effective use. A 505(b)(1) application contains all information as outlined in 21 CFR 314.50.

505(b)(2) NDA (Formerly a "Paper" NDA)

A 505(b)(2) application also contains information required in a 505(b)(1) application necessary to demonstrate safe and effective use of a drug; however, the sponsor can provide data in the application for studies it did not conduct and for which it has not obtained a right to reference.

Section 505(b)(2) was added to the *FD&C Act* by the *Drug Price Competition and Patent Term Restoration Act* of 1984 (*Hatch-Waxman Act*) to allow companies to develop alternative therapies more quickly by relying on existing data. Applicants are able to rely on published literature that supports approval of an application (hence the term "paper" NDA) and on FDA's finding of safety and effectiveness of an approved drug. For example, a 505(b)(2) application can be submitted if the applicant has changed a product's route of administration from an oral form to an intramuscular injection. In this instance, the applicant can rely on the efficacy data and some of the safety data established for the drug's oral formulation that has already been approved by FDA, but will have to conduct studies showing safety and efficacy that relate to the change to the intramuscular form. This pathway may require a comparability study.

ANDA or 505(j)

A 505(j) application is considered abbreviated because, generally, the application is not required to include preclinical and clinical data necessary to demonstrate safety and effectiveness. Instead, it contains chemistry and bioequivalence data to show that the proposed product is identical in active ingredient, dosage form, route of administration, labeling, quality, performance characteristics and intended use to a previously-approved reference product. More information on ANDAs is provided in Chapter 11.

Submission of the NDA and Next Steps

Once the CTD has been compiled and is ready for dispatch, it can be submitted by regular post or express mail to FDA's Document Control Room.

Electronic CTD submissions are submitted either on CD or DVD, or through the FDA Electronic Submissions Gateway (FDA ESG). If submitted on CD or DVD, the disks should be sent by regular post or express mail just like the paper submission. The FDA ESG is a centralized, agency-wide communications point for securely receiving electronic regulatory submissions. It electronically receives, acknowledges, routes to and notifies a receiving center of the receipt of an electronic submission. The FDA ESG is a conduit, or "highway," along which submissions travel to reach their final destination within FDA. FDA ESG staff do not open or review submissions.

Upon receipt of the NDA, FDA has 60 days (also known as the initial filing review period) to determine whether the application is sufficiently complete to allow for a substantive review. If no substantive review issues are identified during the filing review, FDA will notify the applicant to that effect. Note that FDA's filing review represents a preliminary review of the application and is not indicative of deficiencies that may be identified later in the review cycle. FDA will then file, or accept for review, the NDA and will inform the applicant in writing by issuing a letter mandated by *PDUFA* within 14 days of the determination (also called a Day 74 letter).

The *PDUFA* Day 74 letter states the date the NDA was submitted, which is also the date the review clock begins. The *PDUFA* letter provides an "action" date, when FDA commits to providing a decision on the NDA, as well as dates when the applicant can expect to receive feedback from the review division on proposed labeling and postmarketing commitments. The Day 74 letter also identifies the review classification granted by FDA (i.e., standard review or priority review).

During the review period, FDA may ask the applicant for additional information ("solicited" information); this generally will not extend the *PDUFA* action date. However, if the applicant submits a major amendment on its own initiative ("unsolicited" information), FDA usually will determine that an extension to the *PDUFA* action date is needed to review the new information. This extension can be as long as six months. Thus, an applicant's strategy for providing information contained in the NDA should be very carefully planned.

If FDA determines, during the initial review period, that the NDA is not complete, the application will not be accepted for review, which will result in a refuse-to-file (RTF) action. FDA will notify the applicant by letter, telephone conference, fax or secure email within 14 calendar days after the 60 day filing date (by Day 74). FDA will issue a formal RTF letter, which will provide the reasons for the decision (21 CFR 314.101(d) and (e)). An RTF decision generally indicates that the NDA has significant deficiencies and, if reviewed as submitted, is likely to result in a not approvable action or a request for a substantial amount of additional data and/or analysis. By eliminating incomplete or inadequate NDAs from the review queue, FDA is able to focus its limited resources on complete applications.

Note that FDA tends to be more flexible in accommodating drugs intended for critical diseases, particularly when there is no alternative therapy. In such cases, the agency and applicant will often work together to find a balanced resolution to allow NDA review to begin as quickly as possible. Note also that FDA may accept some parts of an NDA and RTF others. The applicant resubmits the NDA after addressing FDA's RTF issues; FDA then determines whether the amended NDA can be filed.

If an applicant strongly disagrees with FDA's decision to RTF an application, the applicant is given 30 days after receiving the RTF letter to request an informal conference with FDA. Following the informal conference, the applicant can request that the agency file the NDA "under protest." In this event, the date of filing will be 60 days after the date the applicant requested the informal conference.

FDA NDA Review Process

Once an application is validated and filed with FDA, it is routed to the project manager in the appropriate review division and to various disciplinary groups (clinical, pharmacology and toxicology, chemistry, etc.) within the review division (**Figure 9-2**). Each disciplinary group completes its review and determines whether the data can support the drug's approval. The review division can notify applicants of serious deficiencies via a "discipline review" letter after each discipline has finished the initial review of its section of the pending application. Communications regarding minor deficiencies or clarifications are often conveyed to the applicant via email, fax or telephone by the FDA project manager. The project manager facilitates minor communications—usually seeking clarification or explanation of data already submitted in the NDA—from the reviewers to the applicant, who provides responses as soon as possible, usually by submitting an amendment to the NDA. Interoffice consults may be necessary, and the applicant can request that the review division arrange interoffice consults when needed. An advisory panel may be convened at this stage.

FDA determines whether it will carry out any bioresearch monitoring (BIMO) or current Good Manufacturing Practice (CGMP) inspections prior to approval. The results of these inspections will allow the agency to determine the credibility and accuracy of the data submitted in the NDA.

Finally, FDA will review the product labeling and determine whether it accurately reflects the product's safety and efficacy and allows physicians and consumers to determine whether the drug's benefits outweigh its risks. The agency will then decide if it is ready to take action on the NDA.

There are three review stages within the agency prior to taking action on an NDA. The primary review stage encompasses the reviews performed by individual disciplinary groups, involving careful assessment and analysis of the raw data submitted in the NDA (**Figure 9-2**). The results of the primary review (which include any postmarketing commitments or requirements) are then reviewed by the division director (secondary review stage), who will determine whether or not to recommend approval of the NDA to the office director. The latter makes the final determination on the NDA and issues either an Approval Letter or a Complete Response Letter.

Advisory Committee Meetings

FDAAA requires FDA to take certain products to an Advisory Committee for discussion. Additionally, FDA can convene an Advisory Committee meeting if there are critical questions regarding the safety or efficacy of the drug or drug class. Most members of this committee are subject matter experts, although there are also a consumer representative and an industry representative. The committee provides FDA with independent opinions and recommendations on the drug. (See Chapter 5 for further information on Advisory Committees.) FDA is not obligated to follow the advice/recommendations from the Advisory Committee, although in practice, it frequently does.

Preapproval Inspections (PAI)

Prior to approving an NDA, FDA may inspect manufacturing facilities (CGMP inspections), as well as facilities or sites where the drug was tested in nonclinical or clinical studies (BIMO inspections). Although the decision is left to the agency's discretion, FDA is likely to conduct PAIs in the following instances:

- new molecular entities (NMEs)
- priority NDAs
- the first NDA filed by an applicant
- for-cause inspections (e.g., if one clinical site had a significantly lower trial outcome than other sites)
- original NDAs, if the CGMP status is unknown, e.g., it has been more than two years since the facility was last inspected

CDER evaluates the adequacy of the NDA's data and relies on the facility inspections to verify the authenticity and accuracy of that data. This ensures that applications are not approved if it is determined that the applicant cannot demonstrate the ability to operate with integrity and in compliance with all applicable requirements. FDA inspects both foreign and domestic facilities and establishments that will manufacture a drug for the US market, or that have completed a study to support the approval of a drug that will be marketed in the US.

FDA Decision on the NDA

Once the NDA is filed, the "review clock" begins (six months for a priority review and 10 months for a standard review). After completing the necessary prior approval

Figure 9-2. Primary NDA Review Stage

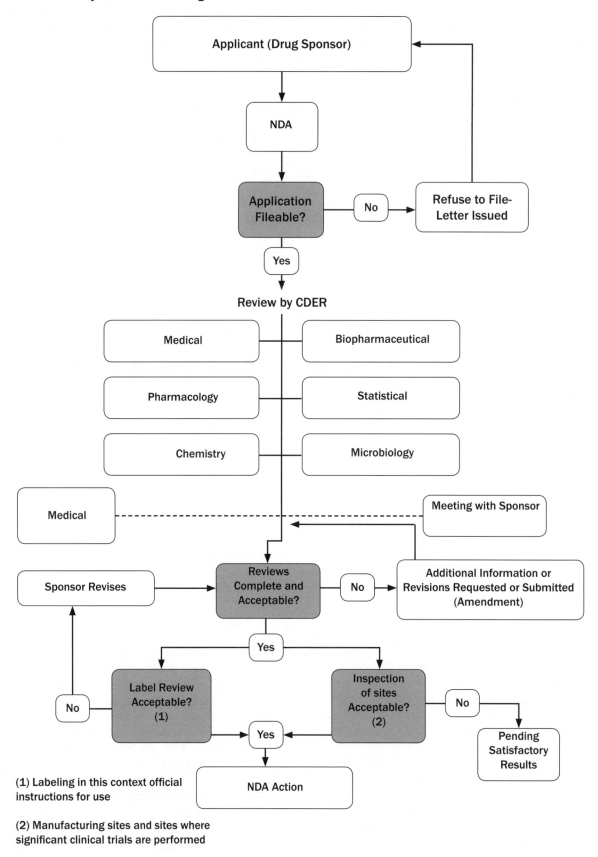

(1) Labeling in this context official instructions for use

(2) Manufacturing sites and sites where significant clinical trials are performed

inspection, FDA will then respond to the applicant with an action letter that indicates approval or "complete response." The latter lists all review deficiencies identified by FDA and identifies steps the applicant must take to get the NDA ready for approval.

Approval letters are issued once FDA has determined that the drug is safe and effective, can be acceptably manufactured and is appropriately labeled. An approval is effective on the date of approval letter issuance, granting authorization to market the drug for sale in the US.

Postmarketing Requirements and Commitments

The NDA approval letter also stipulates any postmarketing requirements and commitments. A postmarketing requirement is a study (e.g., an observational epidemiologic study, an animal study or a laboratory experiment) or clinical trial that the applicant must conduct after the NDA is approved. It includes studies that may be required under the *Pediatric Research Equity Act* (*PREA*) (21 CFR 14.55(b)), the *Animal Rule* (21 CFR 314.610(b)(1)), Accelerated Approval regulations (21 CFR 314.510) or *FDAAA* (Title IX, Section 901). *FDAAA* authorizes FDA to require postmarketing studies or clinical trials at the time of approval, or after approval, if the agency becomes aware of new safety information. The applicant must report the status of each postmarketing requirement annually.

A postmarketing commitment is a written commitment by the applicant to FDA to provide additional information after approval of the NDA. It is not a postmarketing requirement, although 506B-reportable postmarketing commitments require annual status reports to be submitted by the applicant. (506B is the section of the *FD&C Act* that mandates annual status reports and obligates FDA to make certain information about postmarketing commitments publicly available.)

Maintenance of the NDA

After the NDA is approved, there are routine activities that need to continue to support it. This may include the submission of stability data; expedited reporting of serious, unexpected adverse events that occur in the postmarketing setting; submission of periodic safety update reports that provide a review of the drug's safety profile since approval; and submission of Annual Reports. Annual updates to establishment registrations and drug listings may also be necessary. Please refer to Chapter 10 for more information on postmarketing activities.

Programs/Incentives to Expedite Drug Development and Approval

Several programs are intended to provide incentives to manufacturers to expedite the development and approval of drugs, particularly when they are intended to treat serious or life-threatening conditions and/or demonstrate the potential to address unmet medical needs. For example, the President's Emergency Plan for Aids Relief (PEPFAR) supplies antiretroviral HIV therapy, supports prevention and treatment of opportunistic infections, and provides services to prevent and treat malaria, tuberculosis, waterborne illness and other acute infections. Under PEPFAR, FDA has encouraged applicants worldwide to submit US marketing applications for single-entity, fixed-dose combination and co-packaged versions of previously approved antiretroviral therapies, even if the product still has patent or exclusivity market protection in the US. If the product still has marketing protection in the US, FDA issues a "tentative" approval rather than a "full" approval, which signifies that the product meets all safety, efficacy and manufacturing quality standards for marketing in the US, except for the legal market protection. Under PEPFAR, USAID can purchase any drug that has either a full or tentative FDA approval. Additionally, FDA works closely with manufacturers that have not previously interacted with the agency to help them prepare the application and to get ready for PAI inspections of their clinical trials and manufacturing facilities. FDA also provides an expedited review process, with reviews being completed in as little as two weeks after submission of the application.

New Drug Product Exclusivity (Hatch-Waxman Exclusivity)

Under the *FD&C Act*, a holder of an approved NDA for a new chemical entity (NCE) or new molecular entity (NME) is provided protection from competition for a limited period; this is known as new drug product exclusivity. An NCE or NME is a drug that contains an active moiety that has not been previously approved by FDA in any other application submitted under Section 505(b) of the *FD&C Act*.

There are two categories of new drug product exclusivity:

1.   Five-year period of exclusivity for NDAs for products containing chemical entities never previously approved by FDA either alone or in combination. No 505(b)(2) application or ANDA may be submitted during the five-year exclusivity period except that such applications may be submitted after four years if they contain a certification of patent invalidity or non-infringement.

2.   Three-year period of exclusivity for a drug product that contains an active moiety that has been previously approved, but the NDA contains results from new clinical investigations (other than bioavailability studies) that were conducted by the applicant. For example, the changes in an approved drug product that affect its active ingredient, strength, dosage

form, route of administration or conditions of use may be granted exclusivity if clinical investigations were essential to approval of the application containing those changes.

Summary

- A prescription drug is any drug approved or licensed for distribution by FDA that requires a healthcare practitioner's authorization before it can be obtained.
- The *FD&C Act* prohibits introduction of a prescription drug into interstate commerce unless the drug's manufacturer has submitted an NDA and obtained FDA approval.
- Depending upon the type of drug and the disease or condition it diagnoses, treats or prevents, an NDA sponsor must carefully consider a series of options/strategies before an NDA is submitted. A well thought out regulatory strategy is essential to the ultimate success of the drug development program and could shave months, or even years, off the product launch timeline.
- An NDA is required to contain all information pertaining to the drug's development, including chemistry, manufacturing and controls, nonclinical and clinical data. The ultimate goal of the NDA is to provide adequate information to allow FDA to complete its review and provide a decision on the drug's safety, effectiveness and quality.
- There are three different types of NDAs and all should provide adequate information to allow FDA reviewers to conclude both that the drug is safe and effective when used for the proposed indication, and that it can be manufactured consistently under controlled conditions.
- FDA will take action on a submitted NDA by issuing either a complete response letter or an approval letter, based upon its assessment of the application. Complete response letters are issued when deficiencies are identified in the NDA. Approval letters are issued once FDA has determined that the drug is safe, effective, can be acceptably manufactured and is appropriately labeled. FDA can mandate postmarketing requirements or commitments after approval.
- Ongoing maintenance of the NDA is required for as long as it is active. NDA maintenance includes safety reporting, submission of Annual Reports, submission of advertising and promotional labeling and submission of stability data.
- Many incentives and programs are available to expedite drug development, review and approval.

Many of these incentives focus on the development, review and approval of drugs intended to treat serious or life-threatening conditions and/or address an unmet medical need.

References

1. www.fda.gov/Drugs/GuidanceComplianceRegulatoryInformation/LawsActsandRules/ucm084138.htm. Accessed 12 May 2011.
2. www.fda.gov/downloads/Drugs/DevelopmentApprovalProcess/FormsSubmissionRequirements/ElectronicSubmissions/UCM163175.pdf. Accessed 12 May 2011.
3. ICH M2 Expert Working Group. Available at www.ich.org/products/electronic-standards.html. Accessed 12 May 2011.

Recommended Reading

MaPP 6020.4 Classifying Resubmissions of Original NDAs, BLAs, and Efficacy Supplements in Response to Action Letters (www.fda.gov/downloads/AboutFDA/CentersOffices/CDER/ManualofPoliciesProcedures/UCM082002.pdf). Accessed 12 May 2011.

Preapproval Inspections/Investigations (http://www.fda.gov/downloads/Drugs/DevelopmentApprovalProcess/Manufacturing/QuestionsandAnswersonCurrentGoodManufacturingPracticescGMPforDrugs/UCM071871.pdf). Accessed 12 May 2011.

FDA/ORA Bioresearch Monitoring Information (www.fda.gov/ICECI/EnforcementActions/BioresearchMonitoring/default.htm). Accessed 12 may 2011.

Frequently Asked Questions for New Drug Product Exclusivity (www.fda.gov/Drugs/DevelopmentApprovalProcess/SmallBusinessAssistance/ucm069962.htm). Accessed 12 May 2011.

Postmarketing Study Commitments public website (www.accessdata.fda.gov/scripts/cder/pmc/index.cfm). Accessed 12 May 2011.

About the Accelerated Approval Regulations (www.fda.gov/Drugs/DevelopmentApprovalProcess/HowDrugsareDevelopedandApproved/DrugandBiologicApprovalReports/ucm121606.htm). Accessed 12 May 2011.

Postapproval Prescription Drug Submissions and Compliance

By William C. Putnam, PhD, RAC, and Miguel A. de Soto-Perera, PhD

Objectives

- To define and review the postapproval aspects of prescription drugs, including:
  - postapproval reporting requirements for prescription drug marketing applications, including Drug Master Files and associated guidance documents
  - postapproval compliance requirements for prescription drugs and associated guidance documents
  - the effect of changes to approved products and applications
- Understand import and export regulations for approved products

Regulations and Guidance Documents Covered in This Chapter

Regulations

- 21 CFR 201.122 Exemptions from adequate directions for use—Drugs for processing, repacking, or manufacturing
- 21 CFR 207 Registration of producers of drugs and listing of drugs in commercial distribution
- 21 CFR 210 Current Good Manufacturing Practice in manufacturing, processing, packing, or holding of drugs; General
- 21 CFR 211 Current Good Manufacturing Practice for finished pharmaceuticals
- 21 CFR 312.32 IND Safety Reports
- 21 CFR 312.110 Import and export requirements
- 21 CFR 314.70 Supplements and other changes to an approved application
- 21 CFR 314.71 Procedures for submission of supplement to an approved application
- 21 CFR 314.72 Change in ownership of an application
- 21 CFR 314.80 Postmarketing reporting of adverse drug experiences
- 21 CFR 314.81 Other postmarketing reports
- 21 CFR 314.410 Imports and exports of new drugs
- 21 CFR 314.420 Drug Master Files
- 21 CFR 314.550 Accelerated approval of new drugs for serious or life-threatening illnesses—Promotional materials

Guidance Documents

- *Guidance for Industry: Quality Systems Approach to Pharmaceutical Current Good Manufacturing Practice Regulations* (September 2006)
- *Guidance for Industry: Changes to an Approved NDA or ANDA* (November 1999)
- *Guidance for Industry: Changes to an Approved NDA or ANDA: Questions and Answers* (January 2001)
- *Guidance for Industry: Changes to an Approved NDA or ANDA; Specifications—Use of Enforcement Discretion for Compendial Changes* (November 2004)
- *Guidance for Industry: SUPAC-IR: Immediate-Release Solid Oral Dosage Forms, Scale-Up and Postapproval Changes: Chemistry, Manufacturing, and Controls, In Vitro Dissolution Testing and In Vivo Bioequivalence Documentation* (November 1995)

- *SUPAC-IR: Questions and Answers about SUPAC-IR Guidance* (February 1997)
- *Guidance for Industry: SUPAC-MR: Modified-Release Solid Oral Dosage Forms: Scale-Up and Postapproval Changes: Chemistry, Manufacturing, and Controls, In Vitro Dissolution Testing and In Vivo Bioequivalence Documentation* (September 1997)
- *Guidance for Industry: SUPAC-IR/MR: Immediate-Release and Modified-Release Solid Oral Dosage Forms, Manufacturing Equipment Addendum* (January 1999)
- *Guidance for Industry: Nonsterile Semisolid Dosage Forms; Scale-Up and Postapproval Changes: Chemistry, Manufacturing, and Controls, In Vitro Release Testing and In Vivo Bioequivalence Documentation* (May 1997)
- *Draft Guidance for Industry: SUPAC-SS: Nonsterile Semisolid Dosage Forms Manufacturing Equipment Addendum* (December 1998)
- *Guidance for Industry: PAC-ATLS: Postapproval Changes—Analytical Testing Sites* (April 1998)
- *Draft Guidance for Industry: Comparability Protocols—Chemistry, Manufacturing, and Controls Information* (February 2003)
- *Guidance for Industry: Format and Content of the CMC Section of an Annual Report* (September 1994)
- *Guidance for Industry: Providing Regulatory Submissions in Electronic Format—Content of Labeling* (April 2005)
- *Draft Guidance for Industry: CMC Postapproval Manufacturing Changes Reportable in Annual Reports* (June 2010)
- *ICH Q7A: Good Manufacturing Practice Guidance for Active Pharmaceutical Ingredients* (November 2000)
- *ICH Q8(R1): Pharmaceutical Development* (November 2005)
- *ICH Q9: Quality Risk Management* (November 2005)
- *ICH Q10: Pharmaceutical Quality System* (June 2008)

Safety Reporting

- *Guidance: Drug Safety Information—FDA's Communication to the Public* (March 2007)
- *Guideline for Postmarketing Reporting of Adverse Drug Experiences* (March 1992)
- *Guidance for Industry: Postmarketing Adverse Experience Reporting for Human Drugs and Licensed Biological Products: Clarification of What to Report* (August 1997)
- *Draft Guidance for Industry: Postmarketing Safety Reporting for Human Drug and Biological Products Including Vaccines* (March 2001)
- *Draft Guidance for Industry: Providing Regulatory Submissions in Electronic Format—Postmarketing Individual Case Safety Reports* (June 2008)
- *Guidance for Industry: Providing Regulatory Submissions in Electronic Format — Drug Establishment Registration and drug Listing* (May 2009)
- *Draft Guidance for Industry: Postmarketing Adverse Event Reporting for Medical Products and Dietary Supplements During an Influenza Pandemic* (December 2008)
- *Guideline for Drug Master Files* (September 1989)
- *ICH E2A: Clinical Safety Data Management: Definitions and Standards for Expedited Reporting* (October 1994)
- *ICH E2B(R3): Revision of the ICH Guideline on Clinical Safety Data Management—Data Elements for Transmission of Individual Case Safety Reports* (May 2005)
- *ICH E2C(R1): Clinical Safety Data Management: Periodic Safety Update Reports for Marketed Drugs* (November 1996)
- *ICH M1: Medical Terminology (MedDRA)*
- *ICH M2: Electronic Standards for the Transfer of Regulatory Information*

Introduction

Prescription drug manufacturers, distributors and marketers are required to remain in compliance throughout the product lifecycle. This lifecycle starts in early development and extends through the commercial marketing of the product. There are some differences in requirements at the preapproval stage compared with the postapproval stage; however, requirements at both stages are focused on product safety and quality. As in the clinical phases of development, manufacturers of approved products are required to adhere to current Good Manufacturing Practice (CGMP) regulations, and the marketing application sponsor is required to report changes that have a potential effect on the product's safety and quality to the US Food and Drug Administration (FDA). Postapproval requirements for marketing applications and requirements for the production of commercial products are similar for products approved under either a New Drug Application (NDA) or an Abbreviated New Drug Application (ANDA).

This chapter focuses on the CGMP manufacturing regulations and the postapproval maintenance of regulatory submissions (e.g., NDAs, ANDAs and Drug Master Files (DMFs)), addressing postapproval changes to the manufacturing and labeling of prescription drug products and postapproval requirements of commercial prescription drug manufacturing.

The CGMP manufacturing and postapproval application maintenance requirements will be discussed separately.

CGMPs for Processing, Packing or Holding of Drugs and for Finished Pharmaceuticals (21 CFR 210 and 211)

Manufacturers of products undergoing human clinical trials and approved products are required to adhere to CGMP regulations. Title 21 of the US Code of Federal Regulations (CFR) Part 210 outlines the CGMP regulations in 21 CFR 210–226, including the minimum CGMP requirements for methods to be used in, and facilities or controls to be used for, the manufacture, processing, packing or holding of a drug, including those activities for biologic products. Of note, it specifically states that failure to comply with 21 CFR 210–226 shall render the drug adulterated. It also provides clarification on how to handle conflicts between applicable regulations in 21 CFR 210 and other parts of the chapter, i.e., the regulation specifically applicable to the drug product in question shall supersede the more general regulation. Finally, 21 CFR 210 sets forth the definitions as used in Section 201 of the *Federal Food, Drug, and Cosmetics Act (FD&C Act)* and 21 CFR 210–226.

The CGMP regulations for drugs establish the minimum requirements for manufacturing, personnel, equipment, facilities, packaging and the associated process controls. The intention is to ensure that drugs are safe and that requirements are met for quality, identity, strength and purity. Additionally, CGMP regulations require all manufacturing and testing equipment to be qualified as suitable for use and for all operational methodologies and procedures (such as manufacturing, cleaning and analytical testing) utilized in the drug manufacturing process to be validated (according to predetermined specifications) to demonstrate that they can perform their purported function(s) in a reliable and consistent manner.

Active pharmaceutical ingredients (APIs) are subject to the adulteration provisions of Section 501(a)(2)(B) of the *FD&C Act*, which requires all drugs to be manufactured in conformance with CGMPs. The act makes no distinction between an API and a finished pharmaceutical, and failure of either to comply with CGMPs constitutes a violation of the act. FDA has not promulgated CGMP regulations specifically for APIs or drug components (as it has for finished pharmaceuticals).

FDA has long recognized that the requirements in the GMP regulations for finished pharmaceuticals (21 CFR 210 and 211) are valid and applicable in concept to API

manufacturing. These concepts include building quality into the drug by using suitable equipment and employing appropriately qualified and trained personnel, establishing adequate written procedures and controls designed to ensure manufacturing processes and controls are valid, establishing a system of in-process material and final drug tests, and ensuring stability of drugs for their intended period of use. In 2001, FDA adopted an internationally harmonized guidance to industry on API CGMPs in conjunction with regulatory partners in the International Conference on Harmonisation (ICH). This guidance is ICH *Q7A, Good Manufacturing Practice Guidance for Active Pharmaceutical Ingredients*. ICH Q7 (as it is now referred to) represents FDA's current thinking on CGMPs for APIs. Thus, API and related manufacturing and testing facilities that follow this guidance generally will be considered to comply with the statutory CGMP requirement.

CGMP Guidance

In September 2006, FDA published *Guidance for Industry: Quality Systems Approach to Pharmaceutical Current Good Manufacturing Practice Regulations* to help manufacturers implement modern quality systems and risk management approaches to meet the requirements of the agency's CGMP regulations (21 CFR 210 and 211).

The overarching philosophy articulated in both the CGMP regulations and in robust, modern quality systems is: "Quality should be built into the product, and testing alone cannot be relied on to ensure product quality."

This guidance is intended to serve as a bridge between the 1978 regulations and the agency's current understanding of quality systems. In addition to being part of FDA's CGMP initiative, this guidance was issued for a number of reasons:

- to facilitate the development of a quality system that addresses the public and private sectors' mutual goal of providing a high-quality drug product to patients and prescribers that can eventually reduce the number of recalls and returned or defective products
- to harmonize CGMP regulations, to the extent possible, with other widely used quality management systems
- to reduce the number of prior-approval type regulatory submissions through the use of modern quality systems when coupled with manufacturing process and product knowledge and the use of effective risk management practices
- to require a quality system that can provide the necessary framework for implementing Quality by Design (QbD) (building in quality from the development phase and throughout a product's lifecycle), continuous improvement and risk management in

the drug manufacturing process

FDA's *Compliance Program Manual*, which contains instructions to FDA personnel for conducting inspections, is a systems-based approach and is consistent with the robust quality system model presented in this guidance. The six interrelated systems are quality, facilities and equipment, materials, production, packaging and labeling and laboratory controls. The quality system provides the foundation for the manufacturing systems that are linked and function within it. The quality system model described in this guidance does not consider the six manufacturing systems as discrete entities, but instead integrates them into appropriate sections of the model. Those familiar with the six-system inspection approach will see organizational differences in this guidance; however, the interrelationship should be readily apparent. One of the important themes of the systems-based inspection compliance program is that the applicant must have the ability to assess whether each of the systems is in a state of control. The quality system model presented in this guidance also serves to help firms achieve this state of control.

Pharmaceutical Quality System

In April 2009, FDA published *Guidance for Industry: Q10 Pharmaceutical Quality System* to assist pharmaceutical manufacturers by describing a model for an effective quality management system for the industry. ICH's Q10 describes one comprehensive model for an effective pharmaceutical quality system that is based on International Organization for Standardization (ISO) quality concepts, including applicable GMP regulations and complementing ICH's *Q8 Pharmaceutical Development* and *Q9 Quality Risk Management*. Q10 is a model for a pharmaceutical quality system that can be implemented throughout the different product lifecycle stages. Much of the content of Q10 applicable to manufacturing sites is currently specified by regional GMP requirements. Q10 is not intended to create any new expectations beyond current regulatory requirements. Consequently, the content of the guidance that exceeds current regional GMP requirements is optional. Q10 demonstrates industry and regulatory authorities' support of an effective pharmaceutical quality system to enhance the quality and availability of medicines around the world in the interest of public health. Implementation of Q10 throughout the product lifecycle should facilitate innovation and continual improvement as well as strengthen the link between pharmaceutical development and manufacturing activities.

Changes to an Approved Application

Almost all changes to an approved marketing application, either NDA or ANDA, are required to be reported to FDA under the *FD&C Act*. Procedural aspects associated with supplementing an approved application are discussed in 21 CFR 314.71, including:

- Only the applicant (sponsor), or its designated agent, can supplement the application.
- Only information related to the proposed change(s) is required to be submitted.
- Requirements for archival, review and field copies are the same as for original applications.

Changes and the reporting of changes to the chemistry, manufacturing and controls (CMC) and labeling sections of approved applications are discussed in 21 CFR 314.70. The regulations within 314.70 require reporting CMC changes to the drug substance and drug product that may affect the marketed product's identity, strength, quality, purity or potency.

Labeling changes that may affect the proper identification or indications for use for the product must also be reported. It is noteworthy that not all labeling changes require submissions, such as minor editorial or stylistic changes to product information (labeling) that have already been submitted. Typographical and spelling errors and changes in formatting to standard operating procedures or batch records need not be submitted (21 CFR 314.70(a)(1)).

Three categories of postapproval changes are described in 21 CFR 314.70: major (314.70(b)), moderate (314.70(c)(3) and 314.70(c)(6)) and minor (314.70(d)). These changes are categorized based on their potential to adversely affect the drug product's identity, strength, quality, purity or potency. Consequently, the reporting categories and the timing of the ability to distribute product that has been produced under these changes are also stratified. A summary of the postapproval reporting categories, their implementation timeframes and several examples are provided in **Table 10-1**.

FDA will review each supplement and Annual Report. If FDA determines that a supplement or Annual Report is deficient, the sponsor cannot distribute product manufactured with that change until the supplement is amended. If product with the proposed change is already in commercial distribution (e.g., the product was distributed after submission of a Changes Being Effected (CBE)-type supplement) and FDA believes the supplement is deficient, the agency may order the manufacturer to cease distribution of the product until the supplement is appropriately amended.

FDA has issued several guidance documents associated with changes to approved applications that can be found on the agency's website. An index to FDA's guidance documents can be found at www.fda.gov/Drugs/GuidanceComplianceRegulatoryInformation/Guidances/default.htm. If there are changes that are not directly addressed by the regulations, in FDA guidance documents or are multifactorial in nature, consulting the agency is recommended.

Several FDA guidance documents supplement the CFR with respect to reporting requirements associated

Table 10-1. Postapproval CMC Supplements

Type of Change	Postapproval Reporting Category	Implementation	Examples
Major Change Major change has substantial potential to cause an adverse effect on a drug product's identity, strength, quality, purity or potency.	Prior Approval Supplement (PAS)	Approval of the supplement is required prior to distribution of product manufactured using the proposed change(s)	• Establishing a new regulatory analytical procedure including designation of an alternative analytical procedure as a regulatory procedure • A change in qualitative or quantitative formulation
Moderate Change The change has moderate potential to cause an adverse effect on a drug product's identity, strength, quality, purity or potency.	Changes Being Effected in 30 Days Supplement (CBE-30)	Product manufactured using the proposed change(s) may be distributed 30 days after submission of the supplement if the sponsor is not informed otherwise by FDA	• Changes in the size or shape of a container for a sterile drug substance • Relaxing an acceptance criterion or deleting a test to comply with an official compendium that is consistent with FDA statutory and regulatory requirements
Moderate Change The change has moderate potential to cause an adverse effect on a drug product's identity, strength, quality, purity or potency.	Changes Being Effected Supplement (CBE or CBE-0)	Manufacturer can distribute product manufactured using the proposed change(s) immediately following submission of the supplement	• A change in or addition or deletion of a desiccant • Adding or strengthening a contraindication, warning, precaution or adverse reaction on the product labeling
Minor Change The change has minor potential to cause an adverse effect on the drug product's identity, strength, quality, purity or potency.	Annual Report	Product manufactured using the proposed change(s) can be distributed prior to reporting the change; the change is reported in the next Annual Report	• A move to a different manufacturing site for secondary packaging (manufacturing) • Extension of an expiration date based on full shelf-life data when the data were obtained in accordance with an approved stability protocol

with changes to approved applications. The most comprehensive of these documents is *Guidance for Industry: Changes to an Approved NDA or ANDA* (April 2004). This is supplemented by two additional guidance documents: *Guidance for Industry: Changes to an Approved NDA or ANDA: Questions and Answers* (January 2001) and *Guidance for Industry: Changes to an Approved NDA or ANDA: Specifications—Use of Enforcement Discretion for Compendial Changes* (November 2004). Additional guidance can also be found in the *Draft Guidance for Industry: CMC Postapproval Manufacturing Changes Reportable in Annual Reports* (June 2010) and *Guidance for Industry: PAC-ATLS: Postapproval Changes—Analytical Testing Sites* (April 1998). These five FDA guidance documents provide

direction on postapproval changes to:
• components and composition
• manufacturing sites
• analytical testing sites
• manufacturing process
• specifications
• container closure systems
• labeling
• miscellaneous changes
• multiple related changes

FDA has also issued a number of guidance documents to aid manufacturers in determining the amount and type of information (data) required to be submitted to support certain postapproval changes. The most notable of these with respect to drug products are the Scale-Up and Postapproval Changes (SUPAC) guidance documents. The SUPAC guidance documents were written to reduce the reporting requirements for low-risk postapproval changes and reduce the reviewing burden on FDA. They also detail the chemistry and potential bioequivalence study requirements associated with postapproval changes. These documents assess the risk level associated with changes (e.g., manufacturing process, manufacturing site, product formula, equipment, batch size, etc.). The SUPAC documents stratify changes into three levels: 1, 2 and 3. Level 1 changes are filed in an Annual Report and include, for example, site changes within a single facility and process changes within validated ranges. Level 2 changes, such as composition changes and changes in manufacturing equipment, are filed in a CBE-0 or CBE-30 (Changes Being Effected in 30 days) supplement. Level 3 changes are filed in a Prior Approval Supplement (PAS) and can range from site changes to the use of a new manufacturer that does not have experience with the product type. The SUPAC guidance documents include:

- *Guidance for Industry: SUPAC-IR: Immediate-Release Solid Oral Dosage Forms, Scale-Up and Postapproval Changes: Chemistry, Manufacturing, and Controls, In Vitro Dissolution Testing and In Vivo Bioequivalence Documentation* (November 1995)
  - *SUPAC-IR: Questions and Answers about SUPAC-IR* (February 1997)
- *Guidance for Industry: SUPAC-MR: Modified-Release Solid Oral Dosage Forms: Scale-Up and Postapproval Changes: Chemistry, Manufacturing, and Controls, In Vitro Dissolution Testing and In Vivo Bioequivalence Documentation* (September 1997)
  - *Guidance for Industry: SUPAC-IR/MR: Immediate-Release and Modified-Release Solid Oral Dosage Forms, Manufacturing Equipment Addendum* (January 1999)
- *SUPAC-SS: Guidance for Industry: Nonsterile Semisolid Dosage Forms; Scale-Up and Postapproval Changes: Chemistry, Manufacturing, and Controls, In Vitro Release Testing and In Vivo Bioequivalence Documentation* (May 1997)
  - *Draft Guidance for Industry: SUPAC-SS: Nonsterile Semisolid Dosage Forms Manufacturing Equipment Addendum* (December 1998)

A sponsor can reduce the reporting requirements of a postapproval change if the change is implemented under an approved comparability protocol. A comparability protocol fully describes the proposed change, the data that will be generated to support the change and the acceptability criteria for the change. Unless submitted with the original NDA or ANDA, the comparability protocol must be submitted and approved as a PAS. FDA has provided guidance associated with comparability protocols in *Draft Guidance for Industry: Comparability Protocols—Chemistry, Manufacturing, and Controls Information* (February 2003). The reporting requirements associated with postapproval changes may also be reduced if the changes were part of a QbD development and validation program as detailed in ICH's *Q8(R1) Pharmaceutical Development, Q9 Quality Risk Management* and *Q10 Pharmaceutical Quality System.*

A supplement or Annual Report must include a list of all the changes. FDA recommends that the applicant describe each change in enough detail to allow the agency to quickly determine whether the appropriate reporting category has been used. For supplements, this list must be provided in the cover letter (21 CFR 314.70(a)(6)). In Annual Reports, the list should be included in the summary section (21 CFR 314.81(b)(2)(i)). The applicant must describe each change fully in the body of the supplement or Annual Report (21 CFR 314.70(a)(1)). An applicant making a change to an approved application under Section 506A of the *FD&C Act* must also conform to other applicable laws and regulations, including CGMP requirements of the *FD&C Act* (21 U.S.C. 351(a)(2)(B)) and applicable regulations in 21 CFR 210, 211 and 314.

Other Postapproval Requirements

FDA has the authority to withdraw an application (NDA or ANDA) if a sponsor (holder) does not meet the reporting requirements for adverse drug experience (ADE) reports, field events, Annual Reports and advertising and labeling as listed in 21 CFR 314.80 and 314.81 within the required timeframes. FDA withdrawal of an application prevents the sponsor from marketing and distributing the product.

Adverse Drug Experience Reports

Under 21 CFR 314.80, the sponsor is required to review ADE information obtained from all potential sources (foreign and domestic), including:

- marketing experience
- scientific literature (peer-reviewed and non-peer-reviewed)
- unpublished reports
- postmarketing clinical investigations
- postmarketing epidemiological/surveillance studies

Furthermore, the sponsor is required to develop written procedures for collecting, evaluating and submitting postapproval ADE reports to FDA and maintaining records of all ADEs known to the applicant for a period of 10 years, including raw data and any correspondence relating to ADEs. Any company (sponsor, manufacturer, distributor or packer) listed on the approved product labeling is held to these ADE reporting requirements. Obligations of a non-sponsor may be met by submitting all reports of serious ADEs to the sponsor. If a non-sponsor elects to submit ADE reports to the sponsor rather than to FDA, the non-sponsor shall submit each report to the sponsor within five calendar days of receipt of the report, and the sponsor would be responsible for submitting ADEs to FDA.

The sponsor is required to submit the following ADE reports to FDA within the specified timeframes:

- Postmarketing 15-Day Alert Reports—A sponsor shall submit any foreign or domestic ADE that is both serious and unexpected within 15 days following receipt of the information. Additional information shall also be submitted within 15 days of receipt as follow-up reports or as requested by FDA.
- Periodic Adverse Drug Experience Reports—For the first three years following approval, a sponsor shall submit a quarterly, periodic ADE report. Unless otherwise requested by FDA, after three years, the sponsor shall submit the periodic ADE report at annual intervals. The periodic ADE report should contain:
  o a narrative summary and analysis of the report's information, including all ADE information obtained during the reporting period
  o analysis of the 15-day alert reports submitted during the reporting interval
  o any Form FDA 3500A (MedWatch) for an ADE that was not submitted as a 15-day alert report
  o any actions during the reporting period due to ADEs (e.g., labeling changes or additional studies initiated)

A sponsor should protect the privacy of the patient with an ADE by assigning a unique code instead of using the patient's name and address in the reports. A sponsor can include a disclaimer statement in the report indicating that it is not admitting or denying that the ADE report submitted constitutes an admission that the drug caused or contributed to an adverse effect.

An "unexpected" ADE is defined as an ADE not listed in the drug product's current labeling. A "serious" ADE is defined by an experience that results in:

- death
- a life-threatening event
- in-patient hospitalization or prolongation of existing hospitalization
- a persistent or significant disability/incapacity
- a congenital anomaly/birth defect

Other events may be considered serious ADEs if, based on appropriate medical judgment, they may jeopardize the patient or subject and require medical intervention to prevent one of the outcomes listed above.

A 15-Day Alert Report should be submitted if:

- A lack of effect is detected and an increased incident frequency is detected.
- A lack of effect that has severely impacted subject health is detected.
- There are published or unpublished written reports issued (foreign or domestic) of serious, unexpected ADEs.
- There are published or unpublished written reports issued (foreign or domestic) of ADEs if an increased frequency is detected.

Other foreign reports, including serious and non-serious events, are not required to be submitted.

ADE reports can be submitted either via paper or electronically. FDA has provided guidance regarding submission of ADE reports in electronic format. *Draft Guidance for Industry: Providing Regulatory Submissions in Electronic Format—Postmarketing Expedited Safety Reports* (May 2001) and *Draft Guidance for Industry: Providing Regulatory Submissions in Electronic Format—Postmarketing Periodic Adverse Drug Experience Reports* (June 2003) were superseded in June 2008 by *Draft Guidance for Industry: Providing Regulatory Submissions in Electronic Format—Postmarketing Individual Case Safety Reports.*

To encourage healthcare professionals to collect, evaluate and report serious ADEs, FDA developed the MedWatch educational and publicity program in 1993.

Sponsors, manufacturers, distributors and user facilities use MedWatch Form FDA 3500A for mandatory reporting of both adverse events and problems with human drugs and other FDA-regulated products. The MedWatch webpage can be found at www.fda.gov/medwatch/index.html. Foreign reportable ADEs may be submitted on forms developed by the Council for International Organizations of Medical Sciences.

FDA tracks adverse drug reaction reports by entering all safety reports for approved drugs and therapeutic biologic products into the computerized Adverse Event Reporting System (AERS) database, which uses standardized international terminology from the *Medical Dictionary for Regulatory Activities*. FDA uses AERS to facilitate post-marketing drug surveillance and compliance activities. The goal of AERS is to improve the public health by providing the best available tools for storing and analyzing safety data and reports. Data and trends from AERS may lead to FDA action on products, such as "Dear Health Care Professional" letters or requests to a sponsor for additional safety studies. This is part of an FDA initiative to rapidly collect, analyze and disseminate drug safety information. This initiative is highlighted by the FDA *Guidance: Drug Safety Information—FDA's Communication to the Public* (March 2007).

Similar adverse event reporting requirements are associated with the conduct of clinical trials (21 CFR 312.32);

these requirements are discussed in "Chapter 7 Clinical Trials: GCPs, Regulations and Compliance."

Reporting Field Events

The sponsor of an approved application is required by 21 CFR 314.81(b)(1) to report any of the following incidents or occurrences to the appropriate FDA district office within three working days of notification of the event:

- incidents causing the drug product or its labeling to be mistaken for, or applied to, another article
- any bacteriological contamination; any significant chemical, physical or other change or deterioration in the distributed drug product; or any failure of one or more distributed batches of the drug product to meet the specifications established for it in the application

The information may be provided to the appropriate FDA district office by telephone or other rapid means of communication but should be promptly followed by a written Field Alert Report. Two hard copies of the report are required, and the mailing cover must be plainly marked "NDA–Field Alert Report."

Annual Reports

Sponsors of approved applications are required by 21 CFR 314.81(b)(2) to submit an Annual Report within 60 days of the anniversary date of the approval of the NDA or ANDA. If submitting in paper format, two copies of the report should be sent to the FDA division responsible for reviewing the application. Each copy must be accompanied by a completed Form FDA 2252 (Transmittal of Periodic Reports for Drugs for Human Use). The period covered in the report is defined as one full year from the anniversary date.

Following is the type of information that should be reported:

Summary

- summary of significant new information that might affect the drug product's safety, effectiveness or labeling and a description of actions the sponsor has taken or intends to take as a result of this new information
- indication whether labeling supplements for pediatric use have been submitted and whether new studies in the pediatric population have been initiated to support appropriate labeling for the pediatric population

Distribution Data

- distribution data for the commercial drug product, including the National Drug Code (NDC) number and the total number of dosage units of each strength or potency
- quantities distributed for domestic and foreign use

Labeling

- currently used professional labeling, patient brochures or package inserts, as well as representative samples of the package labels
- content of labeling required under 21 CFR 201.100(d)(3) (i.e., the package insert or professional labeling), including all text, tables and figures in electronic format
- summary of any changes in labeling that have been made since the last report, listed by date in the order in which they were implemented or, if no changes, a statement of that fact

Chemistry, Manufacturing and Controls

- CMC changes; reports of experiences; investigations; studies or tests involving physicochemical or any other properties if they affect the drug product's safety or effectiveness
- full description of CMC changes not requiring a supplemental application under 21 CFR 314.70(b)
- updated stability data obtained during the reporting period
- list of outstanding regulatory business, if any

Nonclinical Laboratory Studies

- copies of unpublished reports and summaries of published reports of new toxicological findings in animal studies and *in vitro* studies

Clinical Data

- published clinical trials (or abstracts) of the drug, including clinical trials on safety and effectiveness; clinical trials on new uses; biopharmaceutic, pharmacokinetic and clinical pharmacology studies; and reports of clinical experience related to safety
- review articles or papers describing the drug's use in medical practice
- summaries of completed unpublished clinical trials or prepublication manuscripts

Status Reports of Postmarketing Study Commitments

- status report on each postmarketing study commitment concerning clinical safety, clinical efficacy, clinical pharmacology and nonclinical toxicology

Advertising and Labeling

To comply with 21 CFR 314.81(b)(3), the sponsor must submit specimens of mailing pieces and any other labeling or advertising devised for promotion of a drug product at the time of the promotional material's initial use and at the time of initial publication of an advertisement for a prescription drug product. A copy of the current labeling and a completed Form FDA 2253 (Transmittal of

Advertisements and Promotional Labeling for Drugs for Human Use) are required with each submission.

For new drug products being considered for accelerated approval under 21 CFR 314.550 for treatment of serious or life-threatening illnesses, sponsors must submit copies of all promotional materials, including promotional labeling and advertisements, intended for dissemination or publication within 120 days following marketing approval to FDA for consideration during the preapproval review period. After the first 120 days following marketing approval, the sponsor must submit promotional materials at least 30 days prior to the intended initial dissemination of the labeling or initial publication of the advertisement.

Submission of Patents to the *Orange Book* for Patent Exclusivity

Following approval of an application under *FD&C Act* Section 505, the product will be listed in FDA's *Approved Drug Products with Therapeutic Equivalence Evaluations* (electronic *Orange Book*, www.accessdata.fda.gov/scripts/cder/ob/default.cfm). The electronic *Orange Book* lists patent and exclusivity information associated with each approved product. To add patent information to the *Orange Book*, Form FDA 3542a must be submitted with the application and Form 3524 must be submitted upon or after approval. These forms detail the patent information associated with the product.

Product Complaints

In accordance with CGMP regulations for APIs and finished pharmaceuticals, complaint files are required to be maintained by both sponsors and manufacturing/control sites. Written procedures describing the handling of all written and oral complaints regarding a drug product must be established and followed (21 CFR 211.198). The procedures should include provisions for review by the quality unit of any complaint involving a drug product's possible failure to meet any of its acceptance criteria in the regulatory specification and, for such drug products, a determination of whether there is a need for an investigation in accordance with 21 CFR 211.192.

The established procedures should include provisions for review to determine if the complaint represents a serious and unexpected ADE. A serious and unexpected ADE is required to be reported to FDA in accordance with 21 CFR 310.305 and 514.80.

A written record of each complaint should be kept in a file(s) designated for drug product complaints. The file(s) should be maintained in a location where it can be easily retrieved for review during a regulatory inspection. Written records involving a drug product should be maintained until at least one year after the expiration date of the drug product or one year after the date that the complaint was received, whichever is longer. In the case of certain over-the-counter (OTC) drug products that lack expiration dating because they meet the criteria for exemption under 21 CFR 211.137, the written records should be maintained for three years after distribution.

Product Recalls

Recalls are actions taken by a firm (e.g., a manufacturer or distributor) to effectively remove from the market or correct consumer products that are in violation of laws administered by FDA. Recalls may be conducted on a firm's own initiative, in response to an FDA request or by FDA order under statutory authority. If many lots of product have been widely distributed, a recall is generally more appropriate than seizure and affords better protection for consumers. Seizure, multiple seizure or other court action is indicated when a firm refuses to undertake a recall requested by FDA or when the agency has reason to believe that a recall would not be effective, determines that a recall is ineffective or discovers that a violation is continuing.

There are three classes of recalls:

- Class I Recall—when there is a reasonable probability that the use of or exposure to a suspected product will cause serious adverse health consequences or death
- Class II Recall—when the use of or exposure to a suspected product may cause temporary or medically reversible adverse health consequences, or where the probability of serious adverse health consequences is remote
- Class III Recall—when use of or exposure to a suspected product is not likely to cause adverse health consequences

The product recall process should address the following elements:

- depth of the recall (Depending upon the product's degree of hazard and extent of distribution, the recall strategy should specify the level in the distribution chain to which the recall is to be extended (e.g., to the consumer or user level, the retail level or the wholesale level).)
- public warnings to alert affected parties in urgent situations
- effectiveness checks to ensure that all affected parties have received the recall notification and have taken appropriate action

In some cases, the following situations also are considered recalls:

- withdrawal from the market, which occurs when a product has a minor violation that would not be subject to FDA legal action and the firm removes the product from the market or corrects the violation

- medical device safety alert, which is issued in situations where a medical device may present an unreasonable risk of substantial harm

Regulations related to recalls are found in 21 CFR 7.40–7.59.

Drug Master Files (DMFs)

A DMF (21 CFR 314.420) is a voluntary submission to FDA intended to protect the confidentiality of the information submitted. A DMF provides FDA with details regarding proprietary information such as the chemistry, manufacturing and controls for drug substances, drug products, excipients or packaging materials. Initially, there were five types of DMFs; however, FDA eliminated Type I DMFs in 2000 and requested that information regarding manufacturing sites, facilities, operating procedures, personnel and equipment be submitted in one of the remaining four types of DMFs:

- Type II—manufacture and control information for drug substances, intermediates and materials used in their preparation or similar information for drug products
- Type III—component, composition, controls for release and intended uses of packaging materials
- Type IV—excipients, colorants, flavors, essences or materials used in their preparation
- Type V—FDA-accepted reference information

A DMF is prepared in accordance with FDA's 1989 *Guideline for Drug Master Files*. A DMF may be submitted in hard copy form (in duplicate) using either the Common Technical Document (CTD) or traditional format. It also may be submitted in electronic CTD (eCTD) format. The DMF is accompanied by a statement of commitment, indicating that all information in the DMF is accurate and that any changes will be communicated to FDA. The DMF also includes a list of firms authorized to reference it in other regulatory applications. If the DMF holder restricts the authorization to particular drug products, the list must include the name of each drug product and the application number, if known, to which the authorization applies. A copy of the letter of authorization to reference the DMF is also provided to each of the firms listed.

A DMF may be used to support an Investigational New Drug Application (IND), NDA or ANDA; an amendment or supplement to these; or another DMF. The DMF is a confidential document and is not available for review by the sponsor of the submission in which it is referenced. FDA reviews the DMF only as part of the review of the application that references it and only if the DMF holder supplies the agency with a letter of authorization for that reference. The sponsor's application references the DMF number, and a copy of the letter of authorization is provided. From a regulatory perspective, DMFs are not officially approved by FDA, they are only reviewed. If deficiencies are noted, FDA will provide a list of deficiencies to the DMF holder and notify the application sponsor that such a list has been provided to the DMF holder. FDA will not disclose the deficiencies to the application sponsor. It is the DMF holder's responsibility to provide responses to FDA and supply additional information, if requested.

Annual updates (annual reports) to the DMF are required on the anniversary date of the original submission and should include an updated list of firms authorized to reference the DMF and a list of any changes that have taken place and been reported in an amendment since the last annual report. Any technical changes to a DMF should be submitted in the form of a DMF amendment.

A DMF holder may close a DMF by submitting a request to the Drug Master File staff stating the reason for the closure. The request should include a statement that the holder's obligations have been fulfilled. The agency may close a DMF that has not been maintained by annual reports and/or amendments. The holder will be notified of FDA's intent to close the DMF and will be given 90 days to appropriately update the DMF to prevent closure.

Changes to Drug Master Files Affecting Approved Applications

Changes to DMFs are submitted in the form of DMF amendments, and the firms authorized to reference the DMF are notified of any change. The sponsor of the application assesses the impact of the change to determine the appropriate reporting category (PAS, CBE-30, CBE-0 or Annual Report) and the timing for distribution of drug product manufactured using the change, as discussed previously. The sponsor reports the change to the marketing application as appropriate and references the DMF amendment.

Imports and Exports

Drug substances and drug products must comply with the *FD&C Act* to be imported into the US (21 CFR 314.410). Specifically, drug products must be the subject of an approved NDA or ANDA or an active IND (21 CFR 312.110) to be imported into the US. Drug substances may be imported if they are in compliance with the labeling exemption (21 CFR 201.122) and the drug substance is intended for further manufacturing, packaging or other processing operations. Other articles that are components of or are related to unapproved drug products may be imported, even though they do not strictly comply with the *FD&C Act,* if they are processed and incorporated into products that will be exported from the US by their initial owner or consignee ("Import for Export").

Companies that wish to import regulated products into the US are required to file entry notices and entry bonds with the US Customs Service. Imported products are subject to customs inspection at the time of entry. A notification of the product's entry is provided to FDA, which then determines if the shipment can be admitted through the issuance of a "May Proceed Notice" or "Release Notice." Nonconforming shipments are detained and must either be brought into compliance, destroyed or re-exported; otherwise, the importer will receive a "Notice of Refusal." The burden of proof of compliance with the *FD&C Act* is on the importer, and FDA may detain any shipment that it believes may be unapproved, misbranded or adulterated.

Foreign manufacturers of drug substances and drug products that wish to import products must have a US agent and are required to register with FDA under 21 CFR 207.40 (as described in the Establishment Registration and Drug Listing Forms section of this chapter).

Drug substances and drug products that are the subjects of approved applications may be exported. Drug substances that are the subjects of NDAs or ANDAs may be exported if they have been shown to be within the approved specification and are shipped with the approved labeling. Drug products that are the subjects of approved NDAs or ANDAs may be exported. Drug products that are the subject of active INDs may be exported (21 CFR 312.110).

Drug Establishment Registration and Drug Listing

In accordance with FDA's *Draft Guidance for Industry: Providing Regulatory Submissions in Electronic Format—Drug Establishment Registration and Drug Listing* (July 2008), a voluntary pilot program was initiated to allow firms to transition their submissions from paper to electronic format, i.e., electronic drug registration and drug listing. The pilot program ended 31 May 2009. In May 2009, FDA published *Guidance for Industry: Providing Regulatory Submissions in Electronic Format—Drug Establishment Registration and Drug Listing*, which stated that, effective 1 June 2009, it is a requirement that the information that was traditionally included in Forms FDA 2656, 2657 and 2658 be submitted electronically. Registrants also need to submit the following information in their structured product labeling (SPL) file:

- official contact's name, mailing address, telephone number(s) and email address
- each registered establishment's telephone number
- type of operation(s) performed at each registered establishment

The owner or operator of an establishment entering into the manufacture, compounding, processing, packaging, repackaging or relabeling of a human or veterinary drug, including blood and blood products and biologicals, must register the establishment electronically within five days after beginning to manufacture commercial products or within five days of submitting a marketing application. In addition, each product in commercial distribution should be listed with FDA. The drug listing should also include bulk drugs for commercial distribution, whether or not they are involved in interstate commerce.

Private label distributors are not currently required to register their commercial products. However, if a distributor chooses not to submit drug listing information directly to FDA, the registered manufacturing establishment must submit the drug listing information. If the private label distributor elects to list directly with FDA, a labeler code is obtained and each product is listed using that code.

An NDC number is requested but not required for all OTC products, although most companies list the NDC number on their labels.

After the initial registration, establishments are required to re-register annually. A schedule for annual re-registration is provided in 21 CFR 207.21, based on the first letter of the company name. Establishments also are required to provide updated drug listings. Owners and operators of all registered establishments need to update their drug listing information every June and December or at the discretion of the registrant when a change occurs. If no changes have occurred since the previously submitted list, no drug product listing report is required.

Foreign drug establishments whose drugs are imported or offered for import into the US must also comply with the establishment registration and drug listing requirements. However, if the drugs enter a foreign trade zone and are re-exported from that foreign trade zone without having entered US commerce, compliance is not required. Each foreign drug establishment required to register must submit the name, address and phone number of its US agent (who must reside in the US) as part of its initial and updated registration information. Only one US agent is allowed per foreign drug establishment. The foreign drug establishment or the US agent should report changes in the agent's name, address or telephone number to FDA within 10 business days of the change.

The information required for each establishment includes:

- drug establishment name and full address
- all trade names used by the establishment
- type of ownership or operation (e.g., individually owned, partnership or corporation)
- name(s) of the establishment's owner, operator, partners or officers

For each drug substance (bulk API) and finished dosage form in commercial distribution, the information should include:

- trade name
- NDA or ANDA number or OTC monograph

number
- business type and product type
- packaging type and size
- manufacturing site
- copies of all current labeling and representative sampling of advertising
- quantitative listing of the active ingredients
- NDC number
- for each listed drug product subject to the imprinting requirements of 21 CFR 206, a document that provides the product name; its active ingredient(s); dosage strength; NDC number; manufacturer or distributor name; product's size, shape, color and code imprint (if any); and any other characteristic that identifies the product as unique

The NDC number currently contains 10 digits. The first five digits identify the manufacturer or distributor and are known as the Labeler Code. FDA will expand the Labeler Code from five to six digits when all available five-digit code combinations have been exhausted. FDA assigns Labeler Code numbers and provides them to registrants. The last five digits, identifying the drug product and trade package size and type, are known as a product and package code and are assigned by the registrant.

If any material change to a product occurs—such as a change in the active ingredient, dosage form or route of administration—a new NDC number must be assigned to the product by the registrant and the information must be submitted.

If the registrant decides to discontinue a product, the drug listing should be updated to reflect the discontinuation. The same NDC number may be assigned to another drug product five years after the expiration date of the discontinued product or, if there is no expiration date, five years after the last shipment of the discontinued product into commercial distribution.

Upon application, each business entity will be assigned a distinct, site-specific, nine-digit Data Universal Numbering System (D-U-N-S) number. If the D-U-N-S number for a location has not been assigned, a firm may obtain one at no cost directly from Dun & Bradstreet (www.dnb.com). A D-U-N-S number should be submitted for each site-specific entity (e.g., registrant, establishment, US agent and importer).

Inactivation/Withdrawal of Approved Applications

Under 21 CFR 314.150, an approved application may be withdrawn voluntarily (by the sponsor or applicant) or involuntarily (by FDA). FDA will withdraw approval of an NDA or ANDA at the sponsor's request if the drug covered in the application is no longer being marketed, provided there are no safety or manufacturing issues with the drug. FDA considers a written request for a withdrawal of approval of an NDA or ANDA to be without prejudice to refiling.

On the other hand, FDA will notify a sponsor and, if appropriate, all other persons who manufacture or distribute identical, related or similar drug products of its intent to withdraw approval of an application. For a new drug, the agency will give the sponsor the opportunity for a hearing on the proposal to withdraw approval of the application. FDA may request that a sponsor withdraw the approved application if, among other reasons, it determines that: the drug is unsafe and there is imminent hazard to the public health; the application contains any untrue statement of a material fact; the sponsor deliberately fails to keep adequate records; or the facilities, processes and/or analytical test methods are not suitable for establishing the drug's quality.

FDA may notify a sponsor if it believes a potential problem associated with a drug is sufficiently serious for the drug to be removed from the market. The agency may also ask the sponsor to waive the opportunity for a hearing to permit FDA to withdraw approval of the NDA or ANDA for the product or to voluntarily remove the product from the market. If the sponsor agrees, the agency will not make a finding but will withdraw approval of the NDA or ANDA in a notice published in the *Federal Register* that contains a brief summary of the agency's and the sponsor's reasons for withdrawal.

Change in Sponsor (Ownership) of an Approved Application

A sponsor may transfer ownership of an application (21 CFR 314.72). At the time of transfer, the following information must be submitted to FDA:
- The former owner shall submit a letter or other document that states that all rights to the application have been transferred to the new owner as of the transfer date.
- The new owner shall submit a signed application form and a letter or other document containing the new owner's commitment to agreements, promises and conditions made by the former owner and contained in the application; the date that the change in ownership is effective; and either a statement that the new owner has a complete copy of the approved application, including supplements and records, or has requested a copy of the application from FDA's files. FDA will provide a copy of the application to the new owner under the fee schedule.
- The new owner shall advise FDA of any change in the conditions in the approved application under 21 CFR 314.70, except that the new owner may

advise FDA in the next Annual Report about a change in the drug product's label or labeling to change the product's brand or the name of its manufacturer, packager or distributor.

21 CFR Parts 20, 310, 312 and 314

The Pharmaceutical Regulatory Process. Ira R. Berry (ed.). Marcel Decker, New York, NY (2005).

Summary

- Sponsors of approved marketing applications are required to report almost all changes to FDA under the *FD&C Act.* The reporting requirements for changes are summarized in guidance documents.
- Sponsors of applications are responsible for ensuring that drug substances and drug products for human or veterinary use are manufactured in accordance with applicable GMP regulations.
- Drug manufacturing and control sites are subject to periodic inspection in accordance with FDA's compliance program and applicable GMP regulations.
- Sponsors of approved marketing applications are required to report almost all changes to FDA under the *FD&C Act.* The reporting requirements for changes are summarized in guidance documents.
- Sponsors of approved marketing applications are required to review ADE information obtained from all potential sources. Sponsors are required to report to FDA in 15-Day Alert Reports and periodic ADE reports.
- Sponsors of approved applications are required to submit an Annual Report. Each copy of the report must be accompanied by a completed Form FDA 2252 (Transmittal of Periodic Reports for Drugs for Human Use). The period covered in the report is defined as one full year from the approval anniversary date of the preceding year. The report should include a summary distribution data; labeling; chemistry, manufacturing and controls; nonclinical laboratory studies; clinical data and status reports of postmarketing study commitments.
- DMFs are voluntary submissions to FDA containing detailed, confidential CMC information about drug substances, intermediates, drug products, excipients or packaging materials that may be used for human drugs.
- Manufacturers are required to register drug establishments and provide a current drug product list to FDA on an annual basis. Effective 1 June 2009, the information that was traditionally included in Forms FDA 2656, 2657, and 2658 is required to be submitted electronically in SPL format.

Recommended Reading
ICH and FDA guidance documents listed at the beginning of this chapter

Generic Drug Submissions

By Kurt R. Karst, JD

Objectives

- To gain an understanding of the history of generic drug development in the US
- To gain an understanding of FDA's generic drug approval process and requirements, including the various paths to approval
- To gain an understanding of the concepts of bioequivalence and therapeutic equivalence

Laws, Regulations and Guidelines Covered in This

- *Federal Food, Drug, and Cosmetic Act* of 1938
- *Drug Efficacy Amendments* of 1962
- *Drug Regulation Reform Act* of 1978
- *Drug Price Competition and Patent Term Restoration Act* of 1984 (*Hatch-Waxman Act*)
- *Medicare Prescription Drug, Improvement, and Modernization Act* of 2003
- *Prescription Drug User Fee Act* of 1992
- *Pediatric Research Equity Act* of 2003
- 21 CFR 314 Applications for FDA approval to market a new drug
- 11 CFR 310 Bioavailability and bioequivalence requirements
- 43 *Federal Register* 39,126 (1 September 1978), Abbreviated New Drug Applications; Proposed Related Drug Amendments
- 44 *Federal Register* 2932 (12 January 1979), Therapeutically Equivalent Drugs; Availability of List
- 45 *Federal Register* 72,582 (31 October 1980), Therapeutically Equivalent Drugs; Availability of List
- 45 *Federal Register* 82,052 (12 December 1980), Response to Petition Seeking Withdrawal of the Policy Described in the Agency's "Paper" NDA Memorandum of July 31, 1978
- 46 *Federal Register* 27,396 (19 May 1981), Publication of "Paper NDA" Memorandum
- 54 *Federal Register* 28,872 (10 July 1989), Proposed ANDA Regulations
- 74 *Federal Register* 2849 (16 January 2009) Requirements for submission of bioequivalence data
- Manual of Policies and Procedures 5240.3, "Review Order of Original ANDAs, Amendments, and Supplements" (October 2006)
- *Guidance For Industry: Bioavailability and Bioequivalence Studies for Orally Administered Drug Products—General Considerations* (March 2003)
- *Draft Guidance for Industry: Applications Covered by Section 505(b)(2)* (October 1999)

Introduction

The term "generic drug" is not defined in the *Federal Food, Drug, and Cosmetic Act* of 1938 (*FD&C Act*) or in US Food and Drug Administration (FDA) regulations. It generally is used, however, to refer to a drug product with the same active ingredient as a brand-name drug. Generic drugs cost less because the brand-name drug company has already done the work necessary to develop the active ingredient and show that it is safe and effective.

The first generic drugs were marketed during the period between the enactment of the *FD&C Act* (Pub. L. No. 75-717, 52 Stat 1040 (1938)) and the enactment of the *Drug Efficacy Amendments* of 1962 (Pub. L. No. 87-781, 76 Stat. 780 (1962)). These products were marketed without FDA approval, on the theory that the agency's approval of the brand-name drug under a New Drug Application (NDA) (based only upon safety) made the next version an "old" drug.[1] After 1962, FDA required the submission of an Abbreviated New Drug Application (ANDA) for each generic drug, but did not permit ANDAs to be submitted for brand-name drugs approved after 1962.[2] This meant that a second version of a post-1962 brand-name drug had to obtain full NDA approval. A full NDA was economically prohibitive. (Indeed, even ANDA approval for a pre-1962 drug could be difficult to obtain.)

Competitive pressure drove some generic drug companies to market both pre- and post-1962 drugs without FDA approval, arguing that an active ingredient became available as an "old" drug after initial FDA approval. FDA's attempts to suppress this practice culminated in the 1983 Supreme Court decision in *United States v. Generix Drug Corp.*, 460 U.S. 453 (1983). The court accepted FDA's position that "old drug" status applied not to the active ingredient but to the individual finished product. Hence, each new version of a drug was a "new drug"[3] requiring FDA approval no matter how many times FDA had approved its active ingredient. Aware that its own policies and interpretations were preventing generic competition for post-1962 drugs, FDA took two steps:

1. development of the so-called "paper NDA" policy
2. development of ANDA regulations for post-1962 drug products

In 1978, FDA adopted the paper NDA policy, under which the agency accepted a combination of product-specific data and published literature about an active ingredient to satisfy the approval requirements for a full NDA.[4] FDA's paper NDA policy essentially permitted the sponsor of an application for a "duplicate" of a post-1962 drug product (i.e., a drug product that contained the same active ingredients as an already marketed product, in a similar or identical dosage form and for the same indications) to submit published studies and bridging data in support of its application.[5] However, because the paper NDA approach required published literature rather than information not publicly available, it had limited utility for most drugs.[6]

In 1978, FDA issued proposed regulations in which it expressed its intent to extend its pre-1962 ANDA regulations to post-1962 drugs.[7] FDA began to develop these regulations in the early 1980s. The agency's initiative was controversial because it reportedly would have required a substantial waiting period after initial approval of the brand-name drug before any ANDA could be approved for a generic version. Congressional interest in FDA's initiative, however, coincided with a broader effort to develop legislation that would promote both competition and innovation in the drug industry.[8]

FDA's extended approval process after 1962 undercut the value of drug patents, which are granted early in the development process and whose then 17-year (now 20-year) term was eaten up in large part before marketing approval was granted. Congress engineered a compromise in which brand-name drug companies could obtain a patent term extension and generic drug companies could obtain ANDA approval for pre- and post-1962 drugs. The compromise was enacted in the *Drug Price Competition and Patent Term Restoration Act* of 1984 (*Hatch-Waxman Act*).

The *Hatch-Waxman Act* amended the new drug approval provisions of the *FD&C Act* to add Section 505(j). Section 505(j) formalized the legal structure for generic drugs, under which an ANDA containing bioequivalence data to a Reference Listed Drug (RLD), among other data and information, was sufficient for FDA to consider approval. As explained in "Chapter 12 Patents and Exclusivity," the *Hatch-Waxman Act* also amended the patent laws to authorize a patent term extension for time lost during the regulatory review period.[9]

Under the *FD&C Act* (as amended by the *Hatch-Waxman Act*), ANDA approval is subject to several restrictions. First, non-patent market exclusivity provisions of three or five years were included to compensate brand-name drug companies for allowing reliance on their proprietary research. Second, an ANDA applicant must notify an NDA holder and patent owner if an *Orange Book*-listed patent claims the RLD; if the NDA owner files a patent infringement suit, approval of the ANDA is deferred. Third, an ANDA drug product must contain the "same" active ingredient as the brand-name drug and have essentially the same labeling, including indications, warnings, contraindications, etc.

ANDA Approval Process

The premise of *FD&C Act* Section 505(j) is that an ANDA drug is the "same as" the brand-name drug—i.e., the RLD, defined as "the listed drug identified by FDA as the drug product upon which an applicant relies in seeking approval of its abbreviated application" (21 CFR 314.3(b)).[10] However, "same" does not mean "identical." Differences are allowed in route of administration, dosage form and strength as well as in an active ingredient in a combination drug product. Those differences must first be approved by FDA under a suitability petition as not requiring clinical investigations.[11] *FD&C Act* Section 505(j)(2)(A) states that an ANDA (that is not the subject of an approved suitability petition) must contain information to show, among other things, that the active ingredient, "the route of administration, the dosage form, and the strength

Figure 11-1. OGD ANDA Backlog

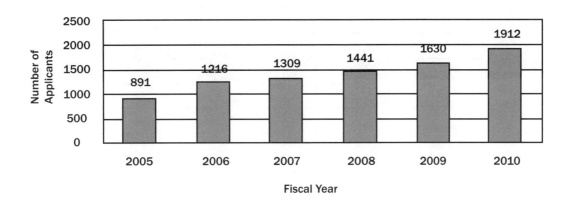

of the new drug are the same as those of the [RLD]."[12]

An ANDA must contain, among other things identified in the *FD&C Act* and in FDA's ANDA format and content regulations at 21 CFR 314.94, information demonstrating that the generic version is bioequivalent to the RLD.[13] (A copy of FDA's ANDA Filing Checklist is included at the end of this chapter.) This information may come from *in vivo* (human) and/or *in vitro* (test tube) studies (21 CFR 320). The purpose of demonstrating bioequivalence is to determine whether changes in a proposed drug product's formulation or manufacturing affect the rate or extent to which the active ingredient reaches the primary site of action. Although data and information demonstrating *in vivo* bioequivalence are often required, FDA may waive this requirement if *in vivo* bioequivalence is considered self-evident (e.g., in the case of many injectable drugs) or for other reasons (21 CFR 320.22).[14]

A drug product is considered bioequivalent to the RLD if:

(i) the rate and extent of absorption of the drug do not show a significant difference from the rate and extent of absorption of the listed drug when administered at the same molar dose of the therapeutic ingredient under similar experimental conditions in either a single dose or multiple doses

or

(ii) the extent of absorption of the drug does not show a significant difference from the extent of absorption of the listed drug when administered at the same molar dose of the therapeutic ingredient under similar experimental conditions in either a single dose or multiple doses and the difference from the listed drug in the rate of absorption of the drug is intentional, is reflected in its proposed labeling, is not essential to the attainment of effective body drug concentrations on chronic use, and is considered medically insignificant for the drug. (*FD&C Act* Section 505(j)(8)(B);

21 CFR 320.1(e))

The choice of which *in vivo* bioequivalence study design to use is based upon the ability of the design to compare the drug delivered by the test (generic) and reference (brand-name) drug products at the drug's particular site of action. In a standard *in vivo* bioequivalence study, single doses of the test and reference drug products are administered to volunteers (usually 24–36 healthy adults), and the rate and extent of absorption of the drug is determined from measured plasma concentrations over time for each subject participating in the study. The extent of absorption (i.e., how much of the drug in the given dose was absorbed) is reflected through various measurements. The preferred study design for oral dosage forms is a single-dose, fasting, two-treatment, two-sequence crossover design with a washout period between treatments.[15] In a crossover study, the subjects receive the test and reference drug products in separate sequences (either test before reference or reference before test), with a period between treatments of no drug administration (the washout period) to ensure the previous dose is cleared from the body before the second dose is administered. To demonstrate *in vitro* bioequivalence, FDA recommends that an applicant use an *in vitro* test (e.g., a dissolution rate test) that has been correlated with *in vivo* data.[16] Over the past couple of years, FDA has begun to publish individual product bioequivalence recommendations on its website. FDA has already published almost 850 product-specific bioequivalence recommendations, and the agency's website is regularly updated with new recommendations.

An ANDA for a generic version of a brand-name drug (the RLD) must also contain one of four possible certifications "with respect to each patent which claims the [brand-name] drug…or which claims a use for such listed drug…and for which information is required to be filed"

Figure 11-2. Median ANDA Approval Times

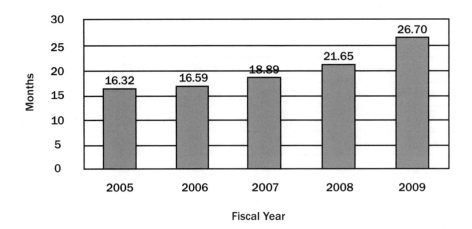

by the NDA holder and that is listed in the *Orange Book* (*FD&C Act* Section 505(j)(2)(A)(vii)). The consequences of the various types of patent certifications are discussed in Chapter 12.

Once an applicant submits an ANDA to FDA, the agency reviews the submission to determine whether the application is sufficiently complete to permit receipt (21 CFR 314.101). FDA generally reviews ANDA submissions within 60 days after they are submitted; however, the agency's decision on whether to receive an ANDA may take longer. If FDA receives an ANDA, the agency performs an in-depth review to determine whether to approve the application. In the past, this review typically took 15–18 months; however, due to a significant backlog of pending ANDAs at FDA—which has increased over the past few years (**Figure 11-1**) and currently stands at about 2,450 original ANDAs—the review process has taken longer in recent years. For example, in Fiscal 2009, the median approval time for an original ANDA was almost 27 months (**Figure 11-2**), and is currently reported to be about 31 months. FDA and the generic drug industry are currently considering the creation of a generic drug user fee system intended to decrease ANDA review times. At the end of its review, the agency either approves or refuses to approve the ANDA (21 CFR 314.127 Refusal to approve an abbreviated new drug application). If approved, the generic drug product is listed in the *Orange Book* and may be identified as a "therapeutic equivalent" to the RLD.

Although FDA generally reviews ANDA submissions on a "first in, first reviewed" basis to ensure fair and even-handed treatment of applicants, there are exceptions. For example, an ANDA applicant may qualify for expedited review. Under FDA's expedited ANDA review policy:

Certain applications may be identified at the time of submission for expedited review. These include products to respond to current and anticipated public health emergencies, products under special review programs such as the President's Emergency Plan for AIDS Relief (PEPFAR),[17] products for which a nationwide shortage has been identified, and first generic products for which there are no blocking patents or exclusivities on the reference listed drug.[18]

FDA's ANDA approval process is illustrated in **Figure 11-3**.

A Few Words on ANDA Suitability Petitions

Two laws enacted over the past several years have significantly affected suitability petitions—with respect to both their availability and their utility.

First, the *Pediatric Research Equity Act* (*PREA*), which was signed into law on 3 December 2003 and amended the *FD&C Act* to add new Section 505B, significantly affected the scope of changes that can be approved under an ANDA suitability petition.[19] Under *PREA* and *FD&C Act* Section 505B, Congress granted FDA the statutory authority to require pediatric studies in certain defined circumstances retroactive to 1 April 1999. Specifically, *FD&C Act* Section 505B states that an applicant "that submits an application (or supplement to an application) under section 505 [of the *FD&C Act*] for a new active ingredient, new indication, new dosage form, new dosing regimen, or new route of administration...shall submit with the application" the results of pediatric studies assessing "the safety and effectiveness of the drug...for the claimed indications in all relevant pediatric subpopulations; and to support dosing and administration for each pediatric subpopulation for which the drug...is safe and effective, [unless FDA]

Figure 11-3. FDA's ANDA Approval Process

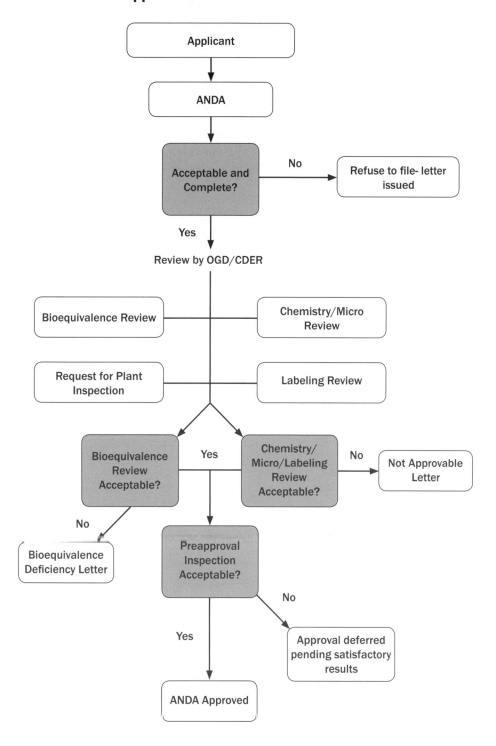

concludes that pediatric effectiveness can be extrapolated from adequate and well-controlled studies in adults, usually supplemented with other information obtained in pediatric patients," or unless FDA defers or partially or fully waives this requirement.[20]

An ANDA requiring an approved suitability petition for a change in the RLD with respect to an active ingredient (in a combination drug), route of administration or dosage form meets the criteria of *FD&C Act* Section 505B(1)(A), because it is a type of application submitted under *FD&C Act* Section 505. The only change permitted by a suitability petition that does not trigger the requirements of *FD&C Act* Section 505B is a change in strength from that of the RLD.

FD&C Act Section 505(j)(2)(C)(i) requires FDA to deny a suitability petition if "investigations must be conducted to show the safety and effectiveness of the drug or of any of its active ingredients, the route of administration, the dosage form, or strength which differ from the listed drug." Thus, unless FDA fully waives the *PREA* pediatric studies requirement, the requirement to conduct (or even a deferral from conducting) pediatric studies triggers the statutory requirement to deny a suitability petition.

Second, the *Medicare Prescription Drug, Improvement, and Modernization Act* of 2003 (*MMA*) (Pub. L. No. 108-173, 117 Stat. 2066 (2003)), amended the *FD&C Act* to preclude a generic applicant with a pending ANDA from amending its application to change the RLD. Specifically, *FD&C Act* Section 505(j)(2)(D)(i), the 505(b)(2) application counterpart for which is at *FD&C Act* Section 505(b)(4)(A), states, "[a]n applicant may not amend or supplement an [ANDA] to seek approval of a drug referring to a different listed drug from the listed drug identified in the application as submitted to [FDA]."[21]

FDA recently addressed *FD&C Act* Section 505(j)(2)(D)(i) in a citizen petition response. The agency determined that an applicant with a pending ANDA subject to an approved suitability petition must submit a new application to the agency as the result of the approval of another applicant's NDA for a drug product that is the pharmaceutical equivalent of the drug product described in the pending ANDA, and which is, therefore, the appropriate RLD that should be cited by the applicant.[22] Thus, if at any time before approval of an ANDA subject to an approved suitability petition (or a 505(b)(2) application), another drug product is approved that is the pharmaceutical equivalent—or that is more pharmaceutically similar to the product in a pending 505(b)(2) application—FDA could require the applicant to cite a new RLD. And, as a result of the statutory prohibition on amending an ANDA to change the RLD, FDA could require the applicant to submit a new application containing a certification or statement to any relevant *Orange Book*-listed patents (as well as required bioequivalence/bioavailability information).

A Few Words on Inactive Ingredients

FD&C Act Section 505(j)(4)(H) states that FDA must approve an ANDA unless, among other things:

(I)nformation submitted in the application or any other information available to [FDA] shows that (i) the inactive ingredients of the drug are unsafe for use under the conditions prescribed, recommended, or suggested in the labeling proposed for the drug, or (ii) the composition of the drug is unsafe under such conditions because of the type or quantity of inactive ingredients included or the manner in which the inactive ingredients are included.

FDA's regulations implementing *FD&C Act* Section 505(j)(4)(H) generally are found in the agency's ANDA content and format regulations at 21 CFR 314.94. Pertinent regulations on inactive ingredient changes for certain types of generic drug products are set forth in 21 CFR 314.94(a)(9). For example, FDA's regulations for parenteral drug products at 21 CFR 314.94(a)(9)(iii) state:

Generally, a drug product intended for parenteral use shall contain the same inactive ingredients and in the same concentration as the [RLD] identified by the applicant under paragraph (a)(3) of this section. However, an applicant may seek approval of a drug product that differs from the reference listed drug in preservative, buffer, or antioxidant provided that the applicant identifies and characterizes the differences and provides information demonstrating that the differences do not affect the safety or efficacy of the proposed drug product.

Preservative, buffer and antioxidant changes in generic parenteral drug products are referred to as "exception excipients," which may differ qualitatively or quantitatively from the RLD formulation. Other regulations under 21 CFR 314.94(a)(9)(iv) identify exception excipients for generic ophthalmic and otic drug products (i.e., preservative, buffer, substance to adjust tonicity and thickening agent). Excipients not identified in these regulations are referred to as "non-exception excipients."

FDA's exception excipient regulations under 21 CFR 314.94(a)(9) find their parallel in 21 CFR 314.127(a)(8)(ii), which addresses the grounds for an FDA refusal to approve an ANDA for a parenteral, ophthalmic or otic drug product. For example, one regulation states: "FDA will consider an inactive ingredient in, or the composition of, a drug product intended for parenteral use to be unsafe and will refuse to approve the [ANDA] unless it contains the same inactive ingredients, other than preservatives, buffers, and antioxidants, in the same concentration as the listed drug."[23] Thus, it is important that a company understand the possible implications of changing certain drug product formulations. If such a change is for a non-exception excipient, FDA would, unless under a narrow exception discussed below, refuse to receive or approve an ANDA. Instead a company would need to submit a 505(b)(2) application for the proposed drug product, which, like other NDAs, is subject to user fees under the *Prescription Drug User Fee Act* (*PDUFA*). For Fiscal 2011, the one-time full application user fee is $1,542,200, and annual product and establishment user fees are $86,520 and $497,200, respectively.

Notwithstanding FDA's exception excipient regulations, the agency has, in very limited circumstances, waived these regulations to permit the receipt and approval of an ANDA for a drug product containing a non-exception excipient change from the RLD.

FDA's regulations at 21 CFR 314.99(b) state that a generic applicant "may ask FDA to waive ...any requirement that applies to the applicant under 21 CFR 314.92–314.99. The applicant shall comply with the requirements for a waiver under 21 CFR 314.90." 21 CFR 314.90, the parallel waiver regulation for 505(b) applicants, describes the information an applicant must submit to support a waiver request, and states that FDA may grant a waiver if the agency finds: "(1) the applicant's compliance with the requirement is unnecessary for the agency to evaluate the application or compliance cannot be achieved; (2) the applicant's alternative submission satisfies the requirement; or (3) the applicant's submission otherwise justifies a waiver."[24] Pursuant to this regulation, FDA may waive its ANDA exception excipient regulations under 21 CFR 314.99(b) so the agency can receive and approve an ANDA.

FDA has granted a 21 CFR 314.99(b) waiver when an ANDA applicant seeks approval to market a drug product containing a non-exception excipient used in a discontinued RLD formulation that is not used in the currently marketed RLD formulation. For example, FDA has allowed applicants seeking approval to market generic Sandostatin (octreotide acetate) Injection to substitute a different tonicity agent (a non-exception excipient change) and buffer system because "the inactive ingredients (including the buffer system and tonicity agent) used in the discontinued formulation of Sandostatin do not make that formulation unsafe...[and because] the discontinued formulation of Sandostatin is no less safe and effective than the new formulation."[25]

Therapeutic Equivalence

The term "therapeutic equivalence" is not defined in the *FD&C Act* or in FDA's ANDA regulations. However, "[d]rug products are considered to be therapeutic equivalents only if they are pharmaceutical equivalents and if they can be expected to have the same clinical effect and safety profile when administered to patients under the conditions specified in the labeling" (i.e., are bioequivalent).[26] "FDA believes that products classified as

therapeutically equivalent can be substituted with the full expectation that the substituted product will produce the same clinical effect and safety profile as the prescribed product."[27]

FDA's regulations define the term "pharmaceutical equivalents" to mean:

(D)rug products in identical dosage forms that contain identical amounts of the identical active drug ingredient, i.e., the same salt or ester of the same therapeutic moiety, or, in the case of modified release dosage forms that require a reservoir or overage or such forms as prefilled syringes where residual volume may vary, that deliver identical amounts of the active drug ingredient over the identical dosing period; do not necessarily contain the same inactive ingredients; and meet the identical compendial or other applicable standard of identity, strength, quality, and purity, including potency and, where applicable, content uniformity, disintegration times, and/or dissolution rates.[28]

As explained above, the term "bioequivalence" is defined in the *FD&C Act* and FDA's regulations.[29]

Because therapeutic equivalence requires two drug products to be pharmaceutically equivalent in order to be substitutable, "pharmaceutical alternatives" are not therapeutic equivalents and are not substitutable for the RLD relied upon for approval. FDA's regulations define "pharmaceutical alternatives" as:

(D)rug products that contain the identical therapeutic moiety, or its precursor, but not necessarily in the same amount or dosage form or as the same salt or ester. Each such drug product individually meets either the identical or its own respective compendial or other applicable standard of identity, strength, quality, and purity, including potency and, where applicable, content uniformity, disintegration times and/or dissolution rates.[30]

Thus, products approved pursuant to an approved suitability petition (i.e., a change in strength, route of administration, dosage form or active ingredient in a combination drug) are pharmaceutical alternatives and are not listed in the *Orange Book* as therapeutically equivalent to the RLD. To give one common example, tablets and capsules are considered different dosage forms. Therefore, they are pharmaceutical alternatives, not pharmaceutical equivalents. Consequently, they will not be "A rated" in the *Orange Book* (described below), even if they are bioequivalent.

Pharmaceutically equivalent prescription drug products (i.e., multisource drug products approved under *FD&C Act* Section 505) usually are identified in the *Orange Book* with either an "A" or "B" therapeutic equivalence code designation, which is further defined by a one-character subcode.[31] (There are six "A" subcodes and 10 "B" subcodes.[32]) The *Orange Book* coding system for therapeutic equivalence evaluations allows users to determine whether FDA has evaluated a particular approved drug product as therapeutically equivalent to other pharmaceutically equivalent drug products (the first character in a code) and provides additional information on the basis of FDA's evaluations (the second character in a code). "A-rated" drug products are considered to be to therapeutically equivalent to other pharmaceutically equivalent products because there are no known or suspected bioequivalence problems or such problems have been resolved with adequate evidence supporting bioequivalence. "B-rated" drug products are not considered to be therapeutically equivalent to other pharmaceutically equivalent drug products because actual or potential bioequivalence problems identified by FDA have not been resolved by adequate bioequivalence evidence.

Drug products assigned an "A" rating fall under one of two categories:

- those active ingredients or dosage forms for which no *in vivo* bioequivalence issue is known or suspected, and for which bioequivalence to the RLD is presumed and considered self-evident based upon other data in an application or by a showing that an acceptable *in vitro* dissolution standard is met
- those active ingredients or dosage forms presenting a potential bioequivalence problem, but the applicant's approved application contains adequate scientific evidence establishing (through *in vivo* and/or *in vitro* studies) the bioequivalence of the product to a selected RLD

Drug products that fall under the first category are assigned a therapeutic equivalence code depending upon the dosage form. These codes include AA, AN, AO, AP or AT.[33] Drug products that fall under the second category are coded AB, the most common code assignment).

Drug products assigned a "B" rating fall under one of three categories:

- FDA has documented bioequivalence problems or a significant potential for such problems (and no adequate studies demonstrating bioequivalence have been submitted to the agency)
- FDA has an insufficient basis to determine therapeutic equivalence (e.g., quality standards are inadequate)
- the drug products are under regulatory review

Drug products that fall under these categories are assigned a therapeutic equivalence code largely based upon dosage form. These codes are B*, BC, BD, BE, BN, BP, BR, BS, BT or BX.[34] FDA's assignment of a "B" rating does not mean that a particular drug product is not safe and effective. (Indeed, the applicant has provided sufficient

data to meet the statutory and regulatory approval criteria.) Rather, a "B" rating means that FDA has identified unresolved actual or potential bioequivalence problems, and that because of those problems a particular drug product cannot be considered to be therapeutically equivalent to other pharmaceutically equivalent drug products.

A generic drug that is a pharmaceutical alternative to an RLD (e.g., tablet versus capsule) is not assigned a therapeutic equivalence code (such drug products are, by definition, not therapeutic equivalents). Instead, they are listed separately in the *Orange Book* as single-source drug products. However, because each *Orange Book*-listed drug product may be designated as an RLD (pursuant to a request to FDA to assign RLD status), a generic applicant could cite the approved drug as the RLD and obtain approval of an ANDA for a pharmaceutically equivalent drug product. In such a case, if the drug is also shown to be bioequivalent to the RLD, FDA could assign both drug products an "A" therapeutic equivalence code appropriate for such a multisource drug product.

Therapeutic equivalence codes are assigned by FDA based upon the agency's scientific and medical evaluations of a marketing application for a generic version of a listed drug. The assignment of a particular therapeutic equivalence code reflects the agency's application of specific criteria to multisource drug products (i.e., those criteria identified in reference 15). As FDA explained in the preamble to the proposal establishing the *Orange Book*:

> The term "therapeutically equivalent drug products" simply means that two such drug products can be expected, in the judgment of FDA, to have equivalent therapeutic effect and equivalent potential for adverse effects when used under the conditions set forth in their labeling. Drug products that are therapeutically equivalent may still vary in certain respects: color, shape, taste, or packaging for example. As a result, patients may not perceive them as identical or equally acceptable. For this reason, it cannot be stated that such drug products are substitutable or interchangeable in all cases. The judgment is not FDA's as to whether different drug products are substitutable or interchangeable for use by a particular patient; rather, it rests with practitioners who, in prescribing and dispensing drug products, can take into consideration the unique characteristics, needs, or problems of individual patients. It is the agency's position, however, that if one therapeutically equivalent drug product is substituted for another under State law, with due professional regard for the individual patient, there is no substantial reason to believe that the patient will receive a drug product that is different in terms of the therapeutic effect intended.[35]

As to the legal status of the *Orange Book*, FDA has commented that it "contain[s] only public information and advice," and that it "[imposes] no requirement or restriction upon any person; it [does] not interpret or apply the [*FD&C Act*] in a manner that creates any obligation on any person; it [makes] no recommendation as to which products persons should purchase, prescribe, or dispense, or conversely, which products should be avoided."[36] However, the criteria FDA uses to assign therapeutic equivalence codes "are regulatory determinations which FDA is statutorily authorized to make."[37]

As to the clinical appropriateness of (and risks associated with) substituting drug products FDA does not consider to be therapeutically equivalent (e.g., a drug product with a two-character "B" therapeutic equivalence code), such issues are generally a matter of state law.[38] FDA emphasized this point in the preamble to the 1979 *Orange Book* proposal: "[A] primary purpose of [the *Orange Book*] is to provide State agencies and officials with information relating to drug products that may be selected for dispensing under applicable State law."[39]

Drug product substitutions must be made in accordance with each individual state's pharmacy practice act. There are, in general, four different approaches taken by such laws:

- the positive formulary approach (requiring that substitution be limited to drugs on a specific list, often the *Orange Book*)
- the negative formulary approach (permitting substitution for all drugs except those prohibited by a particular list—usually drugs for which there are no "A-rated" products listed in the *Orange Book*)
- the combined positive and negative formulary approach
- the "non-formulary" approach (i.e., there is not a clearly defined positive or negative formulary)[40]

In addition, state pharmacy laws may extend the prescribing authority granted to pharmacists beyond substituting a generic drug. For example, pharmacists may be permitted to substitute a product from the same class of drug, even though the drug is not identified in the *Orange Book* as therapeutically equivalent to the prescribed drug product. This procedure is known as "therapeutic interchange." The laws covering therapeutic interchange vary widely from state to state.[41] Thus, the "clinical appropriateness" of substituting drug products FDA does not consider to be therapeutically equivalent is handled on a state-by-state basis. The consequences for violating a particular state substitution law are governed by the laws of that state.

Summary

The term "generic drug" is not defined in the *FD&C Act* or in FDA regulations. It generally is used, however, to refer to a drug product with the same active ingredient as a brand-name drug. Generic drugs cost less because the brand-name drug company has already done the work necessary to develop the active ingredient and show that it is safe and effective. The approval of generic drugs in the US is governed by a tapestry of laws, regulations and FDA policies developed over the past few decades.

FDA has established a generic drug approval process that generally requires applicants to show, through bioequivalence testing, that a proposed drug product is the same as a reference product identified by the agency as the standard for comparison.

References

1. Karst KR. "Marketed Unapproved Drugs–Past, Present and Future?" *Regulatory Affairs Focus*, Vol. 12, No. 2, pp 37–42 (February 2007).
2. ANDAs were permitted under FDA regulations for duplicates (i.e., generic versions). The term *duplicate* applied to a drug product that was the same as an already approved drug product in dosage form, route of administration, kind and amount of active ingredient, indication(s) and any other conditions of use. FDA regulations permitted ANDAs for "similar" and "related" products only if the agency had made a separate finding (following a firm's petition) that an ANDA was appropriate for that drug product.
3. A product that is a "new drug" within the meaning of *FD&C Act* Section 201(p) may not be introduced into interstate commerce unless there is an approved marketing application (e.g., an NDA), or unless an exemption has been granted permitting the introduction of the drug into interstate commerce (e.g., an effective Investigational New Drug Application (IND)).
4. The "paper NDA" policy is described in a 31 July 1979 FDA staff memorandum. The policy was not originally published in the *Federal Register* because FDA determined that rulemaking procedures were not required because "the policy is a lawful exercise of FDA's statutory authority…" 45 *Fed. Reg.* 82,052 (12 December 1980). FDA was challenged on this issue in court and won. See *Burroughs Wellcome Co. v. Schweiker*, 649 F.2d 221, 225 (4th Cir. 1981). Subsequently, in separate litigation, the US District Court for the Northern District of Illinois ruled that upon publication of FDA's policy in the *Federal Register*, the agency could implement it without rulemaking procedures. See *American Critical Care v. Schweiker*, Food, Drug, Cosm. L. Rep. (CCH) 1980-81 Transfer Binder ¶ 38, 110 (N.D. Ill. 1981).
5. The published studies requirement could be met by referencing data available in published literature, laboratory reports, physician evaluation forms and even unpublished reports when available and necessary. However, the underlying data did not have

to be included or referenced, as was required under FDA's old interpretation of "full reports" in *FD&C Act* Section 505(b)(1). Reference to information not publicly available was not permitted, including information in the brand-name product's NDA. The "bridging" data requirement could be met by submitting data from a bioavailability/bioequivalence study comparing the drug that was the subject of the "paper NDA" to the approved drug "to show that the drug is comparable in blood levels (or dissolution rate, as required) to the innovator's product." 46 *Fed. Reg.* at 27,397.

6. FDA revoked the "paper NDA" policy in 1989 when the agency proposed regulations implementing the *Drug Price Competition and Patent Term Restoration Act*, Pub. L. No. 98-417, 98 Stat. 1585 (1984) (*Hatch-Waxman Act*). See FDA, Proposed Rule, ANDA Regulations, 54 *Fed. Reg.* 28,872, 28, 890 (10 July 1989).

7. 43 *Fed. Reg.* 39126, 39128 (1 September 1978).

8. *Drug Regulation Reform Act*, 95th Cong., 2d Sess. (1978); *Drug Regulation Reform Act*, 96th Cong., 1st Sess. (1979).

9. The *Hatch-Waxman Act* also replaced the "paper NDA" with the 505(b)(2) application. The *FD&C Act* describes a 505(b)(2) application as an application "for a drug for which the investigations…relied upon by the applicant for approval of the application were not conducted by or for the applicant and for which the applicant has not obtained a right of reference or use from the person by or for whom the investigations were conducted." *FD&C Act* Section 505(b)(2). A 505(b)(2) application differs from a "paper NDA" in that it permits the sponsor of a drug that may differ substantially from a drug listed in FDA's *Approved Drug Products with Therapeutic Equivalence Evaluations* (commonly referred to as the *Orange Book* because of its bright orange cover) to rely on FDA's determination of the safety and effectiveness of a referenced drug and/or on published studies or studies in an NDA (or NDAs) sponsored by another person, together with studies generated on its own drug product, as a way to satisfy the requirement of "full reports" of safety and effectiveness. As with the old "paper NDA" policy, "bridging" studies to the referenced drug are necessary. An application that is for a duplicate of a drug listed in the Orange Book and eligible for approval under *FD&C Act* Section 505(j) may not be submitted as a 505(b)(2) application.

10. While an ANDA applicant must identify an RLD in its application, a 505(b)(2) applicant must identify a "listed drug" (or drugs) in its application if the applicant seeks to rely on FDA's previous finding of safety or efficacy for that listed drug(s). While there are no FDA regulations governing how a 505(b)(2) applicant should choose a listed drug when various options are present, FDA has spoken to the issue in guidance and in citizen petition responses. FDA has stated that "[i]f there is a listed drug that is the pharmaceutical equivalent of the drug proposed in the 505(b)(2) application, the 505(b)(2) applicant should provide patent certifications for the patents listed for the pharmaceutically equivalent drug." FDA, *Draft Guidance for Industry: Applications Covered by Section 505(b)(2)*, at 8 (October 1999). This serves to "ensure that the 505(b)(2) applicant does not use the 505(b)(2) process to end-run patent protections that would have applied had an ANDA been permitted." FDA, Citizen Petition Response, Docket No. FDA-2004-P-0089 (formerly 2004P-0386), at 9 (30 November 2004) (hereinafter "RLD Choice Petition Response"). Additionally, these provisions "further ensure that the 505(b)(2) applicant (and FDA) can rely, to the maximum extent possible, on what is already known about a drug without having to re-prove (or re-review) what has already been demonstrated." Id.

"When there is no listed drug that is a pharmaceutical equivalent to the drug product proposed in the 505(b)(2) NDA, neither the statute, the regulations, nor the Draft Guidance directly addresses how to identify the listed drug or drugs on which a 505(b)(2) applicant is to rely." Id. In FDA's RLD Choice Petition Response, however, the agency stated that:

it follows that the more similar a proposed drug is to the listed drug cited, the smaller the quantity of data that will be needed to support the proposed change. Accordingly, to avoid unnecessary duplication of research and review, when a section 505(b)(2) application has been submitted and no pharmaceutically equivalent drug product has previously been approved, the 505(b)(2) applicant should choose the listed drug or drugs that are most similar to the drug for which approval is sought. Similarly, if all the information relied on by FDA for approval …is contained in a single previously approved application and that application is a pharmaceutical equivalent or the most similar alternative to the product for which approval is sought, the 505(b)

(2) applicant should certify only to the patents for that application. This is the case even when another application also contains some or all of the same information. Id.

FDA has not defined the factors that should be taken into account when determining "similarity" of drug products; however, FDA likely considers factors such as active ingredient, dosage form, route of administration, and strength. See 21 CFR 320.1(c).

11. See *FD&C Act* Section 505(j)(2)(C); 21 CFR 314.93. As discussed later in this chapter, the *Pediatric Research Equity Act* (*PREA*), Pub. L. No. 108-155, 117 Stat. 1936 (2003), which amended the *FD&C Act* to require that most applications submitted under *FD&C Act* Section 505 include a pediatric assessment (unless otherwise waived or deferred), has significantly restricted FDA's ability to approve suitability petitions. See generally *FD&C Act* Section 505B.

12. FDA has interpreted the term *same as* to mean identical in the context of dosage forms, see 21 CFR 314.92(a)(1), and has used its discretion to interpret the term *identical* to mean products that have the same dosage form identified in the *Orange Book* at Appendix C ("Uniform Terms—Dosage Forms"). See FDA, Citizen Petition Response, Docket No. 1993P-0421, at 3 (12 August 1997) ("[A] proposed drug product has the same dosage form if it falls within the identical dosage form category, as listed in the *Orange Book*, Appendix C.").

13. See *FD&C Act* Section 505(j)(2)(A)(iv).

14. The *FD&C Act* states that an ANDA must include, among other things, "information to show that the new drug is bioequivalent to the [RLD]…," *FD&C Act* Section505(j)(2)(A)(iv), and that FDA must approve an ANDA unless, among other things, "information submitted in the application is insufficient to show that the drug is bioequivalent to the [RLD] . . . ." Id. at Section505(j)(4)(F). However, FDA has discretion to determine how the bioequivalence requirement is met. See *FD&C Act* Section 505(j)(7)(A)(i)(III). FDA's discretion need only be based on a "reasonable and scientifically supported criterion, whether [the agency] chooses to do so on a case-by-case basis or through more general inferences about a category of drugs…." *Bristol-Myers Squibb Co. v. Shalala*, 923 F. Supp. 212, 218 (D.D.C. 1996) (quoting *Schering Corp. v. Sullivan*, 782 F. Supp. 645, 651 (D.D.C. 1992), vacated as moot sub nom, *Schering Corp. v. Shalala*,

995 F.2d 1103 (D.C. Cir. 1993)); see also *Fisons Corp. v. Shalala*, 860 F. Supp. 859, 865 (D.D.C. 1994) (upholding FDA's authority to grant waivers of the requirement for submission of *in vivo* evidence of bioequivalence where bioequivalence can be determined by other available science.).

15. *Guidance for Industry: Bioavailability and Bioequivalence Studies for Orally Administered Drug Products—General Considerations* (March 2003). Although *in vivo* testing is FDA's preferred method for an ANDA applicant to demonstrate bioequivalence, agency regulations state that "bioequivalence may be demonstrated by several in vivo and in vitro methods," which are described at 21 CFR 320.24 in descending order of accuracy, sensitivity, and reproducibility.

16. See 21 CFR 320.24(b)(5). FDA recently amended its ANDA bioequivalence regulations to require applicants to submit data from all bioequivalence studies that the applicant conducts on the "same drug product formulation" submitted for approval. See 21 CFR 314.94(a)(7), 320.21(b)(1); see also FDA, Final Rule, Requirements for Submission of Bioequivalence Data, 74 *Fed. Reg.* 2849 (16 January 2009).

17. The purpose of PEPFAR is to make antiretroviral drug products available to developing countries. The PEPFAR program applies to both NDA and ANDA drug products. In addition to expedited review for PEPFAR ANDAs, the PEPFAR program permits FDA to grant tentative ANDA approval for such applications (if there are *Orange Book*-listed patents covering the RLD) so that such products can be purchased from ANDA applicants with PEPFAR funding.

18. FDA, Manual of Policies and Procedures 5240.3, "Review Order of Original ANDAs, Amendments, and Supplements," at 2 (18 October 2006).

19. Karst KR. "Is the ANDA Suitability Petition Process Dead?" *Regulatory Affairs Focus*, Vol. 10, No. 5, pp 35-6 (May 2005).

20. *FD&C Act* Sections 505B(1)(A), (2)–(4).

21. *FD&C Act* Section 505(b)(4)(A) states that "[a]n applicant may not amend or supplement an application referred to in [*FD&C Act* Section 505(b)(2)] to seek approval of a drug that is a different drug than the drug identified in the application as submitted to [FDA]."

22. FDA, Citizen Petition Response, Docket No. FDA-2008-P-0329, at 16 n. 30 (25 November 2008). FDA also noted that the agency's:

interpretation of § 505(b)(4)(A) of the Act . . . for 505(b)(2) applications is influenced by and intended to be consistent with section 505(j)(2)

(D)(i) regarding ANDAs. Accordingly, a 505(b)(2) applicant may not amend or supplement a 505(b)(2) application to seek approval of a drug that relies on the Agency's finding of safety and/or effectiveness for a drug that is different from the drug identified in a previous submission of the application.

23. 21 CFR 314.127(a)(8)(ii)(B.

24. 21 CFR 314.90(b).

25 FDA, Citizen Petition Response, Docket No. FDA-2005-P-0370, at 6 (25 March 2005).

26. *Orange Book* Preface, 29th ed. (2009), at vii. The *Orange Book* Preface further states:

> FDA classifies as therapeutically equivalent those products that meet the following general criteria: (1) they are approved as safe and effective; (2) they are pharmaceutical equivalents in that they (a) contain identical amounts of the same active drug ingredient in the same dosage form and route of administration, and (b) meet compendial or other applicable standards of strength, quality, purity, and identity; (3) they are bioequivalent in that (a) they do not present a known or potential bioequivalence problem, and they meet an acceptable *in vitro* standard, or (b) if they do present such a known or potential problem, they are shown to meet an appropriate bioequivalence standard; (4) they are adequately labeled; [and] (5) they are manufactured in compliance with Current Good Manufacturing Practice regulations.

27. Ibid.

28. 21 CFR 320.1(c).

29. *FD&C Act* Section 505(j)(8)(B); 21 CFR 320.1(e).

30. 21 CFR 320.1(d)

31. The *Orange Book*, which is published annually and updated monthly, only identifies therapeutic equivalence codes for multisource prescription drug products. Therefore, neither single-source prescription drugs—e.g., a brand-name drug product such as Lipitor (atorvastatin calcium) without generic competition—nor over-the-counter drug products are assigned a therapeutic equivalence code. Once a therapeutically equivalent generic drug is approved, it is listed in the *Orange Book* with a particular therapeutic equivalence code. The RLD and generic equivalent are differentiated from one another by a "+" sign, which denotes the RLD. FDA assigns RLD status to single-source prescription drugs.

32. In certain instances, a number is added to the end of an AB code to make a three character code (e.g., AB1, AB2, etc.).

> Three-character codes are assigned only in situations when more than one [RLD] of the same strength has been designated under the same heading…. For example, Adalat® CC (Miles) and Procardia XL® (Pfizer), extended-release tablets, are listed under the active ingredient nifedipine. These drug products, listed under the same heading, are not bioequivalent to each other. Generic drug products deemed by FDA to be bioequivalent to Adalat® CC and Procardia XL® have been approved, Adalat® CC and Procardia XL® have been assigned ratings of AB1 and AB2, respectively. The generic drug products bioequivalent to Adalat® CC would be assigned a rating of AB1 and those bioequivalent to Procardia XL® would be assigned a rating of AB2.

Orange Book Preface at xv.

33. For example, AO refers to injectable oil solutions, and AT refers to topical products. Some drug products are assigned more than one therapeutic equivalence code. For example, FDA has assigned both AB1 and AB2 codes to several approved levothyroxine sodium drug products because the sponsors conducted studies to establish their drugs' therapeutic equivalence to other RLDs.

34. For example, BT refers to "topical products with bioequivalence issues," and BX refers to "drug products for which the data are insufficient to determine therapeutic equivalence."

35. 44 *Fed. Reg.* 2932, 2937 (12 January 1979); see also *Orange Book* Preface at x–xi.

36. 44 *Fed. Reg.* at 2937; see also *Orange Book* Preface at x.

37. 45 *Fed. Reg.* 72,582, 72,584 (31 October 1980) (*Orange Book* final rule). When Congress amended the *FD&C Act* in 1984, it incorporated the *Orange Book* into the statute as a means of facilitating the approval of generic drugs. See *FD&C Act* Section 505(j)(7). The *Orange Book*'s therapeutic equivalence ratings have been accepted and recognized by the courts. See e.g., *Geneva Pharms. Tech. Corp. v. Barr Labs., Inc.*, 201 F. Supp.2d (S.D.N.Y. 2002) ("The *Orange Book* gives an AB rating to all generic warfarin sodium product[s] available today. Consequently, generic warfarin sodium is eligible for unrestricted substitution for Coumadin under most state pharmacy regulations.").

38. The designation of a drug as "A-rated" to another drug also has been incorporated into the federal Medicaid program. See 42 U.S.C. 1396r-8(e)(4) (setting the standard for upper limits on payment for multi-source drug products based on FDA's therapeutic equivalence evaluations).

39. 44 *Fed. Reg.* at 2938. FDA also commented in the preamble to the agency's final *Orange Book* proposal that:

> one reason FDA is publishing the [*Orange Book*] is in response to requests from several States for assistance in developing their drug product selection legislation. Pharmacies, hospitals, States, and private and public institutions and organizations continue to ask FDA to share its broad knowledge of the safety and effectiveness and quality of drug products, so that they can continue to carry out their duties to protect and promote the public health, both in providing health care services safely and with efficiency and cost-effectiveness, and in advising physicians and pharmacists on drug product selection. 45 *Fed. Reg.* at 72,589.

40. State laws also vary regarding how the final product selection is determined. In the majority of states, prescribers must expressly indicate that substitution is not permitted by writing "Brand Necessary," "Do Not Substitute," "Dispense as Written," "Medically Necessary," or other approved wording on the prescription form. Some states include lines on the prescription form with the phrases "Product Selection Permitted" (or similar wording) and "Do Not Substitute." The prescriber can prevent product substitution by signing on the line. See generally National Association of Boards of Pharmacy, Survey of Pharmacy Law, 2003–2004.

41. Vivian JC. "Legal Aspects of Therapeutic Interchange Programs," *U.S. Pharmacist* (2003).

Helpful References and Resources

FDA's Office of Generic Drugs webpage www.fda.gov/ AboutFDA/CentersOffices/cder/ucm119100.htm. Accessed 4 May 2011.

Federal Food, Drug, and Cosmetic Act www.fda.gov/ RegulatoryInformation/Legislation/default.htm. Accessed 4 May 2011.

The Electronic *Orange Book* www.accessdata.fda.gov/ scripts/cder/ob/default.cfm. Accessed 4 May 2011.

FDA's Paragraph IV Patent Certification List www. fda.gov/Drugs/DevelopmentApprovalProcess/ HowDrugsareDevelopedandApproved/ ApprovalApplications/ AbbreviatedNewDrugApplicationANDAGenerics/ ucm047676.htm. Accessed 4 May 2011.

ANDA Suitability Petition Tracking Reports www. fda.gov/Drugs/DevelopmentApprovalProcess/ HowDrugsareDevelopedandApproved/ ApprovalApplications/ AbbreviatedNewDrugApplicationANDAGenerics/ ucm120944.htm. Accessed 4 May 2011.

CTD Modules/Sections Corresponding to Summary Data Tables in Bioequivalence Submissions to ANDAs www.fda.gov/ Drugs/DevelopmentApprovalProcess/ HowDrugsareDevelopedandApproved/ ApprovalApplications/ AbbreviatedNewDrugApplicationANDAGenerics/ ucm120962.htm. Accessed 4 May 2011.

FDA's Individual Product Bioequivalence Recommendations www.fda.gov/Drugs/ GuidanceComplianceRegulatoryInformation/ Guidances/ucm075207.htm. Accessed 4 May 2011.

FDA Generic Drug Guidance Documents www.fda.gov/Drugs/ GuidanceComplianceRegulatoryInformation/ Guidances/ucm064995.htm. Accessed 4 May 2011.

FDA Generic Drug Manual of Policies & Procedures www.fda.gov/AboutFDA/CentersOffices/CDER/ ManualofPoliciesProcedures/default.htm#generic. Accessed 4 May 2011.

FDA's Dissolution Methods Database www.fda.gov/ Drugs/InformationOnDrugs/ucm135742.htm. Accessed 4 May 2011.

FDA's Inactive Ingredients Database www.fda.gov/ Drugs/InformationOnDrugs/ucm080123.htm. Accessed 4 May 2011.

ANDA FILING CHECKLIST
(CTD or eCTD FORMAT)
FOR COMPLETENESS AND ACCEPTABILITY of an APPLICATION

ANDA:
APPLICANT:
RELATED APPLICATION(S):

DRUG NAME:
DOSAGE FORM:

LETTER DATE:
RECEIVED DATE:

☐ P-IV
☐ FIRST GENERIC
☐ EXPEDITED REVIEW REQUEST (Approved/Denied)
☐ PEPFAR

Electronic or Paper Submission: Type II DMF#

BASIS OF SUBMISSION:
NDA/ANDA:
FIRM:
RLD:

**Document Room Note: for New Strength amendments and supplements, if specific reviewer(s) have already been assigned for the original, please assign to those reviewer(s) instead of the default random team(s).

Review Team:

CHEM Team: ☐ Activity	Bio Team: ☐ Activity
CHEM Team Leader: ☐ **No Assignment Needed in DARRTS**	Bio PM: ☐ FYI
CHEM RPM: ☐ FYI	Clinical Endpoint Team: **(No)** ☐ Activity
DMF Review Team Leader: **Aloka Srinivasan** ☐ FYI	
Labeling Reviewer: ☐ Activity	Micro Review: **(No)** ☐ Activity

Regulatory Reviewer: Date:	Recommendation: ☐ **FILE** ☐ **REFUSE to RECEIVE**

Comments:
Therapeutic Code:
On Cards:
Archival copy:
Sections:

- For More Information on Submission of an ANDA in Electronic Common Technical Document (eCTD) Format please go to: http://www.fda.gov/cder/regulatory/ersr/ectd.htm
- For a Comprehensive Table of Contents Headings and Hierarchy please go to: http://www.fda.gov/cder/regulatory/ersr/5640CTOC-v1.2.pdf
- For more CTD and eCTD informational links see the final page of the ANDA Checklist
- A model Quality Overall Summary for an immediate release tablet and an extended release capsule can be found on the OGD webpage http://www.fda.gov/cder/ogd/

1. Edit Application Property Type in DARRTS where applicable for

   a. First Generic Received
   ☐ Yes ☐ No
   b. Market Availability
   ☐ Rx ☐ OTC
   c. Pepfar
   ☐ Yes ☐ No
   d. Product Type
   ☐ Small Molecule Drug
   e. USP Drug Product (at time of filing review)
   ☐ Yes ☐ No

2. Edit Submission Patent Records
   ☐ Yes
3. Edit Contacts Database with Bioequivalence Recordation where applicable
   ☐ Yes
4. EER (in Draft)
   ☐ Yes

ADDITIONAL COMMENTS REGARDING THE ANDA:

MODULE 1: ADMINISTRATIVE

		COMMENT (S)
1.1	**Signed and Completed Application Form (356h)** (Rx/OTC Status) (original signature)	
1.1.2	**Establishment Information:** 1. Drug Substance Manufacturer 2. Drug Product Manufacturer 3. Outside Testing Facility(ies)	
1.2	**Cover Letter**	
1.2.1	**Form FDA 3674** **(PDF)**	
*	**Table of Contents** (paper submission only)	
1.3.2	**Field Copy Certification** (N/A for E-Submissions) (original signature)	
1.3.3	**Debarment Certification-GDEA** (Generic Drug Enforcement Act)/Other: (no qualifying statement) 1. Debarment Certification (original signature) 2. List of Convictions statement (original signature)	
1.3.4	**Financial Certifications** Bioavailability/Bioequivalence Financial Certification (Form FDA 3454) Disclosure Statement (Form FDA 3455)	

1.3.5	**Patent Information**
	Patents listed for the RLD in the Electronic Orange Book Approved Drug Products with Therapeutic Equivalence Evaluations
	Patent Certification
	1. Patent number(s)
	2. Paragraph: (Check all certifications that apply)
	   MOU ☐ PI ☐ PII ☐ PIII ☐ PIV ☐ (Statement of Notification) ☐
	3. Expiration of Patent(s):
	   a. Pediatric exclusivity submitted? Select
	   b. Expiration of Pediatric Exclusivity?
	4. Exclusivity Statement: State marketing intentions?	

1.4.1	**References**
	Letters of Authorization
	1. DMF letters of authorization
	
	   a. Type II DMF authorization letter(s) or synthesis for Active Pharmaceutical Ingredient
	
	   b. Type II DMF#
	
	   c. Type III DMF authorization letter(s) for container closure
	2. US Agent Letter of Authorization (U.S. Agent [if needed, countersignature on 356h])	

1.12.4	**Request for Comments and Advice** - Proprietary name requested If Yes, did the firm provide the request as a separate electronic amendment labeled "Proprietary Name Request" at initial time of filing 1. Yes 2. No - contact the firm to submit the request as a separate electronic amendment.	
1.12.11	**Basis for Submission** NDA#: Ref Listed Drug: Firm: **ANDA suitability petition required?** If Yes, provide petition number and copy of approved petition **ANDA Citizen's Petition Required?** If Yes, provide petition number and copy of petition	

MODULE 1: ADMINISTRATIVE (Continued)

		COMMENT (S)
1.12.12	**Comparison between Generic Drug and RLD-505(j)(2)(A)** 1. Conditions of use 2. Active ingredients 3. Inactive ingredients 4. Route of administration 5. Dosage Form 6. Strength	
1.12.14	**Environmental Impact Analysis Statement** (cite 21CFR 25.31, if applicable)	
1.12.15	**Request for Waiver** Request for Waiver of In-Vivo BA/BE Study(ies)	
1.14.1	**Draft Labeling** (Multi Copies N/A for E-Submissions) **1.14.1.1** 4 copies of draft for paper submission only (each strength and container) **1.14.1.2** 1 side by side labeling comparison of containers and carton with all differences visually highlighted and annotated **1.14.1.3** 1 package insert (content of labeling) and SPL submitted electronically	
1.14.3	**Listed Drug Labeling** **1.14.3.1** 1 side by side labeling (package and patient insert) comparison with all differences visually highlighted and annotated **1.14.3.3** RLD package insert, 1 RLD label and 1 RLD container label	

MODULE 2: SUMMARIES

		COMMENT (S)

2.3	**Quality Overall Summary (QOS)**
	E-Submission: PDF
	Word Processed e.g., MS Word
	
	A model Quality Overall Summary for an immediate release tablet and an extended release capsule can be found on the OGD webpage http://www.fda.gov/cder/ogd/
	
	Question based Review (QbR)
	
	2.3.S Drug Substance (Active Pharmaceutical Ingredient)
	  2.3.S.1 General Information
	  2.3.S.2 Manufacture
	  2.3.S.3 Characterization
	  2.3.S.4 Control of Drug Substance
	  2.3.S.5 Reference Standards or Materials
	  2.3.S.6 Container Closure System
	  2.3.S.7 Stability
	
	2.3.P Drug Product
	  2.3.P.1 Description and Composition of the Drug Product
	  2.3.P.2 Pharmaceutical Development
	      2.3.P.2.1 Components of the Drug Product
	          2.3.P.2.1.1 Drug Substance
	          2.3.P.2.1.2 Excipients
	      2.3.P.2.2 Drug Product
	      2.3.P.2.3 Manufacturing Process Development
	      2.3.P.2.4 Container Closure System
	  2.3.P.3 Manufacture
	  2.3.P.4 Control of Excipients
	  2.3.P.5 Control of Drug Product
	  2.3.P.6 Reference Standards or Materials
	  2.3.P.7 Container Closure System
	  2.3.P.8 Stability	

2.7	**Clinical Summary (Bioequivalence)**Model BE Data Summary Tables **E-Submission: PDF** **Word Processed: e.g., MS Word** **2.7.1 Summary of Biopharmaceutic Studies and Associated Analytical Methods** **2.7.1.1 Background and Overview** Table 1. Submission Summary Table 4. Bioanalytical Method Validation Table 6. Formulation Data **2.7.1.2 Summary of Results of Individual Studies** Table 5. Summary of In Vitro Dissolution **2.7.1.3 Comparison and Analyses of Results Across Studies** Table 2. Summary of Bioavailability (BA) Studies Table 3. Statistical Summary of the Comparative BA Data **2.7.1.4 Appendix** **2.7.4.1.3 Demographic and Other Characteristics of Study Population** Table 7. Demographic Profile of Subjects Completing the Bioequivalence Study **2.7.4.2.1.1 Common Adverse Events** Table 8. Incidence of Adverse Events in Individual Studies	

MODULE 3: 3.2.S DRUG SUBSTANCE

		COMMENT (S)
3.2.S.1	**General Information** (Do not refer to DMF) **3.2.S.1.1 Nomenclature** **3.2.S.1.2 Structure** **3.2.S.1.3 General Properties**	
3.2.S.2	**Manufacturer** **Drug Substance (Active Pharmaceutical Ingredient)** 1. Name and Full Address(es)of the Facility(ies) 2. Contact name, phone and fax numbers, email address 3. Specify Function or Responsibility 4. Type II DMF number for API 5. CFN or FEI numbers	
3.2.S.3	**Characterization** Provide the following in tabular format: 1. Name of Impurity(ies) 2. Structure of Impurity(ies) 3. Origin of Impurity(ies)	

3.2.S.4	**Control of Drug Substance (Active Pharmaceutical Ingredient)**
	3.2.S.4.1 Specification
	Testing specifications and data from drug substance manufacturer(s)
	3.2.S.4.2 Analytical Procedures
	3.2.S.4.3 Validation of Analytical Procedures
	(API that is USP or reference made to DMF, must provide verification of USP or DMF procedures)
	1. Spectra and chromatograms for reference standards and test samples
	2. Samples-Statement of Availability and Identification of:
	    a. Drug Substance
	    b. API lot number(s)
	3.2.S.4.4 Batch Analysis
	1. COA(s) specifications and test results from drug substance mfgr(s)
	2. Applicant certificate of analysis
	3.2.S.4.5 Justification of Specification	

3.2.S.5	**Reference Standards or Materials** (Do not refer to DMF)	
3.2.S.6	**Container Closure Systems**	
3.2.S.7	**Stability** 1. Retest date or expiration date of API	

MODULE 3: 3.2.P DRUG PRODUCT

		COMMENT (S)
3.2.P.1	**Description and Composition of the Drug Product** 1. Unit composition with indication of the function of the inactive ingredient(s) 2. Inactive ingredients and amounts are appropriate per IIG (per/dose justification) 3. Conversion from % to mg/dose values for inactive ingredients (if applicable) 4. Elemental iron: provide daily elemental iron calculation or statement of adherence to 21CFR73.1200 (calculation of elemental iron intake based on **maximum daily dose (MDD)** of the drug product is preferred if this section is applicable) 5. Injections: If the reference listed drug is packaged with a drug specific diluent then the diluent must be Q1/Q2 and must be provided in the package configuration	
3.2.P.2	**Pharmaceutical Development** Pharmaceutical Development Report	
3.2.P.3	**Manufacture** **3.2.P.3.1 Drug Product** (Finished Dosage Manufacturer and Outside Contract Testing Laboratories) 1. Name and Full Address(es)of the Facility(ies) 2. Contact name, phone and fax numbers, email address 3. Specify Function or Responsibility 4. CGMP Certification (from both applicant and drug product manufacturer if different entities) 5. CFN or FEI numbers **3.2.P.3.2 Batch Formula** **3.2.P.3.3 Description of Manufacturing Process and Process Controls** 1. Description of the Manufacturing Process 2. Master Production Batch Record(s) for largest intended production runs (no more than 10x pilot batch) with equipment specified 3. Master packaging records for intended marketing container(s) 4. If sterile product 5. Reprocessing Statement (cite 21CFR 211.115, submitted by the drug product manufacturer and the applicant, if different entities) **3.2.P.3.4 Controls of Critical Steps and Intermediates** **3.2.P.3.5 Process Validation and/or Evaluation** 1. Microbiological sterilization validation 2. Filter validation (if aseptic fill)	
3.2.P.4	**Controls of Excipients** (Inactive Ingredients) Source of inactive ingredients identified **3.2.P.4.1 Specifications** 1. Testing specifications (including identification and characterization) 2. Suppliers' COA (specifications and test results) **3.2.P.4.2 Analytical Procedures** **3.2.P.4.3 Validation of Analytical Procedures** **3.2.P.4.4 Justification of Specifications:** 1. Applicant COA	

MODULE 3: 3.2.P DRUG PRODUCT (Continued)

		COMMENT (S)

3.2.P.5	**Controls of Drug Product**
	3.2.P.5.1 Specification(s)
	3.2.P.5.2 Analytical Procedures
	3.2.P.5.3 Validation of Analytical Procedures
	(if using USP procedure, must provide verification of USP procedure)
	Samples - Statement of Availability and Identification of:
	    1. Finished Dosage Form
	    2. Lot number(s) and strength of Drug Product(s)
	3.2.P.5.4 Batch Analysis
	    Certificate of Analysis for Finished Dosage Form
	3.2.P.5.5 Characterization of Impurities
	3.2.P.5.6 Justification of Specifications	

3.2.P.7	**Container Closure System** 1. Summary of Container/Closure System (if new resin, provide data) 2. Components Specification and Test Data 3. Packaging Configuration and Sizes 4. Container/Closure Testing (water permeation, light transmission, extractables and leachables when applicable) 5. Source of supply and suppliers address	

3.2.P.8	**3.2.P.8.1 Stability (Finished Dosage Form)**
	1. Stability Protocol submitted
	2. Expiration Dating Period
	3.2.P.8.2 Post-approval Stability and Conclusion
	Post Approval Stability Protocol and Commitments
	3.2.P.8.3 Stability Data
	1. Accelerated stability data
	    a. four (4) time points 0,1,2,3
	          -OR-
	    b. three (3) time points 0,3,6 (if 3 time points for accelerated stability data are submitted then provide 3 exhibit batches along with 12 months of room temperature stability data –Refer to Guidance for Industry Q1A(R2) Stability Testing of New Drug Substances and Products November 2003, Section B)
	2. Batch numbers on stability records the same as the test batch	

MODULE 3: 3.2.R REGIONAL INFORMATION (Drug Substance)

		COMMENT (S)
3.2.R **Drug** **Substance**	**3.2.R.1.S Executed Batch Records for drug substance (if available)** **3.2.R.2.S Comparability Protocols** **3.2.R.3.S Methods Validation Package** Methods Validation Package (3 copies for paper and N/A for E-Submissions) (Required for Non-USP drugs)	

MODULE 3: 3.2.R REGIONAL INFORMATION (Drug Product)

		COMMENT (S)
3.2.R **Drug** **Product**	**3.2.R.1.P.1** **Executed Batch Records** Copy of Executed Batch Record with Equipment Specified, including Packaging Records (Packaging and Labeling Procedures) Batch Reconciliation and Label Reconciliation a. Theoretical Yield b. Actual Yield c. Packaged Yield **3.2.R.1.P.2 Information on Components** **3.2.R.2.P Comparability Protocols** **3.2.R.3.P Methods Validation Package** Methods Validation Package (3 copies for paper and N/A for E-Submissions) (Required for Non-USP drugs)	

MODULE 5: CLINICAL STUDY REPORTS

		COMMENT (S)
5.2	**Tabular Listing of Clinical Studies**	

5.3.1
(complete study data)
	Bioavailability/Bioequivalence
	1. Formulation data same?
	  a. Comparison of all Strengths
	    (check proportionality of multiple strengths)
	  b. Parenterals, Ophthalmics, Otics and Topicals
	    (21 CFR 314.94 (a)(9)(iii)-(v)
	2. Lot Numbers and strength of Products used in BE Study(ies)
	3. Study Type: IN-VIVO PK STUDY(IES)
	  (Continue with the appropriate study type box below)	

	5.3.1.2 Comparative BA/BE Study Reports 1. Study(ies) meets BE criteria (90% CI of 80-125, C max, AUC) 2. Summary Bioequivalence tables: Table 10. Study Information Table 12. Dropout Information Table 13. Protocol Deviations **5.3.1.3 In Vitro-In-Vivo Correlation Study Reports** 1. Summary Bioequivalence tables Table 11. Product Information Table 16. Composition of Meal Used in Fed Bioequivalence Study **5.3.1.4 Reports of Bioanalytical and Analytical Methods for Human Studies** 1. Summary Bioequivalence table: Table 9. Reanalysis of Study Samples Table 14. Summary of Standard Curve and QC Data for Bioequivalence Sample Analyses Table 15. SOPs Dealing with Bioanalytical Repeats of Study Samples **Case Report Forms** should be placed under the study to which they pertain, and appropriately tagged. Refer to The eCTD Backbone File Specification for Study Tagging //www.fda.gov/downloads/Drugs/DevelopmentApprovalProcess/FormsSubmissionRequirements/ElectronicSubmissions/UCM163560.pdf	
5.4	**Literature References**	
	Possible Study Types:	
Study Type	**IN-VIVO BE STUDY(IES) with PK ENDPOINTS** (i.e., fasting/fed/sprinkle) 1. Study(ies) meets BE criteria (90% CI of 80-125, C max, AUC) 2. EDR Email: Data Files Submitted 3. In-Vitro Dissolution	
Study Type	**IN-VIVO BE STUDY with CLINICAL ENDPOINTS** 1. Properly defined BE endpoints (eval. by Clinical Team) 2. Summary results meet BE criteria: 90% CI of the proportional difference in success rate between test and reference must be within (-0.20, +0.20) for a binary/dichotomous endpoint. For a continuous endpoint, the test/reference ratio of the mean result must be within (0.80,1.25) 3. Summary results indicate superiority of active treatments (test & reference) over vehicle/placebo (p<0.05) (eval. by Clinical Team) 4. EDR Email: Data Files Submitted	

Study Type	**IN-VITRO BE STUDY(IES)** (i.e., in vitro binding assays) 1. Study(ies) meets BE criteria (90% CI of 80-125) 2. EDR Email: Data Files Submitted 3. In-Vitro Dissolution	

Study Type	**NASALLY ADMINISTERED DRUG PRODUCTS**
	1. Solutions (Q1/Q2 sameness)
	  a. In-Vitro Studies (Dose/Spray Content Uniformity, Droplet/Drug Particle Size Distrib.,
	    Spray Pattern, Plume Geometry, Priming & Repriming)
	2. Suspensions (Q1/Q2 sameness):
	  a. In-Vivo PK Study
	    1. Study(ies) meets BE Criteria (90% CI of 80-125, C max, AUC)
	    2. EDR Email: Data Files Submitted
	  b. In-Vivo BE Study with Clinical End Points
	    1. Properly defined BE endpoints (eval. by Clinical Team)
	    2. Summary results meet BE criteria (90% CI within +/- 20% of 80-125)
	    3. Summary results indicate superiority of active treatments (test & reference)
	      over vehicle/placebo (p<0.05) (eval. by Clinical Team)
	    4. EDR Email: Data Files Submitted
	  c. In-Vitro Studies (Dose/Spray Content Uniformity, Droplet/Drug Particle Size Distrib.,
	    Spray Pattern, Plume Geometry, Priming & Repriming)	

Study Type	**IN-VIVO BE STUDY(IES) with PD ENDPOINTS** (e.g., topical corticosteroid vasoconstrictor studies) 1. Pilot Study (determination of ED50) 2. Pivotal Study (study meets BE criteria 90%CI of 80-125)	

Study Type	**TRANSDERMAL DELIVERY SYSTEMS**
	1. In-Vivo PK Study
	  a. Study(ies) meet BE Criteria (90% CI of 80-125, C max, AUC)
	  b. In-Vitro Dissolution
	  c. EDR Email: Data Files Submitted
	2. Adhesion Study
	3. Skin Irritation/Sensitization Study	

Updated 03/17/2011

Patents
and Exclusivity

By Kurt R. Karst, JD

Objectives

+ To gain an understanding of the various types of patent and non-patent market exclusivity available to sponsors of brand-name drugs and their effects on generic drug approval
+ To gain an understanding of 180-day marketing exclusivity available to certain generic drug sponsors

Laws, Regulations and Guidelines Covered in This Chapter

+ *Federal Food, Drug, and Cosmetic Act* of 1938
+ *Drug Price Competition and Patent Term Restoration Act* of 1984 (*Hatch-Waxman Act*)
+ *Food and Drug Administration Modernization Act* of 1997
+ *Orphan Drug Act* of 1983
+ *Uruguay Rounds Agreements Act* of 1994
+ 21 CFR 314 Applications for FDA approval to market a new drug
+ 21 CFR 320 Bioavailability and bioequivalence requirements
+ 21 CFR 316 Orphan Drugs
+ 54 *Federal Register* 28,872 (10 July 1989), Proposed ANDA Regulations
+ 59 *Federal Register* 50,338 (3 October 1994), ANDA regulations; patent and exclusivity provisions
+ 68 *Federal Register* 36,676 (18 June 2003), Applications for FDA approval to market a new drug: patent submission and listing requirements and application of 30-month stays on approval of Abbreviated New Drug Applications certifying that a patent claiming a drug is invalid or will not be infringed
+ *Guidance for Industry: Qualifying for Pediatric Exclusivity Under Section 505A of the Federal Food, Drug, and Cosmetic Act* (September 1999)
+ Manual of Policies and Procedures 5240.3, "Review Order of Original ANDAs, Amendments and Supplements" (October 2006)
+ *Draft Guidance for Industry: Applications Covered by Section 505(b)(2)* (October 1978)

Introduction

As discussed in Chapter 11, the *Drug Price Competition and Patent Term Restoration Act* of 1984 (*Hatch-Waxman Act*) amended the *Federal Food, Drug, and Cosmetic Act* of 1938 (*FD&C Act*) to create the contemporary Abbreviated New Drug Application (ANDA) generic drug approval process under Section 505(j). Under the *FD&C Act*'s ANDA statutory provisions and the US Food and Drug Administration's (FDA) implementing regulations, an application containing bioequivalence data to a Reference Listed Drug (RLD), among other data and information, is sufficient for FDA to consider approval. As part of the *Hatch-Waxman Act* compromise, brand-name drug companies may obtain a patent term extension for time lost during the regulatory review period, can submit to FDA for listing certain types of patents in the *Orange Book*, and may also be eligible for a period of non-patent exclusivity. Certain ANDA sponsors may be eligible for a period of 180-day marketing exclusivity for challenging patents listed in FDA's *Orange Book* for the RLD. Under the current law, an ANDA sponsor's eligibility for a period of 180-day marketing exclusivity can be forfeited under various scenarios.

In addition to the incentives created by the *Hatch-Waxman Act*, new or additional incentives have been created by the enactment of several other laws. These laws include the *Orphan Drug Act*, which rewards sponsors for developing products to treat rare diseases and conditions, and the *Best Pharmaceuticals for Children Act*, which rewards sponsors for developing products for children. Each of the types of non-patent exclusivities is discussed in this chapter.

Patent-Related Market Exclusivity
Patent Term Extensions

Under Title II of the *Hatch-Waxman Act*, certain patents related to products regulated by FDA are eligible for extension if patent life was lost during a period when the product was undergoing regulatory review.[1] The "regulatory review period" is composed of a "testing phase" and a "review phase." For a drug product, the testing phase begins on the effective date of an Investigational New Drug Application (IND) and ends on the date a New Drug Application (NDA) is submitted to FDA.[2] The review phase is the period between the submission and approval of the NDA.[3] A patent term may be extended for a period of time that is the sum of one-half of the time in the testing phase, plus all the time in the review phase.[4] The regulatory review period must be reduced by any time that the applicant "did not act with due diligence."[5] The total (calculated) regulatory review period may not exceed five years, and the extended patent term may not exceed 14 years after the date of approval of the marketing application.[6]

As applied to drugs, the patent term extension law provides that the term of a patent claiming the drug (or a use of the drug or a method of manufacturing a drug) shall be extended from the original expiration date of the patent if:

1. the term of the patent has not expired
2. the patent has not been previously extended
3. the extension application is submitted by the owner of record within 60 days of NDA approval
4. the product, use, or method of manufacturing claimed has been subject to a "regulatory review period" before it is commercially marketed
and
5. the NDA is the first permitted commercial use of the drug product[7]

Criterion 5 has been the most controversial. Until recently, the US Patent and Trademark Office (PTO) relied on decisions by the US Court of Appeals for the Federal Circuit in *Fisons v. Quigg*, 8 U.S.P.Q.2d 1491 (D.D.C.1988), *affirmed* 876 F.2d 99 U.S.P.Q.2d 1869 (Fed.Cir.1989), and *Pfizer Inc. v. Dr. Reddy's Labs.*, 359 F.3d 1361 (Fed. Cir. 2004) to support the office's interpretation of the term "product" in 35 U.S.C. §156(a)(5)(A) to mean

"active moiety" (i.e., the molecule in a drug product responsible for pharmacological action, regardless of whether the active moiety is formulated as a salt, ester or other non-covalent derivative) rather than "active ingredient" (i.e., the active ingredient physically found in the drug product, which would include any salt, ester or other non-covalent derivative of the active ingredient physically found in the drug product). In contrast, the Federal Circuit's 1990 decision in *Glaxo Operations UK Ltd. v. Quigg*, 894 F.2d 392, 13 USPQ2d 1628 (Fed. Cir. 1990), construed the term "product" in 35 U.S.C. §156(a)(5)(A) to mean "active ingredient." In 2010, the US Court of Appeals for the Federal Circuit ruled in *Photocure ASA v. Kappos*, 603 F.3d 1372, 1375 (Fed. Cir. 2010) that the term "product" in 35 U.S.C. §156(a)(5)(A) means "active ingredient" rather than "active moiety."

In some cases, a patent that is scheduled to expire before a term extension application can be submitted to the PTO (e.g., if the patent will expire before the NDA is approved) may be granted an interim patent extension.[8]

Two types of interim patent extensions are available:
1. interim patent extensions available during the review phase of the statutory regulatory review period[9]
2. interim patent extensions available during the PTO's review of an application for patent term extension[10]

The cumulative patent time granted under either type of interim patent extension cannot exceed the patent term extension that a company could obtain under regular patent extension provisions. The PTO reviews each application for an interim patent extension to ensure that a patent will not be extended longer than its eligibility under the law.

Orange Book Patent Listing

The *FD&C Act* and FDA regulations require each NDA sponsor to submit with its application "the patent number and the expiration date of any patent which claims the drug for which the applicant submitted the [NDA] or which claims a method of using[11] such drug and with respect to which a claim of patent infringement could reasonably be asserted if a person not licensed by the owner engaged in the manufacture, use, or sale of the drug."[12] FDA regulations clarify that "such patents consist of drug substance (active ingredient) patents, drug product (formulation and composition) patents, and method-of-use patents."[13] Thus, in order to list a patent in the *Orange Book*: the patent must claim the drug or a method of using the drug that is the subject of the NDA; and a claim of patent infringement could reasonably be asserted by the NDA holder or patent owner for the unauthorized manufacture, use or sale of the drug that is the subject of the NDA.[14] Once an NDA is approved, FDA is required to publish information in the *Orange Book* on the patents claiming the drug or a method of using it.[15] If a new patent meeting the requirements of *FD&C Act* Section

Table 12-1. 180-Day Exclusivity Forfeiture Snapshot

- **"Failure to Market":** A first applicant forfeits exclusivity if it fails to market the drug by the **later of** –
  - (1) The **earlier of** 75 days after ANDA **approval**, or 30 months after ANDA **submission**; and
  - (2) Either:
    - – 75 days after favorable court decision on all qualifying patents (**appeals** court, or unappealed district court, decision); or
    - – 75 days after favorable court settlement or consent decree on all qualifying patents; or
    - – 75 days after all qualifying patents are delisted from the Orange Book.

- **Immediate Forfeiture:**
  - – If the ANDA applicant withdraws the ANDA or the application is withdrawn because the applicant failed to meet approval requirements;
  - – If the ANDA applicant amends or withdraws its Paragraph IV certification;
  - – If the ANDA applicant fails to obtain tentative approval within 30 months after filing the application (unless the failure is caused by a review of or change in approval requirements imposed after the ANDA is filed or because of a related citizen petition);
  - – If the ANDA applicant enters into an agreement with another generic applicant, the NDA holder, or patent owner, and the Federal Trade Commission (FTC) files a complaint, and either the FTC or an appeals court rules that the agreement violates antitrust laws; or
  - – If all of the patents certified to in the generic applicant's Paragraph IV certification have expired.

505(b)(1) and FDA patent listing regulations is issued while an NDA is pending FDA review or has received NDA approval, the NDA sponsor must submit information on the patent to FDA within 30 days of issuance.[16]

An ANDA (or 505(b)(2) application) for a generic version of an innovator drug must contain one of four possible certifications "with respect to each patent which claims the [innovator] drug…or which claims a use for such listed drug…and for which information is required to be filed" by the NDA holder and that is listed in the *Orange Book*.[17] If there are patents on the drug and the ANDA applicant does not want to challenge them, the applicant submits a Paragraph III certification, and FDA cannot approve the application until the patents have expired.[18] If the patents have already expired, or if the required patent information has not been filed, the ANDA applicant submits a Paragraph II or Paragraph I certification, respectively, and FDA can approve the application.[19] If the ANDA applicant does want to challenge a patent listed in the *Orange Book*, the applicant submits a Paragraph IV certification claiming that the patent is "invalid or will not be infringed by the manufacture, use, or sale of the new drug for which the [ANDA] is submitted."[20]

As an alternative to these four certifications, if the listed drug is covered by an *Orange Book*-listed "method of use patent which does not claim a use for which the [ANDA] applicant is seeking approval," the application must contain "a statement that the method of use patent does not claim such a use."[21] This is often referred to as a "section viii statement" and permits a generic applicant to "carve out" a patent-protected use from its proposed labeling, provided the omission of such protected information does not "render the proposed drug product less safe or effective than the listed drug for all remaining, non-protected conditions

of use."[22]

An NDA holder or patent owner may choose to sue a generic applicant that submits a Paragraph IV certification. Under certain circumstances, a patent infringement suit may delay ANDA approval for 30 months (i.e., the so-called "30-month stay").[23] If a patent infringement suit is not brought by the NDA holder or patent owner, FDA can approve the ANDA.

Non-patent Statutory Market Exclusivity
Five-Year Exclusivity

Under the *FD&C Act* (as amended by Title I of the *Hatch-Waxman Act*), five-year exclusivity is available to the sponsor of an application (either a full 505(b)(1) NDA or a 505(b)(2) application) for a drug product that does not contain an active moiety previously approved under Section 505(b) of the *FD&C Act* (i.e., an NDA for a New Chemical Entity (NCE)). Five-year exclusivity prevents the submission of an ANDA (and a 505(b)(2) application) that "refers to the drug for which the [approved Section 505(b) NCE NDA] was submitted before the expiration of five years from the date of the approval" of the NCE NDA.[24] Thus, five-year exclusivity is sometimes called "NCE exclusivity." NCE exclusivity prevents the approval of a generic application for the approved active ingredient or any salt or ester of the approved active ingredient for five years. However, five-year exclusivity does not prevent FDA from approving, or a company from submitting, a full Section 505(b)(1) NDA for the same drug.[25]

The *FD&C Act* is ambiguous regarding the meaning of the term "drug" in Sections 505(c)(3)(E)(ii) and 505(j)(5)(F)(ii).[26] Neither provision addresses whether drug means the particular drug product that is the subject of the approved NCE NDA with five-year exclusivity or, more

Table 12-2. Differences Between Applications Submitted and Approved Under *FD&C Act* Section 505

	505(b)(1) NDA	505(b)(2) Application	ANDA
Description	An NDA is an application that contains full reports of investigations of safety and effectiveness (typically data from two adequate and well-controlled studies) that support the intended use of the product.	A 505(b)(2) application is an application submitted under *FD&C Act* Section 505(b)(1) for a drug for which the full reports of investigations of safety and effectiveness relied upon by the applicant for approval of the application were not conducted by or for the applicant, and for which the applicant has not obtained a right of reference or use from the person by or for whom the investigations were conducted.	An ANDA relies on FDA's previous finding that the RLD is safe and effective. ANDAs contain bioequivalence (BE) data to show that the generic product is the "same as" the RLD, and when there is a change permitted by an approved suitability petition (i.e., dosage form, strength, route of administration, change in an active ingredient in a combination drug), data to support that change.
Application Content			
Preclinical Data	X	X The need for preclinical data in addition to those data from studies not conducted by or for the applicant must be made on a case-by-case basis, and will vary depending upon the differences between the listed drug and the 505(b)(2) drug.	Safety and effectiveness presumed based on showing BE to the RLD.
Safety & Effectiveness Data	X	X The applicant must provide any additional clinical data necessary to demonstrate the safety and effectiveness of differences between the original drug and its drug.	Safety and effectiveness presumed based on showing BE to the RLD.
Chemistry, Manufacturing & Controls Data	X	X	X
Pharmacokinetic (PK), Bioavailability (BA), & BE Data	X PK and BA data.	X PK and comparative BA data.	X BE data.
Labeling	X	X Labeling different from listed drug to support approved changes (e.g., new indication); labeling must exclude information in listed drug labeling protected by patent and exclusivity.	X Labeling must be the same as the RLD, except that information protected by patent and exclusivity must be excluded.
Pediatric Use Information	X Data to support pediatric use, unless waived or deferred by FDA.	X Data to support change from listed drug, unless waived or deferred by FDA.	X Pediatric labeling must be the same as the RLD, except that information protected by patent and exclusivity must be excluded.

Patent & Exclusivity Information	X Submit information on patents claiming the drug or a method of use; exclusivity request claiming exclusivity.	X Submit information on patents claiming the drug or a method of use (if any); generally, a patent certification (Paragraph I, II, III or IV) or a "section viii" statement is required; exclusivity request claiming exclusivity and exclusivity statement that the listed drug is subject to exclusivity (if any exists).	X Patent certification (Paragraph I, II, III, or IV) or a "section viii" statement is required; exclusivity statement that the RLD is subject to exclusivity (if any exists).
Financial Disclosure & Debarment Certification	X	X	X
Market Exclusivity			
Five-Year Exclusivity	X Prevents the submission of an ANDA or 505(b)(2) application for five years after NDA approval, except that an ANDA or 505(b)(2) application with a Paragraph IV certification to an Orange Book-listed patent may be submitted after four years.	X Only for applications for NCEs; prevents the submission of an ANDA or another 505(b)(2) application for five years after application approval, except that an ANDA or other 505(b)(2) application with a Paragraph IV certification to an Orange Book-listed patent may be submitted after four years; also subject to NDA holder's exclusivity.	No exclusivity; subject to five-year exclusivity of NDA or 505(b)(2) applicant.
Three-Year Exclusivity	X Only if one or more of the clinical studies, other than BA/BE studies, was essential to the product's approval; prevents FDA from making effective an ANDA or 505(b)(2) application for the conditions of approval of the NDA.	X Only if one or more of the clinical studies, other than BA/BE studies, was essential to the product's approval; prevents FDA from making an ANDA or other 505(b)(2) application effective for the conditions of approval of the 505(b)(2) application; also subject to NDA holder's exclusivity.	Subject to three-year exclusivity of NDA or 505(b)(2) applicant.
Orphan Drug Exclusivity	X Prevents FDA from approving an application for the same drug for the same condition for seven years.	X Prevents FDA from approving an application for the same drug for the same condition for seven years; also subject to NDA holder's exclusivity.	Subject to seven-year exclusivity of NDA or 505(b)(2) applicant.
Pediatric Exclusivity	X Extends by six months all other types of patent and non-patent market exclusivity an NDA holder may have under the FD&C Act for a particular active moiety.	X Extends by six months all other types of patent and non-patent market exclusivity an applicant may have under the FDC Act for a particular active moiety; also subject to NDA holder's exclusivity.	Subject to exclusivity of NDA or 505(b)(2) applicant.
180-Day Exclusivity	Not applicable.	Not applicable.	X Available to any "first applicant" who files an ANDA with a Paragraph IV certification; prevents FDA from approving other ANDAs submitted by applicants who are not "first applicants."

Other			
Adverse Event Reporting Required	X	X	X
User Fees	X	X	Not applicable, but currently under consideration
Orange Book Listing	X Included in the Orange Book as a listed drug; may be identified as a RLD.	X Included in the Orange Book as a listed drug; can be identified as a therapeutic equivalent (e.g, "AB-rated") to the listed drug if BE is demonstrated and is also a pharmaceutical equivalent.	X Included in the Orange Book as a listed drug; can be identified as a therapeutic equivalent (e.g, "AB-rated") to RLD if BE is demonstrated and is also a pharmaceutical equivalent; listed in the Orange Book as a "pharmaceutical alternative" without a therapeutic equivalence evaluation code if approved under an approved suitability petition.

generally, the approved active moiety. FDA identified this ambiguity in the preamble to its proposed rule implementing the exclusivity provisions of the *Hatch-Waxman Act*:

> The language of sections 505(c)(3)[(E)] and 505(j) [(5)(F)][27] of the act is ambiguous as to which ANDAs or 505(b)(2) applications are affected by an innovator's exclusivity. The statutory language allows at least two interpretations. The narrower interpretation of the protection offered by exclusivity is that exclusivity covers only specific drug products and therefore protects from generic competition only the first approved version of a drug…The broader interpretation of the coverage of exclusivity is that it covers the active moieties in new chemical entities… FDA has concluded that the broader interpretation of the scope of exclusivity should be applied to all types of exclusivity conferred by sections 505(c)(3) [(E)] and 505(j)[(5)(F)] of the act. Therefore, when exclusivity attaches to an active moiety or to an innovative change in an already approved drug, the submission or effective date of approval of ANDAs and 505(b)(2) applications for a drug with that active moiety or innovative change will be delayed until the innovator's exclusivity has expired, whether or not FDA has approved subsequent versions of the drugs entitled to exclusivity, and regardless of the specific listed drug product to which the ANDA or 505(b) (2) application refers.[28]

This policy, known as FDA's Umbrella Policy, effectively replaces the term drug in the statutory text with the term "active moiety."[29]

Three-Year Exclusivity

Under the *FD&C Act* (as amended by Title I of the

Hatch-Waxman Act), a sponsor may qualify for a three-year period of exclusivity for an application (a full 505(b) (1) NDA, a 505(b)(2) application or a supplement to either) if the application is for an active moiety that FDA has previously approved and if the application contains "reports of new clinical investigations (other than bioavailability studies)," that were "essential to approval" of the application, and that were "conducted or sponsored by" the applicant.[30] All three of these criteria must be satisfied in order to qualify for three-year exclusivity.[31] Three-year exclusivity is often referred to as "new clinical investigation" or "new use" exclusivity.

Each criterion is defined in FDA's implementing regulations. A "new clinical investigation" is:

> an investigation in humans the results of which have not been relied on by FDA to demonstrate substantial evidence of effectiveness of a previously approved drug product for any indication or of safety for a new patient population and do not duplicate the results of another investigation that was relied on by the agency to demonstrate the effectiveness or safety in a new patient population of a previously approved drug product[32]

An investigation is "essential to approval" of an application if "there are no other data available that could support approval of the application."[33] FDA explained that if the agency was aware of "published reports of studies other than those conducted or sponsored by the applicant, or other information…sufficient for FDA to conclude that a proposed drug product or change to an already approved drug product is safe and effective," then exclusivity would not be appropriate.[34] The applicant must submit a list of all publicly available reports of clinical investigations "that are relevant to the conditions for which the applicant is seeking approval" and explain why these studies or reports do not provide a sufficient basis for approval.[35]

Finally, an investigation is "conducted or sponsored by the applicant" if:

> (B)efore or during the investigation, the applicant was named...as the sponsor of the [IND]...under which the investigation was conducted, or the applicant or the applicant's predecessor in interest, provided substantial support for the investigation. To demonstrate "substantial support," an applicant must either provide a certified statement from a certified public accountant that the applicant provided 50 percent or more of the cost of conducting the study or provide an explanation why FDA should consider the applicant to have conducted or sponsored the study if the applicant's financial contribution to the study is less than 50 percent or the applicant did not sponsor the investigational new drug. A predecessor in interest is an entity, e.g., a corporation, that the applicant has taken over, merged with, or purchased, or from which the applicant has purchased all rights to the drug. Purchase of nonexclusive rights to a clinical investigation after it is completed is not sufficient to satisfy this definition.[36]

Three-year exclusivity prevents FDA from approving[37] an ANDA or a 505(b)(2) application "that relies on the information supporting a change approved in the [NDA or NDA supplement]" until three years after the date FDA approved the application.[38] Although the general rule is that the labeling of a generic drug product approved under an ANDA must have the "same" labeling as the reference listed drug,[39] the sponsor can omit "an indication or other aspect of labeling protected by patent or accorded exclusivity under [505(j)(5)(F)] of the [FD&C Act]."[40] FDA can approve an ANDA with labeling "carve outs" if a particular use of the innovator drug is protected by a patent or period of exclusivity, and other uses are not protected. Before approving such a drug, FDA must first determine that the carve out of the protected information does not "render the proposed drug product less safe or effective than the listed drug for all remaining, non-protected conditions of use."[41]

Pediatric Exclusivity

The *Best Pharmaceuticals for Children Act* amended the *FD& C Act* to create Section 505A, which provides an additional six months of exclusivity to pharmaceutical manufacturers that conduct acceptable pediatric studies[42] of new and currently marketed drug products identified by FDA in a Pediatric Written Request (PWR) for which pediatric information would be beneficial. An initial grant of pediatric exclusivity extends all other types of *Orange Book*-listed patent[43] and non-patent market exclusivity (e.g., five-year NCE exclusivity, three-year new clinical investiga-

tion exclusivity and seven-year orphan drug exclusivity) an application holder may have under the *FD&C Act*.

An important aspect of an initial grant of pediatric exclusivity is that it provides additional market exclusivity not just for the pediatric indications or formulations, but for all protected indications and formulations of that sponsor's drug. Thus, an initial grant of pediatric exclusivity attaches to the patent and non-patent market exclusivities for any of the sponsor's approved drug products (including certain combination products) that contain the active moiety for which pediatric exclusivity was granted, and not to a specific drug product.[44]

While an initial period of pediatric exclusivity is broad, a second period of exclusivity is narrow. Specifically, a second period of pediatric exclusivity attaches only to any period of three-year new clinical investigation exclusivity granted by FDA with respect to a pediatric use supplement containing studies submitted in response to a second PWR issued by FDA.[45] A second period of pediatric exclusivity does not apply to any existing *Orange Book*-listed patent exclusivity or to any existing periods of five-year NCE exclusivity or orphan drug exclusivity. FDA's September 1999 guidance document further explains the scope of a second period of pediatric exclusivity:

> "Pediatric studies submitted in a supplemental application for a drug that has already received one period of pediatric exclusivity may qualify the drug to receive a different 6-month period of pediatric exclusivity if submitted in response to a [PWR]. The different 6-month period of pediatric exclusivity will attach only to any exclusivity period under sections 505(c)(3)(D)(iv) and 505(j)(5)(D)(iv) [(i.e., three-year exclusivity)] granted to the supplemental application for which the studies were completed."[46]

An important exception to the applicability of pediatric exclusivity was added to the law in 2007 relative to new PWRs. Under the exception, FDA will not apply a period of pediatric exclusivity to an unexpired period of patent or non-patent exclusivity if the agency's decision to grant pediatric exclusivity "is made later than 9 months prior to the expiration of such period."[47]

Orphan Drug Exclusivity

Under the *Orphan Drug Act* of 1983 (Pub. L. No. 97-414, 96 Stat. 2049 (1983)), as amended, a manufacturer or sponsor may submit a written request for FDA to designate a drug as a drug for a rare disease or condition (i.e., an "orphan drug"). A "rare disease or condition" is one that affects fewer than 200,000 people in the US, or affects more than 200,000 people but for which the sponsor can show that it will be unable to recover its development and marketing costs from sales of the product in the US.[48]

Once FDA approves a marketing application for a drug

designated as an orphan drug, the agency may not approve another company's version of the "same drug" for the same disease or condition for seven years, unless the subsequent drug is "different" from the approved orphan drug.[49] In addition, the *FD&C Act* and FDA's orphan drug regulations identify circumstances under which the agency can approve another version of the "same drug" for the same orphan disease or condition during the term of another sponsor's orphan drug exclusivity (e.g., failure to assure a sufficient quantity of the drug).[50]

A drug is "different" from an approved orphan drug if it is chemically or structurally distinct. The degree of chemical or structural similarity that allows FDA to determine whether two drugs are "the same" depends upon whether the drugs are small molecules or macromolecules.[51] However, even a drug that is structurally "the same" as an approved orphan drug may be approved for the same condition if it is "clinically superior" to the approved orphan drug. FDA's orphan drug regulations define a "clinically superior" drug as "a drug…shown to provide a significant therapeutic advantage over and above that provided by an approved orphan drug (that is otherwise the same drug)" in one of three ways:

1. greater effectiveness as assessed by effect on a clinically meaningful endpoint in adequate and well-controlled trials
2. greater safety in a substantial portion of the target populations
3. a demonstration that the drug makes a major contribution to patient care[52]

Paragraph IV Litigation and 180-Day Exclusivity

A generic applicant making a Paragraph IV certification must notify the NDA holder and patent owner that an application has been submitted to FDA once the agency determines that the ANDA is substantially complete. If the patent certification is in the ANDA, the applicant must give notice to the NDA holder and patent owner "not later than 20 days after the date of the postmark on the notice with which [FDA] informs the applicant that the application has been filed."[53] If the patent certification is in an amendment or supplement to the ANDA, the applicant must give notice to the NDA holder and patent owner "at the time at which the applicant submits the amendment or supplement, regardless of whether the applicant has already given notice with respect to another such certification contained in the application or in an amendment or supplement to the application."[54] The notice must include a "detailed statement of the factual and legal basis of the applicant's opinion that the patent is not valid or will not be infringed," and must "state that an application that contains data from bioavailability or bioequivalence studies has been submitted…for the drug

with respect to which the certification is made to obtain approval to engage in the commercial manufacture, use, or sale of the drug before the expiration of the patent referred to in the certification."[55]

The NDA holder or patent owner has 45 days from the date of receipt of such notice to file a suit for patent infringement.[56] If a patent infringement suit is brought by the NDA holder or the patent owner within the 45-day period, FDA cannot approve the ANDA until the earlier of:

- the expiration of a single 30-month stay of approval, which may be shortened or lengthened by the court if "either party to the action fail[s] to reasonably cooperate in expediting the action"[57]
- the date on which a district court enters judgment in favor of the defendant (i.e., the ANDA applicant) that the patent is invalid or not infringed (or on the date of a settlement order or consent decree signed and entered by the court stating that the patent that is the subject of the certification is invalid or not infringed)
- if the district court enters judgment in favor of the plaintiff (i.e., the NDA holder or patent owner) and that decision is appealed by the ANDA applicant, the date on which the court of appeals enters judgment in favor of the ANDA applicant that the patent is invalid or not infringed (or on the date of a settlement order or consent decree signed and entered by the court of appeals stating that the patent that is the subject of the certification is invalid or not infringed)

If the judgment of the district court is not appealed or is affirmed by the court of appeals, then ANDA approval can be made effective. An ANDA applicant may also assert a counterclaim "seeking an order requiring the [NDA] holder to correct or delete the patent information submitted by the [NDA] holder…on the grounds that the patent does not claim either the drug for which the application was approved or an approved method of using the drug."[58] An ANDA counterclaimant is not entitled to damages that result from inappropriate listing of patent information.[59]

If a patent infringement suit is not brought by the NDA holder or the patent owner within the 45-day period, FDA can approve the ANDA. In addition, an applicant whose ANDA contains a Paragraph IV certification may bring an action for declaratory judgment on patent infringement or invalidity if it is not sued within the 45-day period.[60] In order to file a declaratory judgment on non-infringement grounds, an ANDA applicant must provide an offer of confidential access to the ANDA to allow the NDA holder or patent owner the opportunity "of evaluating possible infringement of the patent that is the subject of the [Paragraph IV] certification."[61] An ANDA applicant is not entitled to damages even if it obtains a declaratory judgment in its favor.[62]

FD&C Act Section 505(j)(5)(B)(iv) establishes an incentive for generic manufacturers to submit Paragraph IV certifications and to challenge *Orange Book*-listed patents as invalid or not infringed by providing a 180-day period of market exclusivity.[63] This means that, in certain circumstances, an applicant that submits the ANDA containing the first Paragraph IV certification to an *Orange Book*-listed patent is protected from competition from other generic versions of the same drug product for 180 days.

Prior to the enactment of the *Medicare Prescription Drug, Improvement and Modernization Act* of 2003 (*MMA*), 180-day exclusivity was patent-based, such that a period of 180-day exclusivity could arise from each *Orange Book*-listed patent. Pre-*MMA*, 180-day exclusivity (which applies to a dwindling number of pending ANDAs) begins on the date FDA "receives notice from the applicant…of the first commercial marketing of the drug" under the first ANDA, or "the date of a decision of a court in [a patent infringement action] holding the patent which is the subject of the certification to be invalid or not infringed," whichever is earlier. Post-*MMA*, 180-day exclusivity is generally drug-based, such that there is a single 180-day exclusivity period (that can be shared by multiple first applicants) with respect to each listed drug. Also post-*MMA*, there is a single trigger to 180-day exclusivity—first commercial marketing.

Under changes made to the *FD&C Act* by the *MMA*, the first applicant that qualifies for 180-day exclusivity can forfeit exclusivity under various circumstances. While some of the statutory forfeiture provisions are straightforward—e.g., 180-day exclusivity is forfeited if the ANDA sponsor withdraws its exclusivity-qualifying Paragraph IV certification—others are more complex. In particular, the so-called "failure to market" forfeiture provisions under *FD&C Act* Section 505(j)(5)(D)(i)(I) require FDA to calculate a forfeiture date based upon the later of two events. Although FDA has not yet issued proposed regulations implementing the 180-day exclusivity forfeiture provisions added to the *FD&C Act* by the *MMA*, the agency has applied them on a case-by-case basis and has issued several letter decisions describing its interpretation of these provisions. Those letters are posted on FDA's website at www.fda.gov/Drugs/Development ApprovalProcess/HowDrugsareDevelopedandApproved/ ApprovalApplications/AbbreviatedNewDrugApplication ANDAGenerics/ucm142112.htm. Congress enacted the forfeiture provisions to "ensure that the 180-day exclusivity period enjoyed by the first generic to challenge a patent cannot be used as a bottleneck to prevent additional generic competition."[64]

Of the six 180-day exclusivity forfeiture provisions created by the *MMA*, the one provision that appears to have been the basis for the greatest number is *FD&C Act* Section 505(j)(5)(D)(i)(IV), which states that 180-day exclusivity eligibility is forfeited if:

The first applicant fails to obtain tentative approval of the application within 30 months after the date on which the application is filed, unless the failure is caused by a change in or a review of the requirements for approval of the application imposed after the date on which the application is filed.

The *Food and Drug Administration Amendments Act* of 2007 (*FDAAA*) clarified *FD&C Act* Section 505(j)(5)(D)(i)(IV), such that if "approval of the [ANDA] was delayed because of a [citizen] petition, the 30-month period under such subsection is deemed to be extended by a period of time equal to the period beginning on the date on which the Secretary received the petition and ending on the date of final agency action on the petition (inclusive of such beginning and ending dates) . . ."[65] The growing number of 180-day exclusivity forfeitures under *FD&C Act* Section 505(j)(5)(D)(i)(IV) is likely due, in part, to the increasing time it takes FDA's Office of Generic Drugs to review and act on ANDAs.

Exclusivity for Antibiotic Drugs

Until 1997, antibiotic drugs were approved under *FD&C Act* Section 507 and were not entitled to any *Hatch-Waxman* benefits.[66] In 1997, the *Food and Drug Administration Modernization Act* (*FDAMA*) (Pub. L. No. 105-115, 111 Stat. 2295 (1997)), among other things, repealed *FD&C Act* Section 507 and required all NDAs for antibiotic drugs to be submitted under *FD&C Act* Section 505.

FDAMA included a transition provision declaring that an antibiotic application approved under Section 507 before the enactment of *FDAMA* would be considered an application submitted, filed and approved under *FD&C Act* Section 505.[67] Congress created an exception to this transition provision. *FDAMA* Section 125(d)(2) exempted certain applications for antibiotic drugs from those provisions of *FD&C Act* Section 505 that provide patent listing, patent certification and market exclusivity. Specifically, *FDAMA* Section 125(d)(2) exempted an antibiotic application from *Hatch-Waxman* benefits when "the drug that is the subject of the application contains an antibiotic drug and the antibiotic drug was the subject of an application" received by FDA under *FD&C Act* Section 507 before the enactment of *FDAMA* (i.e., 21 November 1997). Thus, applications for antibiotic drugs received by FDA prior to 21 November 1997, and applications submitted to FDA subsequent to that date for drugs that contain an antibiotic drug that was the subject of an application received by FDA prior to 21 November 1997 are within the *FDAMA* Section 125(d)(2) exemption and not eligible for *Hatch-Waxman* benefits. These drugs are referred to as "old antibiotics." Applications for antibiotic drugs not subject to the *FDAMA* Section 125(d)(2) exemption (i.e., so-called "new antibiotics") are eligible for *Hatch-Waxman* benefits.

In October 2008, Congress effectively repealed *FDAMA* Section 125(d)(2) so that old antibiotic drugs are now eligible for some *Hatch-Waxman* benefits. Specifically, Section 4 of the *QI Program Supplemental Funding Act* of 2008 (*QI Act*)—"QI" stands for Qualifying Individual—amended the *FD&C Act* to add new Section 505(v) "Antibiotic Drugs Submitted Before November 21, 1997," to create certain *Hatch-Waxman* benefits for old antibiotics.

Exclusivity for Enantiomers of Previously Approved Racemates

FDA has for decades treated single enantiomers of approved racemates as previously approved active moieties not eligible for five-year NCE exclusivity (but eligible for three-year exclusivity).[68] (In chemistry, enantiomers are stereoisomers that are non-superimposable complete mirror images of one another. Enantiomers may be either "right-handed" or "left-handed." A racemic mixture is one that has equal amounts of "left- and right-handed" enantiomers of a particular chiral molecule.) *FDAAA*, however, amended the *FD&C Act* to add Section 505(u), which permits a 505(b)(1) NDA applicant for an enantiomer (that is contained in a previously approved racemic mixture) containing full reports of clinical investigations conducted or sponsored by the applicant to "elect to have the single enantiomer not be considered the same active ingredient as that contained in the approved racemic drug," and thus be eligible for five-year NCE exclusivity.[69] The enantiomer NDA applicant cannot "rely on any investigations that are part of an application submitted under [*FD&C Act* Section 505(b)] for approval of the approved racemic drug."[70]

There are certain limitations under the new *FD&C Act* §505(u). The enantiomer 505(b)(1) NDA must not be for a condition of use "(i) in a therapeutic category in which the approved racemic drug has been approved; or (ii) for which any other enantiomer of the racemic drug has been approved."[71] In addition, if the enantiomer NDA applicant elects to receive exclusivity, FDA may not approve the enantiomer drug for any condition of use in the "therapeutic category" in which the racemic drug is approved until 10 years after approving the enantiomer.[72] The term "therapeutic category" is defined in *FD&C Act* Section 505(u) to mean "a therapeutic category identified in the list developed by the United States Pharmacopeia pursuant to section 1860D-4(b)(3)(C)(ii) of the *Social Security Act* and as in effect on [27 September 2007]," which FDA must publish and that may be amended by regulation.[73] FDA has not yet published the therapeutic category list. *FD&C Act* Section 505(u) sunsets on 30 September 2012 unless reauthorized (presumably under *PDUFA V*).[74]

Summary

Brand-name drug sponsors may qualify for various types of periods of patent and non-patent exclusivities, which could delay the submission or final approval of a marketing application for a generic version of the brand-name drug. In addition, certain generic drug sponsors may also qualify for their own 180-day period of market exclusivity. Each type of exclusivity is different in scope and is subject to different rules and interpretations.

References

1. Before 8 June 1995, patents typically had 17 years of patent life from the date the patent was issued by the US Patent and Trademark Office (PTO). The *Uruguay Rounds Agreements Act* (*URAA*), Pub. L. No. 103-465, 108 Stat. 4809 (1994), changed the patent term in the US so that patents granted after 8 June 1995 (the effective date of the *URAA*) have a 20-year patent life from the date of the first filing of the patent application with PTO. Under a transition provision in the *URAA*, a patent in effect on 8 June 1995 was awarded a term of the greater of 20 years from the filing of the patent or 17 years from the date of patent issuance. See 35 U.S.C. § 154(c)(1).

2. 35 U.S.C. §156(g)(1)(B)(i).

3. 35 U.S.C. §156(g)(1)(B)(ii).

4. 35 U.S.C. §§156(c)(2) and 156(g)(1)(B).

5. 35 U.S.C. §156(c)(1).

6. 35 U.S.C. §§156(g)(6)(A) and 156(c)(3).

7. 35 U.S.C. §156(a)(1)-(5). The patent term extension law defines the term "drug product" to mean "the active ingredient of a new drug [as defined in §201(p) of the *FD&C Act*]…including any salt or ester of the active ingredient, as a single entity or in combination with another active ingredient." Id. §156(f)(2). With respect to the applicability of patent term extensions to combination drugs, the US Court of Appeals for the Federal Circuit ruled in 2004 that "the statute places a drug product with two active ingredients, A and B, in the same category as a drug product with a single ingredient…. To extend the term of a patent claiming a composition comprising A and B, either A or B must not have been previously marketed." *Arnold Partnership v. Dudas*, 362 F.3d 1338, 1341 (Fed. Cir. 2004).

8. 35 U.S.C. §§156(a)(1), 156 (d)(5) and 156 (e)(2).

9. 35 U.S.C. §156(d)(5).

10. 35 U.S.C. §156(e)(2).

11. Method-of-use patents listed in the *Orange Book* are typically assigned a "patent use code." The *Orange Book* contains hundreds of such use codes.

12. *FD&C Act* §505(b)(1).

13. FDA regulations at 21 CFR 314.53(b)(1) further state: For patents that claim the drug substance, the applicant shall submit information only on those patents that claim the drug substance that is the subject of the pending or approved application or that claim a drug

substance that is the same as the active ingredient that is the subject of the approved or pending application… For patents that claim a drug product, the applicant shall submit information only on those patents that claim a drug product, as is defined in [21 CFR 314.3 (i.e., a finished dosage form that contains a drug substance)], that is described in the pending or approved application. For patents that claim a method of use, the applicant shall submit information only on those patents that claim indications or other conditions of use that are described in the pending or approved application…. Process patents, patents claiming packaging, patents claiming metabolites, and patents claiming intermediates are not covered by this section, and information on these patents must not be submitted to FDA.

14. FDA, Final Rule; Applications for FDA Approval to Market a New Drug: Patent Submission and Listing Requirements and Application of 30-Month Stays on Approval of Abbreviated New Drug Applications Certifying That a Patent Claiming a Drug Is Invalid or Will Not Be Infringed, 68 *Fed. Reg.* 36,676 (18 June 2003).

15. *FD&C Act* Sections 505(b)(1) & 505(c)(2).

16. Ibid Section 505(c)(2); see also 21 CFR 314.53(c)(2)(ii).

17. *FD&C Act* Section 505(j)(2)(A)(vii).

18. Ibid Section 505(j)(2)(A)(vii)(III) and Section 505(j)(5)(B)(ii).

19. Ibid Sections 505(j)(2)(A)(vii)(I)-(II) & (j)(5)(B)(i).

20. Ibid Sections 505(j)(2)(A)(vii)(IV) & 505(j)(5)(B)(iii).

21. Ibid Section 505(j)(2)(A)(viii). For a listed drug covered by a period of five-year NCE exclusivity, generally an ANDA and 505(b)(2) applicant may not reference the listed drug until such exclusivity (described in the next sections) applicable to that listed drug has expired. For this reason, the information in the NDA for the listed drug is sometimes said to be under "data exclusivity."

22. 21 CFR 314.127(a)(7). An ANDA applicant must make an additional certification (or submit an additional "section viii statement") as to any new patent listed in the *Orange Book* while its application is pending if the NDA holder submits the new patent to FDA for *Orange Book* listing within 30 days of patent issuance. See 21 CFR 314.94(a)(12)(vi). A Paragraph IV certification to a later-listed patent will not result in an additional 30-month stay of ANDA approval.

23. *FD&C Act* Section 505(j)(5)(B).

24. Specifically, five-year exclusivity prevents the submission of an ANDA or 505(b)(2) application for five years unless the applicant submits a Paragraph IV patent certification. See *FD&C Act* Sections 505(b)(2)(A) and 505(j)(2)(A)(vii). In this case, the ANDA or 505(b)(2) application can be submitted after four

years; however, "if an action for patent infringement is commenced during the one-year period beginning [four years] after the date of the approval of the [NCE NDA], the thirty-month [stay] period…shall be extended by such amount of time which is required for seven and one-half years to have elapsed from the date of approval of the [NCE NDA]." *FD&C Act* Sections 505(c)(3)(E)(ii) & 505(j)(5)(F)(ii).

25. In addition, it is FDA's policy that five-year exclusivity is not granted for a combination drug containing a previously approved drug. Thus, an application for a two-drug combination containing two previously approved drugs, or even an NCE plus a previously approved drug, is not eligible for five-year exclusivity.

26. A similar ambiguity exists with regard to the scope of three-year exclusivity in Sections 505(c)(3)(E)(iii) and 505(j)(5)(F)(iii) of the *FD&C Act*

27. The original citations are to Sections 505(c)(3)(D) and 505(j)(4)(D) of the *FD&C Act*. These sections were recodified in the *MMA*.

28. 54 *Fed. Reg.* at 28,897.

29. FDA's regulations define the term "active moiety" to mean "the molecule or ion, excluding those appended portions of the molecule that cause the drug to be an ester, salt (including a salt with hydrogen or coordination bonds), or other noncovalent derivative (such as a complex, chelate or clathrate) of the molecule, responsible for the physiological or pharmacological action of the drug substance." 21 CFR 314.108(a).

30. 21 CFR 314.108(b)(4), (5); see also *FD&C Act* Sections 505(j)(5)(F)(iii) and (iv).

31. 21 CFR 314.50(j)(4).

32. 21 CFR 314.108(a).

33. Ibid.

34. FDA, Final Rule: ANDA Regulations Patent and Exclusivity Provisions, 59 *Fed. Reg.* at 50,338, 50,357 (3 October 1994).

35. 21 CFR 314.50(j)(4)(ii).

36. 59 *Fed. Reg.* at 50,368-69; see also 21 CFR 314.50(j)(4)(iii).

37. This is an important difference compared to five-year exclusivity, which prevents the submission of a generic application.

38. 21 CFR 314.108(b)(4), (5).

39. *FD&C Act* Section 505(j)(2)(A)(v).

40. 21 CFR 314.94(a)(8)(iv).

41. 21 CFR 314.127(a)(7).

42. The term "pediatric studies" is defined as "at least one clinical investigation (that, at [FDA's] discretion, may include pharmacokinetic studies) in pediatric age groups (including neonates in appropriate cases) in which a drug is anticipated to be used." *FD&C Act* Section 505A(a).

43. *FD&C Act* Section 505A does not extend the term

of the patent itself, but only the period during which FDA cannot approve (or accept for review) an ANDA or 505(b)(2) application that includes a Paragraph II or Paragraph III certification, or a Paragraph IV certification that concerns a patent that a court has determined is valid and would be infringed. *See FD&C Act* Section 505A(c)(2).

44. See *National Pharmaceutical Alliance v. Henney*, 47 F. Supp. 2d 37 (D.D.C. 1999); and *Guidance for Industry: Qualifying for Pediatric Exclusivity Under Section 505A of the Food, Drug, and Cosmetic Act* (September 1999).

45. *FD&C Act* Section 505A(g).

46. *Guidance for Industry: Qualifying for Pediatric Exclusivity Under Section 505A of the Food, Drug, and Cosmetic Act*, at 14.

47. *FD&C Act* Sections 505A(b)(2), 505A(c)(2).

48. *FD&C Act* Section 526(a)(2).

49. Orphan drug exclusivity operates independently of patent protection and independently of five- and three-year exclusivity (and therefore, pediatric exclusivity as well).

50. *FD&C Act* Sections 527(b)(1) and (2); see also 21 CFR 316.31(a).

51. 21 CFR 316.3(13).

52. 21 CFR 316.3(b)(3)(i)-(iii).

53. *FD&C Act* Section 505(j)(2)(B)(ii)(I).

54. *FD&C Act* Section 505(j)(2)(B)(ii)(II).

55. *FD&C Act* Sections 505(j)(2)(B)(iv)(I)–(II).

56. *FD&C Act* Section 505(j)(5)(B)(iii).

57. *FD&C Act* Section 505(j)(5)(B)(iii).

58. *FD&C Act* Section 505(j)(5)(C)(ii).

59. *FD&C Act* Section 505(j)(5)(C)(iii).

60. *FD&C Act* Section 505(j)(5)(C)(i).

61. Ibid.

62. *FD&C Act* Section 505(j)(5)(C)(iii).

63. A 505(b)(2) application is not eligible for 180-day exclusivity.

64. 149 Cong. Rec. S15746 (daily ed. Nov. 24, 2003) (statement of Sen. Schumer).

65. *FD&C Act* Section 505(q)(1)(G)

66. *Glaxo, Inc. v. Heckler*, 623 F. Supp. 69 (E.D.N.C. 1985).

67. *FDAMA* Section125(d)(1).

68. See 54 *Fed. Reg.* at 28,898. "FDA will consider whether a drug contains a previously approved active moiety on a case-by-case basis. FDA notes that a single enantiomer of a previously approved racemate contains a previously approved active moiety and is therefore not considered a new chemical entity."

69. *FD&C Act* Section 505(u)(1).

70. *FD&C Act* Section 505(u)(1)(A)(ii)(II).

71. *FD&C Act* Section 505(u)(1)(B).

72. *FD&C Act* Section 505(u)(2)(A).

73. *FD&C Act* Section 505(u)(3).

74. *FD&C Act* Section 505(u)(4).

Helpful References and Resources

FDA's Office of Generic Drugs webpage, including exclusivity decisions www.fda.gov/Drugs/DevelopmentApprovalProcess/HowDrugsareDevelopedandApproved/ApprovalApplications/AbbreviatedNewDrugApplicationANDAGenerics/ucm142112.htm. Accessed 13 May 2011.

Federal Food, Drug, and Cosmetic Act www.fda.gov/RegulatoryInformation/Legislation/default.htm. Accessed 13 May 2011.

The Electronic *Orange Book* www.accessdata.fda.gov/scripts/cder/ob/default.cfm. Accessed 13 May 2011.

FDA's Paragraph IV Patent Certification List www.fda.gov/Drugs/DevelopmentApprovalProcess/HowDrugsareDevelopedandApproved/ApprovalApplications/AbbreviatedNewDrugApplicationANDAGenerics/ucm047676.htm. Accessed 13 May 2011.

Over-the-Counter Drug Products

Updated by Alice J. Welenc-Masters, MS and David J. Schifkovitz

Objectives

- Provide an overview of the criteria for marketing over-the-counter (OTC) drugs
- Discuss the drug product classification and regulations surrounding OTC drugs
- Discuss the regulatory pathways available for marketing OTC drugs
- Provide an overview of OTC drug advertising and compliance regulations

Laws, Regulations and Guidelines Covered in this Chapter

- *Federal Food, Drug, and Cosmetic Act* of 1938
- *Durham-Humphrey Amendment* of 1951
- *Fair Packaging and Labeling Act* of 1966
- *Kefauver-Harris Amendments* of 1962
- *Federal Anti-Tampering Act* of 1983
- *Poison Prevention Packaging Act* of 1970
- *Dietary Supplement and Nonprescription Drug Consumer Protection Act* of 2006
- OTC Drug Review and monograph system (21 CFR 328-358)
- OTC Drug Product Labeling Format and Content Requirements (21 CFR 201.66)
- *Guidance for Industry: Labeling OTC Human Drug Products—Questions and Answers* (December 2008)
- *Guidance for Industry: Postmarketing Adverse Event Reporting for Nonprescription Human Drug Products Marketed Without an Approved Application* (July 2009)
- *Draft Guidance for Industry: Time and Extent Applications* (February 2004)
- *Guidance for Industry: Label Comprehension Studies for Nonprescription Drug Products* (August 2010)
- *Guidance for Industry: Contents of a Complete Submission for the Evaluation of Proprietary Names* (February 2010)

Introduction

Over-the-counter (OTC) drugs play a very important role in the daily lives of every person in the US and can be viewed as a cornerstone in the foundation of our healthcare system. Prior to 1951, there was no legal basis for the designation of what was acceptable as an OTC drug product. *The Durham-Humphrey Amendment* to the *FD&C Act* (1951) established three criteria that would limit a drug to prescription status:

- habit forming drugs
- not safe for use unless supervised by a healthcare professional

- limited to prescription use under a New Drug Application (NDA)

All drugs that did not meet these criteria were, by default, OTC.

Typically, OTC drugs have the following characteristics:

- benefits clearly outweigh possible risks
- potential for misuse and abuse is low
- public can use them for self-diagnosed conditions
- can be labeled to help assure appropriate use by the average person
- healthcare practitioners are not needed for their

Table 13-1. NDA vs. OTC Drug Monograph

NDA Route	OTC Monograph route
Premarket approval	No premarket approval (conditions of marketing are codified) • The onus is on the manufacturer/distributor to assure compliance
Confidential filing	Public process
Drug product-specific	Active ingredient-specific • OTC drug therapeutic category
May require a user fee	No user fees
Potential for marketing exclusivity	No marketing exclusivity
Mandated FDA review timelines	No mandated FDA review timelines
May require clinical studies for application • Safety and efficacy • Label comprehension • Actual use • Demonstration of appropriate consumer selection/deselection in OTC setting	Clinical studies for claims support or to amend monograph only

safe and effective use

Regulation of OTC Drugs

In general, regulations applicable to prescription drugs also apply to OTC drug products. Regulations relating to all aspects of drug manufacture and testing (current Good Manufacturing Practices (CGMPs)), facility listing and inspection, drug registration, clinical trials and safety oversight apply equally to prescription and OTC drug products. However, there are important OTC-specific regulations on labeling (Title 21 of the Code of Federal Regulations (CFR) Part 201 *Subpart C Labeling Requirements for Over-the-Counter Drugs)*, on general and administrative procedures for the classification of OTC drugs (21 CFR 330) and on therapeutic categories and related ingredients that have been classified as safe and effective for OTC use under the OTC drug monograph system (21 CFR 331–358).

In addition to the OTC monograph system noted above, OTC drug products are approved for marketing via one of the three NDA routes:

- 505(b)(1)New Drug Application (NDA)
- 505(b)(2) New Drug Application (NDA)
- (505)(j) Abbreviated New Drug Application (ANDA)

A 505(b)(1) application contains full safety and efficacy trial reports. The trials included in this application are conducted either by or for the applicant, or rights have been obtained by the applicant to reference the data. A 505(b)(2) application relies on safety and efficacy data submitted from trials that the applicant did not conduct and did not obtain a right to reference. Essentially, this type of application relies on safety and efficacy data in either the published literature or from data that resulted in an approved NDA previously submitted by another applicant. A (505)(j)

application, commonly referred to as ANDA, is used to gain approval of a generic product.

Table 13-1 summarizes significant differences between the NDA/ANDA and OTC drug monograph pathways to market a product.

OTC Drug Monograph Route

OTC drug monographs are referred to as 'recipe books' covering generally recognized as safe and effective (GRASE) active ingredients (strength and dosage form) and label requirements (indications, warnings and directions for use). In 1972, FDA initiated the OTC Drug Review process as part of the implementation of the *Kefauver-Harris Amendments* of 1962. The OTC Drug Review process encompassed review of the safety and efficacy of those products already on the market. FDA grouped the products into therapeutic drug categories and evaluated the active ingredients rather than assessing each individual product. This enormous undertaking is illustrated in **Table 13-2**. More than 80 therapeutic categories are covered in a process comprised of Advisory Panel expert review and a three-step public rulemaking process (call for information, proposed rules and a codified final rule) published in the *Federal Register*.

The review process commenced with the creation of therapeutic category-specific Advisory Panels composed of subject matter experts. A call for information was published in the *Federal Register* for the public (i.e., industry, healthcare professionals and consumers) to submit data within a defined time period. Advisory Panels held open meetings and reviewed the data to provide expert recommendations, including categorizing active ingredients into one of three categories:

- Category I—generally recognized as safe and effective and not misbranded
- Category II—not generally recognized as safe and

Table 13-2. OTC Monograph Therapeutic Category Subtopics Evaluated* as Part of the OTC Review Process (Therapeutic category subtopics in **BOLD** are codified in the Final Monographs)

Acne	Colloidal Silver	**Nasal Decongestant**
Allergy	**Callus Remover**	**Nighttime Sleep Aid**
Analgesic, External	**Corn Remover**	**Ophthalmic**
Analgesic, Internal	**Dandruff**	Oral Health Care
Anorectal	Daytime Sedative	Oral Would Healing
Antacid	**Decongestant, Nasal**	**Otic**
Anthelmintic	**Dental Care**	Overindulgence, Food & Drink
Antibiotic, First Aid	**Deodorant, Internal**	Pancreatic Insufficiency
Anticaries	**Diaper Rash**	**Pediculicide**
Anticholinergic	Digestive Aid	**Poison Oak/ivy**
Antidiarrheal	Drink Overindulgence	Poison Treatment
Antiemetic	Exocrine Pancreatic Insufficiency	Prostatic Hypertrophy
Antiflatulent	**Expectorant**	**Psoriasis**
Antifungal	**External Analgesic**	**Seborrheic Dermatitis**
Antihistamine	Fever Blister	Sedative, Daytime
Antimalarial	**First Aid Antibiotic**	Skin Bleaching
Antimicrobial	Food Overindulgence	**Skin Protectant**
Antiperspirant	Hair Growth & Loss	**Sleep Aid, Nighttime**
Antipyretic	Hypophosphatemia/ Hyperphosphatemia	Smoking Deterrent
Antirheumatic	**Ingrown Toenail**	**Stimulant**
Antitussive	Insect Bite & Sting	Stomach Acidifier
Aphrodisiac	Insect Repellent, Oral	**Sunscreen**
Astringent	**Internal Analgesic**	Thumbsucking
Benign Prostatic Hypertrophy	**Internal Deodorant**	**Topical Analgesic**
Boil Treatment	Laxative	Vaginal Contraceptive
Bronchodilator	Leg Muscle Cramps	Vaginal Drug Products
Camphorated Oil	**Male Genital Desensitizers**	Vitamins & Minerals
Cholecystokinetic	Menstrual	**Wart Remover**
Cold & Cough	Nailbiting	Weight Control

*Therapeutic category subtopic active ingredients have been implemented as part of therapeutic category Final Monograph, are part of a proposed rule or have been designated by FDA as not GRASE and/or misbranded

effective or is misbranded

- Category III—insufficient data available to permit classification (This category allows a manufacturer an opportunity to show that the ingredients in a product are effective, and if they are not, to reformulate or appropriately relabel the product.)

Advisory Panel recommendations are published as an Advance Notice of Proposed Rulemaking (ANPR) for public review and comment within a defined time period. After collection of public comments, FDA published its conclusions in the form of Tentative Final Monograph (TFM) (Proposed Rule). The TFM is also published for public review and comment. FDA reviewed any additional information submitted prior to publishing a final monograph (FM) (Final

Rule). Once the FM is published, manufacturers of products not complying with FM requirements have a defined time-frame to either withdraw the product from the market, bring the product into compliance with the monograph or submit an NDA. FMs are codified in the CFR. Products complying with monographs can be marketed without preapproval by FDA, provided they are appropriately drug listed, compliant with CGMPs and manufactured in a registered facility.

The monograph process can be very lengthy as there are no defined timelines within which FDA must move from a TFM to an FM. Hence, there are still a number of monographs that have not been finalized. For example, the monograph for oral healthcare drug products is not final, even though the original Advisory Panel provided its expert opinion in 1979. Products meeting the conditions of in-process TFMs can be marketed. FDA can amend FMs as new information becomes available. For example, the *OTC Internal Analgesic Drug Products* monograph (21 CFR 343) was amended in 2009 to include an organ-specific warning statement for acetaminophen and NSAIDs. Two regulatory pathways are available for industry to request that an OTC drug monograph be reopened and/or amended:

1. Citizen Petition
2. Time and Extent Application (TEA)

The Citizen Petition process is codified in 21 CFR 10.30. A Citizen Petition can be used to amend an OTC drug monograph at any stage of the process.

The Time and Extent Application process is codified in 21 CFR 330.14. This process can be used to add an ingredient to an OTC monograph that has been approved under an NDA or has been marketed in another country. This process can only be utilized when the ingredient has been used for a significant time (five or more continuous years in the same country) with a significant marketing distribution (tens of millions of dosage units sold).

NDA Route

Products not covered by the OTC drug monographs are subject to FDA preapproval through the NDA process prior to marketing. There are four NDA routes available for OTC products:

- direct to OTC NDA
- Rx-to-OTC Switch
- NDA Monograph Deviation
- generic (ANDA)

All intended NDAs for OTC products follow the prescription product requirement regarding proprietary names and must be submitted to the Division of Medication Error Prevention and Analysis (DMEPA) for review and approval. Ideally, a primary and an alternate proposed proprietary name should be provided, together with justification and any supporting data the sponsor has generated.

Direct to OTC NDA

Products never available in prescription form can be approved for use in the OTC setting. The same requirements apply for direct to OTC NDA products as for new prescription drug products with the exception that the applicant also needs to prove that the product can be safely used by the wide consumer population without healthcare professional oversight. Colgate Total toothpaste (active ingredients: Sodium Fluoride and Triclosan) and Abreva (active ingredient: docosanol) are examples of direct to OTC NDAs.

Rx-to-OTC Switch

This route is used when it can be demonstrated that a prescription product can be used by the wide consumer population without healthcare professional oversight. FDA evaluates the toxicity and safe consumer use of the product as well as whether the condition can be self-diagnosed and recognized without a healthcare professional's intervention. This route has gained popularity because it can be timed to coincide with patent expiry, allowing an innovator company to market a product for a longer period of time without generic competition and to a wider consumer base. One of the challenges in the switch process is transcribing information from the prescription drug product label to the very limited space of the 'Drug Facts' OTC label format in a manner that consumers comprehend and apply. Some examples of products that were switched are Prilosec OTC (proton pump inhibitor for frequent heartburn), Nicorette (smoking cessation aid), Zyrtec (antihistamine) and Plan B (emergency contraceptive). Several attempts to switch cholesterol-lowering medication to date have failed to meet FDA's criteria for appropriate self-selection.

An Rx-to-OTC switch that creates a new OTC product category is referred to as a first-in-class switch. First-in-class switches are often subject to FDA Advisory Panel review (composed of applicable prescription drug Advisory Committee members and members of the Nonprescription Drug Advisory Committee). Examples of first-in-class switches are Prilosec OTC, Alli (weight loss aid) and Claritin (a non-sedating antihistamine). Rx-to-OTC switches also can be partial or complete. For a complete switch (e.g., Claritin, Nicorette), the full product range and indications are switched. For partial switch, either some product strengths or indications remain prescription (e.g., Prilosec OTC).

To address rules for a partial switch, an ANPR was published in the *Federal Register* in 2005 to elicit comments on whether clarification was necessary in circumstances when an active substance can be marketed simultaneously as OTC and prescription. While the rulemaking process for this issue is not finalized, FDA indicated that it will not allow the same active substance to be marketed in a certain population in prescription status and as an OTC for a subset of that population.

NDA Monograph Deviation

This route can be used when the drug product deviates in any aspect from the OTC drug monograph. The applicant submits an NDA referencing the monograph with data to support safety and efficacy of the drug product with the deviation. This route was utilized to gain approval for a head lice aerosol foam product, Rid Mousse. This drug product met all the conditions of the Pediculicide Final Monograph except for the dosage form.

Generic (ANDA)

The ANDA (505)(j) route can be used when the company intends to market an equivalent OTC drug

Figure 13-1. Example of an OTC Drug Facts Label

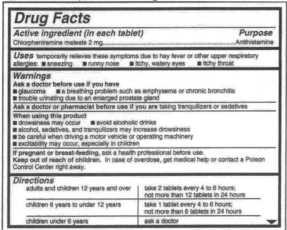

product to one that is already on the market. The same regulations apply here as in prescription products, however the company must submit bioequivalence data in lieu of the safety and efficacy studies. In addition, the product labeling must be the same as for the original product.

Studies Specific to OTC NDA Products

In addition to the safety, efficacy and preclinical studies that might be applicable to OTC NDA products, three other types of studies apply specifically to these products:

- label comprehension
- self-selection
- actual use or OTC simulation trials

Label comprehension studies are used to evaluate the extent to which a consumer can understand the information on the proposed OTC drug label and then apply this information when making drug product use decisions in a hypothetical situation. Label comprehension studies are open label and uncontrolled. No drug product is used in these studies and they do not have to be conducted under an IND; however, it is recommended that they be submitted under an IND to obtain CDER advice on the protocol. FDA issued a guidance document on design aspects of label comprehension testing in August 2010. The guidance describes test standards, hurdle rates and test population literacy demographics.

Identification of a suitable label may take several iterations and should achieve a satisfactory level of comprehension prior to running self-selection and actual use trials (AUT).

Self-selection studies are used to evaluate whether a consumer can make a correct decision about using or not

using a drug product based on reading the information on the drug product label and applying knowledge of his or her personal medical history. Drug product is not used in these studies, although a self-selection measure can be incorporated into the design of AUT.

AUT are used to evaluate consumer behavior—whether a consumer will actually use the product safely without healthcare practitioner supervision and as per the label instructions. These trials are typically designed as "all comers" studies, to measure consumer behavior against the product usage intent described in the product labeling and are conducted under an IND. The product label tested in AUT should have been evaluated previously in the label comprehension study.

OTC "Drug Facts" Label

The information on the label of the OTC drug product is of paramount importance. The label must be able to guide the consumer regarding product selection and use without the need for consultation with a healthcare professional. The Final Rule on the use of "Drug Facts" became effective in 1999. The rule standardized the format, content, headings, graphics and minimum type size requirements to be used on all OTC drug products. An example of a "Drug Facts" label is provided in **Figure 13-1**. All OTC drug products must bear the "Drug Facts" label in accordance with 21 CFR 201.66 and it must be visible to consumers at the time of purchase. All OTC drugs are required to have a clear, simple and readable label that communicates in a very limited space two critical aspects to consumers:

- whether the product is the right product to use to treat their condition
- how to take the product correctly and when to see a healthcare professional

FDA regulations require OTC labeling to be written and tested for use by ordinary people, including those with low comprehension skills, to ensure product information is easy to find and understand including:

- the product's intended uses and results
- active and inactive ingredients
- adequate directions for proper use
- warnings against unsafe use, side effects and adverse reactions

Some OTC drug monographs also provide professional labeling information that includes specific information for healthcare professionals on uses outside the scope of that permitted by OTC consumer drug labeling.

Packaging Requirements

Most OTC drug products must be packaged in tamper-evident packaging as required by 21 CFR 211.132. Statements must be included on both outer and inner cartons that clearly describe the tamper-evident features utilized. In addition, OTC drugs must comply with child-resistant packaging requirements as defined in the *Poison Prevention Packaging Act* of 1970 *(PPPA)*. The US Consumer Product Safety Commission (CPSC) enforces child-resistant packaging requirements. There is a provision in place for one container size to be marketed in non-child-resistant packaging as long as it is adequately labeled and as long as child-resistant packages are also supplied.

FDA Oversight of OTC Drug Products

The Office of Drug Evaluation IV (ODE-IV) has two divisions that have oversight responsibility for OTC drugs. The Division of Nonprescription Clinical Evaluation (DNCE) is responsible for managing INDs and the associated NDAs for those products that are approved under the NDA route. The Division of Nonprescription Regulation Development is responsible for the OTC drug monograph process and the products marketed under the respective monograph.

OTC and prescription drugs generally adhere to the same regulatory requirements. All OTC drug manufacturing activities must comply with 21 CFR 210 and 211, current Good Manufacturing Practices for pharmaceuticals. Drug substance and drug product manufacturing sites are required to be registered with FDA and are subject to prior approval inspections (PAI) for NDA products and routine FDA inspections. All OTC drug products are required to be drug listed, although the National Drug Code (NDC) is suggested but not required to be displayed on the product label. Medical oversight activities for OTC drug products also mimic those required of prescription products. The *Dietary Supplement and Nonprescription Drug Consumer Protection Act* of 2006 mandated safety reporting requirements for OTC drug products marketed without an NDA. Prior to this act, only NDA products were subject to adverse event reporting requirements.

NDA lifecycle management and maintenance activities are identical to those of their prescription counterparts.

Challenges in Assigning a Product Class

Products are classified as drugs based on their intended use as defined by the *FD&C Act*. Intended use can be determined through the product indications/claims, consumer perception or drug ingredients. Because product positioning can define product classification, some cosmetics can be considered unapproved drugs. This is why some cosmetics making drug claims either on the product labeling or through advertising and promotion have been subject to regulatory actions by FDA. Some OTC drug products that make cosmetic-like claims (cleaning)—such as toothpastes—are considered drugs based on the presence of the anti-caries drug ingredient fluoride. In fact, many OTC products meet the definition within the *FD&C Act* of both a cosmetic and a drug because they have two intended uses.

Examples of such products include antidandruff shampoo, deodorants that contain antiperspirant actives, and moisturizers and makeup marketed with sun-protection ingredients. These products must comply with requirements for both cosmetics and drugs. One such requirement for drugs that are also cosmetics is to list inactive ingredients in descending order of predominance as required by the cosmetic regulations, rather than in alphabetical order as required by drug regulations.

Advertising

The Federal Trade Commission (FTC) regulates OTC drug advertising. Since 1971, there has been a Memorandum of Understanding between the FDA and FTC that gives primary responsibility over advertising of OTC drugs to FTC and primary responsibility over OTC drug labeling to FDA. Unlike prescription products, there is no fair balance requirement for OTC drugs, and promotional material is not required to be submitted to FTC prior to distribution. FTC has a number of policy guides on advertising. The National Advertising Division (NAD) of the Council of Better Business Bureaus also oversees advertising either by directly challenging the advertising or resolving the advertising challenge submitted by a competitor.

In addition, the Consumer Healthcare Product Association (CHPA), a not-for-profit trade association that represents the OTC drug industry, has an advertising code of practice.

The regulatory professional should ensure that the advertising standards, including quality claim support data, are available prior to the initiation of advertising.

Summary

Overall, OTC drugs are governed by the same regulatory requirements as those for prescription products. However, unlike prescription products, they must be proven to be safe and effective without healthcare professional supervision. Hence, the information on the label of the OTC drug product is critical. A number of regulatory pathways are available to market OTC drug products in the US. The role of the regulatory professional in creating a strategy for product innovation and product differentiation through claims and/or promotion/advertising, while ensuring compliance with the applicable rules and regulations, is essential in the dynamic and challenging arena of OTC drugs.

References

1. Bureau of Consumer Protection, Health Claims. FTC website. http://business.ftc.gov/advertising-and-marketing/health-claims. Accessed 13 May 2011. Advertising FAQs: A Guide for Small Businesses. http://business.ftc.gov/documents/bus35-advertising-faqs-guide-small-business. Accessed 13 May 2011.

2. CHPA homepage. www.chpa-info.org/ scienceregulatory/science_regulatory.aspx. Accessed 13 May 2011.

3. Is It a Cosmetic, a Drug, or Both? (Or Is It Soap?). FDAwebsite. www.fda.gov/Cosmetics/ GuidanceComplianceRegulatoryInformation/ ucm074201.htm. Accessed 13 May 2011.

4. Drug Applications for Over-the-Counter Drugs. FDA website. www.fda.gov/ Drugs/DevelopmentApprovalProcess/ HowDrugsareDevelopedandApproved/ ApprovalApplications/Over-the-CounterDrugs/ default.htm. Accessed 13 May 2011.

5. Regulation of Nonprescription Products. FDA website. www.fda.gov/AboutFDA/CentersOffices/ CDER/ucm093452.htm. Accessed 13 May 2011.

6. Status of OTC Rulemakings. FDA website. www. fda.gov/Drugs/DevelopmentApprovalProcess/ DevelopmentResources/Over-the- CounterOTCDrugs/StatusofOTCRulemakings/ default.htm. Accessed 14 May 2011.

7. FDA MAPP 6020.5R Good Review Practice: OND Review Management of INDs and NDAs for Nonprescription Drug Products

8. FDA MAPP 6532.1 Over-the-Counter (OTC) Labeling and Use Studies

9. *Guidance for Industry: Label Comprehension Studies for Nonprescription Drug Products* (August 2010). Available at www.fda.gov/downloads/Drugs/ GuidanceComplianceRegulatoryInformation/ Guidances/UCM143834.pdf. Accessed 14 May 2011.

10. *Guidance for Industry: Postmarketing Adverse Event Reporting for Nonprescription Human Drug Products Marketed Without an Approved Application* (July 2009). Available at www.fda.gov/downloads/Drugs/ GuidanceComplianceRegulatoryInformation/ Guidances/UCM171672.pdf. Accessed 14 May 2011.

11. *Draft Guidance for Industry: Time and Extent Applications* (February 2004). Available at www.fda.gov/downloads/Drugs/ GuidanceComplianceRegulatoryInformation/ Guidances/UCM078902.pdf. Accessed 14 May 2011.

12. *Guidance for Industry: Labeling OTC Human Drug Products—Questions and Answers* (December 2008). Available at www.fda.gov/downloads/Drugs/ GuidanceComplianceRegulatoryInformation/ Guidances/ucm078792.pdf. Accessed 14 May 2011.

13. *Guidance for Industry: Contents of a Complete Submission for the Evaluation of Proprietary Names* (February 2010). Available at www.fda.gov/downloads/Drugs/

GuidanceComplianceRegulatoryInformation/ Guidances/UCM075068.pdf. Accessed 14 May 2011.

Chapter 13

Prescription Drug Labeling, Advertising and Promotion

By John Driscoll and Linda Pollitz

Objectives

- Understand the scope of FDA's regulatory authority over prescription drug "labeling"
- Learn the general FDA requirements for the labeling, advertising and promotion of prescription drugs
- Recognize the importance of agency enforcement action in the regulation of promotional materials

Laws, Regulations and Guidance Documents Covered in This Chapter

- *Federal Food, Drug, and Cosmetic Act* of 1938
- *Federal Trade Commission Act* of 1914
- *Kefauver-Harris Drug Amendments* of 1962
- 21 CFR 99 Dissemination of information on unapproved/new uses for marketed drugs, biologics and devices
- 21 CFR 200.5 Mailing of important information about drugs
- 21 CFR 201 Labeling
- 21 CFR 201.56 Requirements on content and format of labeling for human prescription drug and biological products
- 21 CFR 201.57 Specific requirements on content and format of labeling for human prescription drug and biological products described in 101.56(b)(1).
- 21 CFR 202 Prescription drug advertising
- 21 CFR 208 Medication Guides for prescription drug products
- 21 CFR 312.7 Promotion and Charging for Investigational Drugs
- 21 CFR 314.50(l) Applications for FDA approval to market a new drug; content and format; labeling
- 21 CFR 314.70 Applications for FDA approval to market a new drug; supplements and other changes to an approved application
- 21 CFR 314.81(2)(iii) Applications for FDA approval to market a new drug; other postmarketing reports; annual report; labeling
- 21 CFR 314.81(b)(3) Other Postmarket reports
- 21 CFR 314.126 Adequate and well-controlled studies
- 21 CFR 314.550 Promotional materials
- 21 CFR 601.12(f)(4) Advertisements and promotional labeling
- 21 CFR 601.45 Accelerated approval of biological products/promotional materials
- *Guidance for Industry: Dosage and Administration Section of Labeling for Human Prescription Drug and Biological Products—Content and Format* (March 2010)
- *Guidance for Industry: Adverse Reactions Section of Labeling for Human Prescription Drug and Biological Products—Content and Format* (January 2006)
- *Draft Guidance for Industry: Clinical Pharmacology Section of Labeling for Human Prescription Drug and Biological Products—Content and Format* (March 2009)

- *Guidance for Industry: Clinical Studies Section of Labeling for Human Prescription Drug and Biological Products—Content and Format* (January 2009)
- *Guidance for Industry: Content and Format for Geriatric Labeling* (October 2001)
- *Draft Guidance for Industry: Content and Format of the Dosage and Administration Section of Labeling for Human Prescription Drug and Biological Products* (April 2007)
- *Draft Guidance for Industry: Warnings and Precautions, Contraindications, and Boxed Warning Sections of Labeling for Human Prescription Drug and Biological Products—Content and Format* (January 2006)
- *Guidance for Industry and Review Staff: Labeling for Human Prescription Drug and Biological Products — Determining Established Pharmacologic Class for Use in the Highlights of Prescribing Information (October 2009)*
- *Draft Guidance for Industry: Labeling for Human Prescription Drug and Biological Products—Implementing the New Content and Format Requirements* (January 2006)
- *Guidance for Industry: Providing Regulatory Submissions in Electronic Format—Content of Labeling* (April 2005)
- *Draft Guidance: Medication Guides — Distribution Requirements and Inclusion in Risk Evaluation and Mitigation Strategies (REMS)* (February 2011)
- *Draft Guidance for Industry: Public Availability of Labeling Changes in "Changes Being Effected" Supplements* (September 2006)
- *Guidance for Industry: Patient-Reported Outcome Measures: Use in Medical Product Development to Support Labeling Claims* (December 2009)
- *Guidance for Industry: Indexing Structured Product Labeling* (June 2008)
- *Guidance for Industry: SPL Standard for Content of Labeling Technical Qs & As* (December 2005)
- *Draft Guidance for Industry: Providing Regulatory Submissions in Electronic Format—Drug Establishment Registration and Drug Listing* (May 2009)
- *Draft Guidance for Industry: Accelerated Approval Products—Submission of Promotional Materials* (March 1999)
- *Guidance for Industry: Aerosol Steroid Product Safety Information in Prescription Drug Advertising and Promotional Labeling* (December 1997)
- *Draft Guidance for Industry: Brief Summary: Disclosing Risk Information in Consumer-Directed Print Advertisements* (January 2004)
- *Guidance for Industry: Consumer-Directed Broadcast Advertisements* (August 1999)
- *Draft Guidance for Industry and FDA Staff: Dear Health Care Provider Letters: Improving Communication of Important Safety Information* (November 2010)
- *Draft Guidance for Industry and FDA: Consumer-Directed Broadcast Advertising of Restricted Devices* (February 2004)
- *Draft Guidance for Industry: "Help-Seeking" and Other Disease Awareness Communications by or on Behalf of Drug and Device Firms* (January 2004)
- *Guidance for Industry: Industry-Supported Scientific and Educational Activities* (November 1997)
- *Draft Guidance for Industry: Product Name Placement, Size, and Prominence in Advertising and Promotional Labeling* (January 1999)
- *Draft Guidance for Industry: Promoting Medical Products in a Changing Healthcare Environment; I. Medical Product Promotion by Healthcare Organizations or Pharmacy Management Companies (PBMs)* (December 1997)
- *Draft Guidance for Industry: Providing Regulatory Submissions in Electronic Format – Prescription Drug Advertising and Promotional Labeling* (January 2001)
- *Draft Guidance for Industry: Using FDA-Approved Patient Labeling in Consumer-Directed Print Advertisements* (April 2001)
- *Guidance for Industry: Good Reprint Practices for the Distribution of Medical Journal Articles and Medical or Scientific Reference Publications on Unapproved New Uses of Approved Drugs and Approved or Cleared Medical Devices* (January 2009)
- *Draft Guidance for Industry: Presenting Risk Information in Prescription Drug and Medical Device Promotion* (May 2009)
- "PhRMA Code on Interactions with Healthcare Professionals" (July 2008)
- *PhRMA Guiding Principles: Direct to Consumer Advertisements About Prescription Medicines* (December 2008)
- OIG Compliance Guidance (see section IV, "Prescription Drug Promotion—Other Considerations")

Introduction

The *Federal Food, Drug, and Cosmetic Act* of 1938 (*FD&C Act*) grants the US Food and Drug Administration (FDA) broad authority over prescription drug "labeling." Beyond the product's "label" (defined in the act as a display of written, printed or graphic material on the immediate container of a drug), "labeling" is a broader term encompassing any written, printed or graphic material on the drug product; any of its containers or wrappers; or any material issued in association with the drug.

Therefore, in addition to all product container and packaging labels, the regulatory definition of drug "labeling" includes:

- FDA-approved professional labeling (information for healthcare professionals about approved uses of the drug), also referred to as the prescribing information or the "package insert" (PI)
- FDA-approved patient labeling (drug information directed to patients) for some drug products with serious risk(s) in the form of a medication guide
- promotional labeling (any material containing information intended to promote the use of the drug) (Even oral statements spoken by sales representatives are subject to regulation by FDA as "promotional labeling." Unlike the PI and patient labeling, promotional labeling is disseminated by a company without a specific "approval" of the materials by FDA.)

The primary regulations governing FDA-approved prescription drug labeling are in Title 21 of the Code of Federal Regulations (CFR) Part 201. While FDA has issued numerous regulations and guidance documents on the labeling of certain products and within specific therapeutic areas, only the more general labeling requirements are discussed in this chapter. Promotional labeling will be discussed later in this chapter.

General Labeling Requirements (21 CFR 201 Subparts A and B)

The inclusion of certain statements and the appropriate placement and prominence of these statements are key concerns in FDA's regulation of drug labeling.

Some of the most broadly applicable requirements are:

- manufacturer, packager or distributor's name and address (21 CFR 201.1)
- location of National Drug Code (NDC) numbers (21 CFR 201.2) (note: the determination of NDC numbers is included in 21 CFR 207.35)
- statement of ingredients (21 CFR 201.10), including required warning statements for specific ingredients (e.g., FD&C Yellow No. 5 (21 CFR 201.20))
- location of expiration date (21 CFR 201.17)
- location of bar codes (21 CFR 201.25)
- statement of identity (21 CFR 201.50)
- net quantity of contents (21 CFR 201.51)
- statement of dosage (21 CFR 201.55)

Any changes to approved drug product labeling are considered a change to the New Drug Application (NDA) or Biologics License Application (BLA) and are required to be reported to FDA according to the regulations governing supplements to an approved application (21 CFR 314.70). Notably, with the passage of the *Food and Drug Administration Amendments Act* of 2007 (*FDAAA*), FDA was granted new authority to require approved NDA holders to make safety-related labeling changes based on new safety information that becomes available after a drug's approval. Under the new law, NDA holders have a limited time to respond and implement these FDA-requested labeling changes (see Section 505(o)(4) of the *FD&C Act* for details).

Professional Labeling, Including the 2006 Physician Labeling Rule (PLR)

The professional labeling, or package insert, for a drug is a compilation of product information based on FDA's comprehensive review of the sponsor's approved NDA/BLA. The package insert is considered "adequate directions for use," written to direct healthcare professionals' use of a drug product.

In 2006, FDA substantially amended its regulations on the content and format of professional labeling (21 CFR 201.56 and 201.57). These changes to the regulations, referred to as the Physician Labeling Rule (PLR), were intended to enhance healthcare professionals' ability to access, read and use the package insert. Unlike the old package insert format (which was less structured and standardized), the PLR format includes three main sections:

- Highlights of Prescribing Information—intended to provide the a prescriber with one location to find the information they most commonly refer to and consider as most important
- Full Prescribing Information: Contents—a "table of contents" for the Full Prescribing Information
- Full Prescribing Information—in fixed numbered sections

In addition to the organizational changes, FDA has issued several guidance documents articulating new standards for the content of professional labeling. As with the rest of the PLR initiatives, the goal of these guidance documents is to provide standards for the development of clear, concise and useful prescribing information.

An overview of the PLR format, associated regulations and available guidance documents is provided in **Table 14-1**.

Also notable is that the PLR regulations established

Table 14-1. PLR Format, Associated Regulations and Guidance Documents

PLR Format	Associated Regulations/Guidance (if any)
Overall	21 CFR 201.56 and 21 CFR 201.57 *Draft Guidance for Industry: Labeling for Human Prescription Drug and Biological Products—Implementing the New Content and Format Requirements (January 2006)* (Guidance on Drug Names and Dosage Forms planned for calendar year 2011)
Highlights of Prescribing Information Product Names, Other Required Information Boxed Warning Recent Major Changes Indications and Usage* Dosage and Administration Dosage Forms and Strengths Contraindications Warnings and Precautions Adverse Reactions Drug Interactions Use in Specific Populations	21 CFR 201.57(a) **Guidance for Industry and Review Staff: Labeling for Human Prescription Drug and Biological Products—Determining Established Pharmacologic Class for Use in the Highlights of Prescribing Information (October 2009)*
Full Prescribing Information: Contents	21 CFR 201.57(b)
Full Prescribing Information	21 CFR 201.57(c)
Boxed Warning [if applicable]	21 CFR 201.57(c)(1) *Draft Guidance for Industry: Warnings and Precautions, Contraindications, and Boxed Warning Sections of Labeling for Human Prescription Drug and Biological Products—Content and Format (January 2006)*
1 Indications and Usage	21 CFR 201.57(c)(2) (Guidance planned for calendar year 2011)
2 Dosage and Administration	21 CFR 201.57(c)(3) *Guidance for Industry: Dosage and Administration Section of Labeling for Human Prescription Drug and Biological Products—Content and Format (March 2010)*
3 Dosage Forms and Strengths	21 CFR 201.57(c)(4)
4 Contraindications	21 CFR 201.57(c)(5) *Draft Guidance for Industry: Warnings and Precautions, Contraindications, and Boxed Warning Sections of Labeling for Human Prescription Drug and Biological Products—Content and Format (January 2006)*
5 Warnings and Precautions	21 CFR 201.57(c)(6) *Draft Guidance for Industry: Warnings and Precautions, Contraindications, and Boxed Warning Sections of Labeling for Human Prescription Drug and Biological Products—Content and Format (January 2006)*
6 Adverse Reactions	21 CFR 201.57(c)(7) *Guidance for Industry: Adverse Reactions Section of Labeling for Human Prescription Drug and Biological Products—Content and Format (January 2006)*
7 Drug Interactions	21 CFR 201.57(c)(8)
8 Use in Specific Populations	21 CFR 201.57(c)(9) *Guidance for Industry: Content and Format for Geriatric Labeling (October 2001)* (Guidance on incorporation of pediatric information labeling planned for calendar year 2011)
9 Drug Abuse and Dependence	21 CFR 201.57(c)(10)
10 Overdosage	21 CFR 201.57(c)(11)
11 Description	21 CFR 201.57(c)(12)

Table 14-1. PLR Format, Associated Regulations and Guidance Documents

PLR Format	Associated Regulations/Guidance (if any)
12 Clinical Pharmacology	21 CFR 201.57(c)(13) *Draft Guidance for Industry: Clinical Pharmacology Section of Labeling for Human Prescription Drug and Biological Products—Content and Format* (March 2009)
13 Nonclinical Toxicology	21 CFR 201.57(c)(14)
14 Clinical Studies	21 CFR 201.57(c)(15) *Guidance for Industry: Clinical Studies Section of Labeling for Human Prescription Drug and Biological Products—Content and Format* (January 2009)
15 References	21 CFR 201.57(c)(16)
16 How Supplied/Storage and Handling	21 CFR 201.57(c)(17)
17 Patient Counseling Information	21 CFR 201.57(c)(18)
Medication guide [if applicable]	21 CFR 208

minimum requirements for font size and certain other graphic elements (21 CFR 201.57(d)). These requirements vary depending upon the intended use of the labeling (e.g., whether labeling is to accompany the drug product or is for use in accompanying promotional materials). See *Draft Guidance for Industry: Labeling for Human Prescription Drug and Biological Products—Implementing the New Content and Format Requirements* (January 2006) for additional information.

Professional labeling for all drugs approved after June 2001 (or for which an efficacy supplement was approved after June 2001) must be converted to the new PLR format (21 CFR 201.56(c)). Because recreating a product's professional labeling is a difficult and time-consuming process, FDA has instituted a staggered implementation schedule, prioritizing label revision from the most recently approved products to older products. The deadline for submitting revised labeling to meet the new requirement is based upon the date of the most recent NDA efficacy supplement (or the original approval, if there have been no approved efficacy supplements). A table outlining FDA's implementation schedule is provided in Appendix D of the January 2006 draft guidance mentioned above.

Patient Labeling, Including Medication Guide

Patient labeling is product information derived from professional labeling, written in consumer-friendly language, that usually focuses on directions for using the product or risks associated with using the drug. For certain products determined by FDA to pose serious and significant risks, the agency may require a patient medication guide (21 CFR 208).

All medication guides must comply with certain content and format requirements (21 CFR 208.20), including a type size no smaller than 10 points. In addition, medication guides must be distributed to patients each time the prescription drug product is dispensed (21 CFR 208.24).

Because a manufacturer cannot be present as each prescription is distributed, the manufacturer is required to ensure that adequate means exist for dispensers themselves to comply with the requirement. (This is usually achieved by providing sufficient numbers of printed medication guides with each unit of drug product). In February 2011, FDA issued *Draft Guidance for Industry: Medication Guides—Distribution Requirements and Inclusion in Risk Evaluation and Minimization Strategies (REMS)*, clarifying its expectations for the distribution of medication guides.

Electronic Labeling, Including Structured Product Labeling (SPL)

Since 2004, FDA has required the submission of "content of labeling" in electronic format for initial NDA submissions (21 CFR 314.50(l)), labeling supplements and Annual Reports for approved NDAs (21 CFR 314.81(b)). "Content of labeling" is defined as the complete professional labeling, including all text, tables and figures.

Structured Product Labeling (SPL) is the electronic document markup standard adopted by FDA as the mechanism for electronic submission of the content of labeling. The SPL standard uses the extensible markup language (XML) file format with specifications (schema and controlled terminology) as defined by the FDA Data Standards Council. Additional information on SPL, including both technical and nontechnical guidance, can be found on FDA's Structured Product Labeling Resources website.

Prescription Drug Promotion
Background & Enforcement

FDA has regulatory authority over the advertising and promotion for prescription drugs via the *FD&C Act* and monitors company promotional activity through its Division of Drug Marketing, Advertising and Communications (DDMAC). While the language in *FD&C Act* Section 502 is relatively brief and does not specifically define "advertising" or "promotion," FDA has broadly interpreted the act in its regulations and guidances covering drug advertising and promotion. With the passage of the 1962 *Kefauver-Harris Amendments*, the agency gained greater authority over the marketing of prescription drugs. Regulations covering prescription drug promotion are found in 21 CFR 202 and are cross-referenced to 21 CFR 201.

If DDMAC finds advertising or promotion to be violative, the agency has both administrative and judicial tools at its disposal for dealing with violations. FDA's administrative tools include issuing Notice of Violation letters (NOV), often referred to as "Untitled Letters;" issuing Warning Letters; ordering a recall; and calling for the delay, suspension or withdrawal of a product approval. Of these, the most common administrative actions taken by FDA are NOVs and Warning Letters.

NOVs are different from Warning Letters in that they only require the company to stop using the materials that make the claim(s) FDA finds violative. Warning Letters are typically addressed to the company CEO, warn that FDA will take further action if the matter is not immediately addressed, and require corrective action by the company. If the subject of the letter is a product advertisement, this correction is typically a remedial advertisement in each of the same venues where the violative advertisement was run. Warning Letters may also require the company to issue a "Dear Doctor" letter to physicians as described in both 21 CFR 200.5(c)(3) and a draft guidance issued by FDA in November 2010. All letters issued by DDMAC are posted publicly on FDA's "Enforcement Actions" webpage with a copy of the violative promotion; this also serves as one of the most important tools in understanding DDMAC's position on certain topics.

As in other areas of FDA enforcement, judicial tools at FDA's disposal include injunction, seizure or criminal prosecution. However, DDMAC rarely seeks judicial action on its own for promotional violations. DDMAC is more likely to work with the Office of the Inspector General (OIG) or individual state's attorneys general in pursuing companies for significant promotional violations. Additional information on these agencies beyond FDA is provided at the end of this chapter.

In 2010, DDMAC announced a new program, called Truthful Prescription Drug Advertising and Promotion (or more commonly, the "Bad Ad" program). The stated goal of the Bad Ad program is to educate prescribers about their role in reporting to FDA false or misleading detailing by sales representatives and other forms of drug promotion. At a number of major medical meetings throughout 2010, DDMAC distributed materials that encouraged prescribers to recognize and report any activities and promotional messages that they believed were false or misleading. DDMAC, in turn, has promised to review these reports and issue enforcement letters where appropriate. On 3 December 2010, DDMAC sent its first Warning Letter referencing the Bad Ad program.

Summary of Requirements for Advertising and Promotion
No Preapproval Promotion

According to 21 CFR 312.7, sponsors or investigators "shall not represent in a promotional context that an investigational new drug is safe or effective for the purposes for which it is under investigation." The only exceptions to the prohibition on preapproval promotion are disease-state-only promotion, or institutional promotion (which links the name of the drug manufacturer with a field of research); and "Coming Soon" promotions. "Coming Soon" ads reveal only the name of a product that will be available soon, without any written, verbal or graphic suggestions of potential indications or claims of safety or effectiveness. During the preapproval period, a company may choose one of these types of promotional campaigns, but may not switch back and forth between them. The reason is that if a disease awareness campaign is underway for a time (e.g., "Company X is involved in research in the field of diabetes") and then followed by a "Coming Soon" campaign "Coming Soon from Company X: Product Y"), the audience could link the name of the drug with the disease state, which is considered tantamount to preapproval promotion. DDMAC issued a draft guidance in January 2004, entitled *Guidance for Industry: "Help-Seeking" and Other Disease Awareness Communications by or on Behalf of Drug and Device Firms*, to provide clarification on its thinking about preapproval promotion.

Submission and Preclearance of Promotional Materials

With only one exception, all promotional materials must be submitted to DDMAC at the time of its initial publication or dissemination using Form FDA 2253 (21 CFR 314.81(b)(i)).

Manufacturers of products approved under Subpart H (Accelerated approval of new drugs for serious or life-threatening illnesses) are required to submit drafts of all promotional labeling for advisory comment at least 30 days prior to dissemination (21 CFR 314.550 and 601.45). Additionally, for products that are anticipated to receive accelerated approval during the NDA preapproval review period, all promotional materials intended to be used in the first 120 days following marketing approval must be submitted to DDMAC for advisory review prior to the drug's approval. For additional details about the submission of promotional materials for accelerated approval products, see *Draft Guidance for Industry: Accelerated Approval Products—Submission of Promotional Materials* (March 1999).

For drugs approved under standard conditions, it is common industry practice (although not required) to submit a drug's launch materials to DDMAC for advisory comment. DDMAC pays careful attention to launch materials during the first year after a drug's approval. In September 2008, DDMAC issued a letter to a company for violations found in a promotional launch journal advertisement. DDMAC took issue with included claims such as "novel," "next generation" and "unique." The company was asked to pull the advertisement and run a corrective advertising campaign.

Additionally, while not required, it is common industry practice to send direct-to-consumer television advertisements to DDMAC for preclearance prior to dissemination. DDMAC's website explains the submission process for preclearance of TV ads and other materials.

Product Name Placement, Size and Prominence

Promotional labeling must include a reference to the established (generic) name of the drug, per 21 CFR 202.1(b)(1). The regulations require that the most prominent mention of the brand name be accompanied by the generic name "in letters at least half as large as the letters comprising the proprietary name or designation with which it is joined." In January 1999, FDA issued *Draft Guidance for Industry: Product Name Placement, Size and Prominence in Advertising and Promotional Labeling* to clarify issues in this area.

Fair Balance

All claims of effectiveness in a prescription drug advertisement must be accompanied by information about the product's risks, and the risk information must have comparable prominence to the promotional claims (21 CFR 202.1(e)(5)). The omission or minimization of risk information is the most commonly cited concern in DDMAC's enforcement letters.

DDMAC considers many factors when determining "fair balance," including whether the safety and efficacy messages have equal prominence, typography and layout, contrast and white space, or other methods used to achieve emphasis (21 CFR 202.1(e)(7)(viii)). In addition, if promotional material is directed to a consumer audience, the fair balance information should be written in consumer-friendly language.

In May 2009, FDA issued a draft guidance, entitled *Guidance for Industry: Presenting Risk Information in Prescription Drug and Medical Device Promotion,* to shed more light on the factors the agency considers when evaluating the presentation of risk information in advertisements and promotional labeling. This draft guidance includes many helpful, concrete examples to illustrate FDA's thinking on this important topic.

General Requirements for Promotional Claims/"Substantial Evidence"

Promotional materials may not suggest a use of the product that is not approved or otherwise permitted for use in the FDA-approved labeling (i.e., full prescribing information). This is what is commonly referred to as "off-label" use of a product.

In addition to the "on label" requirement, promotional materials may not suggest that a drug is better, safer or more effective than has been demonstrated by "substantial evidence." Generally, FDA's standard for "substantial evidence" in support of a drug product claim is two adequate and well-controlled clinical trials (21 CFR 314.126). Although certain claims may be allowable based upon a single study, DDMAC has on numerous occasions articulated the requirement for two studies for claims of product superiority.

Even if product claims are "on-label," if the claims (either overt or implied) are not supported by substantial evidence, FDA will consider the materials to be misleading and therefore violative. Although the regulations in 21 CFR 202.1(e)(6) and (7) detail the general principles by which FDA will evaluate whether or not promotional materials are misleading (e.g., failure to reveal material facts or improper use of graphics or statistics), reviewing DDMAC enforcement letters is the best way to learn the agency's expectations in this area.

Pharmacoeconomic Claims and Promotion to Formulary Decision Makers

Pharmaceutical companies not only promote their drug products to prescribers, but also to formularies or other related entities that are primarily responsible for managed care coverage and reimbursement decisions. This kind of promotion often focuses on healthcare economic information (pharmacoeconomic claims).

Section 114 of the *Food and Drug Administration Amendments Act* of 1997 (*FDAAA*) provides for a legal mechanism to allow the promotion of pharmacoeconomic claims using a less-stringent standard for the "substantial evidence" standard described above. The law states that pharmacoeconomic claims may be made based on "competent and reliable" evidence, as long as the information directly relates to an approved indication and is only being provided to formularies or other similar managed care decision makers.

Brief Summary & Accompanying Labeling

The 21 CFR 202(l) regulations differentiate materials that constitute advertising from other forms of promotional labeling. The regulations require that prescription drug advertising contain a "[t]rue statement of information in brief summary relating to side effects, contraindications, and effectiveness" (21 CFR 202.1(e)). Promotional labeling that is not an advertisement (or reminder labeling, as described below) must be disseminated with a copy of the full prescribing information.

In January 2004, FDA issued *Draft Guidance for Industry: Brief Summary: Disclosing Risk Information in Consumer-Directed Print Advertisements,* to explain the agency's expectations regarding the Brief Summary in print advertisements directed to consumers. Like "fair balance," FDA encourages sponsors to write a Brief Summary for consumer pieces in language that can be understood by consumers. FDA also recommends that sponsors include a statement in the advertisement reminding consumers that the risk information is not comprehensive, and also provide a toll-free telephone number or website where more information can be found.

Reminder Labeling

An exception to the fair balance and accompanying labeling requirements is reminder labeling (commonly known as "reminder ads"), which, according to 21 CFR 201.100(f), "calls attention to the name of the drug product but does not include indications or dosage recommendations for use… containing no representation or suggestion relating to the drug product." Reminder advertisements are not permitted for products that carry a Boxed Warning in their labeling.

It was common practice for pharmaceutical companies to give away reminder items. In July 2008, the Pharmaceutical Research and Manufacturers of America (PhRMA) issued an updated PhRMA Code on Interactions with Healthcare Professionals (PhRMA Code) that became effective in January 2009. The Advanced Medical Technology Association (AdvaMed) issued similar guidelines to medical device manufacturers.

The PhRMA Code, which is a voluntary non-regulatory standard, prohibits distribution of such non-educational and practice-related promotional materials, which includes reminder items such as pens, notepads and mugs with product logos on them, even if the item is of minimal value and related to the healthcare professional's work or for the benefit of the patient. Most manufacturers have voluntarily adopted the PhRMA Code and are no longer giving away reminder items.

Help-seeking, Bulk-sale and Compounding Drug Advertising

Another exception to the Brief Summary requirement includes "help-seeking advertisements" and bulk-sale and compounding drug advertisements. Help-seeking advertisements are intended to inform consumers about a specific medical condition and encourage them to talk to their healthcare professionals about the condition. They must not mention any product name or imply that a certain prescription drug is intended to treat the medical condition. In January 2004, FDA issued *Draft Guidance for Industry: "Help-Seeking" and Other Disease Awareness Communications by or on Behalf of Drug and Device* Firms. Bulk-sale drugs that are only intended to be used for further processing or manufacturing are also exempt from the Brief Summary requirement, as are drugs sold to pharmacies for the purpose of compounding. As with help-seeking advertisements, neither bulk-sale drugs nor compounding drugs are permitted to make safety or efficacy claims (21 CFR 202.1(e)(2)(ii) and (iii)).

Direct-To-Consumer (DTC) Advertising

Consumer-directed broadcast advertisements (i.e., television and radio) must include a "major statement" of the product's primary risks, in the audio and, for television, video portion of the advertisement. In addition, the advertisement should make "adequate provision… for dissemination of the approved or permitted package labeling in connection with the broadcast presentation" (21CFR 202.1(e)(1)). This is sometimes referred to as the "adequate provision" requirement and, in August 1999, DDMAC issued *Draft Guidance for Industry: Consumer-Directed Broadcast Advertisements* to clarify the approach manufacturers may take to fulfill the requirement. A similar guidance is available for restricted medical devices. As noted previously, most companies submit their television advertisements to DDMAC for advisory comment prior to broadcast.

In addition to other requirements, FDAAA requires that published DTC advertisements include the following statement printed in conspicuous text: "You are encouraged to report negative side effects of prescription drugs to the FDA. Visit www.fda.gov/Safety/MedWatch/default.htm, or call 1-800-FDA-1088."

Internet and Social Media

The Internet, from specific drug websites to sponsored links to social media sites such as YouTube or Facebook, is commonly used for prescription drug promotion. Although DDMAC issued its first letter regarding a promotional website in 1996, FDA has never issued formal regulations or guidance documents on this topic, citing rapidly changing technology as the reason. However, in response to DDMAC's 14 enforcement letters on 3 April 2009 regarding the sponsored link activities of some 47 drug products, criticism arose that FDA's standards had not been clearly communicated to industry. In response, DDMAC held a public hearing in November 2009 to gather comments from industry, trade organizations, physician and patient groups and others on how to appropriately promote medical products using the Internet and social media. DDMAC has expressed strong interest in publishing draft guidances on these topics but as of April 2011, no guidance documents have been issued.

Until such time as guidance is released, regulatory professionals must review the many examples of improper Internet promotion cited in DDMAC enforcement letters to develop their own best judgment and practices for online promotion. Some notable recent examples include a letter for a video posted on YouTube (25 September 2008) and a letter for a Facebook widget placed on a product site (29 July 2010).

Press Releases

Press releases often cause confusion over where the appropriate regulatory jurisdiction lies. Typically, the Securities and Exchange Commission (SEC) regulates how information is communicated to the investment community. Nevertheless, FDA believes that product-specific press releases fall under FDA promotional regulations, thus requiring fair balance and avoiding false or misleading content or preapproval promotion. Many companies have received Warning Letters and Untitled Letters from DDMAC for violative statements in their press releases.

Product Promotion vs. Scientific Exchange

FDA does distinguish between drug promotion and the exchange of scientific information. Truly independent and nonpromotional industry-supported activities, where there is an exchange of scientific information—if done properly—may not be deemed promotional labeling, even if the information being exchanged is considered "off-label." Historically, manufacturers were involved in setting up continuing medical education (CME) programs to facilitate an exchange of scientific information. These events and the manufacturers that organized them fell under harsh scrutiny, however, when it was alleged that the CME events were merely "dressed up product promotion."

In December 1997, FDA issued *Guidance for Industry: Industry-Supported Scientific and Educational Activities* to explain its thinking on this topic. This guidance defines what is considered "nonpromotional" and "educational," and places great importance on keeping the scientific activity independent of influence from manufacturers.

Product Detailing

Product detailing, including the oral statements that company representatives make about their prescription drug products, is also considered promotional labeling. While it is difficult for FDA to monitor conversations, there are several examples of DDMAC issuing Warning Letters and Untitled Letters to companies for presentations that were made to healthcare professionals by sales representatives.

On 1 December 2008, a company received an Untitled Letter based on oral statements made by a sales representative to a healthcare professional. DDMAC's letter specifically stated "On Thursday, January 3, 2009 at approximately 3:00p.m., a sales representative …made an unsolicited sales call to a physician at his office." The letter goes on to describe statements that the representative made—not in response to a specific request from the physician—that described the use of the drug that was not included in the approved PI.

Historically, many conversations that have been the subject of DDMAC letters have occurred and been overheard at exhibit halls at major medical meetings. This is a key enforcement area for DDMAC, and FDA representatives regularly attend major medical meetings and pay close attention to activities in the exhibit halls (see recent letters dated 27 February 2009 and 13 May 2010). With the launch of the "Bad Ad" program in 2010, it is anticipated that more letters will be issued by DDMAC based on conversations between sales representatives and physicians.

Reprints

FDA-cleared or -approved prescription drugs, biologics and medical devices frequently are the subject of medical research, with study results typically published in medical journals, textbooks and other scientific reference publications. Often these studies describe or suggest uses of the products that go beyond the PI, to include "off-label" use. Because manufacturers must limit the promotion of their products to only approved, labeled uses, the promotional use of reprints can be challenging.

In 1997, Section 401 of the *Food and Drug Administration Modernization Act* (*FDAMA*) was written into law in an attempt to address this issue by describing situations where a manufacturer could disseminate reprints containing descriptions of off-label use to healthcare professionals while remaining in a "safe harbor" from being found in violation of the rule against promoting the product for an off label use. The FDA implementing regulations were codified at 21 CFR 99. On 30 September 2006, *FDAMA* Section 401 ceased to be effective and the implementing regulations were no longer applicable.

In January 2009, FDA announced the availability of *Guidance for Industry on Good Reprint Practices for the Distribution of Medical Journal Articles and Medical or Scientific Reference Publications on Unapproved New Uses of Approved Drugs and Approved or Cleared Medical Devices* (*Good Reprint Practices Guidance*). This guidance describes the kind of material that FDA considers to be a true reprint (e.g., one that is peer-reviewed vs. a supplement), what information should accompany the reprint, and appropriate venues for distribution of these reprints.

Other Agencies Beyond FDA

FDA is not the only agency closely tracking prescription drug advertising. Many other government agencies, including the Department of Justice, the Office of the Inspector General (OIG) in the Department of Health and Human Services (DHHS), states attorneys general, the Federal Trade Commission and Congress, closely monitor drug companies' activities.

Government enforcement efforts against the pharmaceutical industry in the US were greatly enhanced, beginning in 2001. The original focus was suspected kickbacks and violations of the pricing statutes (the *Anti-Kickback Statute*). These laws make it illegal for any person—e.g., healthcare provider, office manager or sales agent—to knowingly and willfully solicit, offer, pay or receive "remuneration" (including kickbacks, bribes, rebates or anything of value) directly or indirectly in cash or in kind to any person to induce or cause that person to prescribe a product for which payment may be made in whole or in part under a federal healthcare program (42 USC 1320a-7b).

More recently, the focus of government agencies has been off-label promotion by pharmaceutical and medical device manufacturers in connection with the *False Claims Act* (*FCA*). The *FCA* was born out of the Civil War when fraud was pervasive, particularly by defense contractors who unscrupulously sold bad goods (defective guns, putrid rations, etc.) to the US government and then sought payment for such goods. Under the *FCA*, an individual who is not affiliated with the government can bring a suit claiming fraud. In such cases, the person filing the claim is known as a "whistleblower" and the reward for a successful prosecution was offered as a "qui tam" provision (meaning "he who brings a case on behalf of our lord the King, as well as himself"). The citizen whistleblower in the case is known as a "relator."

While this legislation has undergone some changes over the years, the tenets remain the same: that is, it is unlawful to knowingly present or cause to be presented to the US government a false claim for payment. Modern-day changes to the laws impose treble (triple) damages and civil fines of $5,000–$10,000 per false claim, among other things. In practical application, today, whistleblowers, working with DOJ and states attorneys general, have investigated and brought many high-profile claims against companies for promoting drugs for off-label uses, resulting in false claims for payment submitted to federal insurance programs such as Medicare and Medicaid, which do not provide coverage for off-label uses. In these cases, each off-label prescription is considered one false claim. Many healthcare product manufacturers that settle *FCA* claims also agree to enter into Corporate Integrity Agreements (CIAs) with DHHS, placing strict requirements on corporate compliance for a period of years.

In January 2009, a landmark settlement against a manufacturer was announced wherein the manufacturer agreed to pay $1.415 billion to resolve allegations of off-label promotion of its drug. The settlement included a criminal fine of $515 million, and $800 million in a civil settlement with the federal government and a number of states.

The case was brought by four former sales representatives of the company, and the whistleblowers together received more than $78 million as their share of the settlement. The company also agreed to enter into a five-year CIA with DHHS.

During the same period, another large manufacturer announced that it had settled charges of off-label promotion of one of its popular drugs for $2.3 billion. Although the drug had been removed from the market years before, the company had been plagued by investigations by the US Department of Justice and lawsuits from states attorneys general for alleged off-label promotion tactics connected to the product. These two settlements are the largest to date in any healthcare product cases.

Finally, manufacturers must consider the competition as they develop advertising and promotional materials. Competitors have brought suit against manufacturers for violations of the *Lanham Act*. While this legislation is often thought of in terms of trademark protection, it also allows manufacturers to sue competitors for false advertising. Manufacturers have used courts' interpretation of the act to bring suits charging that comparative claims in advertising are false and misleading, that they deceive a substantial part of the audience viewing the ads and that the deception could influence purchasing decisions. If a plaintiff prevails on a *Lanham Act* false advertising claim, the court can not only bar the advertising, but can also order corrective advertising or a product recall.

Summary

- All drug labeling, including container labels, package inserts, patient labeling, medication guides and promotional labeling (including oral statements) is subject to FDA regulation.
- In 2006, FDA issued the PLR, affecting the content and format of labeling for new prescription drug products.
- A medication guide is a special type of patient labeling for drugs with serious risks and is required to be distributed to the consumer each time a prescription is filled or refilled.
- Structured Product Labeling (SPL) is an electronic document standard adopted by FDA as a mechanism for exchanging drug information.
- FDA monitors prescription drug advertising and promotion through the DDMAC. No drug can be promoted until the NDA has been approved by the FDA.
- Typical FDA enforcement actions include NOVs and Warning Letters. Although rarely used, the agency has other tools at its disposal to deal with violative advertising and promotional materials.
- All advertising and promotional labeling must be submitted at the time of first use with Form FDA

2253, except for products approved under Subpart H ("accelerated approval"), which must be submitted for advisory opinion 30 days prior to initial dissemination. Although not required, it is strongly recommended that launch materials and new television advertisements be submitted to DDMAC for advisory comment prior to dissemination.

- All promotional materials must include a "fair balance" of efficacy and risk information, with the exception of reminder labeling (not allowed for products with a Boxed Warning). Broadcast advertisements must include a "major statement" of risk.

- Promotional materials may not suggest a use for the product that is not approved or otherwise permitted for use in the FDA-approved labeling ("off-label" use) and no claims must be made that a product is safer or more effective than has been established by "substantial evidence" (generally, two adequate and well-controlled clinical trials). *FDAMA* Section 114 allows for the distribution of pharmacoeconomic data using a less-stringent standard as long as certain requirements are met.

- All non-reminder promotional materials must be accompanied by the full prescribing information; advertisements require an accompanying "Brief Summary" of the full PI. Broadcast advertisements must include "adequate provision" for the dissemination of the approved labeling.

- FDA works with other agencies such as the US Attorney's Office and OIG in prosecuting companies alleged to be in violation of the *FCA* or *Anti-Kickback Statute* through off-label promotion. Companies found in violation of the *FD&C Act*, *Anti-Kickback Statute* and/or *FCA* risk disbarment from participation in federal programs (e.g., Medicare) and Corporate Integrity Agreements.

Chapter 14

Medical Device Submissions

By Chas Burr, SM, MBA, FRAPS and John DeLucia, MS, RAC

Objectives

◆ Discuss the types of submissions made to the Center for Devices and Radiological Health (CDRH)

◆ Explain how medical devices are classified and how the classification affects the types of submissions required

◆ Describe the IDE (Investigational Device Exemption) requirements for clinical device studies

◆ Review the types of 510(k) Premarket Notification submissions, when 510(k) submissions are needed and what information is required

◆ Review the types of PMA (Premarket Approval) submissions, when PMA submissions are needed and what information is required

◆ Discuss when Expedited Review should be requested

◆ Explain when an HDE (Humanitarian Device Exemption) is appropriate and what information is required.

◆ Provide an overview of the nature and status of current proposals for change based on recommendations from the August 2010 reports on the 510(k) program and CDRH's use of science in its decision-making.

Laws, Regulations and Guidelines Covered in This Chapter

◆ *Federal Food, Drug, and Cosmetic Act* of 1938

◆ 21 CFR 807 Establishment registration and device listing, premarket notification

◆ 21 CFR 812 Investigational Device Exemptions

◆ 21 CFR 814 Premarket approval

◆ 21 CFR 860 Medical device classification procedures

Introduction

Medical devices were first regulated by the *Federal Food, Drug and Cosmetic Act* of 1938 (*FD&C Act*). It is enforced by the US Food and Drug Administration (FDA). Under the act, devices were examined for adulteration and misbranding but no provision was made for review of their safety or effectiveness prior to marketing. In the late 1960s, FDA started to concentrate on devices that posed problems with safety and effectiveness, requiring recalls and replacements.

The *FD&C Act* was amended in 1976 to include premarket review of medical devices. Under the act's amendments, FDA was authorized to set standards, with premarket clearance for some devices and premarket approval for others. Devices posing little or no risk to users or patients were exempted from standards and premarket clearance, but were not necessarily exempt from complying with parts of the Good Manufacturing Practice requirements for devices under 21 CFR 820, the Quality System Regulation (QSR).

FDA, primarily through the Center for Devices and Radiological Health (CDRH), is responsible for assuring that medical devices are safe and effective. Per the FDA Intercenter Agreement (31 October 1991), the Center for Biologics Evaluation and Research (CBER) has responsibility for devices related to blood and cellular products (see "Chapter 19 Biologics Submissions"). The agency bears this responsibility through authority granted by the *FD&C*

Act, which is carried out in accordance with the regulations found in Title 21 of the Code of Federal Regulations (CFR). Medical devices, referred to as "devices," are defined in Section 201(h) of the *FD&C Act*:

> "The term "device" means an instrument, apparatus, implement, machine, contrivance, implant, in vitro reagent, or other similar or related article, including any component, part, or accessory, which is:
>
> (1) recognized in the official *National Formulary*, or the *United States Pharmacopeia*, or any supplement to them,
>
> (2) intended for use in the diagnosis of disease or other conditions, or in the cure, mitigation, treatment, or prevention of disease, in man or other animals, or
>
> (3) intended to affect the structure or any function of the body of man or other animals, and which does not achieve its primary intended purposes through chemical action within or on the body of man or other animals and which is not dependent upon being metabolized for the achievement of its primary intended purposes."

Medical Device Classification (21 CFR 860)

Medical devices are regulated based upon a classification system that evaluates the risk posed by the product and the level of control needed to adequately assure safety. The device classification system has been modified by subsequent amendments, but generally remains as originally intended. The act defines three classes of medical devices according to increasing complexity and regulatory control:

- Class I—General Controls
- Class II—General Controls and Special Controls
- Class III—General Controls and Premarket Approval

Class I devices are generally low-risk devices, such as nonprescription sunglasses, for which safety and effectiveness can be assured by adherence to a set of guidelines or "general controls." General controls include compliance with the applicable portions of the QSR for manufacturing and recordkeeping; requirements for issuing notices about repair; replacing or refunding money for devices presenting an unreasonable risk of substantial harm; facility registration and product listing; adverse event reporting; and appropriate, truthful and non-misleading labeling, advertising and promotional materials. In rare circumstances, some Class I devices also require premarket clearance by FDA through the 510(k) premarket notification process.

Class II devices are intermediate-risk devices, such as blood glucose test systems and infusion pumps, where general controls are not sufficient to ensure their safety and effectiveness. Class II devices are subject to "special controls," in addition to general controls. Special controls may include performance standards, FDA guidance documents, special labeling requirements, tracking of implantable devices, and other actions the agency deems necessary to assure safety and effectiveness. Most Class II devices are subject to premarket review and clearance by FDA through the 510(k) premarket notification process. At times, the review and requirements are just as rigorous as those for a Class III device.

Class III devices, such as life-sustaining, life-supporting or implantable devices, are considered by FDA to pose the greatest risk. Devices that have a new intended use or employ a unique, new technology that is not substantially equivalent to a legally marketed predicate device are also categorized as Class III. Class III devices are subject to the most rigorous controls, including general controls (like Class I and Class II devices), any relevant special controls (like Class II devices) and, in most cases, premarket approval, which requires the submission of evidence to establish reasonable assurance of the device's safety and effectiveness. Detailed manufacturing information may also be required. FDA may request a panel of outside experts to recommend the action to be taken on the Class III device. However, the agency is not compelled to take the panel's advice.

FDA uses Medical Device Classification Procedures described in 21 CFR 860 to determine device classifications. 21 CFR 862–892 contain resulting classification regulations. A device may be classified by its regulation and by a product code. Product codes may provide more specific designations within a classification regulation. Occasionally, FDA assigns a product code to a category of devices prior to the formal assignment of a regulatory classification. CDRH's Product Classification database[1] can be used to help determine classifications.

Reclassification

The rules and procedures for establishing a device's classification and requesting a change in device classification are contained in 21 CFR 860. Advantages of reclassifying a device from a PMA to a 510(k) route to marketing include reduced fees required by FDA to review the submission; often, reduced information requirements; and reduced requirements for submissions for changes. In Fiscal 2011, the PMA review fee is more than $230,000, while the 510(k) processing fee is approximately $4,300.

Since 1976, the primary reclassification activity has been geared toward down-classifying Class III devices into Class II or I. Generating reclassification data requires considerable effort and resources. If successful, the reclassified device and any substantially equivalent device can be cleared for marketing through the less-burdensome 510(k) process.

It was the intent of Congress that reclassification play a potentially significant role in the medical device clearance process, although CDRH's interpretation of its mandate has not permitted the reclassification process to be utilized to a meaningful extent. A primary obstacle has been the high level of scientific information that CDRH requires to support a device's reclassification. A second obstacle has been difficulty in obtaining agreement among manufacturers whose products have already been cleared by PMAs. Removal of the PMA requirement may be seen as loss of a barrier to entry that limits competitors.

In 2009, FDA initiated the 515 Program Initiative[2] to facilitate reclassifications.

513(g) Request for Designation

It is sometimes unclear into which classification a device falls. A provision in Section 513(g) of the *FD&C Act* allows the device sponsor to request a classification determination from FDA. This requires a letter with a description of the device and a fee payment. The agency usually responds within 60 days with a classification assignment based on the material presented. More information is provided in a CDRHLearn training class.[3]

Exemptions

Most Class I devices, and some Class II devices, are exempt from 510(k) premarket notification requirements. However, they are not exempt from general controls. All medical devices must be manufactured under a quality assurance program, proven suitable for their intended use, appropriately packaged and properly labeled. The establishment and device must be registered and listed with FDA. Establishment registrations and listings are in the public domain. Some Class I devices are exempt from most GMP requirements, with the exception of complaint files and general recordkeeping.

Devices exempt from 510(k) are preamendment devices not significantly changed or modified and Class I and II devices specifically exempted by regulation.

A "preamendment device is one legally marketed in the US before May 28, 1976 that has not been significantly changed or modified and for which a regulation requiring a PMA application has not been published by FDA." Devices meeting this description are referred to as "grandfathered" and do not require a 510(k).

The *FD&C Act* authorizes FDA to exempt certain generic types of Class I devices from the premarket notification requirement. FDA has exempted more than 800 generic types of Class I devices and 60 Class II devices from the premarket notification requirement. Exemptions occur on a periodic basis and are published in the *Federal Register*. The 510(k) exemption has certain limitations. Before deciding that a device is exempt, the sponsor must determine the device's classification status and limitations.

De Novo Process

The *Food and Drug Administration Modernization Act*

of 1997 (*FDAMA*) created a process for the classification of certain low risk devices for which there is no predicate. Before *FDAMA*, such a device would automatically be designated Class III. Reclassification would be required to move the device to Class I or II. Under the de novo process, the sponsor of a device that has received a Not Substantially Equivalent determination can apply for a risk-based determination. The process has proven unwieldy and is rarely used. See the section of this chapter entitled Proposed Submission Changes, which provides details on FDA's plans to address problems in the de novo process.

Combination Products

Until 1990 and the introduction of the *Safe Medical Devices Act*, there was no formal process to establish which FDA center would regulate combination products, such as drug-device, device-biologic or biologic-drug products.

Regulations have now established that FDA makes a determination based on the primary mode of action of the combination product. By making this determination, the agency in effect decides whether the item is a drug, a device or a biologic. Then, FDA determines which center (Center for Drug Evaluation and Research (CDER), CBER or CDRH) is the primary reviewer. However, representatives of the other appropriate centers are included on the review committee.

If it is not clear whether the combination product is a device or drug, the manufacturer may file a Request for Designation with FDA. This compels the agency to classify the combination product and indicate which center which is the primary review group. The agency must respond within 60 days.

For more information on combination products, see Chapter 22.

Investigational Device Exemption (IDE) (21 CFR 812)

The IDE regulations provide a means of distributing devices that are not cleared to be marketed (i.e., by 510(k), PMA or Class I exemption) for the purposes of clinical research or to gather clinical evidence of safety and effectiveness. Guidance is provided at *Device Advice: Investigational Device Exemption (IDE).*[4]

Quoting the regulations (21 CFR 812.1):

"An IDE approved under 812.30 or considered approved under 812.2(b) exempts a device from the requirements of the following sections of the Federal Food, Drug, and Cosmetic Act and regulations issued thereunder: Misbranding under section 502 of the act, registration, listing, and premarket notification under section 510, performance standards under section 514, premarket approval under section 515, a banned device regulation under section 516, records and reports under section 519, restricted device requirements under section 520(e), good manufacturing practice requirements under section 520(f) except for the requirements found in 820.30, if applicable (unless the sponsor states an intention to comply with these requirements under 812.20(b)(3) or 812.140(b)(4)(v)) and color additive requirements under section 721."

FDA regulation and guidance often use the terms, "significant risk" device and "non-significant risk" (NSR) device. In practice, FDA considers the risk of the study, not of the device. For example, a Class III device, depending upon the nature of the study, may be in a significant risk study or a non-significant risk study, or in a study that is exempt from IDE requirements. The rest of this section uses FDA's terminology, e.g., "significant risk device."

A "significant risk device" must comply with full IDE requirements, including FDA approval of an IDE submittal. NSR devices must comply with abbreviated IDE requirements as described in 21 CFR 812.2(b). Abbreviated IDE requirements do not require FDA approval, but do require approval by Institutional Review Boards (IRBs). Abbreviated requirements also include informed consent and some reporting and recordkeeping (see **Table 15-1**). FDA IDE approval is presumed for NSR devices.

A "significant risk" device, per 21 CFR 812.3(m), is:

- intended as an implant and poses a serious risk to patient health
- purported or represented to be of use in supporting or sustaining life and presents a serious risk to patient health
- of substantial importance for diagnosing, curing, mitigating or treating disease or preventing impairment of health and poses a serious risk to patient health
- otherwise presents a potential for serious risk to patient health

A device is exempt from the IDE requirements if it is:

- a device in commercial distribution prior to 28 May 1976
- a device, other than a transitional device, "introduced into commercial distribution on or after May 28, 1976, that FDA has determined to be substantially equivalent to a device in commercial distribution immediately before May 28, 1976, and that is used or investigated in accordance with the indications in the labeling FDA reviewed under subpart E of part 807 in determining substantial equivalence"
  (Note that a "transitional device" is one that FDA considered to be a new drug before 28 May 1976)
- a diagnostic device that:
  o is noninvasive
  o does not require a significant risk invasive

sampling procedure
  o does not intentionally introduce energy into a subject
  o is not used for a diagnostic procedure without confirmation by another established procedure
- a device undergoing consumer preference testing, if the testing is not for determining safety and effectiveness or puts the subject at risk
- a device for veterinary use or research on animals
- a custom device unless it is being used to establish safety and efficacy for commercial distribution

An IDE application includes:

1. sponsor name and address
2. a complete report of prior investigations of the device and an accurate summary of those sections of the investigational plan described in 812.25(a)–(e) or, in lieu of the summary, the complete plan; a complete investigational plan and a complete report of prior investigations of the device if no IRB has reviewed them, if FDA has found an IRB's review inadequate or if FDA requests them
3. a description of the methods, facilities and controls used for the manufacture, processing, packing, storage and, where appropriate, installation of the device, in sufficient detail that a person generally familiar with Good Manufacturing Practices can make a knowledgeable judgment about the quality control used in the manufacture of the device
4. an example of the agreements to be entered into by all investigators to comply with investigator obligations, and a list of the names and addresses of all investigators who have signed the agreement
5. a certification that all investigators who will participate in the investigation have signed the agreement, that the list of investigators includes all who are participating in the investigation, and that no investigators will be added to the investigation until they have signed the agreement
6. a list of the name, address and chairperson of each IRB that has been or will be asked to review the investigation and a certification of the action concerning the investigation taken by each such IRB
7. name and address of any institution at which a part of the investigation may be conducted that has not been identified in accordance with the regulations
8. if the device is to be sold, the amount to be charged and an explanation of why sale does not constitute commercialization of the device; the submitter will also need to demonstrate cost recovery if sale is approved
9. a claim for categorical exclusion under 21 CFR 25.30 or 25.34 or an environmental assessment under 25.40

Table 15-1. Abbreviated IDE Requirements, per 21 CFR 812.2(b)

Requirements	Additional Reference
An investigation of a device other than a significant risk device, if the device is not a banned device.	
Device is labeled per 21 CFR 812.5.	21 CFR 812.5
IRB approves after sponsor presents the IRB with a brief explanation of why the device is not a significant risk device.	
Investigators obtain informed consent from each subject.	
Sponsor monitors investigators and promptly secures compliance or takes appropriate measures if investigators fail to meet requirements.	21 CFR 812.46(a)
Sponsor immediately evaluates unanticipated adverse device effects and takes appropriate action, including termination of the study if there is an unreasonable risk to subject. A terminated study may not be resumed without IRB approval.	21 CFR 812.46(b)
Sponsor keeps records: • basic study information per 21 CFR 812.140(b)(4) • records concerning adverse device effects	21 CFR 812.140(b)(4) and (5)
Investigators keep records: • each subject's documents evidencing informed consent.	21 CFR 812.140(a)(3)(i)
Sponsor reports: • to FDA and IRBs, unanticipated adverse device effects • to FDA and IRBs, any withdrawal of IRB approval • to IRBs, withdrawal of FDA approval • to IRBs, progress reports and final report • to FDA and IRBs, recall and device disposition • to FDA, any report of a failure to obtain informed consent • to FDA, any IRB's determination that a device is a significant risk device • upon request of FDA or IRB, any aspect of the investigation	21 CFR 812 150(b)(1)-(3) and (5)-(10)
Investigator reports • to sponsor and IRB, unanticipated adverse device effects • to sponsor, withdrawal of IRB approval • to sponsor and IRB, any device use without informed consent • upon request of IRB or FDA, any aspect of the investigation	21 CFR 812.150(a)(1), (2), (5), (7)
Sponsor complies with prohibitions against promotion.	21 CFR 812.7

10. copies of all device labeling
11. copies of all forms and informational materials to be provided to subjects to obtain informed consent
12. any other relevant information FDA requests for review of the application
    a. additional information—FDA may request additional information concerning an investigation or revision in the investigational plan. This constitutes a clinical hold. The sponsor may treat such a request as a disapproval of the application for purposes of requesting a hearing.
    b. Information previously submitted—information previously submitted to CDRH need not be resubmitted, but may be incorporated by reference.

FDA requires a risk analysis under 21 CFR 812.25 Investigational Plan. This is a description and analysis of increased risks to which subjects will be exposed by the investigation; the manner in which these risks are minimized; a justification for the investigation; and a description of the patient population, including the number, age, sex and condition.

When considering an IDE application, FDA reviews background information, such as animal testing, bench testing and the clinical protocol, to determine whether the product is safe for testing in humans and whether efficacy can be shown based upon the protocol requirements.

Supplemental IDE Submissions

Supplemental submissions are required for changes in the investigational plan, informed consent or other substantive information. Supplemental IDE submissions include:
- an IDE supplement, which is any additional submission to an IDE after approval of the IDE
- an IDE amendment is any additional submissions to an IDE before approval of the IDE

Institutional Review Board (IRB) Approval

Per 21 CFR 812.42, IRB approval is necessary before an investigation begins. For further information on IRB regulations and consent forms, see 21 CFR 50 and 56, respectively.

Pre-IDE Meeting

Sponsors are encouraged to contact FDA to obtain further guidance prior to the submission of an IDE application. (Pre-IDE Meetings may also be used to obtain guidance on 510(k) submissions even though no clinical data are required.) Early interaction with the agency should help increase the sponsor's understanding of FDA requirements, regulations and guidance documents, and allows FDA personnel to familiarize themselves with the new technologies. Communication with FDA may take the form of a Pre-IDE Meeting and/or a Pre-IDE Submission.

Informal Guidance Meeting

Sponsors are encouraged to meet with the Office of Device Evaluation (ODE) reviewing division so the division can provide advice that can be used to develop supporting preclinical data or the investigational plan. These meetings may take the form of telephone conference calls, video conferences or face-to-face discussions. The sponsor should contact the reviewing division directly or may contact the IDE staff for assistance.

Formal Guidance Meetings

There are two types of formal guidance meetings, a Determination Meeting and an Agreement Meeting.

For a Determination Meeting, a sponsor anticipating the submission of a PMA submits a written request to discuss the types of valid scientific evidence necessary to demonstrate that the device is effective for its intended use. This meeting focuses on the broad outline of clinical trial design. The request and summary information for a meeting should be submitted as a Pre-IDE Submission and identified as a Determination Meeting request. FDA's determination is provided to the applicant in writing within 30 days following the meeting.

For an Agreement Meeting, a sponsor submits a written meeting request to reach an agreement with FDA regarding the agency's review of an investigational plan (including a clinical protocol). The request and summary information should be submitted as a pre-IDE submission and identified as an Agreement Meeting request. This meeting should take place no later than 30 days after receipt of the request. The written request should include a detailed description of the device, a detailed description of the proposed conditions of use of the device, a proposed plan (including a clinical protocol) for determining whether there is a reasonable assurance of effectiveness, and, if available, information regarding the expected performance of the device. If an agreement is reached between FDA and the sponsor or applicant regarding the investigational plan (including a clinical protocol), the terms of the agreement are put into writing and made part of the administrative record by FDA.

To request a formal guidance meeting, use the format in, *Early Collaboration Meetings Under the FDA Modernization Act (FDAMA), Final Guidance for Industry and CDRH Staff.*[5]

It is important to establish a good working relationship with the FDA project officer. The project officer may expedite meeting requests and can also provide clarification, ideas and suggestions.

510(k) Premarket Notification

A 510(k) submission is made for a new or modified device for which the product classification requires a 510(k). Some Class I products, most Class II products and a small number of Class III products require a 510(k). Product families, such as catheters of various sizes or patient monitor systems of varying configurations, can be cleared on a single 510(k) if the intended uses, technological characteristics and issues of safety and effectiveness are essentially the same within the family.

The purpose of a 510(k) is to demonstrate that a new or modified device is "substantially equivalent" in intended use, safety and effectiveness as a "predicate device." A predicate device is a legally marketed device that was cleared onto the market by a 510(k).

The content of 510(k) premarket notifications, described in 21 CFR 807.87, includes: the device name and class, an establishment registration number, an "Indications for Use Statement," a 510(k) summary, proposed labeling, substantial equivalence comparison with the predicate device, supporting performance data and a statement that all data and information submitted are truthful and accurate and that no material fact has been omitted. In particular, the Indications for Use Statement provides the specific indications, clinical settings, target population, anatomical sites, device configuration and other information critical to how the device is intended to be used clinically.

The format and amount of information in a 510(k) varies depending upon the intended use, technology, issues of safety and effectiveness, reliance on standards and special controls and, for modified devices, on the nature of the modification.

For more detail, see *Device Advice: Premarket Notification.*[6] This webpage and three linked guidances provide advice on content and links to required forms. Using the recommended format for 510(k) submissions helps reviewers find required information. Companies preparing 510(k)s help ensure the completeness of the submittal when they combine the preparation guidance with product- and technology-specific guidances.[7] (Note: Refer to the CBER website for guidances specific to 510(k)s reviewed by CBER.[8])

Often, clinical studies are not required for 510(k) devices. However, clinical studies may be necessary if the 510(k) device cannot be shown to be as safe and effective as the predicate device using laboratory tests, such as biocompatibility, engineering, bench performance, design verification and voluntary standards tests.

The required truthful and accurate statement, which must be signed by a designated and accountable person within the company requesting market clearance, is defined in 21 CFR 807.87(k) as:

> "A statement that the submitter believes, to the best of his or her knowledge, that all data and information submitted in the premarket notification are truthful and accurate and that no material fact has been omitted."

The truthful and accurate statement carries significant legal implications and should be taken seriously by the individual signing it. It essentially amounts to a certification and, should FDA subsequently determine that false information or misstatement of material facts were included in the submission, or that material facts were omitted, judicial action could be taken against the person who signed the statement. It is prudent to conduct a formal audit of the information in the 510(k), including pertinent development information, documentation and raw data, prior to signing this statement.

Modifications to 510(k) Devices

A new 510(k) application is required for changes or modifications to an existing device when the modifications could significantly affect the device's safety or effectiveness, or if the device is to be marketed for a new or different indication.

When a 510(k) holder decides to modify an existing device, it must determine whether the proposed modification(s) requires submission of a new 510(k). Changes in indications for use, including a switch from prescription status to over-the-counter availability, require the submission of a 510(k).

Examples of modifications that may require a 510(k) submission include, but are not limited to:
- sterilization method
- structural material
- manufacturing method
- operating parameters or conditions for use
- patient or user safety features
- sterile barrier packaging material
- stability or expiration claims
- design

More detail is provided in the guidance, *Deciding When to Submit a 510(k) for a Change to an Existing Device (K97-1)*.[9]

Not all changes to a device require a new submission to FDA. The sponsor must determine whether the submission criteria are met and proceed accordingly. It is good practice for a sponsor to document and file the review of the changes and the decision that a 510(k) is not required.

If a modification requires a 510(k), but the indication for use and the fundamental technology of the device are not affected, a Special 510(k) may be submitted.

Traditional 510(k)

See the guidance, *How to Prepare a Traditional 510(k)*.[10] The traditional 510(k) format is the default format. Alternatives are the Abbreviated 510(k) and the Special 510(k).

Abbreviated 510(k)

See the guidance, *How to Prepare an Abbreviated 510(k)*.[11] An Abbreviated 510(k) relies on the use of guidance documents, special controls and standards (particularly FDA recognized consensus standards). An Abbreviated 510(k) submission must include required elements. Under certain conditions, the submitter may not need to include test data.

Device sponsors may choose to submit an Abbreviated 510(k) when:
- a guidance documents already exists
- a special control has already been established
- FDA has recognized a relevant consensus standard

In an Abbreviated 510(k) submission, sponsors provide summary reports on the use of guidance documents and/or special controls or Declarations of Conformity to recognized consensus standards to expedite submission review.

An Abbreviated 510(k) that relies on a guidance document should include a summary report that describes the way in which the relevant guidance document was employed. It should also note how the guidance was used during device development and testing. The summary report should include information regarding the sponsor's efforts to conform to the guidance and outline any deviations.

Special controls are a way of providing reasonable assurance of a Class II device's safety and effectiveness. Special controls are defined as those controls (such as performance standards, postmarket surveillance, patient registries, development and dissemination of guidelines, recommendations and other appropriate actions) that establish reasonable assurance of the device's safety and effectiveness. The device classification regulations list special controls for the device, if any.

An Abbreviated 510(k) that relies on a special control(s) includes a summary report that describes adherence to the special control(s). It also notes how the special control(s) was used during device development and testing, including how it was used to address a specific risk or issue. The summary report includes information regarding the sponsor's efforts to conform to the special control(s) and should outline any deviations.

Recognized consensus standards may be cited in guidance documents or individual policy statements, or established as special controls that address specific risks associated with a type of device. FDA has recognized more than 800 standards to which 510(k) submitters can declare conformity. The current list of FDA recognized consensus standards is available in CDRH's standards database.[12]

A submitter may suggest a standard that is not yet recognized by FDA. The submitter should discuss such a strategy with FDA prior to submitting an Abbreviated 510(k) based on an unrecognized standard.

An Abbreviated 510(k) that relies on a standard must include a Declaration of Conformity to the standard.

If FDA determines that an Abbreviated 510(k) does not meet eligibility requirements, the reviewer notifies the sponsor of this decision and offers the option of having the document converted to a traditional 510(k) or withdrawing it for future submission. If the 510(k) is withdrawn and a new one submitted, a new user fee applies. If the 510(k) is converted, the original receipt date remains as the start of the review period. Sponsors should be aware that, in most cases, additional information is necessary for converted submissions.

In the Abbreviated 510(k) process, a sponsor must assess the device's conformance to a recognized consensus standard. Once the assessment is satisfactorily completed, the sponsor may submit the Abbreviated 510(k). Under certain conditions, conformance test data are not required to be submitted in the 510(k). To be sure, consult with the reviewing branch.

The sponsor may use a third party to assess conformance to the recognized consensus standard. The third party performs a conformance assessment with the standard for the sponsor and provides the sponsor with a statement to this effect. For example, a third party may be used to assess conformance to the standard for electromagnetic interference testing and shock hazards, IEC 60601-1-2.

The Abbreviated 510(k) should include a Declaration of Conformity signed by the sponsor, while the third party's statement should be maintained in the Device Master Record (DMR) and Design History File (DHF) (21 CFR 820.30).

Declarations of Conformity to recognized consensus standards should include the following:

- identification of applicable recognized consensus standards met
- statement, for each consensus standard, that all requirements were met except inapplicable requirements or deviations
- identification, for each consensus standard, of any way(s) in which it may have been adapted for application to the device under review (e.g., identification of an alternative series of tests that were performed)

- identification, for each consensus standard, of any requirements not applicable to the device
- specification of any deviations from each applicable standard that were applied
- specification of the differences that may exist, if any, between the tested device and the device to be marketed and a justification of the test results in these areas of difference
- name and address of any test laboratory and/or certification body involved in determining the device's conformance with applicable consensus standards and a reference to any of those organizations' accreditations

Special 510(k)

See the guidance, *How to Prepare a Special 510(k).*[13] If a 510(k) is needed for a device's modification and if the modification does not affect the device's intended use or alter its fundamental scientific technology, summary information resulting from the design control process can serve as the basis for clearing the application along with the required elements of a 510(k).

Modifications to the indications for use or any labeling change that affects the device's intended use are not accepted as a Special 510(k). Special 510(k) sponsors should highlight or otherwise prominently identify changes in the proposed labeling that may result from modifications to the legally marketed device. It should be clearly stated in the Special 510(k) that the intended use of the modified device has not changed as a result of the modification(s). Note that a labeling change from prescription to over-the-counter use, or vice versa, is considered a change in intended use and is not eligible for a Special 510(k) submission.

Special 510(k)s are not accepted for modifications that alter the device's fundamental scientific technology. Such changes include modifications to the device's operating principle(s) or mechanism of action. Specific examples that illustrate types of changes that alter the fundamental scientific technology and should not be submitted as Special 510(k)s include:

- a change in a surgical instrument that uses a sharpened metal blade to one that cuts with a laser
- a change in an in vitro diagnostic device (IVD) that uses immunoassay technology to one that uses nucleic acid hybridization or amplification technology
- incorporation of a sensing mechanism in a device to allow it to function "on demand" rather than continuously

Device modifications that should be appropriate for review as Special 510(k)s include:

- energy type
- environmental specifications

- performance specifications
- ergonomics of the patient-user interface
- dimensional specifications
- software or firmware
- packaging or expiration dating
- sterilization

A sponsor may make changes to the device that do not change the intended use or alter the technology and may not require a 510(k) submission. These changes may be minor but do require appropriate change control in the DMR and DHF.

Third Party Review

See the "Device Advice" guidance *Third Party Review*.[14] *FDAMA* established the Accredited Persons Program. Accredited Persons, which may be companies or individuals, are authorized to perform 510(k) reviews for certain Class II devices. The product classification database includes for each classification, what Accredited Persons, if any, are authorized to perform third party reviews for the device classification. Third party reviews are not subject to an FDA user fee. However, the fee paid to the third party reviewer is usually higher than the FDA 510(k) user fee. Advantages of third party reviews typically include:

- shorter review times
- responsiveness to questions
- expertise in testing, standards and international requirements
- local service, depending upon the location of the third party reviewer's office

Premarket Approval (21 CFR 814)

Premarket Approval (PMA) is the FDA process of scientific and regulatory review to evaluate the safety and effectiveness of Class III medical devices. A PMA is the most stringent type of device marketing application required by FDA. PMA approval is based on a determination by FDA that the PMA contains sufficient "valid scientific evidence" to assure that the device is safe and effective for its intended use(s).

There are essentially two types of PMA Applications:
- Traditional PMA
- Product Development Process

FDAMA introduced other Premarket Approval options:
- Modular PMA
- Streamlined PMA
- Humanitarian Device Exemption

See *PMA Application Methods*.[15]

Traditional PMA

The information required in a PMA is detailed in 21

CFR 814.20(b). In addition to voluntary completion of the applicable sections of a cover sheet, other required information includes:

1. table of contents showing the volume and page number for each item
2. summary of information in the submission, including:
   a. general description of the indications for use
   b. explanation of how the device functions, the scientific concepts upon which the device is based, general physical and performance characteristics, and a brief description of the manufacturing process, if it aids understanding
   c. generic, proprietary and trade name of the device
   d. description of existing alternative practices and procedures for which the device is intended
   e. brief description of the device's foreign and US marketing history by the applicant and/or any other person, including a list of the countries in which it has been marketed and from which marketing was withdrawn because of adverse safety and effectiveness experiences
   f. summary of studies and reports submitted with the PMA, including:
      i. nonclinical laboratory studies
      ii. human clinical investigations, other data, information or reports relevant to an evaluation of the device's safety and effectiveness from any source, known or that reasonably should be known to the applicant
      iii. discussion demonstrating that data and information in the submission constitute valid scientific evidence providing reasonable assurance of the device's safety and effectiveness, and conclusions drawn from the studies with a discussion of risk/benefit considerations and adverse effects
3. complete description of:
   a. device, including photos, drawings and schematics
   b. each functional component and/or ingredient
   c. device properties relative to its specific indications for use
   d. principles of operation
   e. methods, facilities and controls used to manufacture, process, package, store and, if appropriate, install the device
4. references to any performance standard in effect or proposed at the time of submission and any voluntary standard relevant to the device's safety or effectiveness, including adequate information to demonstrate compliance with the applicable standards and an

explanation of any deviation from the standards

5. technical sections containing data and information in sufficient detail to enable approval or disapproval of the application, including results of:
   a. nonclinical laboratory studies in a separate section, including a statement that each study was conducted in accordance with Good Laboratory Practices (21 CFR 58)
   b. human clinical investigations in a separate section, including a statement that each study was conducted in accordance with IRB rules (21 CFR 56), informed consent rules (21 CFR 50) and IDE rules (21 CFR 812)
6. bibliography of all published reports that are known or reasonably should be known concerning the device's safety or effectiveness not submitted under number 5 above:
   a. identification, analysis and discussion of any other data, information and reports relevant to the evaluation of the device's safety and effectiveness from any source that are known or reasonably should be known
   b. copies of all reasonably obtainable published and unpublished reports described in 3d and 3e, if requested by FDA or an FDA Advisory Committee
7. samples of the device and its components, if requested by FDA, submitted or available at a named location if impractical to submit
8. copies of all proposed labeling including labels, instructions for use, installation, maintenance and servicing, and any information, literature and/ or advertising that constitutes labeling (Section 201(m) of the *FD&C Act* and 21 CFR 801 or 809)
9. environmental assessment in accordance with 21 CFR 25.20(n) or justification for categorical exclusion under 21 CFR 25.30 and 25.34
10. disclosure of any financial arrangements between the sponsor and clinical investigators who performed studies included in the submission, or a certification on Form FDA 3454 attesting to the absence of any financial arrangements (21 CFR 54)
11. any other information requested by FDA

Omission of any required information must be identified and justified in a statement attached as a separate section of the PMA. A DMF or other applicable information in FDA files may be incorporated by reference. However, if this information was not submitted by the PMA applicant, the applicant must receive permission from the filer of the information for it to be reviewed by FDA.

The sponsor is required to periodically update a pending PMA with new or newly learned safety and effectiveness information that could reasonably affect the device's

evaluation and labeling (21 CFR 814.20(e)). To ensure adherence to all content and format requirements, manufacturers should carefully review the regulations in 21 CFR 814.20(a)–(h), as well as FDA's guideline on the arrangement and format of a PMA.

Traditional PMA Review Process

The PMA review is performed by an FDA team generally consisting of a medical officer, engineer, biologist, statistician, labeling expert and manufacturing expert. A decision to approve or not approve must be made by FDA within 180 calendar days following receipt of a complete PMA, although, in reality, reviews take much longer.

During the review process, FDA will order an inspection of the sponsor's manufacturing facility to provide evidence that the manufacturer complies with GMP requirements set forth in the QSR (21 CFR 820).

Often, PMAs for important or new technologies will also be reviewed by FDA advisory panels consisting of experts in the medical specialty (e.g., MDs, PhDs, engineers) and consumer and industry representatives. Advisory personnel are not regular employees of FDA, but are paid as "special government employees" for the days they participate as members of a panel. The panel members' recommendation is not binding, however FDA generally follows their advice.

The FDA review process can result in the following outcomes:

- Approval—The PMA substantially meets the requirements of the applicable part of the regulations and the device is safe and effective for its intended use(s).
- Not Approvable—The PMA has major deficiencies and review issues remain that stand in the way of approval (specifically identified in a letter to the applicant). This requires submission of a PMA amendment(s) by the applicant to respond to issues, and results in additional review cycle.
- Denial—The PMA does not meet the requirements of the applicable part of the regulations and the device is not safe and effective for its intended use(s).

PMA Amendments—21 CFR 814.37

Changes or revisions to the original PMA submission are submitted to FDA in the form of amendments. Amendments are also submitted to FDA for changes to PMA supplements.

PMA Supplements

When a significant change to the device approved under a PMA affects the device's safety or effectiveness, a supplement to the original PMA is required. This became law when the *FD&C Act* was amended by Section 515(d)(6).

PMA supplements that are required include:

- new indication for use of the device
- labeling changes
- the use of a different facility or establishment to manufacture, process, sterilize or package the device
- changes in manufacturing facilities, methods or quality control procedures
- changes in sterilization procedures
- changes in packaging
- changes in the performance or design specifications, circuits, components, ingredients, principles of operation or physical layout of the device
- extension of the device's expiration date based on data obtained under a new or revised stability or sterility testing protocol that has not been approved by FDA (If the protocol has been previously approved by FDA, a supplement is not submitted but the change must be reported to FDA in the postapproval periodic reports as described in the Section 814.39(b).)

Supplements that are pending can also be amended with more information.

There are several ways of filing a PMA supplement:

PMA Supplement (180 days)—21 CFR 814.39(a)

The PMA Supplement is for significant changes that affect the device's safety and effectiveness and will require an in-depth review and approval by FDA before implementing the change. This may also require review by an advisory panel.

Special PMA Supplement—Changes Being Effected (CBE)—21 CFR 814.39(d)

The CBE is generally used when the change enhances or increases the device's safety. It does not require FDA approval before making the change. Examples are labeling changes that add more relevant information and increased quality control testing.

30-day Notice and 135 PMA Supplement—21 CFR 814.39(f)

A 30-day Notice is used for modifications to manufacturing procedures or methods that affect the device's safety and effectiveness. If FDA does not respond within 30 days after notification, the change can be made to the device and it can be marketed accordingly. If FDA finds the 30-day Notice is not adequate, but contains data meeting appropriate content requirements for a PMA supplement, the 30-day Notice will become a 135-day PMA Supplement.

PMA Manufacturing Site Change Supplement

When the manufacturing site is changed, a supplement needs to be filed. The site must have received a Quality System/GMP inspection within the last two years. If requirements are not met, a 180-day PMA Supplement must be submitted.

Annual (Periodic) Report or 30-day Supplements—21 CFR 814.39(e)

Changes can also be reported in the Annual Report instead of in a formal supplement. However, to use this approach, a sponsor should seek an advisory opinion from FDA.

"Real-Time" Review Program for PMA Supplements

In April 1996, ODE implemented a pilot program for "Real-Time" reviews of PMA supplements where the sponsor and the FDA review team meet to discuss any concerns FDA may have. Results of the pilot program demonstrated that faster review times for manufacturers and efficient use of FDA staff time were achieved. Because this type of review is not available for all supplements, a sponsor is advised to contact its FDA reviewer to understand the criteria established for the "Real-Time" review program within a particular branch and division within ODE.

The Product Development Protocol (PDP)

The PDP was authorized several years ago as an alternative to the IDE and PMA in *FD&C Act* Section 515(f). For Class III devices subject to premarket approval, the successful completion of a PDP results in market clearance and essentially is a PMA approval.

One intent of the *Medical Device Amendments* of 1976 was to create an alternate pathway for device approval and marketing by having the sponsor and FDA agree early in the development process on items needed for the successful analysis of a Class III device's safety and efficacy.

Once agreement is reached, the PDP contains all the information about design and development activities and acceptance criteria. A project timeline is established and information is furnished to FDA to review in a sequential fashion.

The PDP consists of:
- a description of the device and any changes that may be made to the device
- a description of the preclinical trials, if any
- a description of the clinical trials, if any
- a description of the manufacturing methods, facilities and controls
- a description of any applicable performance standards
- specimens of proposed labeling
- any other information "relevant to the subject matter of the protocol"

Upon completion of clinical studies, reports are furnished to FDA, which has 120 days to act on a PDP. Currently, the PDP approval approach is rarely utilized.

Modular PMA

The *Medical Device User Fee and Modernization Act* (*MDUFMA*) amended Section 515(c) of the *FD&C Act* to allow early FDA review of PMA information submitted in separate modules. Though the Modular PMA has the same content requirements as the Traditional PMA, the sponsor must meet with FDA to come to an agreement with the agency on the content of the PMA "Shell," a framework of modules that identifies the information necessary to support the filing and approval. Generally, this occurs during a pre-IDE submission meeting.

Each module is submitted to FDA as it is completed. The target FDA review period is 90 days for each module or amendment submitted in response to an agency deficiency letter. Upon receipt of the final module, a PMA number is assigned and a 180-day review clock will start. The entire PMA User Fee is due with the submission of the first module.

The Modular PMA is particularly useful for devices at an early stage of development, rather than for devices that are far along in the development process.

Advantages of the Modular PMA may include:
- allows more efficient use of resources
- potentially reduces PMA application review time
- creates ongoing open dialogue between FDA and the sponsor

Disadvantages may include:
- can cost more money and lengthen time to approval
- the need to establish a plan prior to approaching FDA about utilizing the modular approach

To file a Modular PMA, follow FDA's guidance document, *Premarket Approval Application Modular Review* (3 November 2003).[16]

Streamlined PMA

A Streamlined PMA is designed for devices using well-known technologies for well-known disease processes. A PMA may qualify as streamlined if: the device has a review guidance; four or more previous PMAs have been approved for the same type of device; or the device has a study protocol jointly developed by the manufacturer and FDA. The Manufacturing Facility Inspection may be deferred if FDA completed a GMP inspection within past two years. The review time is the same as for Traditional PMAs (180 days).

Humanitarian Device Exemption (HDE)—21 CFR 814 Subpart H

A Humanitarian Use Device (HUD) is intended to benefit patients by treating or diagnosing a disease or condition that affects or is manifested in fewer than 4,000 individuals in the US per year. The number of patient contacts with a device may exceed one per patient, but the total number of patients treated or diagnosed with the device is fewer than 4,000 per year.

The HUD regulation provides a financial incentive for the development of devices for these small populations because manufacturer's research and development costs far exceed market returns for diseases or conditions affecting small patient populations.

A sponsor must receive Humanitarian Use status by submitting a Request for HUD Designation to FDA's Office of Orphan Products Development (OOPD).

The request should include:
- a statement that the applicant is requesting a HUD designation for a rare disease or condition
- the applicant's name and address
- a description of the rare disease or condition for which the device is to be used
- a description of the device
- documentation, with appended authoritative references, to demonstrate that the device is designed to treat or diagnose a disease or condition that affects or is manifested in fewer than 4,000 people in the US per year

A Humanitarian Device Exemption Application (HDE) is similar in both form and content to a Traditional PMA application, however it is exempt from the effectiveness requirements of a PMA. An HDE is not required to contain the results of scientifically valid clinical investigations demonstrating that the device is effective for its intended purpose. An HDE must contain sufficient information for FDA to determine that the device does not pose an unreasonable or significant risk of illness or injury, and that the probable benefit to health outweighs the risk of injury or illness from its use, taking into account the probable risks and benefits of currently available devices or alternative forms of treatment. Finally, the applicant must demonstrate that no comparable devices are available to treat or diagnose the disease or condition, and that they could not otherwise bring the device to market.

The agency has 75 days from the date of receipt to review an HDE. This includes a 30-day filing period during which the agency determines whether the HDE is sufficiently complete to permit substantive review. If FDA notifies the sponsor that the HDE is incomplete and cannot be filed, the 75 day timeframe resets upon receipt of any additional information.

When approved by FDA, an HUD may only be used in facilities that have established a local institutional review board (IRB) to supervise clinical testing of devices and have obtained IRB approval for the use of the device to treat or diagnose the specific disease.

HDE amendments and supplements are subject to the same regulations as those for Traditional PMAs; however, the review timeframe for HDE amendments and supplements is 75 days, the same as for HDE originals.

Expedited Review
Devices Appropriate for Expedited Review

FDA considers a device or combination product containing a device appropriate for expedited review if the device or combination product:

1. is intended to treat or diagnose a life-threatening or irreversibly debilitating disease or condition
2. addresses an unmet medical need, as demonstrated by one of the following:
   a. The device represents a breakthrough technology that provides a clinically meaningful advantage over existing technology. Breakthrough technologies should be demonstrated to lead to a clinical improvement in the treatment or diagnosis of the life-threatening or irreversibly debilitating condition.
   b. No approved alternative treatment or means of diagnosis exists.
   c. The device offers significant, clinically meaningful advantages over existing approved alternative treatments. The device should provide a clinically important earlier or more accurate diagnosis, or offer important therapeutic advantages in safety and/or effectiveness over existing alternatives. Such advantages may include demonstrated superiority over current treatments for effects on serious outcomes, the ability to provide clinical benefit for those patients unable to tolerate current treatments, or the ability to provide a clinical benefit without the serious side effects associated with current treatments.
   d. The availability of the device is in the best interest of patients. That is, the device provides a specific public health benefit or meets the need of a well-defined patient population. This may also apply to a device that was designed or modified to address an unanticipated serious failure occurring in a critical component of an approved device for which there are no alternatives, or for which alternative treatment would entail substantial risk of morbidity for the patient.

Proposed Submission Changes

In 2009, CDRH established two committees—the 510(k) Working Group and the Task Force on the Utilization of Science in Regulatory Decision Making—to address challenges and explore opportunities to improve the 510(k) process. The Institute of Medicine is conducting

an independent evaluation. In addition, CDRH has conducted public meetings and "town hall meetings" to gather input from sponsors and other constituencies affected by the device approval processes.

The Working Group and the Task Force issued 55 recommendations. CDRH reported that in public comments, 28 recommendations were supported, 12 were supported with caveat or modification, and 15 received significant concern. In 2011, CDRH is focusing on implementing the 40 recommendations that received support or support with modification. Recommendations to be implemented include:

- issuing more guidances for the 510(k) program
- increasing and improving training for FDA and industry
- improving CDRH business processes
- streamlining the de novo process

Of the 15 recommendations, seven were referred to the Institute of Medicine, four will be implemented on a case-by-case basis, and one was dropped (with clarification through training). The remaining three will be implemented with significant modifications to address the concerns.

In 2011 and 2012, there will be many changes—hopefully improvements—in CDRH's processes, particularly the 510(k) process. Sponsors should continually review plans and progress online at *CDRH Plan of Action for 510(k) and Science*.[17]

Summary

- FDA regulations for devices comprise sets of rules that classify devices that require agency clearance or approval. Devices may be classified into Class I, II or III. Reclassification or the de novo process allow classifications to be changed, but are complex. Classes I and II may require 510(k) Notification or may be 510(k)-exempt. Except for a small and decreasing number, Class III devices require a PMA. The exceptions require a 510(k).
- Significant risk clinical studies require FDA approval of an IDE.
- Pre-IDE meetings provide a mechanism for sponsors to discuss proposals for submission strategies, as well as clinical trials, with FDA.
- CDRH is implementing a large number of changes to the 510(k) and related device approval and business processes.

References

1. CDRH Product Classification Database, www.accessdata.fda.gov/scripts/cdrh/cfdocs/cfPCD/PCDSimpleSearch.cfm. Accessed 11 April 2011.
2. 515 Program Initiative, www.fda.gov/AboutFDA/

CentersOffices/CDRH/CDRHTransparency/ ucm240310.htm. Accessed 11 April 2011.

3. CDRHLearn class regarding 513(g) Requests for Determination, www.fda.gov/MedicalDevices/ ResourcesforYou/Industry/ucm127147.htm. Accessed 11 April 2011.

4. *Device Advice: Investigational Device Exemption* (IDE), www.fda.gov/MedicalDevices/ DeviceRegulationandGuidance/ HowtoMarketYourDevice/ InvestigationalDeviceExemptionIDE/default.htm. Accessed 11 April 2011.

5. *Early Collaboration Meetings Under the FDA Modernization Act (FDAMA), Final Guidance for Industry and CDRH Staff*, www.fda.gov/ MedicalDevices/DeviceRegulationandGuidance/ GuidanceDocuments/ucm073604.htm. Accessed 11 April 2011.

6. *Device Advice: Premarket Notification*, www.fda.gov/ MedicalDevices/DeviceRegulationandGuidance/ HowtoMarketYourDevice/PremarketSubmissions/ PremarketNotification510k/default.htm. Accessed 11 April 2011.

7. *Device Advice: Device Regulation and Guidance*, www.fda.gov/MedicalDevices/ DeviceRegulationandGuidance/default.htm. Accessed 11 April 2011.

8. *Guidance, Compliance & Regulatory Information (Biologics)*, www.fda.gov/BiologicsBloodVaccines/ GuidanceComplianceRegulatoryInformation/ default.htm. Accessed 11 April 2011.

9. *Deciding When to Submit a 510(k) for a Change to an Existing Device (K97-1)*, www.fda.gov/ MedicalDevices/DeviceRegulationandGuidance/ GuidanceDocuments/ucm080235.htm. Accessed 11 April 2011.

10. *How to Prepare a Traditional 510(k)*, www.fda.gov/ MedicalDevices/DeviceRegulationandGuidance/ HowtoMarketYourDevice/PremarketSubmissions/ PremarketNotification510k/ucm134572.htm. Accessed 11 April 2011.

11. *How to Prepare an Abbreviated 510(k)*, www.fda.gov/ MedicalDevices/DeviceRegulationandGuidance/ HowtoMarketYourDevice/PremarketSubmissions/ PremarketNotification510k/ucm134574.htm. Accessed 11 April 2011.

12. CDRH's Standards database, www.accessdata.fda. gov/scripts/cdrh/cfdocs/cfStandards/search.cfm. Accessed 11 April 2011.

13. *How to Prepare a Special 510(k)*, www.fda.gov/ MedicalDevices/DeviceRegulationandGuidance/ HowtoMarketYourDevice/PremarketSubmissions/ PremarketNotification510k/ucm134573.htm. Accessed 11 April 2011.

14. *Device Advice: Third Party Review*, www.fda.gov/ MedicalDevices/DeviceRegulationandGuidance/ HowtoMarketYourDevice/PremarketSubmissions/ ThirdParyReview/default.htm. Accessed 11 April 2011.

15. *PMA Application Methods*, www.fda.gov/ MedicalDevices/DeviceRegulationandGuidance/ HowtoMarketYourDevice/PremarketSubmissions/ PremarketApprovalPMA/ucm048168.htm. Accessed 11 April 2011.

16. *Premarket Approval Application Modular Review November 3, 2003*, www.fda.gov/ MedicalDevices/DeviceRegulationandGuidance/ GuidanceDocuments/ucm089764.htm. Accessed 11 April 2011.

17. *CDRH Plan of Action for 510(k) and Science*, www. fda.gov/AboutFDA/CentersOffices/CDRH/ CDRHReports/ucm239448.htm. Accessed 11 April 2011.

Medical Device Compliance and Postmarketing Activities

By Richard Angelo, PhD

Objectives

- Develop a basic understanding of FDA regulations that establish compliance and postmarketing requirements for manufacturers and importers of devices marketed in the US
- Learn how to prepare and file establishment registrations and device listings with FDA
- Review FDA's Quality System Regulation (QSR) for medical devices, as well as FDA's approach to medical device manufacturer inspections
- Understand postmarketing requirements for medical device reports (MDRs), corrections and removals (recalls) and medical device tracking
- Review US requirements for importing and exporting devices

Laws, Regulations and Guidelines Covered in This Chapter

- *Pure Food and Drugs Act* of 1906
- *Federal Food, Drug, and Cosmetic Act* of 1938 *(FD&C Act)*
- *FD&C Act* as amended by the *Food and Drug Administration Modernization Act* of 1997 *(FDAMA)*
  - Chapter III—Prohibited Acts and Penalties
  - Chapter V—Drugs and Devices
    - *Section 501—Adulterated Drugs and Devices*
    - *Section 502—Misbranded Drugs and Devices*
    - *Section 506A—Manufacturing Changes*
    - *Section 506B—Reports of Postmarketing Studies*
    - *Section 518(e)—Recall Authority*
    - *Section 519(e)—Device Tracking*
    - *Section 522—Postmarket Surveillance*
  - Chapter VIII—Imports and Exports, Sections 801–803
- 21 CFR Part 7 Enforcement Policy—Voluntary recalls
- 21 CFR Part 803 Medical device reporting
- 21 CFR Part 806 Medical devices; reports of corrections and removals
- 21 CFR Part 807 Establishment registration and device listing for manufacturers and initial importers of devices
- 21 CFR Part 810 Medical device recall authority
- 21 CFR 814.82(a)(2) Condition of approval studies
- 21 CFR Part 820 Quality system regulation
- 21 CFR 821 Medical device tracking requirements
- 21 CFR 822 Postmarket surveillance
- *Guidance for Industry and FDA Staff: Implementation of Medical Device Establishment Registration and Device Listing Requirements Established by the Food and Drug Administration Amendments Act of 2007* (October 2009)

- "How-To" Guide: Device Facility User Fee Process (October 2008)
- *Frequently Asked Questions on Recognition of Consensus Standards* (September 2007)
- *Guidance for Industry and FDA Staff: Recognition and Use of Consensus Standards* (September 2007)
- *Quality System Information for Certain Various Premarket Application Reviews; Guidance for Industry and FDA Staff* (February 2003)
- *Design Control Guidance for Medical Device Manufacturers* (March 1997)
- *Do It By Design: An Introduction to Human Factors in Medical Devices* (January 1997)
- *Medical Device Quality Systems Manual: A Small Entity Compliance Guide* (December 1996)
- *Guidelines on General Principles of Process Validation; Final Guidance for Industry and FDA Staff* (January 2002)
- Comparison Chart: 1996 Quality System Regulation Versus 1978 Good Manufacturing Practices Regulation Versus ANSI/ISO/ASQC Q9001 and ISO/DI 13485
- Compliance Program Guidance Manual 7382.845: *Inspection of Medical Device Manufacturers* (2 February 2011)
- *Guide to Inspections of Quality Systems: Quality System Inspection Technique* (August 1999)
- *Inspection by Accredited Persons Under the Medical Device User Fee and Modernization Act of 2002 and the FDA Amendments Act of 2007; Accreditation Criteria* (August 6, 2009)
- *Draft Guidance for Industry, User Facilities and FDA Staff: eMDR: Electronic Medical Device Reporting* (August 2009)
- *Medical Device Reporting—Remedial Action Exemption; Guidance for FDA and Industry* (September 2001)
- *Medical Device Reporting—Alternative Summary Reporting (ASR) Program* (October 2000)
- *Medical Device Reporting: An Overview* (April 1996)
- *Instructions for Completing FDA Form 3500A* (MedWatch) (July 2009)
- *Regulation of Medical Devices: Background Information for International Officials* (April 1999)
- *Guidance for Industry: Exports and Imports Under the FDA Export Reform and Enhancement Act of 1996* (July 2007)
- *Guidance for Industry: Exports Under the FDA Export Reform and Enhancement Act of 1996* (July 2007)
- *Compliance Policy Guide for FDA Staff,* Section 110.100 Certification of Exports (CPG 7150.01)
- *Medical Device Tracking; Guidance for Industry and FDA Staff* (January 2010)
- *Guidance for Industry: Product Recalls, Including Removals and Corrections* (November 2003)
- *Guidance for Industry and FDA Staff: Procedures for Handling Post-Approval Studies Imposed by PMA Order* (June 2009)
- *Guidance for Industry and FDA Staff: Postmarket Surveillance Under Section 522 of the Federal Food, Drug and Cosmetic Act* (April 2006)
- *General Principles of Software Validation; Final Guidance for Industry and FDA Staff:* (January 2002)
- *Final Guidance for Industry, FDA Reviewers and Compliance on Off-the-Shelf Software Use in Medical Devices* (September 1999)
- *Computerized Devices/Processes Guidance: Application of the Medical Device GMP to Computerized Devices and Manufacturing Processes* (February 1997)
- *Design Control Guidance for Medical Device Manufacturers* (March 1997)

Introduction
History of FDA Medical Device Regulations

All US medical device regulations are codified under 21 CFR Parts 800–899. However, the heritage of these regulations begins with the *Pure Food and Drugs Act* of 1906. This act was the true beginning of federal food and drug legislation intended to protect Americans from harmful substances and the deceptive practices that were becoming more and more common. Medical devices were not represented in the act, in large part because contemporary devices, such as stethoscopes and scalpels, were relatively simple and their corresponding risks, if any, were conspicuous. Although medical devices were considered helpful tools, they bore no significant weight and did not play a crucial role in mediating a caregiver's ability to diagnose or treat patients—medical devices neither gave life nor sustained it. It would soon become apparent, however, that medical devices represented fertile ground for new

and far-reaching technological achievements, along with their accompanying risks. Medical device technology, much like a burgeoning youth, would continue to outgrow its regulatory wardrobe over the next century, requiring federal regulations to expand and change at a pace commensurate with the industry.

The modernization of the *Pure Food and Drugs Act* was driven, in part, by the recognized need to introduce a definition of medical devices into federal law. This modernization initiative resulted in the enactment of the *Federal Food, Drug, and Cosmetic Act (FD&C Act)* of 1938, which was the first law to mandate requirements for exporting unapproved devices. For the next 25 years, medical devices were subject only to the discretionary vigilance activities of the US Food and Drug Administration (FDA), whose charge it was to unilaterally determine whether a device was safe and effective, in the absence of any premarket testing, review or approval process. Accordingly, the agency was further empowered to bring federal charges against manufacturers of products or materials found to be either adulterated (e.g., defective, unsafe or unsanitary), or misbranded (e.g., false or misleading statements, designs or labeling).

In the early 1960s, President Kennedy advocated changes to the ways medical devices entered the US market; however, the changes he sought were not realized until the mid-1970s. As the US prepared to celebrate the bicentennial anniversary of its founding, new legislation was enacted that established the ground rules and standards to which all US medical device manufacturers and importers must now adhere: the 1976 *Medical Device Amendments* to the *FD&C Act*. The new law applied safety and effectiveness safeguards to new devices and required FDA to establish, for the first time: regulations concerning establishment registration and device listing; Good Manufacturing Practices (GMPs) for medical devices; medical device reporting (MDR); and guidelines on policy, procedures and industry responsibilities for field corrections and removals.

Numerous changes to device laws and regulations have been implemented via various amendments to the *FD&C Act* over the years. Three of the most notable changes, mandated by the *Safe Medical Devices Act* of 1990 (*SMDA*) and the *Medical Device Amendments* of 1992, were:

- introduction of the Humanitarian Device Exemption (HDE), the medical device equivalent of orphan drug designation, providing limited exemptions from the law for devices intended to treat or diagnose rare diseases or conditions affecting fewer than 4,000 persons
- promulgation of the Quality System Regulation, resulting in substantial revisions that essentially harmonized US GMPs for medical devices with the European quality system regulations in EN 46001 and ISO 9001,[1] and added significant new the GMP regulation, bringing product development under FDA scrutiny for the first time
- establishment of a regulatory requirement (previously an FDA request) that manufacturers and distributors promptly report field corrections and removals to FDA within 10 days after their initiation
- promulgation of the first device tracking regulation

The *FD&C Act* underwent additional change and reform as a result of the *Food and Drug Administration Modernization Act* of 1997 (*FDAMA*). *FDAMA* empowered FDA to restrict the marketing of products for which the manufacturing processes are so deficient that use of the products could present a serious health hazard. The agency was given authority to take appropriate action if a device manufacturer advocates an off-label use of its product that may be potentially harmful. *FDAMA* further enhanced FDA's risk-based approach to medical device regulation, allocating FDA resources and diligence to the oversight of medical devices presenting the greatest risks to patients. For example, the law exempts from premarket notification Class I devices not intended for a use that is of substantial importance in preventing impairment of human health or that do not present a potential unreasonable risk of illness or injury. The law also directs FDA to focus its postmarket surveillance on higher-risk devices and allows the agency to implement a reporting system that concentrates on a representative sample of user facilities—such as hospitals and nursing homes—where patients may experience deaths and serious illnesses or injuries linked with the use of devices.

In addition, *FDAMA* expanded an ongoing pilot program under which FDA accredits outside (third-party) experts to conduct the initial review of all Class I and low-to-intermediate risk Class II device applications. The act, however, prohibits any accredited person from reviewing devices that are permanently implantable, life-supporting, life-sustaining or for which clinical data are required.

The *Medical Device User Fee and Modernization Act* of 2002 (*MDUFMA*), signed into law 26 October 2002, further amended the *FD&C Act* to include provisions that affect the compliance regulations. Under *MDUFMA*:

- Establishment inspections may be conducted by accredited persons (third parties) under carefully prescribed conditions.
- New labeling requirements were established for reprocessed single-use devices.
- The submission of validation data for some reprocessed single-use devices is required. On 30 April 2003, FDA identified the types of devices subject to this requirement (see 68 FR 23139).

MDUFMA made several other significant changes to the law that involve FDA postmarket surveillance appropriations, combination product review, electronic labeling, electronic registration, devices intended for pediatric use and breast implant reports. Additionally, it requires manufacturer identification on the device itself, with certain exceptions.

Background information, reference materials and additional information about *MDUFMA* can be found on the website of FDA's Center for Devices and Radiological Health (CDRH) (www.fda.gov/MedicalDevices/DeviceRegulationandGuidance/Overview/MedicalDeviceUserFeeandModernizationActMDUFMA/default.htm). *MDUFMA* also imposed various user fees. On 28 September 2007, as part of the *Food and Drug Administration Amendments Act* (*FDAAA*), user fees were reauthorized through Fiscal 2012. New fees include:

- a fee for each 30-day notice submitted to FDA
- a fee for each 513(g) request for classification information submitted to FDA
- an annual fee for periodic reporting made under a condition of approval for a Class III device
- an annual fee for the registration of each medical device establishment

Small businesses may qualify for reduced fees through an application process. However, there is no discount for small businesses on the annual establishment registration fee.

Establishment Registration and Product Listing

Registration and listing information provides FDA with the locations of medical device establishments and what devices are manufactured at each site. Knowing where devices are manufactured increases FDA's ability to prepare for and respond to public health emergencies.

A US establishment owner or operator that initiates or develops medical device specifications; manufactures, assembles, processes, repackages or relabels medical devices for domestic human use; or is an initial importer of medical devices (distributor for a foreign manufacturer), must register the establishment annually with FDA and submit medical device listing information, including activities performed on those devices, for all such devices in commercial distribution. Note that if a device requires a premarket submission (e.g., 510(k), Premarket Approval (PMA), Product Development Protocol (PDP) or HDE) for clearance, the owner or operator should also submit the FDA premarket submission number.

There is a fee for annual registration for some establishment types. On 1 October 2008, FDA instituted a new payment process for those establishments required to pay the device establishment user fee. This process involves first visiting the Device Facility User Fee website (DFUF) to pay the user fee and obtain a Payment Identification Number (PIN). Once the payment has been received and processed, the owner or operator will be notified by email. The email will include directions to return to the DFUF website to obtain the Payment Confirmation Number (PCN) for the order. The PIN and PCN are required as proof of payment before the facility can be registered using the FDA Unified Registration and Listing System (FURLS). Detailed information regarding registration and listing can be found at www.fda.gov/MedicalDevices/DeviceRegulationandGuidance/HowtoMarketYourDevice/RegistrationandListing/default.htm.

Changes brought about by *FDAMA* require foreign manufacturers of devices intended for US commercial distribution to also register with FDA and list their products. Additionally, foreign manufacturers are required to designate a US agent to act as the official correspondent responsible for, among other things, submitting establishment registration, device listing and medical device reports (MDRs). This requirement had been indefinitely stayed in July of 1996, but was later reinstated effective 11 February 2002.[2] The responsibilities of US agents are described at http://www.fda.gov/MedicalDevices/DeviceRegulationandGuidance/HowtoMarketYourDevice/RegistrationandListing/ucm053196.htm. For domestic and foreign registration and listing requirements, see **Tables 16-1** and **16-2**, respectively.

The initial registration and listing must be submitted within 30 days prior to starting any operations at the establishment toward the production and/or commercial distribution of finished devices (see **Table 16-3**). A device family with variations in physical characteristics should be considered a single device for listing purposes, provided the function or intended use does not differ within the family. All subsequent establishment registration and product listing information must be updated annually between 1 October and 31 December, even if no changes have occurred. Failure of an establishment to register or maintain its registration can render its commercial medical device products misbranded and subject to regulatory actions.

After 30 September 2007, *FDAAA* mandated that all registration and listing information be submitted electronically via the FURLS Device Registration and Listing Module (DRLM), unless a waiver has been granted. This electronic registration and listing process replaced the previously used Forms FDA 2891 and 2891a, "Registration of Device Establishment," and Form FDA 2892 "Medical Device Listing." All owners or operators can access FURLS at any time throughout the year to update their registration and listing information as changes occur. Examples of changes to listings include:

- another device being introduced into commercial distribution
- a change to a previously listed device, such as where it is manufactured
- a previously listed device is removed from commercial distribution or commercial distribution is resumed

The information required for registering an establishment and listing medical device products is provided in 21 CFR 807.25 and is clearly cued during the electronic registration process. A permanent establishment registration number will be assigned to each registered device establishment.

FDA requires any person or entity that initiates and develops device specifications and commercially distributes that device to register and list any such medical device products (21 CFR 807.20(a)). A person or entity that only manufactures devices according to another's specifications and does not commercially distribute the devices is not required to register. Registration and listing also are not required of contract sterilizers that do not commercially distribute the devices (21 CFR 807.20 (c)(2)). *FDAMA* repealed the previous requirement in 21 CFR 807.20(c) to eliminate the registration and listing requirements for distributors who are not importers, effective 19 February 1998.

As amended by *FDAMA*, 21 CFR 807 asserts that entities that reprocess single-use devices for reuse in human patients are considered manufacturers; therefore, owners and operators of such establishments also must comply with registration and listing requirements. The FDA guidance,

Table 16-1. Domestic Establishment Registration and Listing Requirements

Establishment Activity	Register	List	Pay Fee
Manufacturer	Yes 807.20(a)	Yes 807.20(a)	Yes
Manufacturer of a custom device	Yes 807.20(a)(2)	Yes 807.20(a)(2)	Yes
Manufacturer of accessories or components that are packaged or labeled for commercial distribution for health-related purposes to an end user	Yes 807.20(a)(5)	Yes 807.20(a)(5)	Yes
Manufacturer of components that are distributed only to a finished device manufacturer	No 807.65(a)	No	No
US manufacturer of export-only devices	Yes 807.20(a)(2)	Yes 807.20(a)(2)	Yes
Relabeler or repackager	Yes 807.20(a)(3)	Yes 807.20(a)(3)	No
Contract manufacturer that commercially distributes the device for the specifications developer	Yes 807.20(a)(2)	Yes 807.20(a)(2)	Yes
Contract manufacturer that does not commercially distribute the device for the specifications developer	No	No	No
Contract manufacturer of a subassembly or component, contract packager or labeler	No	No	No
Contract sterilizer that commercially distributes the device	Yes 807.20(a)(2)	Yes 807.20(a)(2)	Yes
Contract sterilizer that does not commercially distribute the device	No	No	No
Kit assembler	Yes 807.20(a)	Yes 807.20(a)	Yes
Domestic distributor	8007.20(c)(3)	No	No
Specification developer	Yes 807.20(a)(1)	Yes 807.20(a)(1)	Yes
Specification consultant only	No	No	No
Initial distributor/importer	Yes 807.40(a)	No Enforcement Discretion Used for 807.22(c)	No
Device being investigated under IDE	No	No 807.40(c)	No
Reprocessor of single-use devices	Yes 807.20	Yes 807.20	Yes
Remanufacturer	Yes	Yes	No

Enforcement Priorities for Single Use Devices Reprocessed by Third Parties and Hospitals[3] provides additional information about this requirement. *MDUFMA* added new regulatory requirements for reprocessed single-use devices that primarily affect premarket submissions for reprocessed devices, "Information on the *Medical Device User Fee and Modernization Act (MDUFMA)* of 2002" (www.fda.gov/ MecicalDevices/DeviceRegulationandGuidance/Overview/ MedicalDeviceUserFeeandModernizationActMDUFMA/ default.htm).

Quality System Regulation

The Quality System Regulation (QSR), codified under 21 CFR Part 820, went into effect on 18 December 1978,

and defined FDA current Good Manufacturing Practice (CGMP) requirements for medical devices and in vitro diagnostic products. Accordingly, the QSR and CGMP for medical devices should be regarded as synonymous.

Over the next 18 years, only three minor changes[4] would be made to the QSR. However, a substantive revision of the QSR, as authorized by the *SMDA*, was undertaken to add design controls, and to harmonize CGMP and quality system regulations with applicable international standards, such as the International Organization for Standards (ISO) 9001:1994 *Quality Systems—Model for Quality Assurance in Design, Development, Production, Installation and Servicing*, and, at the time, the ISO committee draft (CD) revision of ISO/CD 13485 *Quality Systems—Medical Devices—*

Table 16-2. Foreign Establishment Registration and Listing Requirements

Establishment Activity	Register	List	Pay Fee
Foreign manufacturer	Yes 807.40(a)	Yes 807.40(a)	Yes
Foreign exporter of devices located in a foreign country	807.40 (a)	807.40 (a)	No
Contract manufacturer whose device is shipped to US by the contract manufacturer	Yes 807.40(a)	Yes 807.40(a)	Yes
Contract sterilizer whose sterilized device is shipped to the US by the sterilizer	Yes 807.40(a)	Yes 807.40(a)	Yes
Reprocessor of single-use device	807.20(a)	807.20(a)	Yes
Custom device manufacturers	807.20(a)(2)	807.20(a)(2)	Yes
Relabeler or repackager	Yes 807.20(a)(3)	Yes 807.20(a)(3)	No
Kit assembler	Yes 807.20(a)	Yes 807.20(a)	Yes
Device being investigated under IDE	No 812.1(a)	No 812.1(a) 807.40(c)	No
Specification developer	Yes	Yes	Yes
Remanufacturer	Yes	Yes	No
Manufacturer of components that are distributed only by a finished device manufacturer	No 807.65(a)	No	No
Maintains complaint files as required under 21 CFR 820.198 (Note: register as a manufacturer if physical manufacturing taking place at site, Otherwise register as a specification developer)	Yes	Yes	Yes

Supplementary Requirements to ISO 9001. These QSR revisions went into effect 1 June 1997.

FDA has long been a staunch advocate of the international harmonization of medical device standards and regulations, with a shared goal of mutual recognition of CGMP inspections among major global medical device regulatory authorities. FDA's movement toward harmonization and mutual recognition of medical device CGMP inspections, or Quality System Conformity Assessments, was further galvanized through its collaboration with the Global Harmonization Task Force (GHTF) to develop a final rule that incorporates the harmonized quality system requirements, which are today recognized around the world.

GHTF is a voluntary, international group of representatives from medical device regulatory authorities and trade associations comprising the EU and European Free Trade Association (EFTA), the US, Canada, Japan and Australia. Since its inception in 1992, GHTF has pursued international consensus on medical device regulatory controls and practices. FDA, as one of the founding members of GHTF, has enjoyed a central role in this international collaboration to globally harmonize medical device regulations, standards and practices. This partnership has produced more than 30 voluntary guidance documents in pursuit of its pledge to develop a global regulatory model for medical devices. The GHTF Study Groups are focused in these areas: Study Group 1, Premarket Evaluation; Study Group 2, Postmarket Surveillance/Vigilance; Study Group 3, Quality Systems; Study Group 4, Auditing; and Study Group 5, Clinical Safety/Performance. The GHTF website provides substantial information regarding its mission, charter and study groups, and its final guidance documents may be conveniently downloaded (www.ghtf. org/). In March 2011, GHTF announced its decision to reorganize. The new entity will be comprised solely of the regulatory authorities from the member countries and will focus on finding the optimum ways to achieve harmonization at an operational level in such areas as new science and technologies, information and resource sharing and increased opportunities for technical expert interchanges.

The amended QSR also includes:

- management responsibility and review controls (21 CFR 820.20)
- design controls (21 CFR 820.30)
- purchasing controls (21 CFR 820.50)
- process validation requirements (21 CFR 820.75)
- more robust requirements for corrective and preventive action (21 CFR 820.100)

Table 16-3. Registration and Listing Timelines

Information	Due Date
Establishment name and address	Annually between 1 October and 31 December, and anytime throughout year, but within 30 days of change
Owner/operator name and address	Annually between 1 October and 31 December, and anytime throughout year, but within 30 days of change
Official correspondent name and address	Annually between 1 October and 31 December, and anytime throughout year, but within 30 days of change
Trading name(s)	Annually between 1 October and 31 December, and anytime throughout year, but within 30 days of change
US agent (see foreign establishments)	Anytime throughout year, but within 30 days of change
Owner/operator	Anytime throughout year, but within 30 days of change
Proprietary name	Anytime throughout year, but within 30 days of change
Premarket submission number (for nonexempt devices)*	Annually between 1 October and 31 December, and anytime throughout year, but within 30 days of change
Product code (for exempt devices only)	Annually between 1 October and 31 December, and anytime throughout year, but within 30 days of change

* = For devices requiring 510(k) clearance or PMA approval, examples of change to the premarket submission number may be due to a new 510(k) or PMA supplement submitted for design change of a device.

- service recordkeeping and review requirements (21 CFR 820.200)

Although the original medical device GMPs of 1978 distinguished between requirements for critical and noncritical components and devices, this distinction has since disappeared from the QSR, and all medical devices are now subject to common requirements for specifications, acceptance criteria, identification, supplier agreements and records. As stated in 21 CFR 820.30(a), design controls apply to Class III, Class II and certain Class I devices, as listed.

If a device's failure to perform can result in a significant injury, the QSR requires procedures that allow the identification (21 CFR 820.60) and traceability (21 CFR 820.65) of each unit, lot or batch of finished devices, and, where appropriate, components, during all stages of receipt, production, distribution and installation. This is accomplished through the use of a control number intended to aid in any necessary corrective action. This medical device identification is to be documented in the Device History Record (DHR). Traceability generally applies to the manufacturing process of all eligible devices. This differs from medical device tracking (21 CFR 821), wherein the manufacturer must be capable of tracking (e.g., locating) certain devices from the device manufacturing facility to the actual person for whom the device was indicated. Effective tracking of devices from the manufacturing facility, through the distributor network, to

the patient, is necessary in the event that patient notifications or device recalls are necessary. Device tracking requirements for certain devices are further discussed later in this chapter.

The CDRH *Medical Device Quality Systems Manual: A Small Entity Compliance Guide* contains more than 400 pages of detailed guidance information, illustrations and examples of QSR compliance that manufacturers should consider when designing, manufacturing and distributing medical devices.[5] The manual is available on CDRH's website, and each of the 18 chapters and two appendices is available as a separate document that can be downloaded in text format (www.fda.gov/MedicalDevices/DeviceRegulationandGuidance/PostmarketRequirements/QualitySystemsRegulations/MedicalDeviceQualitySystemsManual/default.htm). The manual explains each of the QSR's major provisions and includes a variety of model procedures and example forms. It can assist manufacturers in establishing or upgrading a quality system that will meet the QSR's intent. Quality system elements are traditionally represented by the following documentation (see **Figure 16-1**):

- The quality manual is a document that states the corporate quality policy, describes quality system components and how the system is implemented, and assigns authority and responsibilities. Quality system components typically are linked by specific reference to quality procedures.

Figure 16-1. Quality System Elements

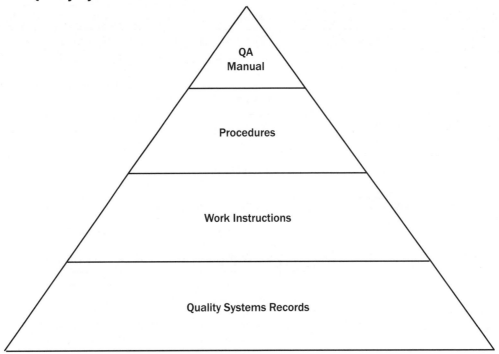

- Quality procedures describe how specific quality system operating processes and controls are implemented. The strength of a set of quality procedures lies in cross-functional and interdepartmental linkages among associated processes and controls.
- Detailed work instructions specify the individual, intradepartmental steps necessary to consistently and reliably perform specific activities, such as those involved in component procurement, inspections, fabrication, assembly and testing, labeling, final acceptance, packaging, shipping, installation, maintenance and servicing of a device.
- Records, forms and reports provide evidence of how the system is functioning.

An important provision of the QSR requires manufacturers to establish and maintain specific records. These records are subject to the document control provisions of 21 CFR 820.40, including change control. Approved device master records (DMRs) as described in 21 CFR 820.181, and Chapter 8 of the CDRH manual, must be maintained. A DMR is analogous to the master batch record in drug manufacturing, and represents the template or stepwise procedure for manufacturing a medical device in accordance with the regulated and validated environment under which it was cleared. For each member (e.g., significant variant) of a family of medical devices being manufactured, there must be a corresponding DMR. Typically a DMR contains, but is not limited to:

- approved component and finished device specifications and drawings, and a complete printout of approved device software code
- production equipment, process and environmental specifications, methods and procedures
- quality assurance procedures and specifications including acceptance criteria and quality assurance equipment, tools and fixtures
- packaging and labeling specifications
- installation, maintenance and servicing procedures

Ideally, a DMR would comprise all of the aforementioned components localized and maintained in a single, physical repository (e.g., a notebook, a server domain, a file drawer, etc.). Alternatively, the DMR, at the very least, must refer to the individual locations of these informational components.

The QSR (21 CFR 820.184) also requires manufacturers to maintain device history records (DHRs). The DHR is simply a copy of the DMR that has been completed (e.g., values entered, process steps checked-off, initials/signatures applied, etc.) during the manufacture of a batch, lot or unit quantity of medical device product to document the production. The DHR is, therefore, comparable to an individual batch record in drug manufacturing. The DHR includes completed forms and reports for each manufactured batch, lot or unit, and demonstrates that devices were manufactured in accordance with the DMR. The DHR shall include, or refer to the location of, the

Figure 16-2. Relationship of Medical Device Records

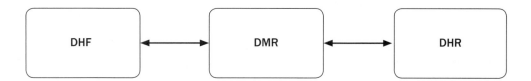

following information:
- dates of manufacture
- quantity manufactured
- quantity released for distribution
- acceptance records that demonstrate that the device is manufactured in accordance with the DMR
- primary identification label and labeling used for each production unit
- device identification(s) and control number(s) used

The QSR (21 CFR 820.30(j)) also requires manufacturers to establish and maintain a design history file (DHF) for each type of device. The DHF shall contain or reference the records necessary to demonstrate that the design was developed in accordance with the approved design plan and the general requirements of design control. All approved changes to a cleared device should be appropriately chronicled in the DHF.

From a quality perspective, consider that all device properties and specifications as documented in the DHR representing a specific batch of product must reconcile with those details as documented in the DMR. Furthermore, all design properties and specifications as documented in the DMR must reside in the DHF (see **Figure 16-2**).

FDA Facility Inspection Programs

A major provision of *MDUFMA* authorizes FDA-accredited third parties to inspect qualified manufacturers of Class II and Class III devices. This initiative is intended to facilitate a greater focus of FDA's inspectional resources on higher-risk devices and provide greater efficiency in scheduling multiple inspections for medical device firms operating in global markets. Certain conditions must apply for a facility to be eligible for third-party inspections, including:
- The most recent inspection must have been classified as "no action indicated" or "voluntary action indicated."
- The establishment must notify FDA of the third party it intends to use, and FDA must agree to the selection.
- The establishment must market a device in the US and must market a device "in one or more foreign countries."

- The third party must be certified, accredited or otherwise recognized by one of the countries in which the device is to be marketed.
- The establishment must submit a statement that one of the countries in which the device is to be marketed "recognizes an inspection of the establishment by [FDA]."

On 28 April 2003, FDA published a *Federal Register* notice providing criteria for the accreditation of third parties to conduct inspections. Commencing 26 October 2003, FDA has maintained a list of firms accredited to conduct third-party inspections on its website (www.accessdata.fda.gov/scripts/cdrh/cfdocs/cfthirdparty/accredit.cfm). An establishment is permitted to select any accredited person to conduct an inspection regarding an eligible medical device product in lieu of an FDA inspection.

A Quality Systems Inspections Technique (QSIT) was validated and subsequently implemented by FDA in July 1999, after the agency determined that it allows more focused and efficient inspections of medical device manufacturers. A QSIT inspections handbook was developed and issued in August 1999 and can be downloaded from the FDA website (www.fda.gov/ICECI/Inspections/InspectionGuides/UCM074883).

The QSIT inspectional approach segments the QSR into seven major subsystems:
1. Corrective and Preventive Action
2. Design Controls
3. Production and Process Controls
4. Management Controls
5. Records/Documents/Change Controls
6. Material Controls
7. Facility and Equipment Controls

QSIT inspections focus on the first four subsystems because they are the primary indicators of QSR compliance, and FDA believes that discrepancies in the last three subsystems will become evident through diligent review of the first four.

An additional resource is FDA's compliance program, which provides guidance manuals to its FDA field and center staff for inspection, administrative and enforcement activities related to the QSR, MDR, medical device tracking

Table 16-4. Summary of Reporting Requirements for Manufacturers

Reporter	What to Report	Report Form Number	To Whom	When
Manufacturer	30 day reports of deaths, serious injuries and malfunctions.	Form FDA 3500A	FDA	Within 30 calendar days from becoming aware of an event.
Manufacturer	Five day reports on events that require remedial action to prevent an unreasonable risk of substantial harm to the public health and other types of events designated by FDA.	Form FDA 3500A	FDA	Within five working days of becoming aware of an event, or whenever FDA makes a written request for the submission a 5 day report.
Manufacturer	Follow-up or supplemental reports on previously reported events—information required under 21 CFR 803 that was not initially provided because it was not known or was not available when the initial report was submitted	Form FDA 3500A	FDA	Within 30 calendar days of becoming aware of the information

regulation (21 CFR Part 821), corrections and removals regulation (21 CFR Part 806), and the registration and listing regulation (21 CFR Part 807). *Compliance Program Manual 7382.845 Inspection of Device Manufacturers* spans five regulations for inspecting medical device firms and provides specific guidance for each. The compliance manual can be downloaded at www.fda.gov/MedicalDevices/DeviceRegulationandGuidance/GuidanceDocuments/ucm072753.htm.

Medical Device Reporting

Medical device manufacturers and importers were first required to report all device-related deaths, serious injuries and certain malfunctions beginning in 1984. In subsequent years, government studies showed that despite full implementation of the MDR regulation, less than 1% of problems occurring in hospitals were being reported to FDA. As a result, the scope of the MDR regulation was extended to require device user facilities to report deaths to both FDA and the manufacturer, and to report serious injuries to the manufacturer. The MDR regulations were amended by the *Medical Device Amendments* of 1992, with a final rule published in 1995, establishing a single reporting standard for device manufacturers, initial importers, domestic distributors and user facilities. The 1995 rule was revised in April 1996 and subsequently amended in March 1997. The *FDAMA* changes to MDR became effective on 19 February 1998. On 26 January 2000,[6] changes to the implementing regulations were published in the *Federal Register*, including:
- Medical device manufacturers, importers and distributors are no longer required to submit an annual certification statement.
- Domestic distributors no longer have to submit MDR reports, but they must continue to maintain records of adverse events and product complaints.
- Importers continue to be subject to the remaining

requirements of the MDR regulation, 21 CFR 803.
- User facilities now submit a report annually instead of semi-annually.

The MDR Rule changes became effective 27 March 2000. Additional information about these updated MDR reporting requirements is available on the CDRH Device Advice webpage (www.fda.gov/MedicalDevices/DeviceRegulationandGuidance/default.htm). The MDR Rule was further amended effective 27 October 2008 to eliminate the requirement for submission of baseline reports, and the use of Form FDA 3417, as the information was considered largely redundant with information provided in individual reports (www.federalregister.gov/articles/2008/06/13/E8-13349/medical-devices-medical-device-reporting-baseline-reports-companion-to-direct-final-rule).

FDA places high priority on compliance with MDR requirements during manufacturing facility inspections. Observed deficiencies are frequently cited on Form FDA 483 and, depending upon their seriousness, can lead to the issuance of a Warning Letter. Adherence to documented procedures that encompass MDR activities, as well as complaints and nonconforming product, is necessary to avoid citations. **Table 16-4** summarizes reporting and recordkeeping requirements for manufacturers and initial importers, and **Table 16-5** provides MDR requirements, including reporting timeframes, for user facilities and domestic distributors. More detailed information regarding reporting requirements is contained in MDR guidance manuals, available on CDRH's website (www.fda.gov/MedicalDevices/DeviceRegulationandGuidance/GuidanceDocuments/default.htm).

Recalls, Corrections and Removals

FDA defines a "recall" as correction or removal of

Table 16-5. Summary of Reporting Requirements for User Facilities and Importers

Reporter	What to Report	Report Form Number	To Whom	When
User Facility	Death	Form FDA 3500A	FDA and manufacturer	Within 10 working days after first becoming aware of the event
User Facility	Serious injury	Form FDA 3500A	Manufacturer; FDA only if manufacturer unknown	Within 10 working days after first becoming aware of the event
Importers	Death or serious injury	Form FDA 3500A	FDA and manufacturer	Not more than 30 calendar days after first becoming aware of the event
Importers	A device malfunction that would likely cause or contribute to a death or serious injury if the malfunction were to recur	Form FDA 3500A	Manufacturer	Not more than 30 calendar days after first becoming aware of the event

a product that is defective, could be a risk to health, or is in violation of the rules administered by the agency. Recalls are classified into a numeric designation (I, II or III) by FDA to indicate the relative degree of health hazard presented by the recalled product. Health hazard evaluation is a key determinant of whether a product should be recalled and includes an assessment of the disease or injury associated with the product, seriousness of the risk posed by the product, likelihood of occurrence and consequences (immediate and long-term). FDA uses the health hazard evaluation as the basis for its recall classification:

- Class I—a situation presenting a reasonable probability that the use of, or exposure to, a violative product will cause serious adverse health consequences or death
- Class II—a situation in which use of, or exposure to, a violative product may cause temporary or medically reversible adverse health consequences or where the probability of serious adverse health consequences is remote
- Class III—a situation in which use of or exposure to a violative product is not likely to cause adverse health consequences

On 19 May 1997, FDA issued a final rule implementing provisions under the *SMDA* that made medical device correction and removal (recall) reporting mandatory instead of voluntary. The new rule was applicable to manufacturers, initial importers and domestic distributors but, because of administrative delays in the Office of Management and Budget (OMB), its effective date was delayed until 18 May 1998.[7] A *FDAMA* provision, which was to be effective 19 February 1998, repealed the requirement for reporting any device removal or correction by domestic distributors.[8] However, FDA's final rule eliminating the requirement for distributor reporting did not become effective until 22 February 1999 due to administrative delays. Recall

regulations include:

- 21 CFR 7, Enforcement Policy, Subpart C, Recalls—which covers voluntary removal of medical device(s)
- 21 CFR 806, Medical Device Corrections and Removals—which covers mandatory notification of correction or removal of a medical device(s)
- 21 CFR 810, Medical Device Recall Authority—which describes the procedures that FDA will follow in exercising its medical device recall authority under section 518(e) of the *FD&C Act*

Device manufacturers and importers for domestic distribution are required to report to FDA any correction or removal undertaken to reduce the risk to human health posed by a device's use. They also are required to report any action taken to remedy an *FD&C Act* violation caused by a device's risk to human health that would cause FDA to act if the manufacturer did not do so voluntarily. Reports of corrections and removals are required for Class I and Class II recalls. Under 21 CFR 806, Class III recalls need not be reported; only recordkeeping requirements would apply. However, FDA has an expectation that all recalls will be reported so that it may review the risk to health and render a final determination on the most appropriate classification.

Information required in such a report is detailed in 21 CFR 806.10(c)(1)–(13) and includes, but is not limited to:

- recalling firm name, address and telephone number
- batch, lot or unit identification numbers and quantity of affected devices manufactured or distributed
- consignee names, addresses and telephone numbers
- copies of all recall-related communications

- names and addresses of recall information recipients

The report must be submitted to the recalling firm's local FDA district office within 10 working days of initiating the recall. Reporting requirements regarding deaths and serious injury apply in accordance with MDR timeframes (see **Table 16-5**). Exemptions from these reporting requirements are provided in 21 CFR 806.1(b) (1)–(4) and include:

- manufacturer's actions to improve a device's performance or quality, which do not reduce a health risk or remedy a violation of the *FD&C Act*
- market withdrawal, defined as a recall of a distributed device that involves a minor or no violation of the *FD&C Act* and would not be subject to legal action by FDA (21 CFR 806.2(h))
- routine servicing, defined as regularly scheduled device maintenance, including the replacement of parts at the end of their normal life expectancy (21 CFR 806.2(k))
- stock recovery, defined as a recall of a device that has not yet been marketed or left the manufacturer's direct control

The recall reporting regulation does not indicate what actions FDA may take upon receiving the report. However, it may be anticipated that the enforcement policy guidelines in 21 CFR 74 would apply, involving periodic progress reports and permitting recall termination only when the agency determines that all reasonable efforts have been taken to recall the affected devices in accordance with the recall strategy and plan. The regulation further clarifies which records must be maintained if a recall is not required to be reported (21 CFR 806.20), as well as information about possible FDA actions to publicly disclose submitted recall reports. Under enforcement, FDA also has the authority to impose a mandatory recall on manufacturers (21 CFR 810).

As noted above, FDA has the authority to impose a mandatory recall on manufacturers under 21 CFR 810. If, after providing the appropriate person with an opportunity to consult with the agency, FDA finds there is a reasonable probability that a device intended for human use would cause serious, adverse health consequences or death, the agency may issue a cease distribution and notification order requiring the person named in the order to immediately:

- cease distribution of the device
- notify healthcare professionals and device user facilities of the order
- instruct these professionals and device user facilities to cease use of the device

The person named in the order will have an opportunity for a regulatory hearing or to provide a written request to FDA asking that the order be modified, vacated or amended. FDA may later amend the order to require a recall of the device.

Additional information concerning recalls, including guidance on recall procedures, effectiveness checks, model press releases, 510(k) requirements during firm-initiated recalls and the FDA recall database, may be found on FDA's website under CDRH Device Advice. In addition, Chapter 7 of the FDA *Regulatory Procedures Manual* provides information on internal FDA procedures used in handling regulatory and enforcement matters for domestic and imported devices.

Exports
Approved or Cleared Devices

There are no export restrictions, approvals, notifications or other requirements for medical devices approved or cleared for marketing in the US, and these may be exported anywhere in the world without prior FDA notification or approval. Although FDA does not place any restrictions on the export of these devices, certain countries may require written certification that a firm or its devices are in compliance with US law. In such instances, FDA will accommodate US firms by providing a Certificate for Foreign Government (CFG). Formerly referred to as a Certificate for Products for Export or Certificate of Free Sale, the CFG uses self-certification to speed the processing of requests, and the certificate is provided on counterfeit-resistant paper bearing an embossed gold foil seal. CDRH requires a fee for the initial certificate and for any additional certificates issued for the same product(s) in the same letter of request.

Requests for a CFG are submitted on Form FDA 3613 and questions regarding the CFG should be directed to the Office of Compliance, Export Certificate Team, at +1 301 796 7400 or via email (exportcert@ cdrh.fda.gov). Additional information about certificate fees for device exports can be found at www.fda.gov/ MedicalDevices/DeviceRegulationandGuidance/ ImportingandExportingDevices/default.htm.

Unapproved or Uncleared Devices

It is only when a device has not been approved or cleared for domestic marketing and is, hence, considered investigational, that legal export provisions become applicable. The basis for the regulation of imports and exports is contained in Chapter VIII of the *FD&C Act*, because there are no regulations in the Code of Federal Regulations (CFR) that cover export requirements, with the exception of 21 CFR 812.18(b) regarding the export of investigational devices. That provision requires a person exporting an investigational device to obtain prior FDA approval as required by Section 801(e) of the act, or to comply with Section 802 of the act.

The export of devices has been regulated since the *FD&C Act* was enacted in 1938. The 1976 *Medical Device Amendments* tightened the rules, requiring a determination by FDA that exporting the device would not pose a public health and safety hazard (essentially an FDA approval to export) and was approved by the recipient country. Despite US medical device firms' positive balance of trade, industry felt the statute's export approval requirements hindered the ability of US manufacturers to enter and compete in foreign markets. Addressing industry concerns, Congress enacted the *Food and Drug Export Reform and Enhancement Act* of 1996 *(FDERA).*[9] In contrast to other *FD&C Act* provisions applicable to medical devices, no regulations have been codified to establish how FDA should manage unapproved device export requirements, except 21 CFR 812.18 regarding the export of investigational devices.

Following is a simplified and abridged summary of unapproved device export requirements. The rules are complex, and this summary is not intended to be inclusive of the requirements applicable to all devices or to any specific device. The statute and guidance documents should be consulted for specific requirements (www.fda.gov/MedicalDevices/DeviceRegulationandGuidance/ImportingandExportingDevices/ucm050521.htm#procedures).

Because the export rules apply to devices that are not approved or cleared for domestic distribution, these devices ordinarily would be considered adulterated, misbranded or both. Essentially, *FDERA* made certain regulatory changes that provide manufacturers with compliance options. When the minimum requirements of Section 801(e)(1) and either Section 801(e)(2) or one or more of the choices under Section 802 of the *FD&C Act* are met, FDA shall deem the devices to be not adulterated or misbranded for the purpose of export.

There are two principal scenarios governing the export of investigational medical devices: a) exportation of Class I and/or Class II devices, and b) the exportation of Class III and/or banned devices. Both scenarios require, at a minimum, that the investigational devices to be exported meet the basic provisions of the *FD&C Act*, as now amended in Section 801(e)(1). These provisions require that the device:

- meet the foreign purchaser's specifications
- not be in conflict with the importing country's laws
- be labeled, "intended for export only" on the outside of the shipping package
- not be sold or offered for sale in domestic commerce

Assuming the device a manufacturer wishes to export complies with these provisions, the remaining regulatory obligations include:

Exportation of Class I and/or Class II Devices

The only additional requirement for exportation is that the manufacturer reasonably believes that the device it is to

export could obtain 510(k) marketing clearance in the US if reviewed by FDA. If the investigational device represents a Class I device that is exempt from premarket notification, then this requirement does not apply. However, if the device represents a Class I or Class II device that is subject to the requirements of premarket notification, then the manufacturer's belief that it would be cleared for marketing must be based upon it being similar in design, construction and intended use to one or more existing, cleared Class I or Class II devices, or it must be a reasonable belief that the investigational device would be regarded as "substantially equivalent" to one or more existing, cleared Class I or Class II devices. Therefore, if this belief of "approvability" is indeed reasonable, the manufacturer can anticipate securing authorization to export the investigational device solely under Section 801(e)(1) of the *FD&C Act*. Certification is required to complete the process.

FDA has implemented a new certification process referred to as a Certificate of Exportability (COE) in an effort to facilitate the export of a medical device under Section 801(e)(1). Persons exporting an article under Section 801(e)(1) must maintain records demonstrating that the investigational product does indeed comply with the four provisions of Section 801(e)(1) listed above. Retention requirements for these records mirror those for GMP documents, or any such quality systems records that apply to the exported product.

Manufacturers applying for a COE are required to sign a statement attesting that they meet the four criteria of Section 801(e)(1). False statements, in such circumstances, are considered violations of United States Code Title 18, Chapter 47, Section 1001. Penalties for a false statement include up to $250,000 in fines and up to five years imprisonment. CDRH requires an initial fee per certificate, and a subsequent nominal fee for each additional certificate issued for the same product(s) in the same letter of request. Original certificates will be provided on special counterfeit-resistant paper with an embossed gold foil seal. CDRH will issue the certification within 20 days upon the firm's demonstration that the product meets the applicable requirements. Requests for a COE are filed on Form FDA 3613a, Supplementary Information Certificate of Exportability Requests. Questions regarding the COE should be directed to the Office of Compliance, Export Certificate Team, at +1 301 796 7400. (exportcert@cdrh.fda.gov).

By meeting the four provisions of Section 801(e)(1) described above—ensuring that records substantiate that compliance, and obtaining a COE—the manufacturer may legally export the investigational device, without FDA permission, in accordance with Section 801(e)(1).

Exportation of Class III and/or Banned Devices

Along with the four basic requirements of Section 801(e)(1), additional provisions found either under

Section 801(e)(2) or Section 802 of the *FD&C Act* allow a manufacturer to export unapproved Class III devices and devices otherwise required to meet a performance standard under Section 514 of the *FD&C Act* (currently, electrode lead wires and patient cables (21 CFR 898) are the only devices with an FDA performance standard under Section 514 of the *FD&C Act*). These devices include investigational devices, that would not be able to obtain Premarket Approval (PMA) or for which a PMA has not been approved, and banned devices (at present, only synthetic hair fibers intended for implant).

Via Section 801(e)(2), a manufacturer electing to comply with Section 801(e)(2) must apply for FDA approval to export and must submit:

- a complete device description
- the device's status in the US
- evidence from the importing foreign governmental authority that the device is not in conflict with its laws (or a notarized certification from a responsible company official in the US that the product is not in conflict with the foreign country's laws),[10] the device's US status is known and the import is permitted
- basic safety data pertaining to the device

Recordkeeping requirements as described above apply for devices exported according to Section 801(e)(2).

An alternative to export under Section 801(e)(2) involves a number of choices under Section 802, which do not require FDA approval but do require the exporter to submit a Simple Notification per 802(g) and maintain substantiating records, should FDA request them. The basic requirements, listed in Section 802(f), call for the devices to:

- satisfy the requirements of Section 801(e)(1)
- be manufactured in acceptable compliance either with US QSR (no deficiencies or satisfactory correction of deficiencies following the most recent FDA inspection) or with an international quality system standard recognized by FDA (currently, none is recognized)
- not be adulterated, other than lack of marketing approval
- not be the subject of a notice by the Department of Health and Human Services that reimportation would pose an imminent hazard nor pose an imminent hazard to the receiving country
- not be mislabeled, except that they must meet the importing country's labeling requirements

Records (Section 802(g), in addition to the requirements per Section 801(e)(1)) must also be maintained for devices exported under Section 802, and other requirements may apply. Even though FDA does not require a firm to obtain written permission prior to export under Section 802, a foreign purchaser may request proof of compliance with US law prior to export. FDA will provide a COE to the exporter under Section 802 to facilitate export of a medical device. Exporting manufacturers should consult Section 802 of the *FD&C Act* for further details specific to their devices.

Imports

Foreign establishments that manufacture medical devices and/or products that emit radiation must comply with applicable US regulations before, during and after importing into the US. These products must meet all applicable FDA regulatory requirements, because FDA does not recognize regulatory approvals from other countries.

Foreign Manufacturers

All foreign manufacturers must meet applicable US medical device regulations to import devices into the US, even if the product is authorized for marketing in another country. These requirements include establishment registration, device listing, manufacturing in accordance with the QSR, medical device reporting of adverse events and a 510(k) or PMA, if applicable. Foreign manufacturing sites are subject to FDA inspection. In addition, the foreign manufacturers must designate a US agent.

Initial Importers

An initial importer is any importer who furthers the marketing of a device from a foreign manufacturer to the person who makes the final delivery or sale of the device to the ultimate consumer or user, but does not repackage or otherwise change the container, wrapper or labeling of the device or device package. The initial importer of the device must register its establishment with FDA. Initial importers are also subject to regulations governing MDR, reports of corrections and removals and medical device tracking, if applicable. Under the MDR regulations, importers are required to report incidents in which a device may have caused or contributed to a death or serious injury, as well as report certain malfunctions. The importers must maintain an MDR event file for each adverse event. All product complaints, MDR and non-MDR events must be forwarded to the manufacturer. Under medical device tracking requirements, certain devices must be tracked through the distribution chain.

Responsibilities of the initial importer, beyond those noted above, may include:[11]

- acting as official correspondent (although this is not required)
- assisting FDA in communications with the foreign establishment and responding to questions concerning the foreign establishment's products that are imported or offered for import into the US
- assisting FDA in scheduling inspections of the foreign establishment if unable to contact the

foreign establishment directly or expeditiously; FDA may provide information or documents to the US agent, and such an action shall be considered equivalent to providing the same information or documents to the foreign establishment

All medical devices imported into the US must meet Bureau of Customs and Border Protection (CBP) requirements in addition to those of FDA. A product that does not meet FDA regulatory requirements may be detained upon entry. Additional information about importing medical devices into the US is available at www.fda.gov/MedicalDevices/DeviceRegulationandGuidance/ImportingandExportingDevices/default.htm.

Medical Device Postmarket Activities

Following market clearance of a medical device, manufacturers and other establishments involved in their commercial distribution must adhere to various postmarketing requirements and applicable regulations. These activities are primarily intended to ensure ongoing monitoring and safety following market approval, and may include a wide array of statutory or voluntary activities for both industry and FDA. These include the use of tracking systems; the reporting of device malfunctions, serious injuries or deaths; and the registration of establishments where devices are produced or distributed.

Some compliance-related activities such as maintaining quality systems, inspections and import/export, although not strictly postmarket, are regarded as essential to the ongoing safety and effectiveness of marketed devices.

Postmarket requirements may also include postmarket surveillance studies required under Section 522 of the act, as well as postapproval studies required at the time of approval of a PMA, HDE or PDP application.

Postmarket activities initiated by FDA may include quality system inspections, monitoring of user reporting and public health notifications. FDA is also involved in disseminating accurate, science-based risk/benefit information for improving the public health.

Medical Device Tracking

Medical device tracking is intended to ensure that a manufacturer can promptly identify product distribution, notify patients and remove a device from the market if requested by FDA. *SMDA* provided for automatic, mandatory medical device tracking by creating a new Section 519(e) of the *FD&C Act*. Subsequently, the device tracking regulations (21 CFR 821) were amended by *FDAMA*, eliminating mandatory tracking and giving FDA discretion to require a manufacturer to adopt a method of tracking a Class II or Class III device. FDA most recently amended the device tracking regulations, effective 9 May 2002, with changes to 21 CFR 821 as follows:

- revising the existing scope and authority: the types of persons subject to tracking are no longer linked to registration requirements; as amended, the tracking requirements apply only to manufacturers that receive a tracking order from FDA
- modifying existing definitions of "importer" and "permanently implantable device"
- adding new patient confidentiality provisions[12]

Accordingly, the amended regulations specify certain devices to which tracking requirements apply. This includes devices, the failure of which would be reasonably likely to have serious adverse health consequences; devices that are intended to be implanted in the human body for more than one year; or devices that are life-sustaining, or life-supporting and are used outside a device user facility. FDA maintains a list of devices subject to tracking regulations.

Manufacturers of a tracked device must establish a written standard operating procedure (SOP), which includes a method for tracking the device throughout distribution, and a quality assurance program including audit procedures. Final distributors of these devices will be required to provide manufacturers with patient information. Device tracking is required for the useful life of the device.

Traceability is distinguished from medical device tracking in that traceability involves the identification of one or more device components or a finished device through the use of control numbers that may facilitate any warranted corrective actions. Therefore, traceability generally applies, and is limited to, the manufacturing stage for all devices. Device tracking, on the other hand, alludes to processes and methods that provide for the pursuit and location of devices that have since been distributed away from the manufacturing facility and may either be stored remotely or may have been prescribed and administered to a patient (e.g., implanted). Information to be maintained through tracking activities includes records concerning the patient and his or her whereabouts; the prescribing and treating physician(s); device identification numbers; and device shipment, treatment initiation and termination dates (21 CFR 821.25). For implants, the explant date and explanting physician information must be maintained. The regulation also requires distributors to provide the manufacturer with specified tracking information (21 CFR 821.30).

Device tracking information is available on CDRH's Device Advice website (www.fda.gov/MedicalDevices/DeviceRegulationandGuidance/default.htm). FDA issued *Medical Device Tracking: Guidance for Industry and FDA Staff* (25 January 2010) to provide manufacturers with more detailed information about device tracking requirements. This guidance can be found at www.fda.gov/MedicalDevices/DeviceRegulationandGuidance/

GuidanceDocuments/ucm071756.htm.

Medical Device Postmarket Transformation Initiative

CDRH has made significant strides toward more robust monitoring of the safety and effectiveness of medical devices and radiation-emitting products in the postmarketing phase. In January 2006, CDRH created the Postmarket Transformation Leadership Team to evaluate current recommendations and to propose a prioritized implementation plan for a transformed postmarket process. The results of this initiative and the subsequent report published in November 2006 provided a vision and an action plan for changes to the medical devices postmarket program.

A key strategic goal of FDA toward the integration of postmarketing initiatives was the establishment and amplification of the interconnections found at all phases of the total product lifecycle (TPLC) (see **Figure 16-3**). This graphic illustrates the links between and interdependence of the regulatory process and lifecycle steps. The diagram further demonstrates the significance and magnitude of postmarketing activities, which comprise half of the critical steps of the TPLC (i.e., manufacturing, marketing, commercial use and obsolescence), and show the inherent balance and flexibility that exists between premarket and postmarket regulation.

As a result of this initiative, the following areas were designated for improvement. They are:

- Create a Culture of Collaboration—CDRH should transform its operations by adding a permanent matrix of cross-cutting, product-related groups over the current functionally based organizational structure to foster information sharing, collaboration and, ultimately, more effective public health promotion and protection. The cross-cutting matrix is designed to ensure that collaboration occurs not just in crisis situations, but also as a part of routine, day-to-day operations.
- Develop World Class Data Systems—Data input, mining, analysis and tracking systems should be strengthened, improved or created as needed for postmarket issues. Improvements to CDRH's critical medical device data and information systems, including the Manufacturer and User Facility Device Experience database (MAUDE) and the MDR system, are highlighted, and additional enhancements to CDRH's analysis and tracking capabilities are being pursued.
- Enhance Risk/Benefit Communication Efforts—CDRH should be a trusted, publicly identifiable source for safety information about medical devices and radiation-emitting products. To that end, an analysis of the communication needs of CDRH stakeholders should be performed. Clinical

practitioners and professional communities should collaborate with the agency to develop a process for the dissemination of risk/benefit information.
- Collaborate on Enforcement Strategies and Outcomes—Both the quantity and quality of CDRH/Office of Regulatory Affairs (ORA) interactions should be transformed through increased collaboration among CDRH, ORA, and the Office of Chief Counsel. Postmarket data and information should be considered when prioritizing inspections and the inspection preparation process should include a review of recent postmarket data. CDRH should develop ways to leverage the audit results obtained by accredited third-party auditing bodies. Enforcement data systems should be updated and employees trained to use them. All available enforcement tools should be used, including civil money penalties.

Numerous priority actions within these four target areas for improvement were undertaken by FDA and significant accomplishments were realized, including the Medical Product Safety Network (MedSun), Unique Device Identification (UDI), safety news, issues, notifications and alerts.

Medical Product Safety Network (MedSun)

MedSun is an adverse event reporting program launched in 2002 by CDRH. Its primary goal is to work collaboratively with the clinical community to identify, understand and remedy problems associated with the use of medical devices. MedSun also serves as a powerful, two-way communications channel between CDRH and the clinical community.

MedSun participants are recruited from all regions of the country using the American Hospital Association (AHA) membership listing. Participants use an Internet-based system as an easy, secure way to report adverse medical device events. Each member facility has online access to the reports submitted to MedSun so that they can be tracked and reviewed at any time.

SMDA defines "user facilities" as hospitals, nursing homes and outpatient treatment and diagnostic centers. The facilities that comprise the MedSun participants are required to report medical device problems that result in serious illness, injury or death. They are also encouraged to voluntarily report other problems with devices, such as "close calls;" potential for harm and other safety concerns. By monitoring reports about problems and concerns before a more serious event occurs, FDA, manufacturers and clinicians work together to prevent serious injuries and death.

Once a problem is identified, MedSun researchers work with each facility's representatives to clarify and understand the issue. Reports and lessons learned are shared with the clinical community and the public, without facility and

Figure 16-3. Total Product Lifecycle

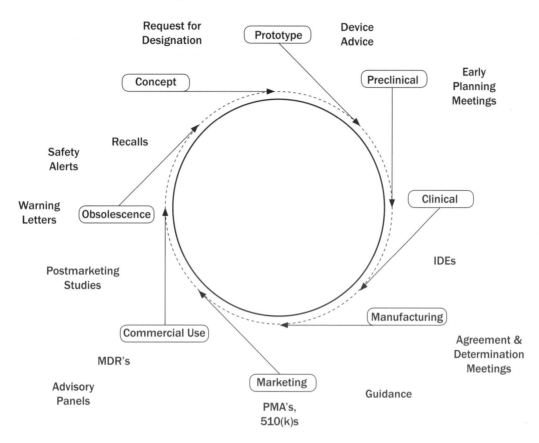

patient identification, so clinicians nationwide may take necessary preventive actions.

Additional information on MedSun can be found at www.fda.gov/MedicalDevices/Safety/MedSunMedicalProductSafetyNetwork/default.htm.

Unique Device Identification

FDAAA contains provisions granting FDA the express authority to propose and ultimately implement regulations requiring medical devices to display a UDI. This new system, when implemented, will require:

- the label of a device to bear a unique identifier, unless an alternative location is specified by FDA or an exception is made for a particular device or group of devices
- the unique identifier to be able to identify the device through distribution and use
- the unique identifier to include the lot or serial number if specified by FDA

The presence of a UDI on a medical device is intended to improve patient safety by reducing device-related medical errors, improving identification of specific devices in adverse event reports and facilitating more-effective

device recalls. Additional information about the requirement of a UDI for medical devices is available at www.fda.gov/MedicalDevices/DeviceRegulationandGuidance/UniqueDeviceIdentifiers/ucm235962.htm.

In 2010, FDA continued to explore what the implementation of the UDI system will mean for various stakeholders. Labeling organizations continued to participate in informal feedback sessions, which included teleconference discussions and practical simulation exercises that provided FDA with a range of information that has further elucidated UDI system needs. Pilot activities conducted internally at FDA identified processes that are well equipped to handle UDI requirements, as well as those that will need to be modified. Fewer issues and questions now remain as FDA nears the release of the UDI regulation.

Safety News, Issues, Notifications, and Alerts

CDRH shares risk communication information with the public primarily through leaflets and Internet sites. Leaflets are mailed to individuals or made available at conferences. The website offers materials on a wide variety of topics of interest to consumers. Information relevant to particular age groups (e.g., children or the elderly) have been developed with those consumers' limitations in mind (e.g., reading level or accessibility needs). These communications are used to inform the public about what to look for in selecting medical devices and products, the availability of new medical devices, product recalls and safety information and how to report adverse events associated with the use of medical devices.

CDRH uses a variety of outreach tools including Urgent Alerts, multimedia outreach, technical publications, presentations and workshops to advise device users about potential risks. These tools utilize a variety of mechanisms, including broadcast media (press releases, talk papers, web-based news programs, websites and television interviews), public health notifications, patient notifications and public meetings to convey risk messages. In addition, staff presentations, CDRH workshops and technical publications, such as standards and guidance documents, convey important safety information to significant stakeholders. FDA's goal is to ensure that healthcare practitioners, industry and the public understand the risks and act appropriately to minimize them.

CDRH staff selects risk communication tools depending upon the urgency of the message, the intended target audience and the outreach goals. An Urgent Alert mechanism is used when the risk associated with a device problem is greatest. Multimedia outreach tools such as website linkages are readily available to keep the healthcare community informed about public health problems.

Urgent Alerts

When a postmarket assessment determines that a public health problem is an imminent hazard, CDRH utilizes experts from all parts of the center to develop Urgent Alerts to notify healthcare professionals and the affected population.

Preliminary Public Health Notification

The Preliminary Public Health Notification is an early alert issued to healthcare practitioners about a device risk. A key determination triggering the issuance of a Preliminary Public Health Notification is the urgency of providing the healthcare community with existing information to make informed clinical decisions about the use of a device or device type, even though information is often incomplete. Factors used to determine urgency include the severity of the potential risk, the population likely to be at risk, the likelihood that adverse events may occur and the need for information and feedback from the healthcare community. CDRH experts use their judgment to predict the impact of these factors. Often, the problem is being actively investigated by CDRH, the industry, another agency or some other reliable entity; hence, updates to the Preliminary Public Health Notification are provided when definitive new information becomes available.

The Preliminary Public Health Notification contains:
- current information on the problem
- analysis of the existing data with a preliminary finding
- preliminary or interim recommendations, usually general reminders (e.g., increase observation of the patient, read the device labeling and/or report adverse events)

The decision to issue a Preliminary Public Health Notification often comes from a Postmarket Issue (PMI) action team or as the result of review of a recall by CDRH. CDRH publishes the Preliminary Public Health Notification on the CDRH and FDA websites and advertises on an office listserv, the MedWatch listserv and any other mechanism considered necessary to ensure that the target audience is made aware of its publication.

Preliminary Public Health Notifications are updated as frequently as necessary to keep the healthcare community aware of the problem. When the agency understands the problem and is able to provide recommendations to mitigate the risk, a Preliminary Public Health Notification will be replaced with a Public Health Notification.

Public Health Notification

Public Health Notifications are important messages about risks associated with the use of medical devices. They are placed on the CDRH and FDA websites and may be disseminated in additional ways to ensure the message reaches the target audience. Public Health Notification recommendations usually come from the PMI team, but in unusual circumstances the decision to issue a notification may be made without convening a PMI team.

Public Health Notifications are issued when:
- The information is important in order to make informed clinical decisions about the use of a device or device type.
- The information is not readily available to the affected target.
- CDRH recommendations will help healthcare practitioners mitigate or avoid the risk.

The decision to issue a Public Health Notification is dependent upon the quality of the information, the significance of the risk, the population at risk, the nature and frequency of adverse events, the urgency of the situation and the expectations of the public.

Press Releases

Press releases approved by CDRH are issued to the media by FDA's Office of Public Affairs whenever there is a need to alert the broader public to a potential health risk associated with an FDA-regulated product. In addition to Class I recalls, press releases are usually issued for seizures of medical devices. Press releases are distributed to a list of critical media nationwide via a listserv. They are also posted on the FDA and CDRH websites.

Multimedia Outreach

CDRH has established a number of methods for making information about public health concerns readily available to the healthcare community and the general public. For example, the Patient Safety News network disseminates information in video format through one of the center's website links. CDRH has also developed a number of relevant and consumer-friendly webpages addressing issues with commonly used medical devices.

Patient Safety News

CDRH leads the agency's production of FDA Patient Safety News (PSN), a monthly television news show distributed by CDRH. The show is broadcast each month on several medical satellite television networks that bring continuing education for healthcare professionals to more than 4,500 US hospitals and long-term care facilities. FDA PSN is a major vehicle for communicating safety messages about medical products to physicians, nurses, pharmacists, risk managers and educators across the nation. It incorporates stories from FDA's three medical product centers (Center for Drug Evaluation and Research (CDER), CDRH and Center for Biological Evaluation and Research (CBER)) on medical errors, patient safety, recalls and alerts and newly approved drugs, devices and biological products.

The show's website is www.accessdata.fda.gov/scripts/cdrh/cfdocs/psn/index.cfm.

Websites

CDRH communicates postmarket safety information through a variety of public websites.

- Medical Device Safety—This website presents a collection of medical device safety information (e.g., recalls, public health notifications, safety tips, "Dear Doctor" letters, etc.) for healthcare professionals. The site is updated regularly to feature high-priority risk messages. CDRH periodically conducts audience analysis and usability studies of this site to make it more accessible and understandable to practitioners (www.fda.gov/MedicalDevices/Safety/default.htm).
- CDRH Consumer Website—The CDRH consumer website provides information about specific devices and device issues for a patient/consumer audience. It includes links to postmarket safety information (including Class I recalls and Public Health Notifications), as well as information geared toward individuals who use devices in their homes. (www.fda.gov/ForConsumers/ConsumerUpdates/ucm149209.htm).
- Disease-Specific Websites (FDA Diabetes Information, Heart Health Online)—CDRH coordinates FDA's disease-specific websites on diabetes and heart disease. These websites are designed to educate patients and caregivers about the types of interventions involving medical devices that prevent and treat disease. Each includes links to appropriate medical device patient labeling and postmarket safety information.
- Device-Specific and Topic-Specific Websites (i.e., LASIK, Phakic Lenses, Whole Body CT Scanning, Cochlear Implants, etc.)—CDRH's device-specific websites provide coordinated postmarket information about specific types of devices. These websites give patients and healthcare professionals easy access to descriptive information, indications for use, risks and precautions and specific safety information.

Postapproval Studies

A postapproval study (PAS), also known as a Condition of Approval study, under 21 CFR 814.82(a)(2), helps ensure the continued safety and effectiveness of an approved, marketed device. CDRH may require such a study, and FDA will state in the PMA approval order the reason or purpose for the requirement, the number of patients to be evaluated and the subsequent reports that must be submitted.

The last few years have seen a greater focus on PAS for FDA-regulated products. Both CDER and CBER now post the status of certain postmarketing studies on CDER's website (www.accessdata.fda.gov/scripts/cder/pmc/index.cfm). In 2005, the Institute of Medicine (IOM) completed a study entitled, "Safe Medical Devices for Children." Among its recommendations, the report urged FDA to establish a system for monitoring and publicly reporting the status of postmarket study commitments involving medical devices.

The new CDRH Postapproval Studies Program encompasses design, tracking, oversight and review responsibilities for studies mandated as a condition of approval of a PMA application. The program helps ensure that well-designed PAS are conducted effectively and efficiently and in the least burdensome manner. On 1 January 2005, oversight responsibility was transferred to CDRH's Office of Surveillance and Biometrics (OSB) and the PAS review functions were integrated into the medical device epidemiology program. This action enabled epidemiologists on the premarketing review teams to begin early planning regarding postmarketing concerns as the product moves through the approval process. In addition, industry is required to consider the design of its postmarketing studies during the approval process. Postmarketing studies are now a standard part of discussions with advisory panels, and products must have a protocol at the time of approval.

CDRH has an automated tracking system that efficiently identifies the reporting status of active PAS ordered since 1 January 2005. This system represents CDRH's effort to ensure all PAS commitments are fulfilled in a timely manner. The effective tracking system is based on study timelines incorporated in study protocols and agreed to by CDRH and the manufacturer. In addition to this internal tracking system, CDRH launched a publicly available webpage (www.accessdata.fda.gov/scripts/cdrh/cfdocs/cfPMA/pma_pas.cfm?sb=dad) to keep all stakeholders informed of study progress. It displays not only PAS reporting status, but also the status (based upon protocol-driven timelines) of each PAS.

Postmarket Surveillance

Premarket review provides limited information on a device's performance, safety and effectiveness. However, it is generally recognized that quality and/or performance issues, along with newly emergent safety signals or efficacy outcomes, may arise after the device has been utilized by a more diverse population and under more varied conditions.

FDAMA modified postmarket surveillance requirements under Section 522 of the *FD&C Act*. Specifically, under the act, the agency may order a manufacturer to conduct postmarket surveillance for any Class II or Class III device, including a device reviewed under the licensing provisions of Section 351 of the *Public Health Service Act*, which meets any of the following criteria:

- The device's failure would be reasonably likely to have serious adverse health consequences.
- The device is intended to be implanted in the human body for more than one year.
- The device is intended to be a life-sustaining or life-supporting device used outside a device user facility.

There are various considerations given when establishing a postmarketing surveillance strategy for a particular device or type of device. A general approach by CDRH is to convene an expert review team within the center to establish the surveillance objective, the information needed to achieve this objective, appropriate sources and mechanisms for obtaining this information and necessary actions needed to address public health concerns. The postmarket surveillance plan will result in the collection of useful data that can reveal unforeseen adverse events, clarify the actual rate of expected adverse events and may provide other information necessary to protect the public health (21 CFR 822.2).

Postmarketing issues or signals may emerge at any point during the device lifecycle and can stem from a variety of sources, such as analysis of adverse event reports, a recall or corrective action, reports from other governmental authorities or the scientific literature. Once such an issue is identified, it is forwarded by the division director to the director of the Issues Management Staff (IMS) in OSB.

An expert review team will consider whether to impose a postmarket surveillance order under Section 522. The expert review team will develop the postmarket surveillance

question(s) and the supporting rationale that will be part of the postmarket surveillance order. The questions focus on confirming the nature, severity or frequency of suspected problems. The OSB director will decide whether to order postmarket surveillance. Although postmarket surveillance will not be used in lieu of adequate premarket testing, it can serve to complement premarket studies.

Manufacturers who do not conduct postmarket surveillance in accordance with the approval plan may be subject to FDA enforcement actions, including civil money penalties (21 CFR 822.20). The results and status of the postmarket surveillance plan are available under the *Freedom of Information Act (FOIA)*, and the overall status of the surveillance, along with a brief description of the plan, may be available via the Internet.

Summary

- Both domestic and foreign medical device manufacturers are required to register their establishments with FDA and list the devices they distribute. The regulations are included in 21 CFR 807 and described in the FDA guidance, *Implementation of Medical Device Establishment Registration and Device Listing Requirements Established by the Food and Drug Administration Amendments Ace* of 2007 (8 October 2009).
- The Quality System Regulation in 21 CFR 820 defines FDA's current GMPs for medical devices. It was substantially augmented in 1996 and now includes premarket product development (design control), as well as installation and servicing.
- FDA's QSIT is an excellent model on which to base or prepare for quality system audits. The QSIT apportions the quality system into seven core subsystems, as follows:
  1. Corrective and Preventive Action
  2. Design Controls
  3. Production and Process Controls
  4. Management Controls
  5. Records, Documents and Change Controls
  6. Materials Controls
  7. Facility and Equipment Controls
  FDA's QSIT inspections generally focus on the first four subsystems because they are primary indicators of compliance.
- Regulations for MDRs in 21 CFR 803 and corrections and removals (recalls) in 21 CFR 806 require filing timely and accurate reports with FDA. The type and severity of adverse experiences occurring determine the timeframe in which these reports must be submitted.
- There are no restrictions for exporting medical devices already cleared or approved for marketing in the US. However, regulations for exporting

unapproved or investigational devices can require careful consideration because they are driven by the device classification, degree of risk and similarity in design, operation and intended use to existing predicate devices in US interstate commerce.

- Device tracking regulations in 21 CFR 821 provide for the post-manufacture identity, distribution, location and patient-specific use of certain eligible significant-risk devices. Traceability requirements in 21 CFR 820 provide for the identity of medical devices or certain components during and throughout the manufacture of the device.

References

1. International Organization for Standardization, ISO 13485:2003 *Medical devices: Quality management systems—Requirements for regulatory purposes.* ISO, Geneva, Switzerland, 2003.
2. US Food and Drug Administration. Foreign Establishment Registration and Listing. *Fed Reg* 27 November 2001, 66, 59138.
3. US Food and Drug Administration. *Enforcement Priorities for Single-Use Devices Reprocessed by Third Parties and Hospitals.* Center for Devices and Radiological Health, Rockville, MD, 14 August 2000. www.fda.gov/MedicalDevices/DeviceRegulationandGuidance/GuidanceDocuments/ucm107164.htm. Accessed 13 April 2011.
4. FDA, *Fed Reg* 21 December 1979, 44, 75628; *Fed Reg* 6 April 1988, 53, 11253; *Fed Reg* 27 March 1990, 55, 11169.
5. Division of Small Manufacturers Assistance (DSMA), *Medical Device Quality Systems Manual: A Small Entity Compliance Guide.* US Food and Drug Administration. Rockville, MD, 1997. www.fda.gov/cdrh/dsma/gmpman.html. Accessed 13 April 2011.
6. US Food and Drug Administration. "Medical Device Reporting: Manufacturer Reporting, Importer Reporting, User Facility Reporting, Distributor Reporting; Final Rule," *Fed Reg* 26 January 2000, 65, 4112.
7. US Food and Drug Administration. "Medical Devices; Reports of Corrections and Removals; Final Rule," *Federal Register* 62:27191 (19 May 1997).
8. US Food and Drug Administration. "Medical Devices; Reports of Corrections and Removals; Direct Final Rule." *Fed Reg* 7 August 1998, 63, 42232 (7 August 1998).
9. Public Law 104-134, as amended by Public Law 104 180.
10. US Food and Drug Administration. "Exports: Notification and Recordkeeping Requirements; Final Rule." *Fed Reg* 19 December 2001, 66, 65429.
11. US Food and Drug Administration. "Device Advice: Establishment Registration." Center for Devices and Radiological Health, Rockville, MD, 28 February 2002.
12. US Food and Drug Administration. "Medical Devices; Device Tracking; Final Rule," *Fed Reg* 8 February 2002, 67, 5943.

Recommended Reading

Device Labeling Guidance # G91-1 (Blue Book Memo) http://www.fda.gov/MedicalDevices/DeviceRegulationandGuidance/GuidanceDocuments/ucm081368.htm. Accessed 20 April 2011.

FDA. Medical Devices; Current Good Manufacturing Practice Final Rule, Quality System Regulation. *Fed Reg* 7 October 1996, 61, 52602–52662. http://www.fda.gov/medicaldevices/deviceregulationandguidance/postmarketrequirements/qualitysystemsregulations/ucm230127.htm. Accessed 13 April 2011.

FDA, Medical Devices, Device Tracking, New Orders to Manufacturers. *Fed Reg* 4 March 1998, 63, 10638–10640. http://www.federalregister.gov/articles/1998/03/04/98-5520/medical-devices-device-tracking-new-orders-to-manufacturers. Accessed 13 April 2011.

Garcia DG. "Medtronic v. Lohr Decision Underscores Importance of Regulatory Compliance." *Med Device & Diag Ind.* March 1997, 97–101.

Gibbs JN. "Treatment IDEs: FDA Proposal Borrows from Treatment INDs." *Reg Aff Focus.* April 1997, 22–23.

Kahan JS. "FDA's New Approach to Export Regulation." *Med Device & Diag Ind.* September 1996, 68–72.

Kahan J. "The Reference List: A Legally Suspect, Dying Program." *Reg Aff Focus.* May 1997, 14–15.

Kingsley PA. (FDA). *Write It Right: Recommendations for Developing User Instruction Manuals for Medical Devices Used in Home Health Care.* FDA, Rockville, MD, FDA, August 1993. http://www.fda.gov/downloads/MedicalDevices/DeviceRegulationandGuidance/GuidanceDocuments/ucm070771.pdf. Accessed 13 April 2011.

Medtronic Inc. v. Lohr, 116 S. Ct. 2240; 1996. Spencer RL. Mandatory Device Recall Procedures. *RAPS News.* September 1994, 5–8.

Webster JL. "Medical Devices, Promotion, Labeling and Advertising." *Reg Aff Focus.* June 1997, 25–27.

Hooten WF. "FDA Makes Quality the Rule." *Med Device & Diag Ind.* January 1997, 114–128.

FDA Regulatory Procedures Manual, "Chapter 7. Recall Procedures" www.fda.gov/ICECI/

ComplianceManuals/RegulatoryProceduresManual/
default.htm. Accessed 13 April 2011.

Recall Procedures and Model Press Releases. www.fda.
gov/Safety/Recalls/default.htm. Accessed 13 April
2011.

510(k) Requirements During Firm-Initiated
Recalls, K95-1—Blue Book Memo.
Issued 21 November 1995. www.fda.gov/
MedicalDevices/DeviceRegulationandGuidance/
GuidanceDocuments/ucm080297.htm. Accessed 13
April 2011.

FDA Recall Database/Medical Device Class I
Recalls. www.fda.gov/MedicalDevices/Safety/
RecallsCorrectionsRemovals/ListofRecalls/. Accessed
13 April 2011.

Acknowledgements

The author wishes to acknowledge and thank Debra
Jarvis-Ferguson for her support, contributions and diligence toward the completion of this chapter.

Advertising, Promotion and Labeling for Medical Devices and IVDs

Updated by Kelly Rowland

Objectives

- Understand the difference between "labels" and "labeling"
- Understand the basic regulatory requirements for labels and labeling for medical devices and in vitro diagnostics (IVDs)
- Understand the basic regulatory requirements for promotion and advertising.
- Explain the jurisdiction for promotion and advertising
- Understand the submission requirements for advertising and promotional materials
- Explain possible enforcement actions for violations of relevant laws and regulations
- Understanding medical device misbranding

Laws, Regulations and Guidelines Covered in This Chapter

- 21 CFR 801 (Subpart A) General labeling provisions
- 21 CFR 801 (Subpart C) Labeling requirements for over-the-counter (OTC) devices
- 21 CFR 801.119 In vitro diagnostic products
- 21 CFR 809 In vitro diagnostic products for human use
- 21 CFR 809.10 General labeling requirements for the content of labeling for In vitro diagnostic products
- 21 CFR 809.20 General requirements for manufacturers and producers of in vitro diagnostic products
- 21 CFR 809.30 Restrictions on the sale, distribution and use of analyte-specific reagents
- 21 CFR 809.40 Restrictions on the sale, distribution, and use of OTC test sample collection systems for drugs of abuse testing
- 21 CFR 99 Dissemination of information on unapproved/new uses for marketed drugs, biologics, and devices
- 21 CFR 99.103 Mandatory statements and information
- *Guidance for Industry and FDA Staff: Use of Symbols on Labels and in Labeling of In Vitro Diagnostic Devices Intended for Professional Use* (November 2004)
- *Guidance for Industry: Alternative to Certain Prescription Device Labeling Requirements* (January 2000)
- *Guidance for Industry: User Labeling for Devices that Contain Natural Rubber (21 CFR §801.437); Small Entity Compliance Guide* (April 2003)
- *Guidance on Medical Device Patient Labeling; Final Guidance for Industry and FDA Reviewers* (April 2001)
- *Guidance for Industry: Designation of Special Controls for Male Condoms Made of Natural Rubber Latex (21 CFR 884.5300); Small Entity Compliance Guide* (January 2009)
- *Human Factors Principles for Medical Device Labeling* (September 1993)
- *Labeling Regulatory Requirements for Medical Devices* (August 1989)
- Device Labeling Guidance #G91-1 (Blue Book Memo) (March 1991)
- *Write it Right: Recommendations for Developing User Instruction Manuals for Medical Devices Used in Home Health Care* (August 1993)

- *Draft Guidance for Industry: Product Name Placement, Size, and Prominence in Advertising and Promotional Labeling* (January 1999)
- *Draft Guidance for Industry: "Help-Seeking" and Other Disease Awareness Communications by or on Behalf of Drug and Device Firms* (January 2004)
- *Draft Guidance for Industry and FDA: Consumer-Directed Broadcast Advertising of Restricted Devices* (February 2004)
- *Guidance for Industry: Good Reprint Practices for the Distribution of Medical Journal Articles and Medical or Scientific Reference Publications on Unapproved New Uses of Approved Drugs and Approved or Cleared Medical Devices* (January 2009)
- *Guidance for Industry: Accelerated Approval Products—Submission of Promotional Materials* (March 1999)

Label and Labeling

As described in Chapter 14, a "label," as defined under the *Federal Food, Drug, and Cosmetic Act (FD&C Act)*,[1] is a display of written, printed or graphic material on the immediate container of any article (in this case a medical device). "Labeling" is a broader term and refers to any written, printed or graphic material on any article (medical device), on any of its containers or wrappers or on any material accompanying it. It includes any form of publicity such as posters, tags, pamphlets, circulars, booklets, brochures, instruction or direction sheets, fillers, etc., as well as labeling intended to be used in promotional activities (sometimes referred to as promotional labeling), for example, on a company's website.

The above phrase "or any material accompanying it" was further defined by the Supreme Court in *Kordel v United States*, 335 U.S. 345 (1948).[2]

A more liberal interpretation meant that a physical association with the device was not necessary. Thus labeling is considered a wide variety of written, printed or graphic matter such as pamphlets, circulars, booklets, brochures, sales sheets, etc., that bear a textual relationship with a drug or device.

The US Food and Drug Administration (FDA) therefore recognizes two types of labeling for drugs and devices: FDA-approved labeling and promotional labeling. FDA-approved labeling is part of the submission process with a new drug application (NDA), a biologics license application (BLA) or a premarket approval application (PMA). For prescription medical device products, the FDA-approved labeling must be included in or within the package from which the drug or device is to be dispensed, or else the product is considered misbranded since it lacks adequate directions for use (*FD&C Act* Section 502(f) and 21 CFR 801.109(c)).

The 510(k) submission process provides draft labeling to the agency, but since this type of submission receives "clearance," the labeling is not FDA-approved. FDA does provide comment and request revisions to package insert labeling, and it is therefore implied that the labeling is cleared during the submission process.

The *FD&C Act* (Section 502(f)(1) and (2)) requires that device labeling bear adequate directions for use, proper operating and servicing instructions, warnings where its use may be dangerous to health or any information necessary to protect the user(s). All devices require directions for use unless specifically exempted by regulation.[3]

The basic outline for labels and/or labeling specific to medical devices includes the following (but is not limited to all label/labeling requirements):

- manufacturer, packer or distributor name and principal place of business
- device name, other required information
- description
- indications and usage
- contraindications
- warnings
- precautions
- use in specific patient populations (if applicable)
- adverse reactions (if applicable)
- prescription device statement or symbol[4]
- date of issue or latest revision of labeling bearing information for use

Additional labeling requirements for over-the-counter (OTC) devices may be found in 21 CFR 801.60. Label/labeling requirements for Investigational Device Exemption (IDE) medical devices are located in 21 CFR 812.

In vitro diagnostic (IVD) products, according to 21 CFR 809.3, are reagents, instruments and systems intended for use in the diagnosis of diseases or other conditions, including a determination of the state of health, in order to cure, mitigate, treat, or prevent disease or its sequelae. IVD products are intended for use in the collection, preparation and examination of specimens taken from the human body. They are considered devices as defined in *FD&C Act* Section 201(h). IVDs are also covered under a separate FDA regulation (21 CFR 809). These devices have their own labels/labeling regulation within that part (809.10).

In addition to some of the basic items outlined above, there are specific requirements determined by the type of IVD:

Label

- proprietary name and established (common or usual) name, if applicable
- indications and usage
- manufacturer, packer or distributor name and place of business

- warnings/precautions per 16 CFR 1500
- IVD use statement and/or reagent use statement
- lot or control number

For a Reagent

- quantity of contents (i.e., weight or volume, numerical count or any combination of these or accurate indication of the package contents)
- proportion or concentration of each reactive ingredient
- storage conditions such as:
  - o temperature
  - o light
  - o humidity
  - o other pertinent factors as applicable
- statement of reagent purity and quality
- if reagent is derived from biological material, the source and a measure of its activity
- expiration date
- statement in reference to any observable indication of an alteration of product

Labeling (i.e., Package Insert, Instruction Manual)

- proprietary name and established (common or usual) name if any
- indication and usage
- type of procedure (qualitative or quantitative)
- warnings/precautions per 16 CFR 1500
- IVD use statement and/or reagent use statement
- summary and explanation of test (history of methodology)
- chemical, physical, physiological or biological principles of the procedure

For a Reagent

- declaration of quantity, proportion or concentration of reactive ingredient
- statement indicating the presence of and characterizing any catalytic or nonreactive ingredients (i.e., buffers, preservatives, stabilizers)
- instructions for reconstitution, mixing, dilution, etc. of reagent, if any
- storage conditions such as:
  - o temperature
  - o light
  - o humidity
  - o other pertinent factors as applicable
- statement of any purification or treatment required for use
- physical, biological or chemical indications of instability or deterioration

A labeling outline for an IVD instrument can be found in 21 CFR 809.10(b)(6). The following is an abbreviated list of the basic requirements for instrument labeling:

- use or function
- installation procedures
- principles of operation
- performance characteristics and specifications
- operating instructions
- calibration procedures, including materials and/or equipment to be used
- operational precautions and any limitations
- hazards
- storage, handling or shipping instructions
- list of all materials provided as well as those materials required but not provided
- calibration details
- details of quality control procedures and materials required (i.e., state if there are both positive and negative controls)
- expected values
- specific performance characteristics (i.e., accuracy, precision, specificity and sensitivity)
- bibliography

Additional labeling requirements for OTC IVDs may be found in 21 CFR 801.60. Analyte-specific reagents (ASRs) are considered restricted devices under the *FD&C Act* (Section 520(e)) and are defined and classified in 21 CFR 864.4020. The associated labeling is regulated by FDA (21 CFR 809.10(e) and 809.30). ASRs are defined as antibodies, both polyclonal and monoclonal; specific receptor proteins; ligands; nucleic acid sequences; and similar reagents that, through specific binding or chemical reaction with substances in a specimen, are intended for use in diagnostic applications for identification and quantification of an individual chemical substance or ligand in biological specimens.[5] Although most are Class I devices, some more-complex ASRs require submission as Class II or III medical devices.

Unlike drug labels or labeling, there are no specific regulations establishing minimum requirements for key graphic elements, (e.g., bold type, bullet points, type size, spacing or use of vertical and horizontal lines) for medical devices and IVDs. Within the labeling requirements, it is recommended that instructions or any specific user-related information be clear, concise and understandable by the user—either a healthcare professional or lay person. Although there are no regulations for key graphic elements in medical device labeling, 21 CFR 801.15 does, in fact, reference some specific labeling format requirements for prescription medical devices. The labeling format for OTC medical devices is described in 21 CFR 801.60 and 801.61. Additionally, guidance documents are available to assist in developing such labels and labeling:

- *Guidance for Industry: Alternative to Certain Prescription Device Labeling Requirements* (January 2000)
- *Guidance on Medical Device Patient Labeling; Final Guidance for Industry and FDA Reviewers* (April 2001)
- Device Labeling Guidance #G91-1 (Blue Book Memo) (March 1991)
- *Write it Right: Recommendations for Developing User Instruction Manuals for Medical Devices Used in Home Health Care* (August 1993)
- *Human Factors Principles for Medical Device Labeling* (September 1993)
- *Guidance for Industry: User Labeling for Devices that Contain Natural Rubber (21 CFR 801.437); Small Entity Compliance Guide* (April 2003)

For IVDs

- *Guidance for Industry and FDA Staff: Use of Symbols on Labels and in Labeling of In Vitro Diagnostic Devices Intended for Professional Use* (November 2004)
- *Guidance for Industry and FDA Staff: Commercially Distributed Analyte-Specific Reagents (ASRs): Frequently Asked Questions* (September 2007)

Since most medical device labeling consists of instructions for using the device properly and safely and, where appropriate, any care instructions for the device, it would only be appropriate to evaluate and include human factors when developing and writing instructional labeling. "Human factors," in this context is the study or evaluation of how people use technology, specifically the interaction of human abilities, expectations and limitations with work environments and system design. FDA's Center for Devices and Radiological Health (CDRH) has a webpage dedicated to human factors (http://www.fda.gov/MedicalDevices/DeviceRegulationandGuidance/PostmarketRequirements/HumanFactors/default.htm), which includes links to specific FDA guidance documents.

It is important that all medical devices contain complete and accurate labeling, as it is essential for the safe and reliable operation of that medical device, whether used by a customer in a home or by a professional in the hospital.[6] In addition to reviewing labeling requirements per 21 CFR 801 (medical devices) and 809 (ASRs and IVDs), two FDA guidance documents are available to manufacturers that contain examples of medical device labeling presentation, format and content. They are *Human Factors Principles for Medical Device Labeling* (September 1993), and *Write It Right, Recommendations for Developing User Instruction Manuals for Medical Devices Used in Home Health Care* (August 1993). These two guidance documents are important reference tools when developing and creating medical

device labeling for both home and professional use.

Furthermore, manufacturers must be aware that if they modify any of their medical devices, the labels/labeling should also be reviewed to ensure that they reflect all current revisions and/or specifications. Therefore, a manufacturer's internal change control process should include a means to capture such label/labeling reviews.

Jurisdiction for Promotional Labeling and Advertising

As noted in Chapter 14, the same agencies have jurisdiction over promotional labeling and advertising of medical devices, including IVDs, as over that for drug products. Healthcare product advertising is regulated by two federal agencies. First, it is regulated by the Federal Trade Commission (FTC) under the *Federal Trade Commission Act* (*FTC Act*).[7] FTC utilizes three legal standards (represented as policy statements) related to the regulation of all advertising: substantiation, deception and fairness. The *FTC Act* prohibits advertising that makes deceptive claims, fails to reveal material information, is unfair, or makes objective claims for which there is not a reasonable basis before the claim was made. FTC has primary responsibility for the advertising of foods, cosmetics, OTC drugs, nonrestricted medical devices and other products whose safety, efficacy and labeling are regulated by FDA.

There is a Memorandum of Understanding (MOU) between FDA and FTC that establishes the division of responsibility between the two agencies with regard to advertising. Though FTC retains legal authority over some aspects of advertising, it generally defers to FDA's more specific authority. Under the MOU, FDA has the primary responsibility for the labeling of foods, drugs, devices and cosmetics.

Each FDA center has its own division responsible for enforcing those regulations. Within the Center for Drug Evaluation and Research (CDER), the Division of Drug Marketing, Advertising and Communication (DDMAC) is responsible for the regulation of prescription drug promotion (see Chapter 14). In 1993, the Center for Biologics Evaluation and Research (CBER) formed the Advertising and Promotional Labeling Staff (APLS) within the Office of Compliance and Biologics Quality to review and monitor the promotion of biologic products. Because some of the regulations are open to interpretation, this can result in the application of different standards to drug and biologic products competing in the same therapeutic class. In 2003, CDRH's Office of Compliance (OC) assumed responsibility for the review and enforcement of restricted medical device advertising and promotional materials.

CDRH has a webpage with links to all guidance documents covering medical devices and radiation-emitting products (http://www.fda.gov/MedicalDevices/DeviceRegulationandGuidance/GuidanceDocuments/default.htm).

The 1976 *Medical Device Amendments* to the *FD&C Act* gave FDA authority over the promotion of restricted medical devices.[8] As defined in Section 520(e) of the act, "restricted medical devices" have the potential for harmful effect or require collateral measures for use. They have no implementing regulation. However, the approval order for a PMA or FDA's recommendations for many devices cleared for marketing via 510(k) may restrict the device's sale, distribution and use as a condition of approval. Under 21 CFR 801(D)(b)(1), labeling must bear the statement: "Caution: Federal law restricts this device to sale by or on the order of a (indicate type of practitioner and, if applicable, required training/experience, and facilities to which use is restricted)." Promotional labeling cannot make claims beyond the intended use for which the device was cleared.

FTC has authority for nonrestricted medical devices.

Promotional Labeling and Advertising

Both the term "advertising" and its regulations are somewhat vague. Generally, advertising is differentiated from promotional labeling simply by the practicality of supplying a copy of the complete prescribing information versus providing only a brief summary. Even though FDA does not specifically define advertising, the agency's interpretation of labeling is broad enough to cover most printed materials, which include most advertising. FDA's view of advertising also includes virtually all promotional activities.

Unlike FDA regulations for prescription drug advertising and promotional materials (21 CFR 202.1), the agency currently has no specific advertising and promotional regulations for medical devices. However, the medical device labeling regulation (21 CFR 801.109(a)(2)) does discuss "other labeling," which FDA considers to be promotional labeling, and Section 502(r) of the *FD&C Act* addresses advertising for restricted devices.

There are three applicable guidance documents that provide current FDA thinking on promotional materials and activities: *"Help-Seeking" and Other Disease Awareness Communications by or on Behalf of Drug and Device Firms (Draft)* (January 2004); *Consumer-Directed Broadcast Advertising of Restricted Devices (Draft)* (February 2004); and *Good Reprint Practices for the Distribution of Medical Journal Articles and Medical or Scientific Reference Publications on Unapproved New Uses of Approved Drugs and Approved or Cleared Medical Devices (Final)* (January 2009).

FDA thus treats press releases, investor relations materials and exhibits as advertising, and these, therefore, are also considered labeling by definition. Additionally, information posted on the Internet is considered promotional labeling rather than advertising.

Misbranding

Section 502 of the *FD&C Act* (21 U.S.C. 352) contains misbranding provisions for prescription devices. A device is misbranded and considered in violation of the law under the act if the device labeling:

1. is false or misleading in any way, and
2. does not contain "adequate directions for use"

In the case of a restricted device, the labeling also must contain:

1. the device's established name printed in type at least half as large as the trade or brand name, and
2. a brief statement of the intended uses, relevant warnings, precautions, side effects and contraindications

The *Medical Device Amendments* expanded the authority of the *FD&C Act* over misbranded medical devices. The amendments contain further conditions under which a device is considered misbranded:

- The device's established name (if applicable), name in an official compendium, or common or usual name is not printed prominently in type at least half as large as used for any proprietary name.
- The device is subject to a performance standard and it does not bear the labeling requirements prescribed in that standard.
- There is a failure to comply with any requirement prescribed under the *FD&C Act* (Section 518, 21 U.S.C. 36h) on notification and other remedies; failure to furnish material or information requested by or under Section 518; or failure to furnish any materials or information requested by or under Section 519 of the act on records and reports.
- The device is commercially distributed without FDA clearance on a 510(k) premarket notification submission.

Scientific Dissemination of Information

In parallel with the rules for drugs outlined in Chapter 14, FDA has traditionally objected to the dissemination of information that is not supported by the approved product labeling, typically referred to as "off-label" information. FDA does not prohibit physicians from prescribing drugs or devices off label, allowing for the appropriate exchange of scientific information. However, the agency historically has had a restrictive policy on off-label information dissemination, and this policy has been repeatedly challenged.

In response to the provisions outlined in the *Food and Drug Administration Modernization Act* of 1997 (*FDAMA*) regarding dissemination of information, FDA codified regulations under 21 CFR 99 entitled, "Dissemination of Information on Unapproved/New Uses for Marketed Drugs, Biologics, and Devices." Note that these regulations do not apply to a manufacturer's lawful dissemination of information that responds to a healthcare practitioner's unsolicited request for information. The regulations state that off-label information concerning the safety, efficacy or benefit of a use that is not included in the approved labeling for a drug or device approved/cleared by FDA may, conditionally, be disseminated to applicable individuals or institutions (healthcare practitioner, pharmacy benefit manager, health insurance issuer, group health plan or federal or state governmental agency). The information disseminated must:

- be about a drug or device that has been approved, licensed or cleared for marketing by FDA
- be in the form of an unabridged, peer-reviewed journal reprint (does not include letters to the editor or abstracts) or reference publication
- not pose a significant risk to public health
- not be false or misleading
- not be derived from clinical research conducted by another manufacturer without permission

The regulations (21 CFR 99.103) also require that the disseminated off-label information prominently display:

- the statement "This information concerns a use that has not been approved (additionally "or cleared" for devices) by the Food and Drug Administration"
- information on the research funding and the association of the authors and investigators with the manufacturer, and a statement, if applicable, if there are products or treatments that have been approved or cleared for the use being presented in the off-label information
- a copy of the approved labeling
- a bibliography of other relevant articles (supporting and not supporting the off-label information)
- any other information that will provide objectivity and balance to the information being presented

The regulations also require that the manufacturer submit the information 60 days before dissemination and eventually submit a supplemental application for the new use that is the subject of the disseminated information.

The requirements in these regulations have been legally challenged by claiming protection under the First Amendment's provisions for freedom of speech. In response to such challenges, FDA clarified that rather than defining the requirements, these regulations provide sponsors with a "safe harbor" to disseminate information on unapproved new uses for marketed drugs, biologics and devices under specific conditions without threat of enforcement action. It should be noted that this safe harbor allows for the dissemination of information regarding the safety, effectiveness or benefits of new uses of approved or cleared products but does not provide for statements about approved uses that FDA would otherwise find misleading. FDA stated that it reserves the right, on a case-by-case basis, to prosecute a manufacturer for misbranding its product if it can be

shown that the company was promoting an unapproved use. The effects of these rulings/notices have not yet been tested, leaving this a gray area, open to various interpretations by most companies.

The provisions above are still found in 21 CFR 99, but did sunset in September 2006. In January 2009, the guidance entitled, *Good Reprint Practices for the Distribution of Medical Journal Articles and Medical or Scientific Reference Publications on Unapproved New Uses of Approved Drugs and Approved or Cleared Medical Devices* was issued. This set of draft guidelines is different from 21 CFR 99 in two important aspects:

1. manufacturers are no longer required to submit promotional materials for distribution to FDA for review
2. a new product submission is no longer required for the new use(s) being promoted

Much of this draft guidance originates from the regulations found in 21 CFR 99 and provides for:

- various types of reprints, articles and reference publications that are permitted to be distributed
- manner of the dissemination of scientific and medical information

Enforcement

FDA can enforce violations of the *FD&C Act* or agency regulations through a variety of mechanisms, including Notices of Violations (NOV) or "untitled letters," Warning Letters and, if the violation warrants, referring the issue for judicial action. With regard to devices, FDA will look at such things as a company website, videos, brochures, flyers/promotional flyers, advertisements in journals, bulk mailings, press releases and newsletters. FDA usually sends an NOV for the least violative practices that, in the agency's opinion, do not greatly jeopardize the public health. An NOV usually requires only that the company stop using materials that contain the claim the agency found to be violative. FDA may also issue a Warning Letter with or without a prior NOV letter. Warning Letters contain stronger language and generally are addressed to the company's CEO. In addition to requiring the company to cease using the violative materials, Warning Letters may require the company to provide corrective actions. For example, a company may be required to run a remedial advertisement to reach the same audience as the original violative advertisement or disseminate corrective information through the issue of a "Dear Healthcare Professional" letter as described in 21 CFR 200.5(c)(3). Warning Letters also frequently direct the sponsor to provide FDA with information on any other promotional items that contain similar messages. All FDA Warning Letters, regardless of issuing center or office, are available at www.fda.gov/ICECI/EnforcementActions/WarningLetters/default.htm.

If FDA is not satisfied by the sponsor's response to the actions, it may choose to recommend enforcement action in the form of injunctions, seizures and/or criminal prosecution. The judicial branch of the federal government carries out these activities. One possible outcome is that the company agrees to enter into an arrangement with the government, called a consent decree, that places severe restrictions on company operations to ensure the firm comes into compliance.

Actions That May be Brought by Competitors

The *Lanham Act* of 1946 (*US Trademark Act*) allows private parties a course of action against false and misleading advertising. Trademarks themselves identify the source of a product. The *Lanham Act* prohibits the use of another's mark and false or unfair advertising and is administered by the Patent and Trademark Office (PTO). This act has been amended several times, including the *Trademark Law Revision Act* of 1988, which made it easier to register trademarks, and the *Trademark Dilution Act* of 1995, which prohibited the use of terms that would dilute a trademark (e.g., Buick aspirin). Although not often invoked in these cases, state laws covering false advertising, defamation and disparagement also can be applied to comparative advertising. FTC brings cases, primarily before administrative judges, against those companies it believes are making misleading statements in their promotions. In cases of fraud, FTC brings these into federal court. Many companies will settle out of court, agreeing to "cease and desist" while not admitting guilt.

Summary

- Labeling subject to FDA regulations includes the container label, the package insert used by the physician, patient labeling/medication guide and promotional labeling.
- FDA and FTC regulate healthcare product advertising. FDA regulates advertising for drugs (CDER, DDMAC) and restricted medical devices (CDRH, OC) under the *FD&C Act* and biologics (CBER, APLS) under the *PHS Act*. FTC regulates food, cosmetics, OTC drugs and nonrestricted medical devices under the *FTC Act*.
- Advertising and promotional materials must not be false or misleading, must present fair balance, and must reveal material facts.
- Advertising and promotional labeling are not allowed for unapproved products or unapproved uses of an approved product.
- FDA does, conditionally, allow for the appropriate exchange of scientific materials (unsolicited requests, scientific exhibits).
- FDA can enforce violations through Notices of

Violation, Warning Letters, or judicial action (consent decrees, injunctions and seizures).

References

1. *Food, Drug, and Cosmetic Act* of 1938 (under Title 21 of the United States Code (U.S.C.)).
2. *Kordel v United States*, 335 U.S. 345 (1948) (available at http://supreme.justia.com/us/335/345/).
3. 21 CFR Part 801, Subpart D.
4. *Guidance for Industry: Alternative to Certain Prescription Device Labeling Requirements* (January 2000).
5. 21 CFR 864.4020(a)
6. *Human Factors Principles for Medical Device Labeling* (September 1993).
7. *Federal Trade Commission Act* of 1914 (*FTC Act*).
8. *Public Health Service Act* of 1944 (*PHS Act*), 42 USC Section 351 [262].
9. *Trademark Act* of 1946 (*Lanham Act*), 15 USC Chapter 22.

Chapter 17

In Vitro Diagnostics Submissions and Compliance

By Michael Wienholt, RAC (US, EU)

Objectives

- Know the definition of an in vitro diagnostic device (IVD)
- Understand the risk-based classification of IVDs
- Understand the regulatory submission types and their requirements
- Understand the labeling requirements for IVDs
- Know where to find additional information

Laws, Regulations and Guidance Documents Cited in This Chapter

- 21 CFR 50 Protection of human subjects
- 21 CFR 56 Institutional review boards
- 21 CFR 801 Labeling
- 21 CFR 809 In vitro diagnostic products for human use
- 21 CFR 812 Investigational device exemptions
- 21 CFR 814 Premarket approval of medical devices
- 21 CFR 820 Quality system regulation
- 21 CFR 862 Clinical chemistry and clinical toxicology devices
- 21 CFR 864 Hematology and pathology devices
- 21 CFR 866 Immunology and microbiology devices
- 42 CFR 493 Laboratory Requirements
- *Guidance for Industry and FDA Staff: In Vitro Diagnostic (IVD) Device Studies—Frequently Asked Questions* (June 2010)
- *Guidance for Industry and FDA Staff: Administrative Procedures for CLIA Categorization* (May 2008)
- *In Vitro Diagnostic Devices: Guidance for the Preparation of 510(k) Submissions* (January 1997)
- *New Section 513(f)(2)—Evaluation of Automatic Class III Designation, Guidance for Industry and CDRH Staff* (February 1998)
- *Guidance for the Content of Premarket Submissions for Software Contained in Medical Devices* (May 2005)

The Definition of an IVD

"In vitro diagnostics" (IVDs) are defined in Title 21 of the Code of Federal Regulations (CFR) Part 809.3 as "those reagents, instruments, and systems intended for use in the diagnosis of disease or other conditions, including a determination of the state of health, in order to cure, mitigate, treat, or prevent disease or its sequelae. Such products are intended for use in the collection, preparation and examination of specimens taken from the human body."

The definition given in 21 CFR 809.3 also states that IVDs are devices as defined in Section 201(h) of the *Federal Food, Drug, and Cosmetic Act (FD&C Act)* and that they may also be biological products regulated under Section 351 of the *Public Health Service Act (PHS Act)*. IVDs may be considered to be a subset of medical devices, the defining characteristic being the use of specimens taken from the human body. The US Food and Drug Administration's (FDA) classification rules define more than 500 different types of medical devices that meet the definition of an in vitro diagnostic product. Worldwide, the IVD industry accounts for more than $50 billion annually in diagnostic tests alone.

Additionally, the labeling regulation in 21 CFR 809.10 defines two other types of products: Research Use Only (RUO) and Investigational Use Only (IUO). Both RUO and IUO products are considered to be pre-commercial and, under specific circumstances, may be shipped without fully complying with the labeling requirements that apply to commercial IVDs.

RUO products are those "in the laboratory research phase of development, and not represented as an effective in vitro diagnostic product" (21 CFR 809.10(c)(2)(i)). Such products must be prominently labeled with the following statement: "For Research Use Only. Not for use in diagnostic procedures." RUO products are reagents, instruments or test systems that are under development and being evaluated for their potential use as IVDs, or are used in basic life science research and not intended for further development for a clinical diagnostic use.

IUO products are those "being shipped or delivered for product testing prior to full commercial marketing (for example, for use on specimens derived from humans to compare the usefulness of the product with other products or procedures which are in current use or recognized as useful)" (21 CFR 809.10(c)(2)(ii)). IUO products are reagents, instruments or test systems that are being used in a "clinical investigation or research involving one or more subjects to determine the safety and effectiveness of a device" (21 CFR 812.3(h)). Such products must be prominently labeled with the following statement: "For Investigational Use Only. The performance characteristics of this product have not been established."

Finally, the classification rules in 21 CFR 864 define two additional types of specimen preparation reagents: General Purpose Reagents (GPR), and Analyte Specific Reagents (ASR).

GPR products are chemical reagents having "a general laboratory application, that is used to collect, prepare, and examine specimens from the human body for diagnostic purposes, and that is not labeled or otherwise intended for specific diagnostic application" (21 CFR 864.4010(a)). Importantly, GPRs are classified as Class I (general controls) and exempt from premarket notification, subject to the limitations described in 21 CFR 864.9. Such products must be labeled in accordance with 21 CFR 809.10(d) with basic identifying information, warnings and precautions, and the statement: "For Laboratory Use."

ASR products are "antibodies, both polyclonal and monoclonal, specific receptor proteins, ligands, nucleic acid sequences, and similar reagents which, through specific binding or chemical reaction with substances in a specimen, are intended for use in a diagnostic application for identification and quantification of an individual chemical substance or ligand in biological specimens" (21 CFR 864.4020(a)). Information on the classification of ASRs is given in 21 CFR 864.4020(b). ASRs are Class I and exempt from premarket notification except when they are used in blood banking tests that have been classified as Class II (e.g., cytomegalovirus serological reagents), and when they are intended to be used as components in Class III tests used in contagious fatal diseases (e.g., tuberculosis) or blood donor screening (e.g., blood group typing or hepatitis). ASRs must be labeled in accordance with 21 CFR 809.10(e)(1). Class I ASRs must bear the statement: "Analyte Specific Reagent. Analytical and performance characteristics are not established." Class II and III ASRs must bear the statement: "Analyte Specific Reagent. Except as a component of the approved/cleared test (Name of approved/cleared test), analytical and performance characteristics of this ASR are not established."

FDA Classification and Regulation of IVDs

As with all other medical devices, IVDs are regulated according to a risk-based classification scheme based upon the intended use. Factors that determine the classification of IVDs include whether the device is intended for diagnosis, monitoring or screening of a specific disease or condition; the patient population in which it will be used; the type of specimen to be tested; and the consequence of a false test result.

FDA classifies IVD products into Class I, II or III depending upon the level of control necessary to ensure that the devices are reasonably safe and effective when they are placed on the market. The classification determines the regulatory pathway to market. The CFR lists the classification of existing IVDs in 21 CFR 862 (clinical chemistry and toxicology devices), 864 (hematology and pathology devices) and 866 (immunology and microbiology devices).

Class I IVDs are the lowest risk category. Most are exempt from premarket review and are subject to General Controls only. (Some Class I IVDs do require submission of a premarket notification 510(k). These are termed "Reserved Devices" and include a total of 44 devices in 21 CFR 862, 864 and 866.) General Controls apply to all medical devices, regardless of class, and include establishment registration as a manufacturer, distributor, repackager or relabeler; listing the devices intended to be marketed with FDA; manufacturing in accordance with Good Manufacturing Practices (21 CFR 820), including maintenance of records and providing reports to FDA; and labeling in accordance with 21 CFR 801 and 809.

Approximately 50% of the IVDs currently marketed are regulated as Class I. Some examples of Class I IVDs include clinical chemistry tests for urine pH and osmolality, reagents and kits for immunohistochemistry stains, and serological reagents for immunology and microbiology.

Class II IVDs are those products that pose a moderate risk of harm due to a false test result. They are typically more complex in their design and mode of operation. Most Class II products require submission of a premarket notification 510(k) that includes evidence for a determination of "substantial equivalence" to a similar product already on the market. In addition to General Controls, Class II products require "Special Controls" to assure safety and effectiveness. Special Controls include certain mandatory performance standards, special labeling requirements and requirements for postmarket surveillance.

Approximately 42% of the IVDs currently marketed are regulated as Class II. Some examples of Class II IVDs include clinical chemistry tests for newborn screening for metabolic disorders, hematology tests for sickle cell hemoglobin and microbiology tests for pathogenic organisms that cause such diseases as meningitis.

Class III IVDs are those products that present a potential high risk of harm due to a false test result. These typically employ complex methodologies and algorithms for calculating a result and may be intended for diagnosis of serious infectious diseases. Class III products are those for which General Controls and Special Controls alone are not sufficient to provide assurances of safety and effectiveness. They are subject to the most rigorous premarket scrutiny, often requiring extensive clinical data. Class III products require submission of a Premarket Approval application (PMA) which includes a complete description of the manufacturing process and clinical evidence (diagnostic sensitivity and specificity) of safety and effectiveness in the intended use population.

Approximately 8% of the IVDs currently marketed are regulated as Class III. Some examples of Class III IVDs include tests for screening for various cancers (e.g., breast, prostate) and tests for screening the blood supply for infectious agents such as Hepatitis B and C.

Under an intercenter agreement that became effective in October 1991, two centers within FDA share responsibility for regulating IVDs—the Center for Devices and Radiological Health (CDRH) and the Center for Biologics Evaluation and Research (CBER). CDRH was assigned the lead role for policy development, procedural regulations, regulating all IVDs not assigned to CBER, small business assistance programs, registration and listing, GMP advisory activities and medical device reporting. CBER was assigned the lead role in regulating all IVDs for screening or confirmatory laboratory tests associated with blood banking operations, as well as those medical devices intended for use in collecting, processing, storing and administering blood products and their components. Each center retains authority for surveillance activities and compliance actions, issuing Special Controls guidance documents and performance standards, and for review of IDE, 510(k) and PMA submissions.

The Office of Blood Research and Review (OBRR) within CBER administers the premarket review and postmarket surveillance and compliance programs for IVDs assigned to the center. The Office of In Vitro Diagnostic Device Evaluation and Safety (OIVD) within CDRH administers the premarket review and postmarket surveillance and compliance programs for all other IVDs. OIVD is also responsible for making complexity categorization and waiver determinations under the *Clinical Laboratory Improvement Amendments* (*CLIA*) of 1988, which set standards and certification requirements for clinical laboratory tests. OIVD is organized into three principal divisions: the Division of Chemistry and Toxicology Devices (DCTD), the Division of Immunology and Hematology Devices (DIHD) and the Division of Microbiology Devices (DMD). On an annual basis, OIVD processes more than 1,000 premarket submissions and more than 2,000 *CLIA* determinations, and implements more than 150 compliance actions.

The Application of the *CLIA* to IVDs

As stated above, *CLIA* set standards and certification requirements for clinical laboratory tests. OIVD is responsible for the program for complexity categorization and waiver determinations of commercially marketed in vitro diagnostic tests under CLIA. Categorization is the process by which FDA assigns IVDs to one of three *CLIA* complexity categories based upon the potential risk to the public health. The categories are Waived, Moderate Complexity and High Complexity. FDA evaluates seven criteria to determine the complexity of an IVD and assigns a number score (1 = Low; 2 = Intermediate; 3 = High) to each. The evaluation criteria include: the scientific or technical knowledge required to perform the test; necessary training and experience; the complexity of the preparation of reagents and test materials; characteristics of the operational steps; the need for calibration, QC and proficiency testing; troubleshooting and maintenance; and the difficulty of interpreting the test results. The scores for each criterion are then totaled. Tests receiving scores of 12 or less are assigned Moderate Complexity. Tests receiving scores of 12 or higher are assigned High Complexity. Waived tests are those tests that were specified in the regulations that *CLIA* implemented (42 CFR 493) or tests that are granted a waiver by FDA following review of an application containing valid scientific data that demonstrates the test is simple to use, accurate and unlikely to pose a risk of harm to the patient if the test is performed inaccurately. Manufacturers apply for a CLIA categorization during the premarket review process. Further information can be found in *Guidance for Industry and FDA Staff: Administrative Procedures for CLIA Categorization.*

Premarket Submission Types for IVDs

As discussed above, the classification of an IVD determines the regulatory pathway to market. Class II IVDs require submission of a premarket notification 510(k) at least 90 days prior to placing the device on the market. The 510(k) must contain evidence that the device to be marketed is "substantially equivalent" to (i.e., as safe and effective as) to another device that is already legally marketed. This is termed the "predicate device." A predicate device is one that has a similar intended use and similar technological characteristics. Once FDA has determined that the new device is substantially equivalent (SE) to the predicate device, the new device is "cleared" for marketing in the US. If FDA determines that the new device has no predicate or that its performance is not equivalent to the predicate, then a "not substantially equivalent" (NSE) decision is rendered. The content and format of a 510(k) is given in *In Vitro Diagnostic Devices: Guidance for the Preparation of 510(k) Submissions.* The evidence establishing substantial equivalence to the predicate consists of nonclinical and clinical performance data. This includes analytical sensitivity and specificity, precision, reproducibility and reagent and sample stability. FDA recommends the use of standards published by the Clinical Laboratory Standards Institute (CLSI) to guide the evaluation of analytical performance. Additionally, a method comparison study showing similar clinical performance as the predicate device is also required. This is typically done by calculating the percent agreement between the two methods using retrospectively collected clinical samples. OIVD posts a summary of the 510(k) review on the FDA website that details the basis for the SE determination. These summaries provide manufacturers with valuable information on the choice of likely predicates and data requirements for establishing substantial equivalence to a predicate.

Class III IVDs require submission of a PMA. The required elements of a PMA are given in 21 CFR 814. PMAs are reviewed under a 180-day timeline. For most PMAs, a clinical study using prospectively collected samples is required to establish the device's safety and effectiveness. Such studies must be conducted in accordance with the informed consent regulations in 21 CFR 50 and the Institutional Review Board regulations in 21 CFR 56. If the device is the first of its kind, or if FDA's review of the PMA raises significant questions regarding safety and effectiveness, FDA may seek advice or a determination of approvability of a PMA from an advisory panel comprised of external experts. In most cases, an inspection of the manufacturer's facility by FDA is required prior to approval of a PMA. FDA will often place postapproval requirements on manufacturers of Class III devices as a condition of approval. These may include additional studies of safety and effectiveness and periodic reporting of the results of such studies. Once a formal approval order is issued, FDA posts a Summary of Safety and Effectiveness Data (SSED) on the FDA website.

Another important premarket mechanism is the de novo reclassification. This was created by the *Food and Drug Administration Modernization Act* of 1997 (*FDAMA*) as a way of classifying new, lower risk devices that were automatically placed in Class III when the original classification rules were established. Such devices have no predicate, but are devices for which Special Controls would be an appropriate means of controlling risks and ensuring that the devices are reasonably safe and effective. De novo allows a manufacturer of an IVD that has been found NSE due to the lack of a predicate device to submit a petition to have a risk-based classification made for the device (often Class II) without submitting a PMA. The petition must include identification of the IVD's risks and benefits, the Special Controls the manufacturer believes will adequately control risks and ensure safety and effectiveness, and a recommendation as to whether the IVD should be placed in Class I or Class II. FDA will make a classification determination within 60 days. If the IVD is placed in either Class I or II, it may be legally marketed and will then become a predicate for any future device having the same intended use and technological characteristics. The de novo process is explained in detail in *New Section 513(f)(2)—Evaluation of Automatic Class III Designation, Guidance for Industry and CDRH Staff.*

The Pre-IDE Submission

In 1995, FDA issued a memorandum introducing the pre-IDE submission as a mechanism for sponsors of Investigational Device Exemption (IDE) applications under 21 CFR 812 to submit preliminary information to FDA prior to submitting an IDE. Since most IVDs are exempted from the IDE regulations, the pre-IDE has become an informal method for manufacturers to obtain advice and comment on the regulatory pathway and proposed studies prior to submission of a 510(k) or PMA. In fact, OIVD routinely requests that manufacturers submit a pre-IDE when a new device has novel performance characteristics or a new intended use. This is specifically designed for those devices that are likely to require a *de novo* petition, *CLIA* waiver application or complex 510(k) or PMA submission for multiplex tests or companion diagnostics. A pre-IDE may also be useful when a manufacturer is submitting its first ever premarket application. A pre-IDE should be submitted when the intended use (including the target patient population) has been defined and the manufacturer is ready to discuss the analytical and clinical performance studies that may be required for clearance or approval. The pre-IDE process begins with the submission of a written request to the Document Mail Center. The exchange of information between the submitter of a pre-IDE and FDA may take the form of written memoranda or in-person meetings or teleconferences. An important consideration regarding the pre-IDE is that it is nonbinding on both the manufacturer and the FDA.

The pre-IDE package consists of a cover letter with contact information, a brief device description, proposed intended use, predicate device (if known) and any specific questions the manufacturer has regarding the proposed analytical and clinical performance studies or regulatory pathway. Typically, FDA will respond to a pre-IDE submission within 60 days by returning a pre-IDE review memo to the submitter. This document will contain FDA's most current thinking regarding how the device is likely to be regulated and the data likely to be required in a 510(k) or PMA submission. A manufacturer may request a pre-IDE meeting with FDA in person, and vice versa.

Software Considerations for IVDs

Many IVDs employ software to control instrumentation and to calculate complex algorithms prior to providing the test result. As is the case for other medical devices, FDA regulates the software that is integral to the operation and safety of diagnostic test systems. Therefore, a certain amount of information related to the design and development of software must be included in premarket submissions. The extent of the documentation to be included in a 510(k) or PMA is based on the software "Level of Concern." FDA defines the Level of Concern as Minor, Moderate or Major depending upon the role of the software in causing, controlling or mitigating hazards that may result in injury to the patient or device operator. FDA classifies most IVD software as Moderate Level of Concern. Among the software documentation required to be submitted in premarket applications, the most important is a risk analysis. This must include the hardware and software hazards identified in the course of design and development, an assessment of their severity and the mitigations implemented to control them. To the extent that software plays a role in mitigating hazards associated with the laboratory examination of clinical specimens (e.g., user errors; incorrect or delayed diagnostic results), the hazard analysis must address the severity of the harm resulting from software failures. FDA defines these terms and the level of software verification and validation documentation required in *Guidance for the Content of Premarket Submissions for Software Contained in Medical Devices.*

Recent Trends in IVD Compliance— Laboratory Developed Tests (LDTs)

Recently, FDA has begun focusing attention on the marketing of so called "home brew" tests by clinical laboratories that have historically been regulated under *CLIA*. Since the passage of the *CLIA* regulations in 1988, diagnostic tests have reached the market in one of two ways: FDA clearance or approval of a premarket application submitted by a commercial manufacturer, or the offering of such tests directly to clinicians by *CLIA*-licensed laboratories. In a regulatory practice known as "enforcement discretion," FDA allowed the commercialization of such "laboratory developed tests" (LDTs) without premarket review. Over the past decade, FDA has become increasingly concerned with the lack of oversight of such tests, particularly a subset of molecular diagnostic tests that purported to predict the genetic risk of developing clinical diseases that were marketed on direct-to-consumer (DTC) websites. Specifically, FDA cited concerns over the apparent lack of clinical validation, absence of premarket review of diagnostic claims and the lack of postmarket surveillance and reporting. Beginning in 2000, FDA published a number of draft guidance documents related to the use of ASRs in the development of such tests, and began exercising its authority over ASRs and ROUs.

In June of 2010, FDA sent a number of regulatory letters to companies operating *CLIA*-certified laboratories offering DTC genetic tests. This was followed on 19–20 July 2010 by an unprecedented two-day public meeting in which FDA, industry and the public gave their perspectives on FDA oversight of LDTs. During the meeting, FDA stated its concerns that the *CLIA* regulations alone were insufficient to evaluate evidence of analytical and clinical validation of test performance of LDTs. FDA was further concerned about the lack of quality system requirements on ASRs, design controls (particularly with regard to validation of software) and postmarket surveillance (e.g., recalls and medical device reporting).

During the course of the FDA public meeting on LDTs, OIVD issued additional regulatory letters to manufacturers of genetic tests. Subsequently, on 22 July 2010 the Subcommittee on Oversight and Investigations of the US House of Representatives Committee on Energy & Commerce held a hearing on "Direct-To-Consumer Genetic Testing and the Consequences to the Public Health" where testimony was provided by representatives of CDRH, the General Accounting Office and several companies offering DTC genetic tests. Since then, FDA has been conducting an internal review prior to preparing further guidance on these matters.

FDA has stated that it will apply a risk-based classification to higher risk LDTs similar to the current regulations that apply to commercial IVDs. This would bring FDA oversight to tests intended for companion diagnostics associated with drug therapy, screening or diagnosis of cancer and other tests for potentially fatal communicable diseases.

Summary

IVDs are a subset of medical devices that are "intended for use in the collection, preparation, and examination of specimens taken from the human body." FDA's classification rules define more than 500 different types of medical devices that meet the definition of an IVD.

Research Use Only (RUO) and Investigational Use

Only (IUO) products are considered to be pre-commercial, and under specific circumstances, may be shipped without fully complying with the labeling requirements that apply to commercial IVDs.

IVDs are regulated according to a risk-based classification scheme as either Class I, II or III, based upon their intended use. Factors that determine the classification of IVDs include whether the device is intended for diagnosis, monitoring or screening of a specific disease or condition; the patient population in which it will be used; the type of specimen to be tested; and the consequence of a false test result.

Most Class I IVDs are exempt from premarket review and are subject to General Controls only. Class II IVDs require submission of a premarket notification 510(k) at least 90 days prior to placing the device on the market. The 510(k) must contain evidence that the device to be marketed is "substantially equivalent" to (i.e., as safe and effective as) another device that is already legally marketed. This is termed the "predicate device." A predicate device is one that has a similar intended use and similar technological characteristics. Class III IVDs require submission of a PMA. For most PMAs, a clinical study using prospectively collected samples is required to establish the safety and effectiveness of the device. Such studies must be conducted in accordance with the Informed Consent regulations and the Institutional Review Board regulations.

General Controls apply to all IVD devices, regardless of class, and include establishment registration as a manufacturer, distributor, repackager or relabeler; listing the devices intended to be marketed with FDA; manufacturing in accordance with GMPs (21 CFR 820), including maintenance of records and providing reports to FDA; and labeling in accordance with 21 CFR 801 and 809.

The Office of In Vitro Diagnostic Device Evaluation and Safety (OIVD) website (www.fda.gov/MedicalDevices/ ProductsandMedicalProcedures/InVitroDiagnostics/default. htm) is the primary source of information on IVD regulations, guidance documents, *CLIA* categorizations, relevant standards, assistance and guidance on pre- and postmarket issues and information on cleared or approved IVDs.

Sources of Additional Information

The Office of In Vitro Diagnostic Device Evaluation and Safety (OIVD) website (www.fda.gov/MedicalDevices/ ProductsandMedicalProcedures/InVitroDiagnostics/default. htm) is the primary source of information on IVD regulations, guidance documents, CLIA categorizations, relevant standards, assistance and guidance on pre- and postmarket issues, and information on cleared/approved IVDs.

The Association of Medical Diagnostics Manufacturers (AMDM) website (http://amdm.org/) contains archived FDA presentations from public meetings and web links to FDA resources.

Biologics Submissions

By Marcia Gaido, PhD, RAC

Objectives

- Learn the history of biologics regulation and understand the types of products classified as biologics
- Understand the organizational structure and responsibilities of the review offices of CBER
- Understand the changes to biologics regulation resulting from the *Biologics Price Competition and Innovation Act* of 2009 (*BPCI Act*), as part of the *Patient Protection and Affordable Care Act* (*PPAC Act*), signed into law on 23 March 2010
- Understand CBER's Investigational New Drug (IND) process including clinical, manufacturing and preclinical requirements for biologics
- Understand the contents of the Biologic License Application (BLA), the BLA review process, advisory committees and lot release protocols
- Become familiar with several licensing issues including the submission and review of Drug Master Files (DMFs), special manufacturing arrangements for biologics and the "Animal Rule"

Laws, Regulations and Guidelines Covered in This Chapter

- *Public Health Service Act*, Section 351—including new Section (k) Licensure of Biological Products as Biosimilar or Interchangeable
- *Federal Food, Drug, and Cosmetic Act* of 1938
- 21 CFR 210 Current Good Manufacturing Practice in manufacturing, processing, packing, or holding of drugs, general
- 21 CFR 211 Good Manufacturing Practice for finished pharmaceuticals
- 21 CFR 600 Biological products: general
- 21 CFR 601 Biologics licensing
- 21 CFR 610 General biological products standards
- 21 CFR 312 Investigational new drug application
- 21 CFR 314 Applications for FDA approval to market a new drug
- 21 CFR 25 Environmental impact considerations
- ICH *M4: The Common Technical Document*
- *Guidance for Industry M4Q: The CTD—Quality*
- *Guidance for Review Staff and Industry—Good Review Management Principles and Practices for PDUFA Products* (April 2005)
- Collaboration of CBER Offices on Issues Related to the Release of Pre-Licensing and Routine Lots, *SOPP 8408* (November 1996)
- Administrative Processing of Biologics License Applications (BLA), *SOPP 8401* (May 2007)
- *Draft Guidance for Industry: Analytical Procedures and Methods Validation—Chemistry, Manufacturing, and Controls Documentation* (August 2000)

- *Guidance for Sponsors, Industry, Researchers, Investigators, and Food and Drug Administration Staff: Certifications To Accompany Drug, Biological Product, and Device Applications/Submissions: Compliance with Section 402(j) of The Public Health Service Act, Added By Title VIII of The Food and Drug Administration Amendments Act of 2007* (April 2008)
- ICH *S6: Preclinical Safety Evaluation of Biotechnology-Derived Pharmaceuticals* (July 1997)
- *Guidance for Industry: Providing Regulatory Submissions in Electronic Format—Human Pharmaceutical Product Applications and Related Submissions Using the eCTD Specifications* (June 2008)
- *Guidance for Industry: Preparation and Public Availability of Information Given to Advisory Committee Members* (August 2008)
- *Draft Guidance for the Public and the Food and Drug Administration Staff on Convening Advisory Committee Meetings* (August 2008)
- *Guidance for Industry: Formal Dispute Resolution: Appeals Above the Division Level* (February 2000)
- SOPP 8001.5, "Intercenter Consultative/Collaborative Review Process" (August 2002)
- *Guidance for Industry: Cooperative Manufacturing Arrangements for Licensed Biologics* (November 2008)
- *Guidance for Industry: Submitting Type V Drug Master Files to the Center for Biologics Evaluation and Research* (August 2001)
- *Guideline For Drug Master Files* (September 1989)
- SOPP 8110, "Investigational and Marketable Applications: Submission of Regulatory Documents to CBER" (February 2003)
- *Guidance for Industry: Container Closure Systems for Packaging Human Drugs and Biologics: Chemistry, Manufacturing, and Controls Documentation* (May 1999)
- *Guidance for Industry: Environmental Assessment of Human Drug and Biologics Applications* (July 1998)
- *Guidance for Industry: Gene Therapy Clinical Trials—Observing Subjects for Delayed Adverse Events* (November 2006)
- *Guidance for Industry and FDA Staff: Interactive Review for Medical Device Submissions: 510(k)s, Original PMAs, PMA Supplements, Original BLAs, and BLA Supplements* (February 2008)
- *Guidance for Industry and Review Staff: Target Product Profile—A Strategic Development Process Tool* (**March 2007**)
- *Guidance for Industry: Pharmacogenomic Data Submissions* (March 2005)
- *Draft Guidance for Industry: Pharmacogenomic Data Submissions—Companion Guidance* (August 2007)
- *Draft Guidance for Industry: Animal Models—Essential Elements to address Efficacy under the Animal Rule* (January 2009)
- *Guidance for Industry—Assay Development for Immunogenicity Testing of Therapeutic Proteins* (December 2009)
- *Draft Guidance for Industry: Investigational New Drugs (INDs) - Determining whether Human Research Studies can be Conducted without an IND* (October 2010)
- *Draft Guidance for Industry: Adaptive Design Clinical Trials for Drugs and Biologics* (February 2010)
- *Guidance for Industry: Drug-Induced Liver Injury: Premarketing Clinical Evaluation* (July 2009)
- *Draft Guidance for Industry: Codevelopment of Two or More Unmarked Investigational Drugs for Use in Combination* (December 2010)
- *Draft Guidance for Industry: Qualification Process for Drug Development Tools* (October 2010)
- *Draft Guidance for Industry: Clinical Pharmacogenomics: Premarketing Evaluation in Early Phase Clinical Studies* (February 2011)
- *Drug Diagnostic Co-Development Concept Paper* (April 2005)

Introduction

Biologics are drug products derived from living sources, including humans, animals and microorganisms. The *Public Health Service Act* (*PHS Act*, 42 United States Code (U.S.C.) 262), Section 351(i) defines a biological product as "any virus, therapeutic serum, toxin, antitoxin, vaccine, blood, blood component or derivative, allergenic product, protein (except any chemically modified synthetic polypeptide), or analogous product... that is intended for use in the diagnosis, cure, mitigation, treatment, or prevention of disease."

Pursuant to Section 351(a) of the *PHS Act*, a biologics license must be in effect for any biological product introduced or delivered for introduction into interstate commerce. A submission for a biologic product approval is called a Biologic License Application (BLA). Biological products subject to the *PHS Act* also meet the definition of "drugs" under Sections 201(g) of the *Federal Food, Drug, and Cosmetic Act* of 1938 (*FD&C Act*) and, as such, must comply with Title 21 of the Code of Federal Regulations (CFR) Parts 210 and 211, current Good Manufacturing Practices (CGMPs).

The primary US Food and Drug Administration (FDA) reviewing center for a biological product is the Center for Biologics Evaluation and Research (CBER); however, there are exceptions. For instance, well-characterized proteins, such as therapeutic monoclonal antibodies, are reviewed by the Center for Drug Evaluation and Research (CDER). A combination product comprised of a biologic and a drug or a device may instead be reviewed by CDER or by the Center for Devices and Radiological Health (CDRH) as the lead center, depending upon the "primary mode of action" determination made by the Office of Combination Products (see "Chapter 22 Combination Products"). However, redundant product submissions for combination products are not ordinarily required; for instance, a biological/drug product combination that is accepted for review as a BLA generally does not also require a New Drug Application (NDA) for approval. Because of the many similarities and overlaps in how drugs and biologics are regulated, many sections of this book on chemical entities also apply to biologics; thus, this chapter emphasizes topics that are of particular interest or distinction for biologics.

Center for Biologics Evaluation and Research

CBER's regulatory authority is derived from the *PHS Act*, Section 351(a), and, as is the case with many regulations, the development of those for biologics has been fueled by tragedy. For instance, the very first biologics regulation, the *Biologics Control Act*, approved in 1902, came in response to the deaths of 13 children who contracted tetanus by taking horse diphtheria antitoxin. In 1955, in what came to be known as the Cutter Incident, several thousand children were exposed to live polio virus upon vaccination with the new Salk polio vaccine (seven lots were found deficient in viral inactivation), resulting in 260 people contracting polio. As a result, the Laboratory of Biologics Control became the Division of Biologics Standards (DBS) within the National Institutes of Health (NIH) to strengthen and expand its biologics control. DBS continued to oversee the control and release of biologics until 1972 when, in reaction to DBS's failure to implement an effectiveness review equivalent to that performed for drugs, it was moved from NIH to FDA and renamed the Bureau of Biologics. **Table 19-1** lists these and other key milestones in the regulatory oversight of biologics.

Over time, biological products have become increasingly diverse, and now include products such as cellular, tissue and gene therapies, and xenotransplantation products that were not considered when biologics were initially defined in the *PHS Act*. Current biological products regulated by CBER include:

- viral-vectored gene insertions, i.e., gene therapy
- products composed of human or animal cells or from physical parts of those cells, i.e., cell therapy
- allergen patch tests
- allergenics—extracts used for the diagnosis, prevention or treatment of allergies
- monoclonal antibodies, growth factors or other proteins when used solely as *ex vivo* reagents in a

manufacturing process, or used solely as reagents in the production of a product under CBER's jurisdiction
- vaccines, including therapeutic vaccines
- toxoids and toxins intended for immunization
- antitoxins, antivenins and venoms
- blood, blood components and related products (e.g., clotting factors)
- plasma expanders
- in vitro diagnostics used to screen donor blood, blood components and cellular products, and to diagnose, treat and monitor people with infectious diseases such as HIV, hepatitis, etc.
- devices used in collection, processing, testing, manufacture and administration of licensed blood, blood components and cellular components
- tissues—human cells or tissue intended for implantation, transplantation, infusion or transfer into a human recipient is regulated as a human cell, tissue and cellular and tissue-based product (HCT/P) (Note: CBER does not regulate the transplantation of vascularized human organs such as kidney, liver, heart, lung or pancreas)
- xenotransplantation—transplantation, implantation or infusion into a human recipient of either live cells, tissues or organs from a nonhuman animal source; or human body fluids, cells, tissues or organs that have had *ex vivo* contact with live nonhuman animal cells, tissues or organs

Effective 30 June 2003, oversight responsibility for the class of biological products, variously termed "specified," "well-characterized" or "therapeutic" biological products, was transferred from CBER's Office of Therapeutics Research to CDER's Office of New Drugs (OND), Office of Drug Evaluation VI. More recently, the review of therapeutic proteins was dispersed within CDER, so instead of all applications going to one office, they now go to the appropriate therapeutic review division within OND.

This product class is comprised of biotechnology products and naturally and synthetically derived proteins including the following:
- monoclonal antibodies for *in vivo* use (monoclonals for *in vitro* use remained under CBER's jurisdiction)
- proteins intended for therapeutic use, including cytokines (e.g., interferons), enzymes (e.g., thrombolytics) and other novel proteins, except those specifically assigned to CBER (e.g., vaccines and blood products); this category includes therapeutic proteins derived from plants, animals or microorganisms, and recombinant versions of these products
- immunomodulators (non-vaccine and non-allergenic products intended to treat disease by

Table 19-1. History of Biologics Regulation

Year	Regulatory Action
1902	• *Biologics Control Act* (Virus-Toxin Law) later called the *Public Health Service Act*—required regulation of vaccine and antitoxin producers including licensing and inspections of manufacturers and the interstate sale of serum, vaccines and related products
1903	• First biologics regulations by Public Health Service Hygienic Laboratory—"Poison Squad," effect of food preservatives and artificial colors on public health
1906	• *Pure Food and Drugs Act*—Prohibited "misbranding and adulteration"
1930	• PHS Hygienic Lab became NIH
1937	• NIH reorganized, Hygienic Lab became Division of Biologics Standardization
1938	• *Food, Drug, and Cosmetics Act (FD&C Act)*—Products must be shown to be 'safe;' authorized factory inspections
1944	• *PHS Act*—Required Product License Application/Establishment License Application (PLA/ELA, precursor to the BLA); gave seizure power
1955	• Division of Biologics Control became an independent entity within the National Institutes of Health, after polio vaccine thought to have been inactivated is associated with about 260 cases of polio
1972	• Division of Biologics Standardization, which was responsible for regulation of biologics, including serums, vaccines and blood products, transferred from NIH to FDA, became what is now called CBER
1982	• Bureau of Drugs and Bureau of Biologics combined to form National Center for Drugs and Biologics (ODRR and OBRR)
1988	• FDA becomes part of Department of Health and Human Services (DHHS), Center for Drug Evaluation and Research (CDER) and Center for Biologics Evaluation and Research (CBER)
1995	• Regulatory Initiative REGO IIb—Eliminate ELA requirement and lot release requirement for specified biotechnology products
1997	• *Food and Drug Administration Modernization Act (FDAMA)*—Revised *PHS Act* and eliminated the ELA for all biologics
2003	• Review of "well-characterized" proteins transferred to CDER
2009	• *Biologics Price Competition and Innovation Act of 2009 (BPCI Act)* created an abbreviated approval pathway for biosimilars

inhibiting or modifying a pre-existing immune response)
• growth factors, cytokines and monoclonal antibodies intended to mobilize, stimulate, decrease or otherwise alter the production of hematopoietic cells *in vivo*

These products continue to be regulated as licensed biologics (i.e., BLA) per 21 CFR 601.2(a). It is important to note that CDER already had responsibility for hormone protein products, e.g., insulin, growth hormone and pituitary hormones (regardless of the method of manufacture) as part of an October 1991 Intercenter Agreement between CBER and CDER; however, these products have been regulated as NDAs. This is now changing. Under the *BPCI Act*, proteins (with the exception of synthetic polypeptides) that have been approved under Section 505 (as an NDA) of the *FD&C Act* will be considered licensed biologics (i.e., BLAs), and will be required to comply with Section 351 of the *PHS Act* within 10 years of the date of enactment of the *BPCI Act* (i.e., March 2020).

Within CBER, the organizational structure for reviewing the widely diverse range of biological product submissions is divided into three main review offices:

• Office of Blood Research and Review (OBRR) (see Chapter 24)
• Office of Cellular, Tissue and Gene Therapies (OCTGT)
  o Division of Cellular and Gene Therapies (DCGT)
  o Division of Clinical Evaluation and Pharmacology and Toxicology (DCEPT)
  o Division of Human Tissues (DHT) (see Chapter 25)
• Office of Vaccine Research and Review (OVRR)
  o Division of Bacterial, Parasitic and Allergenic Products (DBPAP)
  o Division of Viral Products (DVP) (reviews viral vaccines and related products)
  o Division of Vaccines and Related Products Applications (DVRPA)

OCTGT regulates cellular and gene therapy products, including therapeutic cancer vaccines. DCGT (within OCTGT) reviews cell therapy products that include: progenitor cells such as stem cells; differentiated cells such as epithelial cells, reproductive cells, islet cells, dendritic cells and T lymphocytes; and tissue-engineered products, which may include cells that are embedded in a scaffold for use in treating damaged or diseased tissues. An Investigational New Drug Application (IND) is needed for studying such cell therapies when the cells are more than "minimally manipulated" or if they are used for nonautologous treatments. Minimal manipulation is defined in 21 CFR 1271.3(f) as processing that does not alter the relevant biological characteristics of the cells or tissues.

DCGT also reviews "human gene therapy products," which are defined as products that introduce genetic material into the body, to replace faulty or missing genetic material, or to treat or cure a disease or medical condition. Gene therapies include replication-deficient viral vectors, plasmid DNA vectors, various types of transgenes delivered by those vectors, as well as replication competent or attenuated viruses for the treatment of various types of cancer via viral lysis of tumor cells. FDA has not yet approved any human gene therapy product. Clinical gene therapy protocols are also governed by NIH's Recombinant DNA Advisory Committee (RAC) for clinical sites that receive NIH-funding, and information related to these clinical trials is tracked within the joint NIH/FDA Genetic Modification Clinical Research Information System (GeMCRIS). GeMCRIS enables faster reporting and better monitoring of adverse events in human gene transfer trials. CBER works closely with NIH to monitor safety and serious adverse events in gene therapy trials.

OVRR reviews vaccines that are of a heterogeneous class of medicinal products containing antigenic substances capable of inducing specific, active and protective host immunity against an infectious agent or pathogen. Vaccines can be either preventive, as with childhood vaccines, or therapeutic, as with cancer vaccines. Vaccines may be:

- live attenuated preparations of bacteria, viruses or parasites
- inactivated (killed) whole organisms
- living irradiated cells
- crude fractions or purified immunogens, including those derived from recombinant DNA in a host cell
- conjugates formed by covalent linkage of components
- synthetic antigens
- polynucleotides (such as plasmid DNA vaccines)
- living vectored cells expressing heterologous immunogens
- cells pulsed with immunogen

Vaccine-related products include *in vivo* diagnostic antigens used for detection of existing specific immune response by skin testing, and microbial-derived proteins such as botulinum toxins. Prophylactic vaccines approved for marketing usually require additional postmarketing studies to further establish their safety and effectiveness. Because the majority of vaccines are given to healthy individuals, and because of the public health advantage of childhood vaccines, the *National Childhood Vaccine Injury Act* was established to compensate patients who suffer serious injuries related to vaccines.

OVRR is responsible for reviewing allergenics, which include two types of products: allergen patch tests and allergenic extracts. Allergen patch tests are diagnostic tests applied to the surface of the skin to determine the specific causes of contact dermatitis, and are manufactured from natural substances or chemicals (e.g., nickel, rubber and fragrance mixes) known to cause contact dermatitis. Allergenic extracts are used to diagnose and treat allergic diseases, such as allergic rhinitis (hay fever), allergic sinusitis, allergic conjunctivitis, bee venom allergy and food allergies. Allergenic extracts are currently manufactured in two forms: standardized and unstandardized. Prior to release, standardized allergenic extracts are compared to US reference standards for potency. CBER maintains these reference standards and distributes them to manufacturers.

Through OBRR, CBER regulates blood products, described further in Chapter 24. However, CBER also regulates all medical devices associated with the collection and testing of licensed blood and cellular products. In addition, these products must comply with all appropriate medical device laws and regulations. Jurisdiction of medical device review by CBER and CDRH is governed by a 31 October 1991 FDA Intercenter Agreement.

IND Process for Biologics

The IND regulations (21 CFR 312) also apply to clinical testing of biologics. Recent guidance has clarified when clinical testing under an IND would not be required. Studies that could be exempt from the IND requirements include: certain research using marketed products, bioavailability/bioequivalence studies (these studies are now subject to safety reporting requirements, however) and studies using radioactive versions of both approved and unapproved drugs due to the lower radiation doses being used (some of these studies may require oversight by the Radioactive Drug Research Committee).

An IND for a biologic may be submitted in electronic Common Technical Document (eCTD) format, and guidance is available for mapping the IND sections to their appropriate location in the CTD. Just as for NDA-regulated drugs, Forms FDA 1571, 1572 and 3674 (Certificate of Compliance) should be submitted with the IND. Form FDA 3674 is an *FDAAA* requirement following the addition of Section 402(j) to the *PHS Act*, expanding the current database known as ClinicalTrials.gov to include mandatory registration and reporting of results for applicable clinical trials of human drugs (including biological products) and devices.

The following *Prescription Drug User Fee Act* (*PDUFA*) meetings with FDA are also applicable to biologics:

- Type A—to resolve a clinical hold or Refusal to

File, to resolve a dispute or to discuss a special protocol assessment (SPA)

- Type B—key milestone meetings to include Pre-IND, End-of-Phase 1 (for products developed under 21 CFR 601 Subpart E), End-of-Phase 2/Pre-Phase 3 and Pre- BLA
- Type C—for any other purpose

The required sections of the IND—including the clinical development plan; the proposed clinical protocol; Investigator's Brochure (IB); chemistry, manufacturing and controls (CMC); preclinical (pharmacology/toxicology); and previous human experience—are the same as for NDA drugs. Regulations related to financial disclosure, special INDs, orphan products, fast track, accelerated approval, clinical hold, pediatric studies/waivers (including the six months of additional exclusivity) and the SPA are all applicable for biologics as well. With the passing of the *BPCI Act*, the additional six months of market exclusivity for pediatric indications now applies to biologics as well; however, biologics are allowed a 12-year exclusivity period instead of the five years allowed for NDA drugs (seven years for orphan products). While there has been harmonization for regulatory submissions and programs between NDA and BLA products, a number of distinct development issues, discussed in more detail below, are specific to biologics. To accommodate these issues related to biologics, CBER provides a number of guidance documents, including some entitled "Points to Consider," that represent its current thinking on a variety of topics. In addition, some guidances from the International Conference on Harmonisation (ICH) are applicable to biologics. CBER also makes its internal Standard Operational Procedures and Policies (SOPPs) available to help sponsors prepare for interacting with the center.

Preclinical Development Considerations for Biologics

The preclinical safety package for a biologic can be quite different from the toxicology package for NDA drugs. Small-molecule drugs typically follow the M3 and Safety series of ICH guidance pretty closely, while special consideration must be given to biologics for all types of toxicological assessments in order to perform relevant preclinical testing in an appropriate model. Some of these principles are discussed in ICH *S6: Preclinical Safety Evaluation of Biotechnology-Derived Pharmaceuticals*. For instance, proteins are typically not active in all species, so selecting the correct species in which to assess the therapy is very important. In cases where there is no animal in which the biologic can function, either due to lack of specificity or due to anti-drug antibodies, preparing an analogous product, i.e., an animal homologue of the product intended for humans (e.g., a mouse monoclonal

antibody that binds to the same intended target in mice), can be warranted to assess potential safety issues. Another consideration is that the maximum tolerated dose (MTD) is usually not reached for biologics because biologics are not typically inherently toxic, thus it is difficult to provide drug concentrations at high enough levels to induce overt toxicity. Consequently, clinical dosing may be based on the biologically effective dose rather than the MTD. However, an attempt to cover the planned maximum human dose (preferably with up to a 10-fold safety margin) should be assessed in the safety studies. Typically, the doses are calculated with scaling for size in animals, with the exception of certain complex products with limited planned dosing, e.g., a vaccine, where the whole maximum human dose is assessed without adjusting for size. The route of administration for the toxicity assessment should correspond to the clinically intended route of administration. The total number of doses and dosing schedule should be at least equal to but more typically exceed the number of doses planned for the clinic. For example, vaccines usually test "N plus 1" in the preclinical models (perhaps two doses total), whereas a protein intended for longer-term treatment might undergo three months of daily or weekly dosing (as determined by its pharmacokinetics (PK)) to help inform human dose selection.

Safety pharmacology and acute toxicity studies typically are not performed as separate studies for biologics; instead, safety pharmacology endpoints are incorporated into the multiple-dose toxicity testing. While genotoxicity and carcinogenicity testing are usually not relevant for biologics, there are some biologics whose reproductive and developmental toxicity should be evaluated, especially if the product is to be given to pregnant women or women of child-bearing potential. For other biologic products, no preclinical toxicology testing is warranted, e.g., for cellular therapies, since the transfer of cells from one species to another is not valid due to immunological rejection and thus provides no relevant information with regard to evaluating safety. Thus, the preclinical testing strategy for a biologic needs to be science-based, flexible and discussed with health authorities to ensure acceptability.

Immunogenicity is also of concern in preclinical models for biologics since anti-drug antibodies could neutralize the drug's effects, thereby preventing development of potential toxicity reactions. Therefore, the occurrence of immunogenicity reactions needs to be carefully assessed in animal studies so preclinical data can be appropriately interpreted. Additionally, the manufacturing process utilized for preparing test articles for the preclinical studies needs to be representative of the process used for the GMP material. Ideally, the test articles would be the GMP material, to prevent the need to provide comparability data and to obviate immunogenicity and potency concerns related to any process changes.

Clinical Development Considerations for Biologics

Clinical study design and requirements for providing safety and effectiveness data are not different for biological drugs than for small molecule drugs; however, there may be additional safety concerns related to immunogenicity with biological products. Thus, additional testing may be required during the clinical trial to assess immunogenicity and the potential development of autoimmunity. As is the case for NDA drugs, clinical trials for biologics are conducted in phases. Once the study biologic's initial safety has been characterized in Phase 1 trials, Phase 2 trials are performed with larger groups (20-300) to assess how well the biologic works, and to evaluate Phase 1 safety and dosing assessments in a larger group of subjects. Phase 2 studies are sometimes divided into Phase 2A and Phase 2B. Phase 2A is designed to assess dosing requirements and can also include combination dosing studies if the biologic is to be administered in combination with another therapy. Phase 2B is designed to study efficacy and can include exploratory end points to assess other pharmacodynamic markers, safety and efficacy endpoints and patient populations in order to better design the Phase 3 trial(s). Phase 3 studies are typically randomized controlled studies in larger patient groups (300 or more, depending upon the disease or medical condition studied) and are aimed at being the definitive assessment of how effective the drug is, in comparison with the current standard of care. It is common practice for certain Phase 3 trials to continue while the regulatory submission is pending review. This allows patients to continue to receive possibly life-saving drugs until the drug is approved. These trials (often called Phase 3B trials) can be used to show that the drug works for additional types of patients or diseases beyond the original indication for which the drug received marketing approval, to obtain additional safety data, or to support marketing claims for the drug. While not required in all cases, two successful Phase 3 trials demonstrating a drug's safety and efficacy normally are recommended in order to obtain approval from the appropriate regulatory agencies.

Numerous ICH efficacy (E1–E16) and multidisciplinary (M3) guidelines cover topics relevant to the clinical development of biologics. In addition, FDA routinely publishes guidance documents that provide information about the clinical development process both for specific disease indications as well as for more general topics, which are easily searchable on the FDA website.

One of the newer clinical guidance documents discusses how to design clinical trials with adaptive features (i.e., changes in design or analyses guided by examination of the accumulated data at an interim point in the trial). These adaptive trial designs may make the studies more efficient (e.g., shorter duration, fewer patients), more likely to demonstrate an effect of the drug if one exists, or more informative (e.g., by providing broader dose-response information).

Another recent draft guidance lays out considerations for the codevelopment of two or more unmarketed drugs for use in combination, which will be of increased importance as the understanding of overall disease treatment response improves to allow multiple therapeutic targets to be addressed in combination.

FDA has issued several recent guidances on the use of pharmacogenomics (PGx) in the drug development process. PGx studies can contribute to a greater understanding of inter-individual differences in the efficacy and safety of investigational biologics. Across the drug development continuum, genomic data may be used for understanding PK variations and variability in clinical response; elucidating the molecular basis for lack of efficacy or adverse events; and designing clinical trials to test for effects in identified subgroups, possibly for use in study enrichment strategies. Drug product labeling has increasingly included preapproval information on the likelihood of treatment response based on genetic or genomic status. In addition, codevelopment of a drug-diagnostic combination is an area of rapidly evolving technology and will involve regulation of products across the FDA centers (CBER, or CDER, the Center for Devices and Radiological Health (CDRH) and the Office of Combination Products (OCP)). Drug-test combinations could potentially yield important information to healthcare providers regarding topics such as differential diagnosis of a disorder or identification of a patient subset, identification of responders to a specific drug or targeted therapy, identification of individuals at risk for adverse events, monitoring responses to drugs, and providing individualized therapy.

FDA also provides guidance on key safety issues relevant to drug development such as understanding the risks of prolonged QT interval related to drug treatment, or considerations for monitoring a drug's ability to cause drug-induced liver injury. FDA published a recent guidance on immunogenicity, *Assay Development for Immunogenicity Testing of Therapeutic Proteins* (December 2009), which is particularly relevant for biologics because treatment with therapeutic proteins can frequently stimulate an immune response. The clinical effect of these immune responses to therapeutic proteins, however, has ranged from none to extremely harmful. Such varied immune responses can affect both the product safety and efficacy and the immunogenicity rates observed during clinical trials, which are included in the product labeling. Thus, the development of valid, sensitive immune assays is a key aspect of product development. For new products, assay development and validation pose many challenges and an evolving approach is typically utilized during product development. Because immunogenicity poses a high risk, and real-time data concerning patient responses are needed, there should generally be a preliminary validated assay to be used during Phase 1. Even though immunogenicity in animal models is not predictive of immunogenicity in humans, it may reveal potential antibody-related toxicities that should be monitored in clinical trials. Multiple approaches may be appropriate for immunogenicity testing during clinical trials; however, testing strategies should address sensitivity (to detect clinically relevant levels of antibodies); interference (from the matrix or from on-board product); functional or physiological consequences (such as neutralizing activity and ability to induce hypersensitivity responses); and risk-based application (risk to patients of mounting an immune response to product). The rationale for the immunogenicity testing paradigm should be provided in the IND.

Manufacturing of Clinical Trial Material for Biologics

The CMC section is a critical component during the preparation of IND and BLA submissions for biologics because of the complexity of most biological products. The goal of CMC development is to provide an established process that assures consistent production of a quality product. The amount of information required to assure proper identity, quality, purity, potency and strength will vary with the phase of the clinical investigation. During Phase 1, attention is paid to characterizing the drug substance and drug product using qualified assays. Testing should demonstrate clearance of impurities and contaminants and of safety-related issues such as viral clearance or sterility (aseptic manufacturing), development of a suitable reference standard, and development of a stability program to support the use of the biologic during the clinical trial. Submissions include:

- description of all materials and components
- analytical tests
- characterization of biological source materials (e.g., cell line, vectors, cell bank, viral seed and donor)
- description of the manufacturing process through final formulation and filling
- description of critical process controls
- lot release data (including material used in toxicological testing and planned for clinical trial use)
- stability data

The presence of adventitious agents is of particular concern with biological products, especially vaccines that contain animal materials and/or cellular substrates. An adventitious agent is an infectious agent that is extraneous to the product; potential agents include transmissible spongiform encephalopathy (TSE), viruses and oncogenic agents. Testing and clearance of known agents must be demonstrated to be sufficiently sensitive; testing should also be capable of detecting unsuspected agents. Suitable tests may include techniques such as cell culture, polymerase chain reaction (PCR), electron microscopy and egg or animal inoculation. In addition, sourcing of materials to avoid animal-derived materials can help reduce exposure of materials and substrates to specified risk materials for TSE.

As the process is optimized and additional knowledge is gained, changes to the process will inevitably take place; thus, careful attention is required to evaluate changes made during development and to demonstrate comparability for these manufacturing changes. Information amendments are required during the IND stage for significant changes and any changes that are likely to affect safety and efficacy prior to the use of the revised process material in clinical studies. Inability to assure the product's quality, stability and/or comparability can lead to a clinical hold. During development to Phase 3, specifications for testing will evolve and become more defined; critical assays will need to be validated and determined to be reproducible, quantitative, sensitive, specific and biologically relevant; and the manufacturing process will be optimized. Activities required for process development and optimization are discussed in a recently finalized guidance, *Guidance for Industry: Process Validation: General Principles and Practices* (January 2011), which describes three stages for the process development lifecycle including: Process Design, Process Qualification and Continued Process Verification. For biologics, the process needs to be validated, i.e., qualified, prior to submitting the BLA and the process validation is included in the BLA. This is in contrast to NDA products where the process validation is reviewed as part of the Preapproval Inspection (PAI) program.

Unique requirements for biologics are found in the General Biological Product Standards (21 CFR 610). Under these standards, to receive the license, the product must be shown to be "safe, pure, and potent." In addition, an inspection must confirm that the production facility assures that the product meets these standards. The biological standards provide specific tests to be performed on each lot prior to release:

- potency—ideally via a product-specific bioassay that correlates with the *in vivo* mechanism of action or is predictive of function, and in place for final product lot release by Phase 3
- general safety test—intraperitoneal injection of drug product into two mice and two guinea pigs, if applicable (not required for well-characterized biologics)
- sterility—similar to USP Chapter 71
- purity—essentially free of extraneous material such as residual solvents, antibiotics, animal products, contaminating cell populations and co-purifying proteins; also includes residual moisture and pyrogenic substances (e.g., endotoxin)
- identity—if product is comprised of multiple components (e.g. cell lines, proteins), the test method should identify all components
- constituent materials—all ingredients should meet general standards of purity and quality
- mycoplasma, if applicable

Table 19-2. Key CMC Guidance for Development of Biological Products

ICH Guidelines Specifically Targeted at Biotech Products
• Q5A(R1): Viral Safety Evaluation of Biotechnology Products Derived from Cell Lines of Human or Animal Origin (March 1997)
• Q5B: Quality of Biotechnological Products: Analysis of the Expression Construct in Cells Used for Production of rDNA Derived Protein Products (November 1995)
• Q5C: Quality of Biotechnological Products: Stability Testing of Biotechnological/Biological Products (November 1995)
• Q5D: Derivation and Characterisation of Cell Substrates Used for Production of Biotechnological/Biological Products (July 1997)
• Q5E: Comparability of Biotechnological/Biological Products Subject to Changes in Their Manufacturing Process (November 2004)
• Q6B: Specifications: Test Procedures and Acceptance Criteria for Biotechnological/Biological Products (March 1999)
FDA Points to Consider and Other Applicable CMC Guidance Documents
• Guidance for Industry: CGMP for Phase 1 Investigational Drugs (July 2008)
• Guidance for Industry: Content and Format of Investigational New Drug Applications (INDs) for Phase 1 Studies of Drugs, Including Well-Characterized, Therapeutic, Biotechnology-Derived Products (November 1995).
• Guidance for Industry: INDs for Phase 2 and 3 Studies of Drugs, Including Specified Therapeutic Biotechnology-Derived Products, Chemistry, Manufacturing, and Controls Content and Format (February 1999)
• Draft Guidance for Industry: Potency Tests for Cellular and Gene Therapy Products (October 2008)
• Guidance for Food and Drug Administration Reviewers and Sponsors: Content and Review of Chemistry, Manufacturing, and Control (CMC) Information for Human Somatic Cell Therapy Investigational New Drug Applications (INDs) (April 2008)
• Guidance for Food and Drug Administration Reviewers and Sponsors: Content and Review of Chemistry, Manufacturing, and Control (CMC) Information for Human Gene Therapy Investigational New Drug Applications (INDs) (April 2008)
• Draft Guidance for Industry: Validation of Growth-Based Rapid Microbiological Methods for Sterility Testing of Cellular and Gene Therapy Products (February 2008)
• Draft Guidance for Industry: Characterization and Qualification of Cell Substrates and Other Biological Starting Materials Used in the Production of Viral Vaccines for the Prevention and Treatment of Infectious Diseases (September 2006)
• Guidance for Industry: Container Closure Systems for Packaging Human Drugs and Biologics—Chemistry, Manufacturing, and Controls Documentation (May 1999)
• Guidance for Industry: Guidance for Human Somatic Cell Therapy and Gene Therapy (March 1998)
• Proposed Approach to Regulation of Cellular and Tissue-Based Products (February 1997)
• Points to Consider in the Manufacture and Testing of Monoclonal Antibody Products for Human Use (February 1997)
• Guidance for the Submission of Chemistry, Manufacturing, and Controls Information and Establishment Description for Autologous Somatic Cell Therapy Products (January 1997)
• Guidance for Industry for the Submission of Chemistry, Manufacturing, and Controls Information for a Therapeutic Recombinant DNA-Derived Product or a Monoclonal Antibody Product for In Vivo Use (August1996)
• Guidance on Applications for Products Comprised of Living Autologous Cells Manipulated ex vivo and Intended for Structural Repair or Reconstruction (May 1996)
• Points to Consider in the Manufacture and Testing of Therapeutic Products for Human Use Derived from Transgenic Animals (1995)
• Points to Consider in the Characterization of Cell Lines Used to Produce Biologicals (July 1993)
• Supplement to the Points to Consider in the Production and Testing of New Drugs and Biologics Produced by Recombinant DNA Technology: Nucleic Acid Characterization and Genetic Stability (April 1992)
• Points to Consider in the Collection, Processing, and Testing of Ex-Vivo Activated Mononuclear Leukocytes for Administering to Humans (August 1989)
• Guideline on Validation of the Limulus Amebocyte Lysate Test as an End-Product Endotoxin Test For Human and Animal Parenteral Drugs, Biological Products, and Medical Devices (December 1987)
• Points to Consider in the Production and Testing of New Drugs and Biologicals Produced by Recombinant DNA Technology (April 1985)
• Draft Guidance for Industry: Early Clinical Trials with Live Biotherapeutic Products: Chemistry, Manufacturing, and Control Information (December 2010)
• Guidance for Industry: Process Validation: General Principles and Practices (January 2011)

Alternative methods are permitted if they are equal to or greater than the assurances provided by the specified method and must be validated by the end of Phase 3 to show equivalency to the established method. The standards also include testing requirements for communicable disease agents (if applicable), product dating periods and product labeling requirements (i.e., the product package to be labeled with the biologic's proper name; the manufacturer's name, address and applicable license number; and the expiration date).

The amount of information on analytical procedures and methods validation necessary for submission will vary with the phase of the investigation (21 CFR 312.23(a)(7)). For general guidance on analytical procedures and methods validation information to be submitted for Phase 1 studies, sponsors can refer to FDA's *Guidance for Industry: Content and Format of Investigational New Drug Applications (INDs) for Phase 1 Studies of Drugs, Including Well-Characterized, Therapeutic, Biotechnology-Derived Products* (November 1995). And for Phase 2 or Phase 3 studies, FDA's *Guidance for Industry: INDs for Phase 2 and 3 Studies of Drugs, Including Specified Therapeutic Biotechnology-Derived Products, Chemistry, Manufacturing, and Controls Content and Format,* (draft guidance published April 1999). All analytical procedures should be fully developed and validated when the BLA is submitted. The requested format and content of analytical procedures for the BLA are the same as for an NDA; however, for the BLA, analytical information is submitted in the BLA rather than as a separate methods validation package.

A number of sources of guidance for the appropriate development of CMC processes and testing should be consulted, including ICH guidelines, CBER Points to Consider and other FDA guidances. Key CMC-related guidances are listed in **Table 19-2**. In addition, there are several general and specific chapters in the *United States Pharmacopoeia* (USP) relevant to biologics, including specific chapters on methods such as capillary electrophoresis and peptide mapping, viral safety evaluation and cell and gene therapies that can be consulted.

BLA Format and Content

BLAs are required for all biological products submitted to CBER and for well-characterized proteins regulated by CDER. The Application to Market a New Drug, Biologic or Antibiotic Drug for Human Use is submitted on Form FDA 356h, the same form used for the NDA, in accordance with 21 CFR 601. Major sections of the NDA and BLA are the same, with a few exceptions. For instance, a facility description is required for CBER-reviewed products but not those reviewed by CDER, and a Field Copy Certification only applies to NDA products. Also, biologics typically are categorically excluded from requiring an environmental assessment under 21 CFR 25.5(c).

The BLA may also be submitted in eCTD format and should follow the ICH M4 guidance. Due to the broad diversity of products regulated by CBER, specific requirements related to elements necessary for each sponsor's distinct product BLA should be discussed and planned throughout development. The contents and requirements should be carefully mapped out, presented and discussed at the Pre-BLA meeting to prevent miscommunication and potential Refusal to File (RTF) action.

BLA Review Process

The BLA review process, like the NDA review, is divided into five phases:

1. filing determination and review planning
2. review
3. Advisory Committee meeting preparation and conduct
4. action
5. post-action

Under the *PDUFA* provisions, submission of a major amendment during the last three months of a review may trigger a three-month extension of the review clock. For combination biological products, CBER may need to undertake formal consultative or collaborative reviews with CDER or CDRH, which involve formal procedures.

Per 21 CFR 601.2, an application for licensure is not considered as filed until CBER has received all pertinent information and data from the manufacturer. An RTF decision may be made on applications that contain incomplete or inadequate information required under section 351 of the *PHS Act*, the *FD&C Act* or in FDA regulations (e.g., 21 CFR 601.2). RTF decisions, therefore, can be based upon:

- administrative incompleteness of an application (i.e., clear omission of information or sections of information required)
- scientific incompleteness of an application (i.e., omission of critical data, information or analyses needed to evaluate safety, purity and potency or provide adequate directions for use (21 CFS 601.2))
- inadequate information content or organization in an application that precludes substantive and meaningful review (e.g., illegibility; data tabulations (line listings) or graphical displays that cannot be interpreted)
- technically deficient electronic submission

In summary, CBER's initial decision on whether to file a BLA or supplement will be based upon a threshold determination of whether the information submitted to support licensure is sufficiently complete to permit a substantive and meaningful review. An RTF may also apply if the application contains uncorrected deficiencies (e.g., manufacturing or product specifications), which were clearly communicated to the applicant before application submission or, for electronic submissions, contains technical deficiencies sufficient to require resolution before a meaningful review can occur. An RTF is not a final determination concerning potential approvability; it can be an early opportunity for the applicant to develop a complete application, but will delay, at least for a time, a full review of the application.

By contrast, issuance of a Complete Response (CR) Letter (after a complete review) is generally based on critical omissions of data or analyses as well as an adverse judgment about the data, conclusions, rationale, etc., presented in the application. For example, a CR Letter could be issued if CBER concludes that effectiveness has not been demonstrated; an analysis was incorrectly carried out; clinical trials were poorly designed or conducted; safety has not been adequately demonstrated; or outstanding compliance issues remain. These judgments would not serve as the basis for an RTF unless the deficiencies were so severe as to render the application incomplete.

Other action letters include the Information Request (IR) letter and the Discipline Review (DR) letter. An IR letter requests further information or clarification that is necessary to complete the discipline review. A DR letter is sent to convey early thoughts on possible deficiencies found by a discipline review team at the conclusion of its review. Generally, each discipline reviews a different section of the BLA or BLA supplement. These disciplines include, but are not limited to: clinical review; CMC review; preclinical pharmacology and toxicology review; and human pharmacokinetics and bioavailability review. A single DR letter may contain comments from multiple discipline reviews if it is more efficient to do so. Neither an IR letter nor a DR letter necessarily reflects input from upper supervisory levels (i.e., division or office directors).

Biosimilars

The *Drug Price Competition and Patent Term Restoration Act of 1984* (*Hatch-Waxman Act*) amended the *FD&C Act* and created the section 505(j) generic drug approval pathway. This pathway does not apply to the well-characterized proteins regulated by CDER or to any other biologics regulated by FDA; however, there has been considerable interest in establishing a regulatory approval pathway for follow-on biologics. This has now been accomplished with the *Patient Protection and Affordable Care Act* (*PPAC Act*) signed into law in March 2010, which amended the *PHS Act* to create an abbreviated approval pathway for biological products that are demonstrated to be "highly similar" (biosimilar) to or "interchangeable" with an FDA-approved biological product. These new statutory provisions are referred to as the *Biologics Price Competition and Innovation Act* of 2009 (*BPCI Act*). The goal of the *BPCI Act* is similar in concept to that of *Hatch-Waxman Act* since the *BPCI Act* aligns with

FDA's policy of permitting appropriate reliance on what is already known about a drug, thereby saving time and resources and avoiding unnecessary duplication of human or animal testing.

Under the *BPCI Act*, a sponsor may seek approval of a "biosimilar" product under the new section 351(k) of the *PHS Act*. A biological product may be demonstrated to be "biosimilar" if data show that it is "highly similar" to the reference product, notwithstanding minor differences in clinically inactive components, and that there are no clinically meaningful differences between the biological product and the reference product in terms of safety, purity and potency. In order to meet the higher standard of interchangeability, a sponsor must demonstrate that the biosimilar product can be expected to produce the same clinical result as the reference product in any given patient and, for a biological product that is administered more than once, that the risk of alternating or switching from the reference product to the biosimilar product is not greater than the risk of maintaining the patient on the reference product. Interchangeable products may be substituted for the reference product by a pharmacist without the intervention of the prescribing healthcare provider.

An application submitted under this subsection should include information demonstrating that the product is biosimilar to a reference product based on data derived from: analytical studies that demonstrate that the biological product is highly similar to the reference product, notwithstanding minor differences in clinically inactive components; animal studies (including the assessment of toxicity); and a clinical study or studies (including the assessment of immunogenicity and pharmacokinetics or pharmacodynamics) sufficient to demonstrate safety, purity and potency in one or more appropriate conditions of use for which the reference product is licensed and intended to be used and for which licensure is sought for the biological product. To be approved as a biosimilar, the following criteria must also be met:

- the biological product and reference product utilize the same mechanism or mechanisms of action for the condition or conditions of use prescribed, recommended or suggested in the proposed labeling (but only to the extent that the mechanism(s) of action are known for the reference product)
- the condition or conditions of use prescribed, recommended or suggested in the labeling proposed for the biological product have been previously approved for the reference product
- the route of administration, dosage form and strength of the biological product are the same as those of the reference product
- the facility in which the biological product is manufactured, processed, packed or held meets standards designed to assure that the product continues to be

safe, pure and potent

The approval of a biosimilar application under Subsection 351(k) of the *PHS Act* may not occur until 12 years after the date on which the reference product was first licensed. In addition, an application under Subsection 351(k) may not be accepted for review until four years after the date on which the reference product was first licensed. The *BPCI Act* also provides for an extension of exclusivity for biologics (to match that of drugs) of six months for pediatric indications, making the exclusivity period 12 years and six months (also adds six months to existing patents).

Lot Release Protocols

In accordance with 21 CFR 610.2(a), samples of any lot of licensed biological product, together with the protocols showing results of applicable tests, may be required to be submitted to CBER at any time for review and confirmatory testing. The timely review of test results and sign-off on lot release protocols are important elements of the biologicals approval process. Early communication and collaboration are essential during the approval process with respect to review of test protocols, sample requirements and development of new testing procedures. This requirement has been waived for the well-characterized biologics regulated by CDER.

Advisory Committee Meetings

The *Federal Advisory Committee Act* of 1972 is the legal foundation defining how federal Advisory Committees operate. Advisory Committees are groups of experts from outside the agency that FDA sometimes turns to for advice on complex scientific, technical and policy issues. Advisory Committees provide independent, professional expertise related to the development and evaluation of FDA-regulated products, such as human and animal drugs, blood and other biological products, medical devices and foods. For example, an Advisory Committee may provide advice to help FDA weigh the risks and benefits of a new potential treatment for a disease. In general, Advisory Committees include a chairman, several members, plus representatives of consumer groups, industry and sometimes patients. Additional experts with special knowledge may be added for individual meetings as needed. Although the committees provide advice to the agency, FDA makes the final decisions. The current CBER Advisory Committees include:

- Allergenic Products
- Blood Products
- Cellular, Tissue and Gene Therapies
- Transmissible Spongiform Encephalopathies
- Vaccines and Related Biological Products

In some cases, FDA is required by law to refer an issue to an Advisory Committee. In others, it has discretion to consider whether to refer a matter to an Advisory Committee. The guidance proposes three factors for FDA to consider when deciding whether to voluntarily refer a matter to an Advisory Committee:

1. issues of significant public interest
2. issues so controversial that it would be highly beneficial to obtain the advice of an Advisory Committee
3. issues that require specific expertise for the review process

When one of these factors is present, FDA should refer the matter to an Advisory Committee. The guidance also proposes that, for all first-of-a-kind or first-in-class products for human use, FDA either refer the product to an Advisory Committee or provide a summary of the reasons why it did not before approval in the action letter. As is true for drugs, a biological product sponsor may request an Advisory Committee meeting as part of formal dispute resolution proceedings; however, FDA is not obligated to schedule a meeting if it is not deemed necessary.

Once the review has progressed within the reviewing division, CBER will notify the sponsor 55 days in advance if it has determined that an Advisory Committee meeting is required. The sponsor prepares materials for Advisory Committee review and designates which materials are publically releasable under the *Freedom of Information Act* (*FOIA*) and which are to be treated as proprietary, non-public materials. FDA may disagree with the sponsor's designations and request that additional information be made public. In general, product information that is not in the labeling, such as manufacturing processes, formulation information and quality control testing, as well as the raw data from preclinical and clinical studies, can be considered exempt from *FOIA*. Advisory Committee members, however, will receive both sets of materials. During the meeting, sponsors may be permitted to make presentations but they are not allowed to approach committee members without the consent of a federal officer. The function of Advisory Committees is advisory only and therefore, once the meeting is held, FDA is not obligated to adopt the committee's recommendation(s). Instead, all matters under FDA consideration must still be determined in accordance with applicable laws.

Licensing Issues
Cooperative Manufacturing Arrangements

CBER, in conjunction with CDER, has issued guidance allowing different licensing strategies in the production of biological products that are subject to licensure under section 351 of the *PHS Act* for meeting the increased need for flexible manufacturing arrangements. These include:

Short Supply

When a licensed biologic is in short supply, the manufacturer may obtain an initial or partially manufactured version of the product from an unlicensed, but registered, facility when the product is shipped solely to the licensee and when the licensee can ensure the product made at the unlicensed facility will be manufactured in full compliance with applicable regulations. The license holder must update its license with FDA to explain this arrangement. This provision is most commonly used to obtain source materials such as those used in producing allergenic extracts; specific types of human plasma containing rare antibodies; venoms used in producing antitoxins and antivenins; and recovered plasma.

Divided Manufacturing

Divided manufacturing is an arrangement in which two or more manufacturers, each registered with FDA and licensed to manufacture a specific biological product in its entirety, participate jointly in the manufacture of that product by only performing part of the approved process. BLAs should be updated to describe the role of each manufacturer and may need to demonstrate equivalency and stability of the intermediate products during shipment. The intermediate should also be labeled "for further manufacturing use" as part of the proper name. Each licensed manufacturer must notify the other licensee(s) and the appropriate FDA center regarding proposed changes in the manufacture, testing or specifications of its product, in accordance with 21 CFR 601.12.

Shared Manufacturing

Shared manufacturing is an arrangement in which two or more manufacturers are registered and licensed for specific aspects of a product's manufacture, but neither is licensed for the product's total manufacturing process. A common shared manufacturing arrangement makes one manufacturer responsible for an intermediate product and another for the final product. All license applications or supplements under a shared manufacturing arrangement should be submitted concurrently to FDA for BLA review. Lack of one or more related applications may result in an RTF action.

Contract Manufacturing

In this arrangement, the sponsor holds the license, and the contract facilities, while listed in the BLA, are considered to be under the license holder's control. Therefore, sponsors must establish, maintain and follow procedures for receiving information from the contract manufacturing facility on all deviations, complaints and adverse events that may affect product quality. Specific identification of the contractor in the product labeling is not required since it does not hold the license.

Drug Master Files

A drug master file (DMF) is a submission to FDA, usually concerning confidential CMC information of a drug product component, that permits the agency to review the information in support of a third party's submission. DMFs are optional and are categorized in 21 CFR 314.420 as follows:

- Type I—Reserved, no longer applicable
- Type II—Drug substance, drug substance intermediate and material used in their preparation, or drug product
- Type III—Packaging material
- Type IV—Excipient, colorant, flavor, essence or material used in their preparation
- Type V—FDA accepted reference material

Submitted DMFs are only reviewed in conjunction with a sponsor's IND or BLA when that DMF is referenced and there is a letter of authorization granting FDA permission to access the DMF in support of the submission. If there are deficiencies in the DMF, the DMF holder will be notified to provide additional information. The sponsor will also be notified in either an IR or CR Letter; however, no confidential details about the deficiency will be included in this communication. If there are no deficiencies, the holder will not receive any communication. DMFs should be updated annually, although FDA does not send reminders. After three years of holder inactivity, FDA will notify the holder that the DMF will be closed; the holder has 90 days to either close the DMF or provide an annual update to keep it open.

A DMF's content should be based upon applicable guidance and the submission should follow the M4Q CTD-Quality format. The submission must also contain a statement of commitment to CGMP compliance. One commonly used DMF submission for CBER is the Type V, under which CBER accepts:

- facility information in support of gene- and cell-based therapies (which may be used to support clinical trials and to facilitate IND review)
- production facility information for a contract manufacturer to confidentially provide a list of other products manufactured in the facility (this information was formerly filed as a Type I DMF)
- submissions from contract testing facilities such as cell bank testing and viral clearance studies

Before submitting any other types of information in a Type V DMF, a letter of intent should be submitted to FDA to determine the suitability of the DMF submission.

Animal Rule

In May 2002, FDA published "Approval of Biological Products when Human Efficacy Studies are not Ethical or Feasible" (21 CFR 601 Subpart H and 21 CFR 314 Subpart I), also known as the "Animal Rule." In addition, FDA published draft guidance in 2009, *Animal Models —Essential Elements to Address Efficacy Under the Animal Rule*, to outline critical characteristics to consider when developing an animal model for this purpose. Under this rule, FDA can rely upon the evidence from animal studies to provide substantial evidence of the effectiveness of these products when:

- There is a reasonably well-understood pathophysiological mechanism for the toxicity of the chemical, biological, radiological or nuclear substance and its amelioration or prevention by the product.
- The effect is demonstrated in more than one animal species expected to react with a response predictive for humans.
- The animal study endpoint is clearly related to the desired benefit in humans.
- The data or information on the product's pharmacokinetics and pharmacodynamics are sufficiently well understood to allow selection of an effective dose in humans and it is therefore reasonable to expect the product's effectiveness in animals to be a reliable indicator of its effectiveness in humans.

To date, CBER has not approved any new products under the Animal Rule. However, several products are in development and are moving toward approval through this mechanism. CDER has approved one product thus far using the Animal Rule.

Critical Path Initiative at CBER

The Critical Path Initiative is FDA's national strategy to drive innovation in the scientific processes through which medical products are developed, evaluated and manufactured. The CPI was launched in 2004 and has had the following areas of focus:

- developing better evaluation tools such as biomarkers and new assays
- streamlining clinical trials by modernizing the clinical trial sciences to make trials safer and more efficient
- harnessing bioinformatics (e.g., moving from a paper-based to an electronic environment for exchanging information and overseeing the safety of FDA-regulated products)
- moving manufacturing into the 21st century, using tools such as process analytical technology and nanotechnology
- developing products to address urgent public health needs, including improved antimicrobial testing, new animal models to test bioterrorism countermeasures and vaccine testing
- focusing on at-risk populations, such as pediatrics

Beginning in 2010, CPI at CBER began a new project aimed at enhancing the development and availability of diagnostics and therapies for tropical diseases, especially tuberculosis (TB)—an effort strongly supported by Congress since TB continues to be a major global killer, and, because of multi-drug resistance, remains a threat to US health and security. Among the key CPI focus areas going forward are: supporting partnerships to accelerate the development of personalized medicine; new approaches to toxicology; new efforts to help meet unmet US and global public health needs; and increased support of informatics activities to facilitate FDA's ability to carry out its mission as efficiently as possible.

Other CBER priorities include preparing for pandemic or emerging threats by increasing the availability of safe and effective treatments and developing drugs and biologics that will reduce or prevent exposure to biological warfare agents. Thus, CBER plays a critical role in preserving public health by controlling these and other emerging infectious disease threats—recognized as a critical local, national and worldwide priority.

Summary

- Biologics are drug products derived from living sources, e.g., humans, animals and microorganisms, which are approved for licensure (using a BLA) under the *PHS Act*, unlike small-molecule drugs, which are approved under the *FD&C Act*. CBER is the primary reviewing center for biologics and is organized into three offices for the review of blood products, of vaccines and of cell, tissue and gene therapy products.
- The review of "well-characterized" biological products was moved from CBER to CDER in 2003. This category is comprised of biotechnology products and naturally and synthetically derived proteins and includes products such as monoclonal antibodies, cytokines, growth factors, enzymes, immunomodulators and thrombolytics.
- The IND process for biologics is much the same as for drugs; however, there are a number of preclinical, clinical and manufacturing guidance documents to assist sponsors with the issues unique to the development of biological products.
- The BLA format and general review process are also similar to that for drugs, including the utilization of the eCTD format for submissions. One unique aspect of a CBER review is the requirement for lot release protocols that the agency may then use to perform postapproval lot release testing of sponsors' products; this requirement has been waived for the well-characterized products reviewed by CDER.
- CBER (and CDER, for well-characterized proteins) allow different licensing strategies to be

used in the production of biological products to meet the increased need for flexible manufacturing arrangements including short supply, and shared and divided manufacturing.

- It is now possible for a sponsor to seek approval of a "biosimilar" product under new Section 351(k) of the *PHS Act*. The sponsor must show that the product is highly similar to the reference product and that there are no clinically meaningful differences between the biological product and the reference product in terms of safety, purity and potency. However, to meet the higher standard of interchangeability, a sponsor must demonstrate that the risk of alternating or switching between use of the biosimilar product and the reference product is not greater than the risk of maintaining the patient on the reference product.

Biologics Compliance

By Marcia Gaido, PhD, RAC

Objectives

- Understand general biologics licensing standards
- Understand the organization, roles and responsibilities of CBER's Office of Compliance and Biologics Quality
- Learn general regulatory compliance principles for biologics preapproval including chemistry, manufacturing and controls (CMC), change control, IND safety reports, role of Bioresearch Monitoring, product naming and prelicense inspections
- Learn general regulatory postapproval compliance principles for biologics including inspections, postapproval commitments, change control, biologic deviations reporting and import/export
- Understand risk management plans for biologics including setting up Risk Evaluation and Mitigation Strategies (REMS)
- Understand Food and Drug Administration (FDA) enforcement activities for biologics

Laws, Regulations and Guidance Documents Covered in This Chapter

- Sections 351 and 361 of the *Public Health Service Act* of 1946
- *Federal Food, Drug, and Cosmetic Act* of 1938
- The *Food and Drug Administration Amendments Act of 2007 (FDAAA)*
- 21 CFR 600 Biologics general
- 21 CFR 601 Biologics licensing
- 21 CFR 610 General biological products standards
- Compliance Program Guidance Manual—Inspection of Biological Drug Products—7345.848
- *Regulatory Procedures Manual*, Chapter 9, Subchapter 9.3, "Importation of Biological Products," Office of Regulatory Affairs, US Food and Drug Administration
- *Guidance for Industry: Comparability Protocols—Chemistry, Manufacturing, and Controls Information* (February 2003)
- *Guidance for Industry: Comparability Protocols—Protein Drug Products and Biological Products—Chemistry, Manufacturing, and Controls Information* (September 2003)
- ICH; *Comparability of Biotechnological/Biological Products Subject to Changes in Their Manufacturing Process Q5E* (June 2005)
- *Guidance For Industry: Changes to an Approved Application for Specified Biotechnology and Specified Synthetic Biological Products* (July 1997)
- *SOPP 8410: Determining When Prelicense/Preapproval Inspections are Necessary* (December 2001)
- *SOPP 8001.4: Review of CBER Regulated Product Proprietary Names* (November 2008)
- *Draft Guidance for Industry: Contents of a Complete Submission for the Evaluation of Proprietary Names* (November 2008)
- *Guidance for Industry: Regulation of Human Cells, Tissues, and Cellular and Tissue-Based Products (HCT/Ps)—Small Entity Compliance Guide* (August 2007)

- *Exports Under the FDA Export Reform and Enhancement Act of 1996* (July 2007)
- *Draft Guidance for Industry: Postmarketing Safety Reporting for Human Drug and Biological Products Including Vaccines* (March 2001)
- *Guidance for Industry: Biological Product Deviation Reporting for Licensed Manufacturers of Biological Products Other than Blood and Blood Components* (October 2006)
- *SOPP 8404: Refusal to File Procedures for Biologics License Applications* (August 2007)
- *Guidance for Industry: Good Pharmacovigilance Practices and Pharmacoepidemiologic Assessment* (March 2005)
- *Guidance for Industry: Premarketing Risk Assessment* (March 2005)
- *Guidance for Industry: Changes to an Approved Application: Biological Products* (July 1997)
- *Guidance for Industry: Format and Content of Proposed Risk Evaluation and Mitigation Strategies (REMS), REMS Assessments, and Proposed REMS Modifications* (September 2009)
- *Draft Guidance for Industry: Safety Reporting requirements for INDs and BA/BE Studies* (September 2010)
- *Guidance for Industry: Postmarketing Studies and Clinical Trials—Implementation of Section 505(o)(3) of the Federal Food, Drug, and Cosmetic Act* (April 2011)
- *Medications Guides - Distribution Requirements and Inclusion in Risk Evaluation and Mitigation Strategies (REMS)* (February 2011)

Introduction

Biologics licensing standards per the *Public Health Service Act* of 1946 (*PHS Act*) and Title 21 of the Code of Federal Regulations (CFR) 600.3 provide that biologics must be "safe, pure, and potent." Under 21 CFR 601.20, there must be a demonstration upon inspection that the production facility assures that the product meets these standards and complies with the applicable regulations. Therefore, processes and methods to ensure these attributes are in place for licensure must be developed during the Investigational New Drug Application (IND) stage. These attributes are defined as follows:

- Safety—relative freedom from harmful effect to persons affected, directly or indirectly, by a product when it is prudently administered, taking into consideration the product's character in relation to the recipient's condition at the time
- Purity—relative freedom from extraneous matter in the finished product, whether or not harmful to the recipient or deleterious to the product; purity includes, but is not limited to relative freedom from residual moisture or other volatile and pyrogenic substances
- Potency—specific ability or capacity of the product, as indicated by appropriate laboratory tests or by adequately controlled clinical data obtained through the administration of the product in the manner intended, to effect a given result

Additional information related to chemistry, manufacturing and controls (CMC) product development and biologics submissions can be found in "Chapter 19 Biologics Submissions."

Upon approval of a Biologics License Application (BLA), a manufacturer receives a license to market its product in interstate commerce. The compliance and surveillance activities related to biologics licenses during the lifecycle of biological products are overseen by the Office of Compliance and Biologics Quality (OCBQ) within the US Food and Drug Administration's (FDA) Center for Biologics Evaluation and Research (CBER). OCBQ comprises three divisions and their associated branches, as listed below:

- Division of Case Management
  - o Advertising and Promotional Labeling Branch
  - o Biological Drug and Device Compliance Branch
  - o Blood and Tissue Compliance Branch (see "Chapter 24 Blood and Blood Products" and "Chapter 25 Tissue Products")
- Division of Inspections and Surveillance
  - o Bioresearch Monitoring Branch
  - o Program Surveillance Branch
  - o Program Inspection Branch
- Division of Manufacturing and Product Quality (DMPQ)
  - o Product Release Branch
  - o Manufacturing Review Branch I
  - o Manufacturing Review Branch II

These divisions carry out a wide range of activities including:

- conducting pre-license and preapproval inspections of manufacturing facilities and products under clinical study
- monitoring the safety, purity and potency of biological products through review of:
  - o Biological Product Deviation Reports (BPDRs) and Human Cell, Tissue, and Cellular and Tissue-Based Products (HCT/P) Deviation Reports
  - o investigations into transfusion- and donation-related fatalities and other adverse events

- o product recalls
- monitoring research (bioresearch monitoring (BIMO)) conducted on biological products and assessing the protection of human research subjects' rights, safety and welfare and research data quality and integrity
- monitoring import and export activities
- reviewing product advertising and promotional labeling (see "Chapter 21 Biologics, Labeling, Advertising and Promotion")
- monitoring reports of biological product shortages and helping to prevent or alleviate shortages of biological products, working with all parties involved to ensure medically necessary products are available within the US
- initiating regulatory action to address noncompliance with FDA regulations

These activities include both pre- and postapproval compliance surveillance activities, described in more detail below.

Preapproval Compliance
CMC Change Control

During the IND stage, CMC change control includes providing information amendments to the IND that provide data substantiating the comparability or improvements related to manufacturing changes, prior to making the change. During product development, it is likely there will be multiple changes in the manufacturing process that could impact drug product quality, safety and efficacy. Comparability studies generally are performed to demonstrate that nonclinical and clinical data generated with pre-change product are applicable to post-change product, to facilitate further development and, ultimately, to support the marketing authorization. Comparability studies conducted for products in development are influenced by factors such as the stage of product development, the availability of validated analytical procedures and the extent of product and process knowledge, which can vary based on the manufacturer's experience with the process. Due to the limitations of analytical tools in early clinical development, physicochemical and biological tests alone might not be adequate to determine comparability, and it may become necessary to bridge nonclinical and/or clinical studies.

When process changes are introduced in later stages of development and no additional clinical studies are planned to support the marketing authorization, the comparability study should be as comprehensive as one conducted for an approved product. However, some comparability study outcomes on quality attributes may still require additional nonclinical or clinical studies.

IND Safety Reporting

Premarketing expedited safety reports are required for serious and unexpected adverse experiences associated with the use of the biologic, as is the case for drugs (21 CFR 312.32). These requirements were recently amended to update the definitions used for safety reporting and to clarify when to submit expedited safety reports. In summary, expedited safety reporting applies to suspected adverse reactions that are both serious and unexpected, and where there is a reasonable possibility of a causal relationship between the drug and the adverse event. For other adverse events, the sponsor should collect the information and develop a process for ongoing evaluation of accumulating safety data. The new ICH Development Safety Update Report, not yet adopted in the US, is consistent with this safety reporting framework.

Additional safety reporting guidance is available for specific biological products, such as those used in gene therapy clinical trials. In gene therapy trials, where there is heightened concern related to the potential for delayed adverse events as a consequence of persistent biological activity of the transferred genetic material, long-term follow-up studies for safety are recommended. Adverse events associated with gene therapy trials may also need to be reported to the National Institutes of Health (NIH) if the trial includes NIH-funded sites.

Bioresearch Monitoring (BIMO)

BIMO refers to FDA's compliance program of Good Clinical Practice (GCP) and Good Laboratory Practice (GLP) inspections during development. BIMO covers clinical investigators, institutional review boards (IRBs), sponsors, contract research organization (CRO) monitors, in vivo bioequivalence laboratories and facilities and GLP facilities. The emphasis in clinical inspections is on how sponsors assure the validity of the data clinical investigators submit to FDA, and the adherence of sponsors, CROs and monitors to applicable regulations, such as adverse event reporting and the test article's integrity from the time of manufacture until receipt by the investigator. To carry out these responsibilities, BIMO staff conduct preapproval data audit inspections, investigate complaints, answer questions about GCP and help evaluate data integrity concerns.

Biological Product Naming

The nonproprietary/proper name for a new biological product, as for drugs, is determined by submitting an application and fee to the United States Adopted Names Council (USANC), which is part of the American Medical Association (see www.ama-assn.org). Sponsors should provide several selections and the naming rationale to USANC. When submitting suggested names, consideration should be given to the naming conventions used by USANC to assess submissions (i.e., use of common stems and/or syllables for existing products or product classes). For biologics, CBER has developed naming conventions for certain product categories, e.g., cellular therapies, which must be followed to the extent possible. Thus, sponsors may want to discuss nonproprietary name selection with CBER prior to submission to USANC, to assist in the naming process. For well-characterized proteins, certain suffixes are standard and must be included in the nonproprietary name, e.g., monoclonal antibodies use -mab as the final syllable.

The proprietary name for a new biological is approved by CBER and reviewed by OCBQ's Advertising and Promotional Labeling Branch (APLB). Two names may be submitted, with a clear indication of the sponsor's preference. The rationale for the choice, with summaries from marketing research studies, should be included. These studies should be designed to assess similar sounding names and to assess how names may be interpreted, including foreign language translations. Also included in the application are full descriptions of the product, therapeutic category and/or indication and the setting for use (e.g., doctor's office, hospital or home). Proprietary name submissions can be made any time after Phase 2, but a recommendation made prior to product approval will be reevaluated within 90 days of approval to ensure that no new products have entered the marketplace that could give rise to confusion because of similarity in spelling or pronunciation.

Pre-License Inspection

A pre-license inspection is an inspection of an establishment that has not yet been licensed or approved by CBER for the product under review, and may include all facilities involved in manufacturing the biologic, regardless of the manufacturing arrangement (e.g., contract, divided, shared). The inspection can also include establishments that already have one or more biologics license(s) or approvals for other products. *PHS Act* Section 351 and Section 704 of the *Federal Food, Drug and Cosmetic Act* of 1938 (*FD&C Act*) provide the regulatory authority to conduct inspections at any establishment where biological products are manufactured.

CBER's policy is that a pre-license or preapproval inspection generally will be necessary for a BLA or supplement if any of the following criteria are met:

1. The manufacturer does not hold an active US license or, in the case of a contract manufacturer, the facility is not approved for use in manufacturing a licensed product.

2. FDA has not inspected the establishment in the last two years.

3. The previous inspection revealed significant Good Manufacturing Practice (GMP) deficiencies in areas related to the processes in the submission (similar processes) or systemic problems, such as quality

control (QC)/quality assurance (QA) oversight.

4. The establishment is performing significant manufacturing step(s) in new (unlicensed) areas using different equipment (representing a process change). This would include currently dedicated areas that have not been approved as multiproduct facilities, buildings or areas.

5. The manufacturing process is sufficiently different (new production methods, specialized equipment or facilities) from that of other approved products produced by the establishment. Points to be considered:
   - Do differences in the process (e.g., different types of columns) or particulars (e.g., different production cell lines) require an on-site determination of GMP compliance?
   - Are the analytical methods accurate or sensitive enough to detect problems?
   - Are different processes or equipment being used?

In some cases, CBER relies on inspections to obtain validation and facility information that previously may have been submitted in the BLA; thus, greater coordination and efficiency are required in planning and conducting inspections. However, some BLAs and supplements include manufacturing establishments that use production areas common to other licensed products, so conducting a pre-license or preapproval inspection prior to approval of every BLA or supplement may not be necessary. In such cases, both the director of the division with product responsibility and the director, Division of Manufacturing and Product Quality (DMPQ), OCBQ, must concur in the decision to waive an inspection, or the inspection should be scheduled according to established procedures.

Inspections for biologics are much the same as those for other drugs. Systems-based inspections include review of:
- production and process controls
- failure investigations
- buildings and facilities
- equipment cleaning and maintenance
- laboratory controls
- quality unit/systems

In addition, the CMC section of the BLA will be compared to manufacturing site documents during the inspection to establish the BLA submission's accuracy and integrity. Because of the complexity of the process involved in the manufacture of biologics, the investigator is likely to spend considerably more time observing the process than is typical for small-molecule inspections. The investigator usually works with the manufacturer to schedule an appropriate time to conduct the inspection so the entire manufacturing process can be observed; any delay by the sponsor in this activity may delay the BLA review. Another difference is that the CMC product specialist for the BLA review generally will participate in a biologics inspection.

Postlicensing Compliance Activities
Annual Progress Reports of Postmarketing Studies

Routine Annual Reports, such as those required under NDA or ANDA regulations, are not mandatory for licensed biological products. However, the regulations do require Annual Reports for products marketed under a BLA for certain situations such as: making changes to the application (21 CFR 601.12(d)); providing information related to pediatric studies (21 CFR 601.28); and providing status reports on postmarket study requirements related to clinical safety, clinical efficacy, clinical pharmacology or nonclinical toxicology (21 CFR 601.70).

The *Food and Drug Administration Amendments Act* of 2007 (*FDAAA*), which does apply to both drugs and biologics, gave FDA authority to require additional postmarketing studies related to assessing known safety risks, including both signals of serious risk and potential serious risks associated with use of the drug. *FDAAA* also gave FDA authority to require labeling changes based on the results of such studies. Section 505(o)(3)(E)(ii), enacted under *FDAAA*, stipulates that the following information be provided in the Annual Report for required postmarketing studies: a timetable for the completion of each study; periodic reports on the status of required studies, including whether enrollment has begun, the number of participants enrolled and whether any difficulties in completing the study have been encountered; and registration information with respect to clinical trial certification. In addition, *FDAAA* requires that applicants report on each study "otherwise undertaken by the applicant to investigate a safety issue." The status of other types of postmarketing commitments (e.g., those concerning chemistry, manufacturing, production controls and studies conducted on an applicant's own initiative) are not required to be reported under Sections 314.81(b)(2)(vii) and 601.70.

Once a required postmarketing study commitment has been made, an Annual Report is due each year within 60 days after the anniversary date of application approval, and must be accompanied by a completed transmittal Form FDA 2252. Sponsors must continue to report on the progress of the commitment until the postmarketing study is completed or terminated, unless the postmarketing study commitment is either no longer feasible or would no longer provide useful information (as agreed with FDA). Failure to comply with the timetable, the periodic reporting submissions or other requirements of section 505(o)(3)(E)(ii) will be considered a violation unless the applicant demonstrates good cause for the noncompliance (only as agreed with FDA). Violations could result in civil penalties of up to $250,000 per violation, and the penalties can be increased (i.e., doubled) if the violation continues for more than 30 days, and can continue to double for subsequent 30-day periods.

Inspections

After licensure, two other types of inspections may take place: the routine, periodic inspection that should occur every two years (biennial) and a directed (for cause) inspection. CBER and the Office of Regulatory Affairs (ORA) have built a partnership to focus resources on inspectional and compliance issues in the biologics area. To accomplish this, a group of specialized investigators, called Team Biologics, has been formed to inspect licensed biological drug and device product facilities regulated by CBER. The goal of Team Biologics is to assure the quality and safety of biological products and to quickly resolve inconsistencies.

Import/Export

CBER oversees the import and export of biologics to determine whether imported biological products, drugs and devices regulated by the center comply with the requirements of the *FD&C Act*, the *PHS Act* and the regulations promulgated under these statutes. Imported products regulated by FDA are subject to inspection at the time of entry by the US Customs and Border Protection (CBP) (see www.cbp.gov). Shipments found not to comply with the law are subject to detention. For imports, FDA works with CBP to verify licensure; FDA may perform random sampling, and will issue import alerts for products that do not comply. A foreign manufacturer must have a US license to import a biological product into the US. Per FDA's *Regulatory Procedures Manual*, Chapter 9, Subchapter 9.3, "Importation of Biological Products," licensed biologics that have been lot-released (or are exempt) by CBER may be imported into the US and may proceed through Customs without FDA examination. Entry documents for IND biologics must declare a valid, active IND number. Products in short supply may also be imported under 21 CFR 601.22; however, these products must be registered with CBER and this will be verified by CBP. Under 7 CFR Chapter III, and overseen by the US Department of Agriculture (USDA), biological products may also require an Animal and Plant Health Inspection Service (APHIS) permit to enter the country if the product contains certain microbial, plant- or animal-derived materials or is otherwise a regulated product such as a genetically engineered organism.

A licensed biologic may be exported without FDA authorization (*Guidance for Industry: FDA Export Certificates* (August 2002)) and in accordance with Section 801(e) Exports or 802 Export of Certain Unapproved Products of the *FD&C Act* or Section 351(h) of the *PHS Act*, which states that a biologic is not adulterated or misbranded if it:
- accords to the specifications of the foreign purchaser

- is not in conflict with the laws of the country to which it is intended for export
- is labeled on the outside of the shipping package that it is intended for export
- is not sold or offered for sale in domestic commerce

FDA supplies a Certificate to Foreign Government, if requested, for the export of products that can be legally marketed in the US. It also supplies a Certificate of Exportability for the export of products that cannot be legally marketed in the US but meet *FD&C Act* requirements.

Import for export, per the *FDA Export Reform and Enhancement Act* of 1996, allows the importation of drug and device components for incorporation into a finished product that can then be exported in accordance with 801, 802 and *PHS Act* 351h.

Postapproval Changes

In accordance with Section 506A(b) of the *FD&C Act* (21 USC 356a), the effect of any postapproval CMC changes on a product's identity, strength, quality, purity or potency, as they may relate to the product's safety or efficacy, must be assessed. Such changes may include changes to:
- manufacturing process
- analytical procedures
- manufacturing equipment
- manufacturing facilities
- container closure systems
- process analytical technology (PAT)

Before distributing a product made using a change, sponsors are required to demonstrate, through appropriate validation and/or other clinical or nonclinical laboratory studies, the lack of adverse effect of the change on identity, strength, quality, purity or potency as they may relate to the product's safety or effectiveness.

Sponsors should assess the change to determine the correct product reporting category:
- Prior Approval Supplement (PAS)—Major changes that require supplement submission and approval prior to distribution of the product made using the change (21 CFR 601.12(b)). A PAS is used to report changes that have a substantial potential to adversely affect a product's identity, strength, quality, purity or potency as they may relate to the product's safety or effectiveness. Examples include: a change in manufacturing processes or analytical methods that result in change of specification limits; a change to larger-scale production; major construction; a change in the stability protocol or acceptance criteria; and extension of the expiration dating period.
- Changes Being Effected in 30 Days (CBE-30)— Moderate changes (CBE-30) require a supplement

to FDA 30 days prior to distribution (21 CFR 601.12(c)(3)). A CBE-30 is used to report changes that have moderate potential to adversely affect a product's identity, strength, quality, purity or potency as they may relate to the product's safety or effectiveness. Examples include: addition of a duplicated process chain or unit process; change in the site of testing from one facility to another (e.g., from a contract lab to the sponsor; from an existing contract lab to a new contract lab; from the sponsor to a new contract lab).
- CBE—A CBE reports changes that have minimal potential to adversely affect a product's identity, strength, quality, purity or potency as they may relate to the product's safety or effectiveness. A CBE supplement would be received by FDA before, or concurrently with, distribution of the product made using the change. Examples include: addition of release tests and/or specifications; tightening of specifications for intermediates; and minor changes in fermentation batch size using the same equipment and resulting in no change in specifications of the bulk or final product.
- Annual Report—Minor changes can be included in the Annual Report, which is submitted within 60 days of the anniversary date of product approval. These are changes that have minimal potential to adversely affect a product's identity, strength, quality, purity or potency as they may relate to the product's safety or effectiveness. Examples include: an increase in the scale of aseptic manufacturing for finished product without a change in equipment, e.g., increased number of vials filled; modifications in analytical procedures with no change in the basic test methodology or existing release specifications provided the change is supported by validation data; and establishment of a new working cell bank derived from a previously approved master cell bank according to an SOP on file in the approved license application.

By using a comparability protocol that has been previously reviewed by FDA, the sponsor may be able to file certain CMC changes made under the protocol under a less-restrictive reporting category, e.g., a change that would normally be a CBE-30 may be allowed as a CBE if it has already been approved as a comparability protocol. While the submission of a comparability protocol is not required to make changes, in many cases, using one will facilitate the subsequent implementation and reporting requirements of CMC changes, which could result in moving a product into distribution more quickly than if a protocol were not submitted.

A comparability protocol is a well-defined, detailed,

written plan for assessing the effect of specific CMC changes on a particular drug product's identity, strength, quality, purity and potency as they may relate to the product's safety and effectiveness. A comparability protocol describes the changes that it covers and specifies the tests and studies that will be performed, including establishing analytical procedures and acceptance criteria to demonstrate that specified CMC changes do not adversely affect the product. However, it is important to note that comparability protocols are not recommended for CMC changes that cannot be definitely evaluated, that require a new IND, or that require efficacy, safety (clinical or nonclinical) or pharmacokinetic/pharmacodynamic data to evaluate the effect of the change (e.g., certain formulation changes or clinical or nonclinical studies to qualify new impurities).

The FDA review committee will determine whether the changes reported in the supplement require on-site review. If the review committee determines an inspection is necessary for one or more establishments included in the supplement, the inspection(s) will be performed prior to sending the action letter for the supplement. Failure to comply with the reporting requirements outlined in 21 CFR 601.12 could result in a request by FDA that all changes be submitted as a PAS. Two examples of failing to comply are constantly downgrading changes (e.g., from a PAS to a CBE) and failing to supply sufficient information to support the changes.

Similarly, under 21 CFR 601.12(f), changes to a product package label, container label and package insert require one of the following:

- submission of a supplement with FDA approval needed prior to product distribution, in cases such as the addition of superiority claims or changes based upon additional preclinical and/or postmarketing clinical studies
- submission of a supplement with product distribution allowed at the time of supplement submission (does not require a 30-day wait) in cases such as strengthening cautionary statements or instructions
- submission of the final printed label in an Annual Report in cases such as editorial changes and changes in how the product is supplied, provided there is no change in dosage strength or form

Additionally, under 21 CFR 601.12(f)(4), changes to advertising and promotional labeling must comply with the provisions of 21 CFR 314.81(b)(3)(i), which requires the submission to FDA of specimens of mailing pieces and any other labeling or advertising devised for promotion of a drug product at the time of initial dissemination of the labeling, and at the time of initial publication of the advertisement for a prescription drug product. Mailing pieces and labeling designed to contain samples of a drug product are required for the submission to be complete,

with the exception of the sample of the drug product itself. (See "Chapter 21 Biologics Labeling, Advertising and Promotion" for more on labeling.)

Postmarketing Reporting Requirements

Postmarketing expedited reporting requirements for serious and unexpected adverse experiences from all sources (domestic and foreign) related to biologics are similar to those for drugs and are stated in 21 CFR 600.80 and 600.81. Reporting requirements include: Postmarketing 15-day "Alert Reports," which include reports based on scientific literature; Postmarketing 15-day Alert Report follow-ups, which are also required to be reported within 15 days of receiving new information; and periodic adverse experience reports. The reporting format for individual case study reports is the MedWatch mandatory reporting form, Form FDA 3500A. However, adverse events related to vaccines must be reported on a separate form under the Vaccine Adverse Event Reporting System (VAERS). Foreign adverse experience may be reported using either the 3500A or, if preferred, a CIOMS I form. Sponsors may request waivers for filing Form FDA 3500A for non-serious, expected adverse experiences; however, FDA does not intend to grant waivers within one year of licensure for new biological molecular entities, blood products, plasma derivatives or vaccines. For biological combination products, reports must be filed with both centers. Adverse events related to vaccines are also monitored by the Centers for Disease Control (CDC). The VAERS reporting system is not linked to the vaccine injury compensation program.

Periodic adverse experience reports include summaries of serious and unexpected adverse experiences as well as reports of nonserious expected adverse experiences. Periodic reports are made at quarterly intervals for three years from the date of issuance of the biologics license, and then annually. The licensed manufacturer is required to submit each quarterly report within 30 days of the close of the quarter (the first quarter beginning on the date of issuance of the biologics license) and each Annual Report within 60 days of the anniversary date of the issuance of the biologics license.

Distribution reports for biological products, including vaccines, are also required under 21 CFR 600.81; this requirement is unique for biologics with approved BLAs. The distribution report includes the bulk, fill and label lot numbers for the total number of dosage units of each strength or potency distributed, expiration date and distribution date. The licensed manufacturer submits this report every six months to either CBER or CDER, as applicable.

Risk Assessment

Risk assessment should occur throughout a product's lifecycle, from the early identification of a potential product and preclinical testing, through the premarketing development process, and after approval during marketing.

Premarketing risk assessment represents a key step in this process, and product approval requires that a product's underlying risks and benefits have been adequately assessed. The adequacy of this risk assessment is a matter of both quantity (ensuring that enough patients are studied) and quality (the appropriateness of the assessments performed, the appropriateness and breadth of the patient populations studied, and how results are analyzed). In reaching a final decision on approvability, both existing risk information and any outstanding questions regarding safety are considered in a product's risk assessment and weighed against the product's demonstrated benefits. The fewer a product's demonstrated benefits, the less acceptable may be higher levels of demonstrated risks.

For assessing risk in the postapproval setting, labeling and routine reporting requirements are sufficient to mitigate risks and preserve benefits for the majority of approved products. However, in other cases, FDA has requested additional risk minimization strategies, which were originally called Risk Minimization Action Plans, or RiskMAPs. Since the passage of *FDAAA,* these safety plans are now called Risk Evaluation and Mitigation Strategies, or REMS. A REMS is a strategy to manage a known or potential serious safety risk associated with a drug or biological product while preserving its benefits. FDA also has the authority to apply the REMS retroactively, and require sponsors to submit a REMS for an already approved product.

A REMS can include a medication guide, a patient package insert, a communication plan for healthcare professionals, various elements to assure safe use, and an implementation system. The medication guide is the most commonly used REMS, with more than 150 approved drugs now requiring a medication guide. Medication guides are utilized when specific information is necessary to prevent serious adverse effects, when patient decision making should include knowledge about a serious side effect, or if patient adherence to directions for use is essential for the product's effectiveness. The responsibility for ensuring that the medication guides are available to patients lies with the sponsor, not the pharmacist.

The elements to assure safe use (ETASU) may include one or more of the following requirements:

- Healthcare providers who prescribe the drug must have particular training or experience or be specially certified.
- Pharmacies, practitioners or healthcare settings dispensing the drug must be specially certified.
- The drug is dispensed to patients only in certain healthcare settings, such as hospitals.
- The drug is dispensed to patients with evidence or other documentation of safe use conditions, such as laboratory test results.
- Each patient using the drug is subject to certain monitoring requirements.

- Each patient using the drug is enrolled in a registry.

The REMS must also include a timetable for assessment; the minimum timeframe for assessments is at 18 months, three years and seven years after approval.

Biological Product Deviation Reporting (BPDR)

Manufacturers of licensed biological products are required to report events that represent unexpected or unforeseeable events or deviations from current Good Manufacturing Practice (CGMP), applicable regulations, applicable standards or established specifications that may affect a product's safety, purity or potency per 21 CFR 600.14. Prior to 2001, this reporting was termed "error and accident" reporting. The BPDR is reported on Form FDA 3486—Biological Product Deviation Report Form and the appropriate deviation code designating the type of event must be included. The report must not be dated more than 45 calendar days from the date when information that reasonably suggests a reportable event has occurred is discovered. Events that are reportable are those that occur at the sponsor's facility or at a facility under the sponsor's control, e.g., a contract manufacturer, and include events for products that have been distributed and are no longer under the sponsor's control. Therefore, procedures for the investigation of any unexplained discrepancy or failure of a lot to meet any of its specifications should include provisions for timely investigation; an appropriate corrective action plan to prevent recurrence; procedures to gain control of unsuitable products in a timely manner; and appropriate disposition of all affected products (in-date and expired). All BPDRs should be submitted to OCBQ, except in the case of biological products transferred to CDER in 2003.

FDA Enforcement Actions
Regulatory Action Letters

CBER may issue several types of regulatory action letters. These letters are ordinarily issued to biological product manufacturers in an effort to stop practices that are in violation of the regulations and to promote corrective action. Examples of regulatory action letters issued by CBER include:

- Warning Letters
- Notice of Initiation of Disqualification Proceedings and Opportunity to Explain (NIDPOE) Letters
- Untitled Letters
- Administrative License Action Letters
- Orders of Retention, Recall, Destruction and Cessation of Manufacturing Related to Human Cell, Tissue, and Cellular and Tissue-Based Products (HCT/Ps)

Warning Letters are issued for violations considered to be of regulatory significance and are issued to achieve voluntary compliance. Significant violations are those violations that may lead to enforcement action if not promptly and adequately corrected. A Warning Letter is issued to a responsible individual or firm to establish prior notice that the agency considers one or more products, practices, processes or other activities to be in violation of the *FD&C Act*, its implementing regulations and other federal statutes. A Warning Letter is one of FDA's principal means of achieving prompt voluntary compliance with the *FD&C Act*.

A NIDPOE Letter informs the recipient clinical investigator that the agency is initiating an administrative proceeding to determine whether the clinical investigator should be disqualified from receiving investigational products pursuant to FDA regulations. Generally, the agency issues a NIDPOE letter when it believes it has evidence that the clinical investigator repeatedly or deliberately violated FDA's regulations governing the proper conduct of clinical studies involving investigational products or submitted false information to the sponsor.

An Untitled Letter is an initial correspondence with a sponsor citing violations that do not meet the threshold of regulatory significance for a Warning Letter. CBER has issued Untitled Letters, for example, after its review of a manufacturer's advertising and promotional labeling, after an inspection under CBER's Bioresearch Monitoring program or by Team Biologics and as a result of Internet website surveillance.

Administrative License Action Letters include license revocation and suspension. License revocation is the cancellation of a license and the withdrawal of the authorization to introduce biological products into interstate commerce. Examples of grounds for revocation include: FDA's inability to gain access for inspection; the manufacturer's failure to report a change as required; failure of the product or establishment to conform to standards in the license or to comply with CGMPs; or the product not being safe or effective, or being misbranded. Except in the case of license suspension or willful violations, CBER will issue a Notice of Intent to Revoke License Letter and provide an opportunity for the sponsor to demonstrate or achieve compliance before initiating revocation proceedings and issuing a license revocation letter. The licensee has 10 days to notify FDA of its commitment to, and plans for, achieving compliance, and then has 30 days to submit a comprehensive report with rigid timetables.

License Suspension is a summary action that provides for the immediate withdrawal, without prior notice or a hearing, of the authorization to introduce biological products into interstate commerce when there are reasonable grounds to believe that the product is a danger to public health (*PHS Act* Section 351). The Department of Justice does not need to concur. All product shipping and manufacturing activities must cease until the license is reactivated.

An Order of Retention, Recall, Destruction, or Cessation of Manufacturing may be issued when there are reasonable grounds to believe that an HCT/P is violative, or if the HCT/P is infected or contaminated and is a source of dangerous infection to humans; or if an establishment does not provide adequate protections against the risks of communicable disease transmission.

Recalls

Recalls are generally voluntary acts by sponsors because FDA has limited statutory authority to prescribe a recall. However, the *National Childhood Vaccine Injury Act* of 1986 amended the *PHS Act* to provide recall authority for biological products (42 U.S. 262). Therefore, FDA can order a recall if the biological product constitutes an imminent or substantial hazard to public health per *PHS Act* Section 351(a), or if it is considered a "dangerous" medical device per the *FD&C Act*. Recalls can be ordered for any reason, but if a recall is due to misbranding or adulteration, FDA should be notified to prevent further action. Companies can expect to work closely with the agency during a recall. There are four key stages in the recall process: discovery, planning, implementation and termination of the recall event. Final disposition of the recalled product should be discussed with FDA and typically involves destruction.

Judicial Enforcement

FDA's civil and criminal enforcement actions include:

- Seizure—an action taken to remove a product from commerce because it is in violation of the law. FDA initiates a seizure by filing a complaint with the US District Court where the product is located. A US Marshal is then directed by the court to take possession, i.e., seize the goods where they are found, until the matter is resolved.
- Injunction—a civil action taken against an individual or firm seeking to stop continued production or distribution of a violative product until the firm complies with FDA requirements.
- Prosecution—a criminal action taken as the result of acts prohibited in the *FD&C Act* that can be directed at the responsible persons in management, even if they are unaware of the violative conduct and even without intent.

For more information on FDA enforcement actions, see "Chapter 31 FDA Inspections and Enforcement Options."

Summary

- The compliance and surveillance activities related to biologics licenses during the lifecycle of biological products are overseen by the Office of Compliance and Biologics Quality, CBER.
- Biologics licensing standards per the *PHS Act* and 21 CFR 600.3 provide that biologics must be "safe,

pure, and potent." Compliance activities prior to approval include safety reporting, CMC change control and compliance with GMPs, GCPs and GLPs to ensure readiness for BIMO and/or pre-license inspections.

- For import and export of biological products, a US license is required for a foreign manufacturer to import and distribute a biological product in the US, whereas a licensed biologic may be exported from the US without FDA authorization.

- Postapproval compliance activities include post-marketing commitments, three categories of CMC change control (PAS, CBE and Annual Report), which can be reduced by using comparability pro-tocols, postmarketing safety reporting and biologic product deviation reporting (BPDR).

- *FDAAA* authorized Risk Evaluation and Mitigation Strategies (REMS), which are safety plans designed to manage a known or potential serious risk associated with a drug or biological product if FDA determines that such a plan is necessary to ensure the product's benefits outweigh its risks.

- In cases where CBER identifies areas of noncompli-ance, it may issue any of several types of regulatory action letters, up to and including license revoca-tion, to stop practices found to be in violation of the regulations and to promote corrective action. CBER also has options for judicial enforcement including seizure, injunction and prosecution, if warranted.

Biologics Labeling, Advertising and Promotion

Updated by Moulakshi Roychowdhury, PharmD, JD

Objective

+ Review the general FDA regulations for labeling, promotion and advertising of biological drugs under the jurisdiction of the CBER
+ Understand the application of these regulations through the study of related FDA guidance documents and enforcement letters

Laws, Regulations and Guidelines Relevant to this Chapter

Regulations

+ *Federal Food, Drug, and Cosmetic Act* of 1938
+ 21 CFR 99 Dissemination of information on unapproved/new uses for marketed drugs, biologics and devices
+ 21 CFR 201 Labeling
    o 21 CFR 201.56–58 Labeling requirements
    o 21 CFR 201.80 Specific requirements on content and format of labeling for human prescription drug and biological products
    o 21 CFR 201.200 Disclosure of drug efficacy study evaluations in labeling and advertising
+ 21 CFR 202.1 Prescription drug advertisements
+ 21 CFR 203 Prescription drug marketing
+ 21 CFR 208 Medication guides for prescription drug products
+ 21 CFR 312.6–7 Labeling and promotion for investigational new drugs
+ 21 CFR 314.70 Supplements and other changes to an approved application
+ 21 CFR 314.81 Other post-marketing reports
+ 21 CFR 601.2 Applications for biologics licenses; procedures for filing
+ 21 CFR 601.12 Changes to an approved application
+ 21 CFR 601.25 Review procedures to determine that licensed biological products are safe, effective, and not misbranded under prescribed, recommended, or suggested conditions of use
+ 21 CFR 601.45 Promotional materials
+ 21 CFR 610 Subpart G Labeling standards
+ Other labeling related chapters:
    o 21 CFR 606.120–122
    o 21 CFR 660.2(c)
    o 21 CFR 660.28
    o 21 CFR 660.35
    o 21 CFR 660.45
    21 CFR 660.55
    o 21 CFR 801

    o   21 CFR 809

Guidelines

◆ *Final Guidance on Industry-Supported Scientific and Educational Activities* (November 1997)
◆ *Guidance for Industry: Changes to an Approved Application: Biological Products* (July 1997)
◆ *Draft Guidance for Industry: Product Name Placement, Size, and Prominence in Advertising and Promotional Labeling* (January 1999)
◆ *Draft Guidance for Industry: Accelerated Approval Products—Submission of Promotional Materials* (March 1999)
◆ *Guidance for Industry: Consumer-Directed Broadcast Advertisements* (August 1999)
◆ *Draft Guidance for Industry: Providing Regulatory Submissions in Electronic Format—Prescription Drug Advertising and Promotional Labeling* (January 2001)
◆ *Draft Guidance for Industry: Brief Summary: Disclosing Risk Information in Consumer-Directed Print Advertisements* (January 2004)
◆ *Draft Guidance for Industry: "Help-Seeking" and Other Disease Awareness Communications by or on Behalf of Drug and Device Firms* (January 2004)
◆ *Guidance for Industry: Providing Regulatory Submissions in Electronic Format—Content of Labeling* (April 2005)
◆ *Draft Guidance for Industry: Labeling for Human Prescription Drug and Biological Products—Implementing the New Content and Format Requirements* (January 2006)
◆ *Guidance for Industry: Indexing Structured Product Labeling* (June 2008)
◆ *Guidance for Industry: Good Reprint Practices for the Distribution of Medical Journal Articles and Medical or Scientific Reference Publications on Unapproved New Uses of Approved Drugs and Approved or Cleared Medical Devices* (January 2009)
◆ *Draft Guidance for Industry: Presenting Risk Information in Prescription Drug and Medical Device Promotion (May 2009)*

Definitions

Label—The *Federal Food, Drug, and Cosmetic Act* of 1938 (*FD&C Act*) defines a "label" as a display of written, printed or graphic material on the immediate container of a drug.

Labeling—"Labeling" is defined by the US Food and Drug Administration (FDA) as any written, printed or graphic material on the drug, on any of its containers or wrappers, or on any material accompanying it. Therefore, it includes, but is not limited to, professional labeling (generally referred to as the package insert or prescribing information (PI)) and patient labeling (patient package insert (PPI) or a medication guide).

The umbrella term "labeling" for drugs and devices generally is divided by FDA into two subcategories that are regulated by FDA under the *FD&C Act*:

1. FDA-approved labeling is initially prepared for the original Biologic License Application (BLA) submission and then included with subsequent supplements. This includes the PI. This document includes the details and directions healthcare providers need to prescribe the product properly. It is also the basis for how sponsors can advertise their products. FDA-approved labeling may also include a PPI; when the information is for an especially risky or difficult-to-use drug, the PPI is referred to as a medication guide. Risk Evaluation and Mitigation Strategy (REMS) (described later in this chapter) may also be a component of labeling. The FDA-approved labeling must be included in the package when a drug is dispensed.

2. Promotional labeling is, generally, any product material (other than the FDA-approved labeling as defined above) intended to promote the use of a drug. Unlike FDA-approved labeling, promotional labeling does not have to physically accompany the drug or be inserted in the package when a drug is dispensed. However, as per the regulations, promotional labeling must be disseminated with the full FDA-approved labeling.

Labeling Regulations and Requirements
Labeling Filed With Original BLA Submissions

Biologics labeling begins with filing of the first BLA for a biological drug product. The BLA is a request for permission to introduce, or deliver for introduction, a biologic product into interstate commerce (21 CFR 610.2). Labeling information is required in BLA submissions to FDA for approval (21 CFR 610.2). This labeling information represents the proposed labeling a sponsor intends to use for postapproval marketing. The content and format are regulated by 21 CFR 201.56–57 and 21 CFR 610.60–68 and further explained in various guidance documents, e.g., *Draft Guidance for Industry: Labeling for Human Prescription Drug and Biological Products—Implementing the New Content and Format Requirements* (January 2006). Typically, four types of labeling information are required to be submitted in the original BLA: 1) draft container and carton labels, 2) new PI format, 3) annotated draft labeling text and 4) structured product labeling (SPL). In addition, some biologics require the submission of a medication guide or REMS.

Container and Carton Labels
Container Label

Per 21 CFR 610.60, the container label should bear the following information:

1. proper name of the product
2. manufacturer name, address and license number
3. lot number or other lot identification
4. expiration date
5. recommended individual dose, for multiple dose containers
6. the statement: "Rx only" for prescription biologics
7. medication guide, if required

In special cases, certain information may be expanded or omitted. For example, expansion may be needed if the container is not inserted in any package, or text can be omitted if the container is too small to affix a label containing all the information listed above (see 21 CFR 610.60(b), (c) and (d)). To allow visual inspection of the contents, the label should not cover the container completely.

Package (Carton) Label

Per 21 CFR 610.61, the package label should contain:

1. proper name of the product
2. manufacturer name, address and license number
3. lot number or other lot identification
4. expiration date
5. preservatives, if any
6. number of containers, if more than one
7. amount of product in the container
8. recommended storage temperature
9. the words "shake well" or "do not freeze," as required
10. recommended individual dose, for multi-dose container
11. type and calculated amount of antibiotics added during manufacture
12. adjuvant, if present
13. product source, when it is a factor in safe administration
14. minimum potency of product or the statement: "No US standard of potency"
15. the statement: "Rx only" for prescription biologics
16. reference statement to PI inside the package for any other pertinent information

The font size, type, color, position and legibility of container and package labels should meet the requirements in 21 CFR 610.62. Divided manufacturing responsibility should also be shown on either the package or the container label. Bar code label requirements under 21 CFR 201.25 apply to all biologics except biological devices or blood and blood components intended for transfusion, which follow the requirements in 21 CFR 606.121(c)(13).

New Package Insert Format

The plain package insert format, also called the "draft package insert" or "draft labeling text," is required. It contains information about the sponsor's proposed labeling and should conform to the format required by regulations and guidance.

Annotated Labeling

The draft labeling text, once completed, needs to be annotated with relevant sections in the BLA submission (e.g., Module 5 clinical study reports) to substantiate each claim in the labeling. This is a separate file from the draft labeling text required in the initial submission and is called "annotated labeling."

Structured Product Labeling (SPL)

SPL, another separate file containing all the draft labeling text in extensible markup language format (XML), is also required by the Center for Drug Evaluation and Research (CDER) under 21 CFR 601.14 and must be submitted in the initial BLA filing. Instructions on preparing SPL are detailed in *Guidance for Industry: Providing Regulatory Submissions in Electronic Format—Content of Labeling* (April 2005) and *Guidance for Industry: Indexing Structured Product Labeling* (June 2008). Based on these guidance documents, the content of SPL labeling files is placed in a single folder named "SPL" in the electronic submission. This requirement applies to both small molecular and biological products under the jurisdiction of CDER. The Center for Biologics Evaluation and Research (CBER) will soon require SPL for BLAs under its jurisdiction. SPL in XML format enables healthcare professionals and other users to rapidly search and sort product information using new computer technologies.

Risk Evaluation and Mitigation Strategy (REMS)

Under the *Food and Drug Administration Amendments Act* of 2007 (*FDAAA*) a REMS is required for some drugs, including biologics.

"Drug and biological products deemed to have in effect an approved REMS are those that on March 25, 2008 (the effective date of Title IX, subtitle A of FDAAA), had in effect "elements to assure safe use". "Elements to assure safe use" include the following: (1) Health care providers who prescribe the drug have particular training or experience, or are specially certified; (2) pharmacies, practitioners, or health care settings that dispense the drug are specially certified; (3) the drug is dispensed to patients only in certain health care settings, such as hospitals; (4) the drug is dispensed to patients with evidence or other documentation of safe use conditions, such as laboratory test results; (5) each patient using the drug is subject to certain monitoring; or (6) each patient using the drug is enrolled in a registry (see section 505-1(f)(3) of the act)."[1]

A drug will not be deemed to have a REMS if it has only a medication guide (see below), patient package insert and/or communication plan.

Because of this new regulation, a BLA sponsor needs to determine whether it is required to submit a proposed REMS in the BLA. If a REMS is required, it should be submitted to FDA prior to approval.

Medication Guide

A medication guide applies primarily to human prescription drug products used on an outpatient basis without direct supervision by a healthcare professional (21 CFR 208.1 (a)). It is approved by FDA and distributed to patients when FDA determines that such a guide is necessary to patients' safe and effective use of drug products (21 CFR 208.1 (b)). The drug product is the basis for determining whether to file a medication guide in the original BLA. Self-injectable insulin to treat type I diabetes is an example of a product requiring a medication guide. Many new biologics, however, require healthcare professionals to administer the drug to patients in hospitals or special treatment centers to ensure safe use. Because these products often target severe diseases and unmet medical needs, patients need to be monitored closely by healthcare professionals after administration. In such cases, a REMS is often required instead of a medication guide.

Postapproval Labeling Changes
Lifecycle Management

The labeling lifecycle begins when the draft labeling is submitted to FDA. During the BLA review phase, the labeling content may be revised either by the sponsor or at the agency's request. Once the labeling is modified and approved by FDA, the sponsor can begin to commercialize the product by promoting and advertising the approved labeling information through various marketing channels such as television, newspapers, magazines, the Internet, direct-to-consumer marketing, etc. However, changes to the initially approved labeling may be required, to add and/or delete any information or to clarify specific information to prevent misunderstanding in the marketplace.

Furthermore, the initially approved full labeling may need to be adapted based on the type of marketing channel used for promotion and advertising, e.g., a television advertisement is usually limited to a brief summary of the full labeling due to time constraints (21 CFR 202.1 (e)) and a direct-to-consumer (DTC) promotional piece should

be written in language that can be readily understood by ordinary consumers rather than healthcare professionals.

Any information disseminated initially by the sponsor to healthcare professionals and/or directly to consumers must follow FDA requirements (21 CFR 314.81(b)(3)(i) and 601.12(f)(4)) and be submitted to the agency at the time of dissemination. Each submission is required to be accompanied by Form FDA 2567 or its equivalent and must include a copy of the product labeling. For products approved under the accelerated approval program (21 CFR 314 Subpart H or 21 CFR 312 Subpart E), promotional labeling and advertising must be submitted prior to dissemination (21 CFR 314.550 and 601.45).

All of these activities constitute lifecycle management of pre- and postapproval promotion and advertising.

Preparing Changes to Labeling

The labeling change lifecycle may be managed per *Guidance for Industry: Changes to an Approved Application—Biological Products* (July 1997). Postapproval changes to labeling information require submission to CDER or CBER in one of the following ways:

- Prior Approval Supplement (PAS)—Supplement submission and FDA approval are required before dissemination of the labeling change (e.g., changes to a medication guide, highlights of prescribed information) per 21 CFR 314.70(b)(2)(v).
- Changes Being Effected (CBE)—Supplement submission is required but FDA approval is not necessary before dissemination of labeling changes (e.g., to add or strengthen a contraindication, warning, precaution or adverse reaction; to add or strengthen a statement about drug abuse, dependence, psychological effect or overdosage; to add or strengthen an instruction about dosage and administration that is intended to increase the safe use of the drug product; to delete false, misleading or unsupported indications for use or claims for effectiveness) per 21 CFR 314.70(c)(6)(iii). Subsequent FDA approval, however, is required.
- Annual Report—Information on labeling submitted in an Annual Report is described in 21 CFR 314.81(b)(2)(iii). It should include a summary of any labeling changes since the last Annual Report (e.g., a change in labeling description or how the drug is supplied without change of dosage strength or form, an editorial change in labeling) per 21 CFR 314.70(d)(2)(ix-x).

Depending upon the category into which a change falls, the sponsor needs to develop a strategy, collect necessary information and submit the relevant regulatory documents to FDA.

Biologics Advertising and Promotional Labeling Requirements
Regulatory Oversight of Biologic Advertising & Promotion Labeling

FDA has primary jurisdiction over prescription advertising under the 1962 *Kefauver-Harris Drug Amendments* to the *FD&C Act*, over restricted medical devices and biologics advertising under the *Public Health Service Act* (*PHS Act*), and over veterinary medicines under the *FD&C Act*.

Biologics are approved primarily by CBER. At CBER, the Advertising and Promotional Labeling Branch (APLB) within the Office of Compliance and Biologics Quality is responsible for reviewing and monitoring biologic product promotion. Specific oversight activities include reviews of final and draft advertising and promotional labeling of licensed biological products to ensure that product communications are fair-balanced (with risks and benefits), truthful, non-misleading and in compliance with federal laws and regulations.

Regulatory oversight of promotion serves to ensure the following overarching principles of advertising and promotional labeling:

- Drug promotion must be consistent with approved product labeling or package insert (PI).
- Claims must be supported by substantial evidence.
- Promotion must not be false or misleading.
- Promotion must be fair-balanced.
- Promotion must reveal all material information.

It should be noted that the following requirements apply to any prescription product advertising and promotional labeling, regardless of the medium by which it is communicated—television, print media, Internet or other. Various guidance documents referenced here can be found on the FDA, CBER and CDER websites.

Preparing Advertisements and Promotional Labeling for Submission
Submitting at First Use

Sponsors are required to submit all biologic advertisements and promotional labeling to APLB at the time of dissemination, also referred to as "time of first use" on Form FDA 2253 (21 CFR 314.81(b)(i)). The form requires sponsors to indicate the type of piece that is being submitted, using the specific coding provided on the form, and the initial date of dissemination. While CDER's Division of Drug, Marketing, Advertising and Communications (DDMAC) and CBER's APLB require the same form for these submissions, each center provides slightly different directions on the form that the sponsor should be careful to note when completing it. Current information on how to submit biologic advertising and promotional labeling can be found at www.fda.gov/ BiologicsBloodVaccines/DevelopmentApprovalProcess/ AdvertisingLabelingPromotionalMaterials/ucm118171. htm. Failure to submit advertising and promotional labeling on Form FDA 2253 constitutes a violation of 21 CFR 314.81(b)(i).

Products that Require Prior Submission

While most products' materials can be submitted to FDA for the first time at the time of dissemination, there is an exception that requires prior submission for products approved under the accelerated approval program (21 CFR 601.45) and for products that may cause fatalities or serious damage about which information has not been widely publicized (as described in 21 CFR 202.1(j)(1)). In these cases, approval by FDA prior to dissemination is required:

- The sponsor of an accelerated approval product must submit to APLB, during the preapproval review period, all advertisements and promotional materials intended to be published within 120 days after approval. After 120 days postapproval, the applicant must submit materials at least 30 days in advance of publication. Once submitted, the sponsor must wait the minimum 30 days to receive advisory comments (often referred to as "pre-clearance") from APLB. If no comments are received at 30 days, the sponsor can choose to withdraw the submission and move ahead with the use of the piece. After receiving advisory comments or choosing to withdraw and move ahead with the piece, the sponsor still is required to submit the pieces on Form FDA 2253 at the time of dissemination.
- Products that are covered under 21 CFR 202.1(j)(1), such as those causing fatalities or serious damage but about which information has not been widely publicized, must obtain FDA approval in a similar manner prior to dissemination.

Advisory Comments/Pre-Clearance

While not a requirement, sponsors have the option of requesting APLB advisory comments on draft advertising and promotional materials (this is often referred to in industry as "pre-clearance"). Advisory comments can only be requested for draft materials that have not yet been published or disseminated and are not currently in use or in the public domain. When sponsors are uncertain about certain promotional campaigns or language, this can be a very valuable option. APLB strongly encourages the use of this option when launching a new product or indication. Specific directions on how to submit draft materials for advisory comments can be found at www.fda.gov/ BiologicsBloodVaccines/DevelopmentApprovalProcess/ AdvertisingLabelingPromotionalMaterials/ucm118171. htm.

Note that even after submitting material for advisory

comments or withdrawing a submission for advisory comments, the sponsor is still required to submit the pieces on Form FDA 2253 at time of dissemination/first use.

Misconception Regarding Submissions

A common misconception heard in industry is that if APLB does not comment on a piece when submitted at first use on Form FDA 2253, the piece is deemed to be "approved" by APLB. This misconception can wrongly encourage the continued use of inappropriate or violative materials. In general, the submission on Form FDA 2253 is for documentation purposes and does not constitute any type of "approval" by APLB.

Content and Format of Advertising and Promotional Labeling

The requirements for promotional and advertising materials of biologic products are described in detail in 21 CFR 202, as well as in relevant guidance documents such as *Draft Guidance for Industry: Product Name Placement, Size, and Prominence in Advertising and Promotional Labeling* (January 1999) and *Draft Guidance for Industry: Presenting Risk Information in Prescription Drug and Medical Device Promotion (May 2009).*

Presentation of Product Name

As indicated in 21 CFR 202.1 and the draft guidance documents, product names in advertising and promotional labeling should be presented as follows

- The entire proprietary (brand/trade) name, including the ingredients and dosage form if it is approved as such in the PI, should be presented together without any intervening written or graphic matter.
- The established (generic) name should be printed in letters that are at least half as large as the letters comprising the proprietary name, and the prominence of the established name must be comparable with the prominence of the proprietary name.
- The order of ingredients and respective quantities should be listed in the same manner as they are listed in the PI, and the information presented concerning the quantity of each ingredient should also correspond with the PI.

Product Claims
Must be Consistent With Approved Product Use/ Indication

As indicated in 21 CFR 202.1, all advertising and promotional labeling may only "recommend or suggest" the approved use of the product as indicated in the product PI. Any suggestions or recommendations inconsistent with the specific product use/indication presented in the label could constitute off-label promotion or broadening of the indication. For example, in June 2003, APLB issued an enforcement letter to a company that promoted a product for a general condition when the drug was only approved for a "moderate to severe" condition. Failure to clarify the claim with the limitation of "moderate to severe" constituted broadening of the indication.

To determine whether or not a product claim is consistent with the approved use of the product, FDA looks not just at the product indication, but also at the clinical trials section of the PI. The clinical trials section of the PI provides study background, patient populations included and study results. Generally, if a product is promoted for use in a patient population broader than that which was tested in the clinical trials used for product approval, this may constitute broadening of the indication and be considered a violation of the regulations.

Substantial Evidence or Substantial Clinical Evidence

In addition to maintaining consistency with the approved use of the product, all claims of safety and effectiveness must be supported by either substantial evidence or substantial clinical evidence. Substantial evidence is generally accepted as evidence stemming from two adequate and well-controlled trials. Ideally, the trials would be prospective, randomized, blinded and minimize confounding variables. In July 2009, APLB issued a letter to a company for presenting safety claims stemming from postmarketing data (adverse event rates observed in practice) in an exhibition panel; postmarketing data do not constitute substantial evidence (they are not from a well-controlled clinical trial) and, therefore, the panel was deemed to be misbranded.

Product claims that are held to this standard include not just verbal and textual communications, but also graphics. Graphics in advertising and promotional labeling must be consistent with the FDA-approved product label and be supported by substantial evidence. For instance, a patient depicted in an advertisement generally should represent the average patient in the clinical trials conducted for product approval. An example of an inconsistent advertising claim would contain a graphic of a patient climbing a mountain when the product is indicated for a seriously physically disabling disease; if the majority of patients in the clinical trial had seriously debilitating physical disabilities, this depiction could constitute overstating the product's efficacy.

Fair Balance and Presentation of Risk Information

The manner in which a product's risks are presented in advertising and promotional labeling in comparison to the efficacy information is of utmost importance to APLB. Essentially, safety and effectiveness claims in advertising and promotional labeling must be fairly balanced with risk information. In addition, the risk information must be presented with equal prominence to the promotional claims (21 CFR 202.1(e)(5)). Material facts about the product being promoted also must be communicated, including facts about consequences that may result from the use of the product as suggested in the promotional piece (21 CFR 202.1 (e)(5)(iii)).

Draft Guidance for Industry: Presenting Risk Information in Prescription Drug and Medical Device Promotion (May 2009) provides insight into FDA's thinking on appropriate risk presentation and the various factors used to evaluate adequate risk disclosure. A key aspect of the draft guidance is that when FDA evaluates risk communication in promotional pieces, it does not look only at specific risk statements, but rather at the net impression. The net impression is the message communicated by the promotional piece in its entirety; the piece as a whole should convey an accurate and non-misleading impression of the product's benefits and risks. Furthermore, even if individual claims are not misleading, if the piece as a whole provides a misleading impression (e.g., that the drug is safer than has been proven by substantial evidence), the piece may be deemed to be violative.

Provided below are some general factors that FDA will consider when reviewing risk communication:

- Consistent use of language appropriate for target audience—If a promotional piece is directed toward patients, it should be written in patient-friendly language likely to be understood by the general public.
- Use of signals—Headlines and subheads should accurately identify the risk information.
- Framing risk information—Information should be stated clearly and specifically without inaccurately emphasizing positive or negative aspects.
- Hierarchy of risk information—The ordering of risks is important and generally the serious risks should be communicated first to ensure increased emphasis.
- Quantity—The amount of benefits conveyed generally should not exceed the amount of risks conveyed (fair-balance) in number, completeness, time and space.
- Formatting—The layout, location of risk information and the contrast between text and background will be evaluated to ensure that the benefits are not highlighted more than the risk information.

Consistent with these guidelines, APLB issued an enforcement letter to a company in May 2010 for an audio news release in which efficacy claims were presented in a "slow and deliberate manner that is understandable in terms of the pacing and articulation" while the risk information was presented in a "fast and inarticulate" manner. APLB stated that the piece "fail[ed] to present information about risks of a drug with a prominence reasonably comparable

with the presentation of information relating to the effectiveness." In this example, the benefits were highlighted more than the risk information and, thus, the risks associated with the product were minimized.

Misconception About Fair Balance

In previous years, there may have been a general misconception that merely providing a statement of the serious and most common risks in any piece, regardless of the amount of benefits/effectiveness claims provided would be sufficient risk disclosure. This statement of risks was often referred to as the "Fair-Balance Statement." Through more recent enforcement letters and the draft guidance, it has become clear that FDA is looking not for a concise statement, but rather for a balance (as described in the section above) between benefit and risk information and disclosure of material information.

Distinctions Between Advertising and Promotional Labeling

While "advertising" is technically not defined in the CFR, 21 CFR 202.1(l)1 states that advertisements subject to Section 502(n) of the *FD&C Act* include advertisements published in journals, magazines, other periodicals and newspapers; and broadcast through media such as radio, television and telephone communications systems. This is not a comprehensive list of advertising media subject to regulation. For example, FDA also regulates advertising on the Internet or on electronic bulletin boards.

Generally, advertising and promotional labeling are treated in the same manner, except for the three following distinctions.

Broadcast Advertising

Television and radio advertising (broadcast advertising) must include a statement of the drug's most important risks; this statement is called the "Major Statement" (21 CFR 202.1(e)(1)). This presentation must be spoken, and it can also be included in the video portion of a television advertisement.

The law enables broadcast advertising to include only the most important risk information if the advertisement makes "adequate provision" and directs viewers and/or listeners on how they can obtain the full FDA-approved prescribing information. Broadcast advertisements can meet the "adequate provision" requirement by communicating the following sources for locating a drug's prescribing information:

- website address
- toll-free telephone number
- current issue of a magazine running a print advertisement
- referring to a healthcare provider (e.g., a doctor)

Brief Summary in Print Advertising

Regulations allow advertising to contain a "statement of information in brief summary relating to side effects, contraindications, and effectiveness" (21 CFR 202.1(e)) rather than requiring dissemination of the full FDA-approved labeling (PI), which must be presented directly adjacent to the advertisement. Promotional labeling must always be disseminated with the full PI.

Draft Guidance for Industry: Brief Summary: Disclosing Risk Information in Consumer-Directed Print Advertisements provides the following advice:

- Risk information in Brief Summaries should be presented in patient-friendly language (language that can be easily understood).
- Consumers should be directed to a toll-free number or a website for additional information.
- A statement clarifying that the Brief Summary does not provide a comprehensive list of risks associated with the product should be included.

Food and Drug Administration Amendments Act (FDAAA) of 2007

Section 906 of *FDAAA* went into effect in March 2008, and mandates that all published direct-to-consumer advertisements for prescription drugs include the following statement printed in conspicuous text: "You are encouraged to report negative side effects of prescription drugs to the FDA. Visit www.fda.gov/medwatch, or call 1-800-FDA-1088." This requirement only applies to advertising and not to promotional labeling.

General Exception to Risk Disclosure Requirement: Reminder Labeling

"Reminder labeling" is the only type of pharmaceutical promotional labeling that is exempt from the requirement to disclose risk information (21 CFR 201.100(f)). Reminder labeling generally calls attention to the biologic product's name but does not include indications or dosage recommendations for use. Promotional labeling qualifies as a reminder if the following elements are met:

- The product proprietary name and established name of each active ingredient are disclosed.
- Certain specific descriptive information relating to quantitative ingredients statements, dosage form, quantity of package contents, price and other limited information may be included.
- The product indication or dosage recommendation is not conveyed.
- There are no claims or representations about the product.
- The product does not have a "black box" warning in its labeling.

Note that merely indicating a patient population in the material, either through text or a graphic, would be a violation of this exemption and require the sponsor to provide risk disclosure. For instance, if along with the name, Product X, there was a graphic of a child in the background, this would provide a representation about the product in that it is appropriate for use in a pediatric population; therefore, the sponsor would have to include the appropriate risk disclosure.

Nonpromotional Communications

The following communications are generally not considered to be "promotional" in nature; however, they are still monitored by FDA to ensure that they do not cross the line into advertising and promotional labeling.

Preapproval Product Communications

FDA generally prohibits any promotional activity and claims of safety and efficacy for investigational products prior to approval. Specifically, 21 CFR 312.7(a) states: "A sponsor or investigator, or any person acting on behalf of a sponsor or investigator, shall not represent in a promotional context that an investigational new drug is safe or effective for the purposes for which it is under investigation or otherwise promote the drug."

However, companies often need to provide product information to the public prior to approval (e.g., clinical trial recruitment, press releases, etc.). In these instances, the following guidelines can help ensure that product information is not linked to promotional claims of safety and efficacy:

- When presenting efficacy information, provide an objective presentation of data; state all endpoints and provide data without bias.
- When presenting safety information, include all grades of adverse events with material percentages and/or incidences.
- Avoid characterizing data descriptions such as well-tolerated, revolutionary or robust.
- Always clarify that the product is not yet approved by using descriptions such as "investigational" or "study medication."

It is important to note that this regulation applies not only to sponsors, but also to investigators. In recent years, FDA has issued enforcement letters to investigators who, in their product communications, suggested that a product was safe or efficacious prior to approval.

Scientific Exchange

21 CFR 312.7 continues: "This provision is not intended to restrict the full exchange of scientific information concerning the drug, including dissemination of scientific findings in scientific or lay media. Rather, its intent is to restrict promotional claims of safety or effectiveness

of the drug for a use under which it is under investigation and to preclude commercialization of the drug before it is approved for commercial distribution."

Scientific media include journal publications and scientific abstracts and presentations at purely scientific forums. To determine whether a communication is truly a scientific exchange, FDA generally looks at who is communicating it as well as the media by which it is communicated. If a promotional individual (e.g., pharmaceutical sales representative) provides the communication in a promotional venue (e.g., promotional presentation), this most likely will not be considered a scientific exchange. However, if a clinical researcher from the company, in response to a request from a medical society, provides a presentation on current findings in a purely scientific forum, this may qualify as a scientific exchange.

The nuances are slight and sometimes difficult to discern, therefore this is an area of much discussion. Consequently, in one-on-one communications, sponsors generally do not allow any proactive communication of information that may be deemed inconsistent with the label, and restrict any sharing of additional information to reactive responses to unsolicited requests from medical customers. Also, many sponsors hire medical professionals to fill this communication role.

Dissemination of purely scientific information before a drug is approved is generally allowed since there is no promotional activity or commercial incentive involved and the sponsor is not allowed to sell an IND biologic. *Final Guidance on Industry-Supported Scientific and Educational Activities* (November 1997) states that truly independent and nonpromotional industry-supported activities have not been subject to FDA regulation. Thus, the agency does not have specific regulations for such an activity.

Disease Awareness and "Help-Seeking" Advertising

"Help-seeking" communications or advertisements are disease awareness communications directed at consumers or healthcare practitioners that discuss a particular disease or health condition, but do not mention any specific drug or device or make any representation or suggestion concerning a particular drug or device. Because no drug is mentioned or implied, this type of communication is not considered to be a product advertisement, and therefore, it is not subject to the requirements of the *FD&C Act* or FDA regulations (see *Draft Guidance for Industry: "Help-Seeking" and Other Disease Awareness Communications by or on Behalf of Drug and Device Firms* (January 2004)).

To qualify as a disease awareness and help-seeking advertisement as outlined in the draft guidance, a piece must meet the following elements:
- It should discuss a disease or health condition.
- If it is directed toward consumers, it should advise

the consumer to "see your doctor."
- If it is directed at healthcare practitioners, it should encourage awareness of the signs of disease/conditions to assist in diagnosis.
- It should not mention or identify a particular drug.
- It should not contain any representation or suggestion relating to the drug.

The most important element here is that the piece should not mention or identify a particular drug. The guidance also provides principles on how to help ensure that a help-seeking or disease awareness communication is not linked to product promotion and does not identify a product. Essentially, the guidance suggests that help-seeking and disease awareness communications should be distinct from commercial and product marketing communications. FDA will examine the following elements to determine whether or not they are distinct:
- Perceptual similarity—themes, presentation (branding) elements, colors, logos, graphics (Do the two presentations look alike?)
- Physical proximity (Are the advertisements running close to one another?)
- Linking by audience (Is the audience able to associate the two presentations with one another?)

Also, when a communication relates to a drug or device that is the only one in its diagnostic or therapeutic class or the only product manufactured by a company, the agency may treat the communication as labeling or advertising under the *FD&C Act*.

FDA Oversight and Enforcement

FDA can enforce violations of the *FD&C Act* or agency regulations through a variety of mechanisms, including: Notices of Violations (NOVs), also known as Untitled Letters; Warning Letters; and, if the violation warrants, referral for judicial action. All three mechanisms are intended to induce compliance with regulations.

NOVs are reserved for those violations that are generally less serious and do not greatly jeopardize public health, but are still serious concerns. An NOV usually requires only that the sponsor discontinues use of the violative materials along with any other pieces that may contain a similar violation.

Warning Letters are generally reserved for more serious violations that may pose a risk to public safety. They typically contain stronger language and are usually addressed to the company's CEO. In addition to ceasing use of the violative materials, Warning Letters also may require the company to conduct corrective actions. For example, a company may be required to run a remedial advertisement to reach the same audience as the original violative advertisement, or disseminate corrective information through a "Dear Healthcare Professional" letter as described in 21 CFR 200.5(c)(3). Generally, the corrective action is meant to be communicated in the same medium as the original violative piece. Warning Letters frequently direct the sponsor to provide FDA with information on any other promotional items that contain similar messages. All FDA Warning Letters, regardless of issuing center of office, are available at http://www.fda.gov/ICECI/EnforcementActions/WarningLetters/default.htm#browse.

In determining whether a sponsor should be issued an enforcement letter and, if so, which grade, FDA often looks at the following elements:

- Do the product materials have recurrent violations?
- Is there a pattern and/or consistency of these violations through different forms of media?
- Is there a risk to public health?

If FDA is not satisfied by the sponsor's response to the Warning Letter, it may recommend such enforcement actions as injunctions, seizures and/or criminal prosecution. The Department of Justice (DOJ) carries out these activities. One possible outcome is that the company agrees to enter into an arrangement with the government, called a consent decree, which places severe restrictions on the company's operations to ensure that it comes into compliance.

Corrective actions that can be taken by FDA on inadequate dissemination of medical and scientific information relating to an unapproved use of an approved biologics are outlined in 21 CFR 99.401–405.

Summary

- Promotion and advertising activities are generally prohibited for investigational products prior to FDA-approval.
- The lifecycle of labeling usually begins with the original BLA, when draft labeling information is prepared and submitted by the sponsor to FDA for review and approval. The draft labeling information should contain, at a minimum, container and carton labels, package insert, annotated labeling and SPL. The draft labeling information may also contain a REMS and a medication guide. Upon approval, the labeling content can be appropriately applied to promotional and advertising activities.
- The content and format of labeling information are subject to FDA regulations.
- Postapproval changes to the ordinal labeling as well as promotional labeling and advertising content need to be reported to FDA. Depending upon the nature of the change, it is reported via one of three mechanisms: Prior Approval Supplement, Changes Being Effected or Annual Report.
- Biologics labeling, whether contained in the original BLA or submitted as a postapproval change,

is reviewed and approved under the jurisdiction of CDER and CBER. In CDER, DDMAC reviews, approves and monitors all labeling. In CBER, APLB oversees all labeling activities.

- Advertising and promotional labeling utilize many formats, including direct-to-consumer, reminder advertisements, print advertisements and radio/television broadcasting. Each is governed by specific regulations.
- Generally, advertising and promotional labeling must be consistent with the FDA-approved product labeling, must be supported by substantial evidence, must not be false or misleading, and must reveal all material information.
- Product communications intended to be "nonpromotional" in nature can be subject to FDA regulations if they make product claims.
- Dissemination of scientific or medical information regarding an approved biologic must be conducted in accordance with the *FD&C Act* and should adhere to appropriate regulatory guidelines.
- Disease awareness and "help-seeking" advertising do not mention any specific drug or make any representations about a drug, and therefore, are not subject to the requirements of the *FD&C Act*.
- FDA uses a variety of enforcement tools, such as Notices of Violations, Warning Letters and other corrective actions to ensure industry compliance with the *FD&C Act* and to ensure safe and effective use of biologics in patients.

References

1. FDA, *Federal Register* 73:16313 (27 March 2008).

Combination Products

By Mark D. Kramer, MS, RAC

Objectives

- Review the regulatory definition of a combination product
- Understand the overall regulatory scheme for combination products
- Explain how combination product jurisdictional determinations are made
- Discuss the premarket review process for combination products
- Describe the proposed combination product postmarket safety reporting regulation
- Describe the proposed CGMP requirements for combination products
- Discuss relevant combination product guidance documents
- Discuss how user fees are applied for combination products

Laws, Regulations and Guidelines Covered in This Chapter

- 21 CFR 3 Product jurisdiction
- Proposed 21 CFR 4 Regulation of combination products
- 21 CFR 210 Current Good Manufacturing Practice in manufacturing, processing, packing, or holding of drugs; general
- 21 CFR 211 Current Good Manufacturing Practice for finished pharmaceuticals
- 21 CFR 820 Quality system regulation
- *Federal Food, Drug, and Cosmetic Act* of 1938
- *Safe Medical Devices Act* of 1990
- *Medical Device User Fee and Modernization Act* of 2002
- *Public Health Service Act* of 1944

Introduction

Combination products raise a variety of regulatory and review challenges. Although the US regulatory frameworks for drugs, devices and biological products share many of the same basic features, each is also somewhat unique. Drugs, devices and biological products each have their own types of marketing applications, Good Manufacturing Practice (GMP) regulations and adverse event reporting requirements. When drugs and devices, drugs and biologics or devices and biologics are combined to create a new product, consideration must be given to how the combination product as a whole will be regulated.

Until 1990, there was no clear process or mandate for the

US Food and Drug Administration (FDA) to determine the regulatory pathway of "borderline" products, or products comprised of more than one type of regulated article. The *Safe Medical Devices Act* of 1990 (SMDA) introduced the notion of a combination product in Section 503(g) of the *Federal Food, Drug, and Cosmetic Act* of 1938 (*FD&C Act*), and provided that a combination product be assigned to a lead agency center based on its "primary mode of action" (PMOA). In 1991, FDA implemented the *SMDA* provision in Title 21 of the Code of Federal Regulations (CFR) Part 3. This regulation vested jurisdictional authority for both combination and non-combination products in FDA's Product Jurisdiction Officer (originally FDA's Office of the Ombudsman, and later reassigned to FDA's newly established Office of Combination Products in 2003).

Part 3 also established a "Request for Designation" (RFD) process to determine which FDA center would be assigned review responsibility for combination products, or for any product for which jurisdiction is unclear or in dispute. This regulation was intended to eliminate in most cases, but did not preclude, the need for separate approvals for each individual component of a combination product.

Despite the changes brought with the *SMDA*, the perception persisted that combination products were still vulnerable to "falling through the cracks" between the medical product centers. To address these issues, in the *Medical Device User Fee and Modernization Act* of 2002, Congress amended Section 503(g) of the *FD&C Act* to mandate that FDA establish an Office of Combination Products (OCP) with the following responsibilities for combination product assignment, premarket review and postmarket regulation:

- prompt assignment of the center with primary jurisdiction ("lead center") for the review and regulation of a combination product
- ensure timely and effective premarket review by overseeing the timeliness of and coordinating reviews involving more than one center
- ensure consistent and appropriate postmarket regulation
- resolve disputes regarding review timeliness
- review/revise agreements, guidance and practices specific to the assignment of combination products
- report to Congress on the activities and impact of OCP

While not part of its statutory mandates, OCP also works with FDA centers to develop guidance and regulations to clarify combination product regulation, and serves as a focal point for combination product issues for internal and external stakeholders. Note that OCP does not itself review combination products, but assigns the product to the lead reviewing center and oversees the intercenter consultation process.

Definition of a Combination Product

A "combination product" is defined in 21 CFR 3.2(e) as a combination of two or more different types of regulated products, i.e.,

- a drug and a device
- a device and a biological product
- a drug and a biological product
- a drug, a device and a biological product

The individual components (called "constituent parts") of a combination product can be:

- physically or chemically combined (21 CFR 3.2(e) (1)[1])

- co-packaged (21 CFR 3.2(e)(2)[2])
- separate, cross-labeled products (21 CFR 3.2(e)(3)[3] and (e)(4)[4])

Combinations of two drugs, two devices or two biological products are not combination products as defined by 21 CFR Part 3.

Examples of combination products include:
- drug-coated or drug-eluting device
- drug packaged with a syringe or injector pen
- controlled-release drug delivery device
- orthopedic implant coated or packaged with biologic growth factor
- chemotherapy drug and monoclonal antibody (biologic) conjugate
- scaffold (device) seeded with autologous cells (biologic)
- cross labeled drug/ *in vitro* pharmacogenomic test

A list of recent FDA examples of combination approvals can be found at www.fda.gov/CombinationProducts/ AboutCombinationProducts/ucm101598.htm.

Determining Combination Product Jurisdiction and Regulatory Path

FDA is required to assign a combination product to a lead center based on its PMOA. In the 25 August 2005 *Federal Register*, FDA promulgated a final regulation (PMOA rule) to describe the principles for how combination products will be assigned to an agency center. The regulation defined "mode of action" and "primary mode of action," and set forth an algorithm for how FDA would assign combination products for which the PMOA cannot be determined with "reasonable certainty."

FDA defined "mode of action" as the means by which a product achieves an intended therapeutic effect or action. For purposes of this definition, "therapeutic" action or effect includes any effect or action of the combination product intended to diagnose, cure, mitigate, treat or prevent disease, or affect the structure or any function of the body. Because combination products are comprised of more than one type of regulated article (biological product, device or drug), and each constituent part contributes a biological product, device or drug mode of action, combination products will typically have more than one identifiable mode of action. The respective definitions of biological product, device and drug mode of actions are closely related to the statutory definitions of a biological product, device and drug, respectively:

1. A constituent part has a biological product mode of action if it acts by means of a virus, therapeutic serum, toxin, antitoxin, vaccine, blood, blood component or derivative, allergenic product or analogous product applicable to the prevention, treatment or

cure of a disease or condition of human beings, as described in section 351(i) of the *Public Health Service Act*. [Note: while not currently reflected in the definition of a biological product mode of action, it should be noted that the statutory definition of a biological product was amended in 2010 to also include proteins (except any chemically synthesized polypeptide).]

2. A constituent part has a device mode of action if it meets the definition of device contained in section 201(h)(1) to (h)(3) of the *FD&C Act*, it does not have a biological product mode of action, and it does not achieve its primary intended purposes through chemical action within or on the body of man or other animals and is not dependent upon being metabolized for the achievement of its primary intended purposes.

3. A constituent part has a drug mode of action if it meets the definition of drug contained in section 201(g)(1) of the *FD&C Act* and it does not have a biological product or device mode of action.

"PMOA" is defined as "the single mode of action of a combination product that provides the most important therapeutic action of the combination product." The regulation further clarifies that PMOA is the "mode of action expected to make the greatest contribution to the overall intended therapeutic effects of the combination product." For example, if the PMOA of a drug-device combination product is attributable to its device constituent part, CDRH would have primary jurisdiction for the combination product, whereas if the PMOA of a drug-device combination product is attributable to its drug constituent part, CDER would have primary jurisdiction.

In cases where FDA is unable to determine the most important therapeutic action with reasonable certainty, 21 CFR 3.4 sets out an "assignment algorithm," describing the assignment process. First, FDA would look at historical precedents to assign the combination product to the agency component that regulates other combination products that present similar questions of safety and effectiveness with regard to the combination product as a whole. When there are no other combination products that present similar questions of safety and effectiveness with regard to the combination product as a whole, FDA would look to direct the most appropriate assignment based on the safety and effectiveness questions raised by the new combination product. FDA assigns the product to the agency component with the most expertise related to the most significant safety and effectiveness questions presented by the combination product. For example, if the most significant safety and effectiveness issues presented by a drug-device combination product in this scenario were attributable to the drug constituent part, the combination product would likely be assigned to CDER.

Understanding the regulatory pathway early in the development phase of a combination product is often essential for the sponsor to establish a realistic regulatory strategy. There are two ways in which a manufacturer can seek FDA's feedback for determining the product's jurisdiction: informal processes or formal processes. Informal processes involve seeking advice from center or OCP staff, typically by telephone, email or meeting. Informal procedures are generally appropriate where the most important therapeutic action of the combination product is clear or when FDA has previous experience with similar combination products for which jurisdiction has been previously determined. However, one of the disadvantages of the informal approach is that the advice is not binding on FDA and may be subject to change.

Formal designation of a product, whether a single entity (i.e., non-combination drug, device or biologic) or a combination product, is achieved by submitting a Request for Designation (RFD). An RFD is a written submission to OCP requesting designation of the center with primary jurisdiction for a product. An RFD submission is not necessary for every product, but it is generally indicated when the jurisdiction of a single entity or combination product is unclear or in dispute.

FDA action on an RFD is a binding jurisdictional determination with respect to center assignment and is subject to change only under conditions specified in 21 CFR 3.9 and Section 563 of the *FD&C Act*. However, while a designation is binding as to assignment of a particular product, such assignment pertains only to the product described in the RFD. For example, if the product's configuration, composition, modes of action, intended use or any other key aspect changes after the designation letter is issued, it may be necessary to submit a new RFD to determine the modified product's appropriate assignment.

An RFD is limited by regulation to 15 pages, including attachments. Under the regulation, if FDA does not provide an answer within 60 days of the RFD filing date, the sponsor's request for classification or assignment is granted.

As described in 21 CFR 3.7(c), the following information is required in an RFD submission. FDA has issued a guidance document *How to Write a Request for Designation* that further elaborates on these requirements:[5]

- sponsor's identity, including company name and address, establishment registration number, company contact person and telephone number
- product description, including:
  - o classification, name of the product and all component products
  - o common, generic or usual name of the product and all components
  - o proprietary name
  - o identification of any component of the product

that already has received premarket approval, is marketed as not being subject to premarket approval, or has received an investigational exemption

- o status of any discussions or agreements between the sponsors regarding the use of this product as a component of a new combination product
- o chemical, physical or biological composition
- o status and brief report of the results of developmental work, including animal testing
- o description of the manufacturing processes, including the sources of all components
- o proposed use or indications
- o description of all known modes of action, the sponsor's identification of the single mode of action that provides the most important therapeutic action of the product and the basis for that determination
- o schedule and duration of use
- o dose and route of administration of drug or biologic
- o description of related products, including their regulatory status
- o any other relevant information
- sponsor's recommendation as to which agency component should have primary jurisdiction

FDA generally reviews an RFD for completeness within five working days of receipt. An incomplete RFD is "not filed" and the applicant is notified of the information necessary to permit OCP to undertake a substantive review. If an RFD is filed, the sponsor is notified of the filing date, as well as the date by which OCP will respond. Within 60 days after the filing of the RFD, OCP issues a letter specifying the agency component with primary jurisdiction for the product's premarket review and regulation. The designation letter usually also identifies any consulting agency components, and sometimes also describes the regulatory authorities (e.g., device or drug provisions of the *FD&C Act*) to which the product will be subject.

If the sponsor disagrees with the designation, it may request that OCP reconsider the decision. The Request for Reconsideration (RFR) must be submitted within 15 days of receipt of the designation letter, may not include new information, and must not exceed five pages. OCP will in turn respond in writing to the RFR within 15 days.

A variety of resources is available to help sponsors understand the jurisdiction of a combination product. The original such resources were the three intercenter agreements (ICAs) between CBER and CDER, CDER and CDRH, and CBER and CDRH, established in 1991. The usefulness of the ICAs has decreased over time due to organizational realignments within FDA, the development of new products not envisioned in the original ICAs, new

uses of existing products, and laws that have been enacted since 1991. In 2006 (71 *FR* 56988[6]), the agency announced that it had reviewed these agreements and preliminarily proposed to continue using the CBER-CDRH and CDER-CDRH ICAs as they provide helpful, nonbinding guidance, with the understanding that they should not be independently relied upon as the agency's most current, complete jurisdictional statements. Due to the transfer of many therapeutic biologic products from CBER to CDER in 2003, the agency stated that the CBER-CDER ICA is out of date.

The 2006 notice also explains that while FDA does not plan to update the existing ICAs, it believes transparency in jurisdictional decision making should result in greater predictability and reduce ambiguity about FDA perspectives. A number of mechanisms have been implemented by FDA to provide this transparency. For example, the agency has used its website to disseminate information concerning product jurisdiction. Some examples of these are:

- Jurisdictional determinations—Approximately 250 capsular descriptions of selected RFD decisions have been posted on OCP's website (www.fda.gov/ CombinationProducts/JurisdictionalInformation/ RFDJurisdictionalDecisions/ CapsularDescriptions "One-Liners"/default.htm)
- Jurisdictional updates—Detailed statements on updated classification and assignment of specific product classes are available on OCP's website (www.fda.gov/CombinationProducts/ JurisdictionalInformation/JurisdictionalUpdates/ default.htm)
- RFD decision letters—For approximately 50 products covered by an RFD that have since been approved or cleared, the OCP website includes the written jurisdictional determination respecting the RFD, redacted to remove trade secret and confidential commercial information in accordance with the *Freedom of Information Act* (www.fda.gov/ CombinationProducts/JurisdictionalInformation/ RFDJurisdictionalDecisions/ RedactedDecisionLetters/default.htm)

Premarket Review

The assigned lead center has primary responsibility for the review and regulation of a combination product; however a second center is often involved in the review process, especially to provide input regarding the "secondary" component. In some cases, secondary center involvement may be extensive, depending upon the issues raised by a particular product or submission.

To make the combination product review process more efficient, FDA established a standard operating procedure (SOP), the *Intercenter Consultative and Collaborative Review Process*.[7] This SOP provides the procedures for FDA staff to follow when requesting, receiving, handling, processing and tracking formal consultative and collaborative reviews of combination products, devices, drugs and biologics. The objectives of the SOP are to improve intercenter communication on combination products as well as the timeliness and consistency of intercenter consultative and collaborative reviews.

While a combination product's PMOA dictates the lead center assignment, it does not dictate the regulatory authorities that may be applied to a combination product. In most cases, the lead center applies its usual regulatory pathway. For example, a drug-device combination product assigned to CDRH is typically reviewed under the 510(k) or Premarket Approval Application (PMA) process, while a drug-device combination product assigned to CDER will typically be reviewed under a New Drug Application (NDA). In most cases, a single marketing application is sufficient to review a combination product, but in some cases, particularly where the two components are themselves separate products, two applications (e.g., a PMA and an NDA) may be desirable or required.

FDA published the concept paper "Number of Marketing Applications for a Combination Product" for stakeholder comment.[8] The document describes FDA's thinking about when single or separate marketing applications may be appropriate for the constituent parts of a combination product. While separate marketing applications are sometimes appropriate, normally only one investigational application (Investigational New Drug (IND) or Investigational Device Exemption (IDE)) is submitted to authorize a clinical investigation of a combination product.

It is recommended that the sponsor contact the agency, ideally during early product development, to determine the nature of technical and scientific information that may be necessary for investigational and marketing applications for a combination product. In September 2006, FDA published *Guidance for Industry and Staff: Early Development Considerations for Innovative Combination Products,*[9] which provides helpful perspectives on combination product development.

Special consideration should also be given to intellectual property when more than one manufacturer is co-developing a combination product. For example, the sponsor of an IDE or PMA for a device-drug combination product may not be given access by the drug manufacturer to confidential/trade secret drug information, such as drug synthesis, formulation, purification or manufacturing processes, yet such information may be required for regulatory purposes.

Confidentiality of such information can usually be maintained while providing FDA the necessary information to support the investigational or marketing application in one of two ways. One is through a letter of authorization (LOA), which allows the applicant to cross-reference

an existing application and allows FDA to consider this information in its review of the application used for the combination product. The second alternative is the use of master files. Drug Master Files (DMFs) or Device Master Files (MAFs) are voluntary submissions to FDA used to provide confidential information about a product or process (e.g., manufacturing processes or toxicology data) that one sponsor wishes to keep confidential but which is necessary for the other sponsor to support the premarket review process. It should be noted that FDA does not approve information or data in a master file, but rather accesses and reviews the information in the context of the referring application. Additional information on DMFs can be found in 21 CFR 314.420 and on FDA's website.

New Regulations Proposed in 2009 for Combination Products

In late 2009, FDA published two proposed rules that would amend the combination product regulations by creating new 21 CFR 4. Subpart A would address current GMP (CGMP) requirements for combination products, while Subpart B would promulgate postmarketing safety reporting requirements for combination products. A similar legal framework underlies both proposed rules and sets forth FDA's view that drugs, devices and biological products do not lose their individual regulatory identities when they become constituent parts of a combination product. Under this framework, in general, the CGMP and postmarket safety reporting requirements specific to each constituent part of a combination product also apply to the combination product itself. However, rather than impose duplicative requirements for manufacturers to fully comply with both sets of requirements, the proposed rules set out a streamlined framework whereby a manufacturer would comply with one set of requirements, as well as specific, additional provisions to ensure that any unique requirements attributable to the "other" component are not lost if the product were to comply with only one set of requirements. The application of this general approach is further described below for both postmarket safety reporting and CGMP requirements.

Good Manufacturing Practice Requirements

In 2004, FDA published *Draft Guidance for Industry and FDA: Current Good Manufacturing Practice for Combination Products,* on the applicability of GMP requirements to combination products. In the 23 September 2009, *Federal Register,*[10] FDA proposed codifying an approach similar to the one taken in the draft guidance, by establishing new 21 CFR 4, Subpart A. The proposed rule embodies the legal framework that, in FDA's view, a drug-device combination product is both a drug and a device, and both sets of CGMP requirements (21 CFR 210 and 211 for drugs and 21 CFR 820 for devices) apply to the combination product itself.

However, the proposed rule recognizes that 21 CFR 210 and 211 and 820 are similar in most respects. In this context, for single entity and co-packaged combination products, the rule provides a streamlined approach as an alternative to fully implementing and complying with both sets of CGMP requirements. Under this streamlined approach, a manufacturer could choose to operate under and comply with either 21 CFR 210 and 211 or 21 CFR 820, rather than both, provided that additional specific aspects of the other CGMP framework are also incorporated.

Specifically, under the proposed rule, a manufacturer choosing to operate under and comply with drug CGMP regulations under 21 CFR 210 and 211 for its single-entity or co-packaged drug-device combination product, would also be considered to have complied with all provisions of the device Quality System Regulation at 21 CFR 820, if it complies with the following specific provisions from 21 CFR 820:

1. 820.20 Management responsibility
2. 820.30 Design controls
3. 820.50 Purchasing controls
4. 820.100 Corrective and preventive action
5. 820.170 Installation
6. 820.200 Servicing

In an analogous manner, a manufacturer choosing to operate under and comply with device CGMP requirements under 21 CFR 820 for its single-entity or co-packaged drug-device combination product, would also be considered to have complied with all provisions of the drug CGMP requirements in 21 CFR 210 and 211, if it complies with the following specific provisions from 21 CFR 210 and 211:

1. 211.84 Testing and approval or rejection of components, drug product containers, and closures
2. 211.103 Calculation of yield
3. 211.132 Tamper-evident packaging for over-the-counter (OTC) human drug products
4. 211.137 Expiration dating
5. 211.165 Testing and release for distribution
6. 211.166 Stability testing
7. 211.167 Special testing requirements
8. 211.170 Reserve samples

Under the proposed rule, the streamlined approach may be used when two or more types of constituents are manufactured in the same facility. When manufacture of a constituent part occurs at a separate facility from all other types of constituent parts, the proposed rule would require the manufacture of that part to occur under the CGMP regulations applicable to that part. For example, the manufacture of a drug constituent part at a facility separate from all other combination product constituent parts would be subject to 21 CFR 210 and 211, while the facility where that drug constituent part is manufactured with the device into a single-entity or co-packaged constituent part could implement the streamlined approach.

For a combination product that includes a biological product constituent part, in addition to demonstrating compliance with either the drug CGMPs or the device Quality System Regulation, along with 21 CFR 210 and 211, the CGMP operating system would also have to comply with additional CGMP requirements that apply to that constituent part as a biological product (see 21 CFR 600–680). Similarly, if the combination product includes a human cellular or tissue (HCT/P) constituent part, it would also have to be shown to comply with the requirements of 21 CFR 1271.

Finally, for combination products where the constituent parts are separately packaged (21 CFR 3.2(e)(3) and (e)(4)), under the proposed rule, each constituent part would remain separate for purposes of applying the CGMP regulations. For example, for a combination product comprised of a drug and a cross-labeled but separately packaged delivery device, the drug constituent part would be subject to 21 CFR 210 and 211, while the delivery device would be subject to 21 CFR 820.

The proposed requirements are not currently in effect and may be revised to incorporate stakeholder comments, but it is expected that the final rule will be similar in overall approach. FDA encourages manufacturers to consider CGMP requirements for combination products early in the development process and to contact FDA for guidance as appropriate.

Postmarket Safety Reporting for Combination Products

The 1 October 2009 proposed rule,[11] which has not been finalized as of the date of this publication, recognizes that the individual reporting requirements for drugs (21 CFR 310 and 314), devices (21 CFR 803) and biological products (21 CFR 600 and 606) share many similarities and have a common underlying purpose, i.e., to protect the public health by ensuring a product's continued safety and effectiveness. For example, each set of regulations requires reports of death and serious adverse events; each provides for periodic and follow-up reports; and each provides a method to signal certain types of safety events that warrant expedited reporting. Despite these similarities, each set of regulations also has certain reporting standards and timeframes with unique requirements based upon the characteristics of the products for which the regulations were designed. For example, the drug reporting provisions have no requirement analogous to device malfunction reporting, while the device reporting provisions have no requirement analogous to drug 3-day Field Alert

Table 22-1. Unique Proposed Postmarket Safety Reporting Provisions for Combination Products

Type of Requirement	Name of Requirement	Regulatory Citation
Device	5-Day Report	21 CFR 803.53(a)
Device	30-Day Device Malfunction Report	21 CFR 803.20(b)(3)(ii)
Drug/Biological Product	15-Day Alert Report	21 CFR 314.80(c)(1) and (e) 21 CFR 600.80(c)(1) and (e)
Drug	3-Day Field Alert Report	21 CFR 314.81(b)(1)
Biological Product	Expedited Blood Fatality Report	21 CFR 606.170

Reporting. The intent of the proposed rule is to consolidate the requirements so that a combination product is subject primarily to the reporting requirements associated with the type of marketing application under which the product is approved or cleared, while at the same time ensuring that the public health benefit of the specific unique provisions is not lost if the combination product were subject solely to the reporting requirements associated with the type of marketing application.

FDA has identified five such provisions, described in **Table 22-1**, that are unique to drugs, devices and biological products that FDA believes need to be preserved to appropriately reflect the combination nature of the product and to ensure consistent and appropriate postmarketing safety reporting for combination products.

Under the proposed rule, a drug-device combination product approved or cleared under the device provisions of the *FD&C Act* would be subject to Medical Device Reporting under 21 CFR 803, and in addition, would be subject to 15-Day Alert Reporting under 21 CFR 314.80(c)(1) and 3-Day Field Alert Reporting under 21 CFR 314.81(b)(1). A drug-device combination product approved under the drug provisions of the *FD&C Act* would be subject to the drug reporting provisions under 21 CFR 314.80 and 314.81, as well as 5-Day Reporting under 21 CFR 803.53(a) and 30-Day Malfunction Reporting under 21 CFR 803.20(b)(3)(ii). Expedited blood fatality reporting under 21 CFR 606.170 would apply to combination products with a blood constituent part.

The proposed rule also describes how reporting would work in less frequent situations, e.g., where there are separate marketing applications for the constituent parts of the combination product or where there are multiple reporters (i.e., one application holder for one constituent part of the combination product, and a second application holder for another constituent part of the combination product). In the case of multiple reporters, each reporter would be subject to the applicable requirements for that reporter's constituent report. The application holder for the device constituent part would submit in accordance with 21 CFR 803, while the application holder for the drug constituent part would submit in accordance with 21 CFR 314. In addition, to ensure each reporter is aware of and can investigate and follow-up on events the other may learn about that may impact a constituent part, the proposed rule would require each application holder to submit information learned about the "other component" to the other manufacturer for investigation or follow-up, or to FDA.

The proposed requirements are not currently in effect and may be revised to incorporate stakeholder comments, but it is expected that the final rule will be similar in overall approach.

User Fees for Combination Products

FDA published *Guidance for Industry and Staff: Application User Fees for Combination Products*[12] in April 2005, to clarify the application of user fees for combination products. The guidance explains that a combination product, as defined in 21 CFR 3.2(e), is subject to the application fee associated with the type of application submitted for the product's premarket approval or clearance. For example, a biologic-device or a drug-device combination product for which a PMA is submitted is subject to the PMA fee under *MDUFMA*. Likewise, a combination product for which an NDA is submitted is subject to the NDA fee under the *Prescription Drug User Fee Act* (*PDUFA*).

In specific situations, a sponsor may opt to submit separate marketing applications for each constituent part of the combination product, even though one application (covering the entire combination product) would suffice. Usually, this is done to pursue some type of benefit such as new drug product exclusivity, orphan status or proprietary data protection when two firms are involved. Because the submission of two applications when one would suffice places an extra burden on FDA resources, a user fee for each application would ordinarily be required.

However, in cases where two marketing applications are required by FDA for the combination product (rather than at the discretion of the sponsor), an "innovative combination product waiver" might allow for reduction of the dual application user fees. More information on the eligibility for fee reduction provided by this waiver is available in the guidance document referenced above.

Summary

* As defined in 21 CFR 3.2(e), a combination product" is any combination of a drug and a device; a biological product and a device; a drug and a biological product; or a drug, a device and

a biological product. There are four definitions within 3.2(e) explaining these combinations.

- The *FD&C Act* gives OCP broad responsibilities covering the lifecycle of combination products. However, primary responsibility and oversight reside with the lead center (CDRH, CDER or CBER) to which the product is assigned.

- OCP is responsible for the prompt assignment of a lead center that will have primary jurisdiction for the review and regulation of a combination product based upon a determination of its primary mode of action (PMOA).

- Formal designation of a single entity (i.e., drug, device or biologic) or combination product is achieved by submitting a Request for Designation (RFD).

- In 2009, FDA proposed new regulations for postmarket safety reporting and CGMP requirements for combination products. The proposed regulations are predicated on the general legal framework that a combination product is subject to the legal authorities governing its constituent parts, however streamlined approaches are proposed that recognize the similarities while also preserving the unique differences among the underling regulations.

- A marketing application for a combination product is subject to the usual fee associated with that type of application. In unique situations where two applications are required and the eligibility criteria are met, an "innovative combination product waiver" may apply.

References

1. 21 CFR 3.2(e)(1): a product comprised of two or more regulated components, i.e., drug/device, biologic/device, drug/biologic or drug/device/biologic, that are physically, chemically or otherwise combined or mixed and produced as a single entity.

2. 21 CFR 3.2(e)(2): two or more separate products packaged together in a single package or as a unit and comprised of drug and device products, device and biological products or biological and drug products.

3. 21 CFR 3.2(e)(3): a drug, device or biological product packaged separately that, according to its investigational plan or proposed labeling, is intended for use only with an approved, individually specified drug, device or biological product where both are required to achieve the intended use, indication or effect and where, upon approval of the proposed product, the labeling of the approved product would need to be changed, e.g., to reflect a change in intended use, dosage form, strength, route of administration or significant change in dose.

4. 21 CFR 3.2(e)(4): any investigational drug, device or biological product packaged separately that, according to its proposed labeling, is for use only with another individually specified investigational drug, device or biological product where both are required to achieve the intended use, indication or effect.

5. www.fda.gov/RegulatoryInformation/Guidances/ucm126053.htm. Accessed 17 May 2011.

6. http://edocket.access.gpo.gov/2006/pdf/E6-15967.pdf. Accessed 17 May 2011.

7. www.fda.gov/downloads/RegulatoryInformation/Guidances/UCM126016.pdf. Accessed 17 May 2011.

8. www.fda.gov/downloads/CombinationProducts/RequestsforComment/UCM108197.pdf. Accessed 17 May 2011.

9. www.fda.gov/downloads/RegulatoryInformation/Guidances/ucm126054.pdf. Accessed 17 May 2011.

10. http://edocket.access.gpo.gov/2009/pdf/E9-22850.pdf. Accessed 17 May 2011.

11. http://edocket.access.gpo.gov/2009/pdf/E9-23519.pdf. Accessed 17 May 2011.

12. www.fda.gov/downloads/RegulatoryInformation/Guidances/UCM147118.pdf. Accessed 17 May 2011.

Recommended Reading

Product Jurisdiction, 21 CFR 3 www.accessdata.fda.gov/scripts/cdrh/cfdocs/cfCFR/CFRSearch.cfm?CFRPart=3&showFR=1. Accessed 17 May 2011.

FDA Guidance *How to Write a Request for Designation.* www.fda.gov/RegulatoryInformation/Guidances/ucm126053.htm. Accessed 17 May 2011.

Review of Agreements, Guidances, and Practices Specific to Assignment of Combination Products http://edocket.access.gpo.gov/2006/pdf/E6-15967.pdf. Accessed 17 May 2011.

Intercenter Consultative and Collaborative Review Process. www.fda.gov/downloads/RegulatoryInformation/Guidances/UCM126016.pdf. Accessed 17 May 2011.

Number of Marketing Applications for a Combination Product. www.fda.gov/downloads/CombinationProducts/RequestsforComment/UCM108197.pdf. Accessed 17 May 2011.

Early Development Considerations for Innovative Combination Products. www.fda.gov/downloads/RegulatoryInformation/Guidances/ucm126054.pdf. Accessed 17 May 2011.

Proposed Rule: Postmarket Safety Reporting for Combination Products http://edocket.access.gpo.

gov/2009/pdf/E9-23519.pdf. Accessed 17 May
2011.

Proposed Rule: Current Good Manufacturing Practice
Requirements for Combination Products http://
edocket.access.gpo.gov/2009/pdf/E9-22850.pdf.
Accessed 17 May 2011.

Application User Fees for Combination Products.
www.fda.gov/downloads/RegulatoryInformation/
Guidances/UCM147118.pdf. Accessed 17 May
2011.

Regulation of Products for Small Patient Populations

Updated by Hari Nagaradona, PhD

Objectives

- Review regulations for small patient populations
- Recognize that orphan products include not only drugs but also devices and medical foods
- Understand the regulatory history and processes for each classification
- Understand differences between patent protection and exclusivity provisions
- Review the EU, Australian and Japanese processes for orphan products and efforts for global harmonization
- Gain knowledge regarding orphan products and HUDs and the HDE process

Laws, Regulations and Guidelines Covered in This Chapter

- *Orphan Drug Act* of 1983, Public Law 97-414, 1983 with amendments in 1985 and 1988
- 21 U.S. Code 360bb(a)(2) Designation of drugs for rare diseases or conditions
- 21 CFR 316.3(b)(13) Definition of same drug
- 21 CFR 814.20(b)(10) Proposed labeling and 21 CFR 814.102 Designation of HUD status
- 21 CFR 814, Subpart H Humanitarian Use Devices
- 21 CFR 814.104 Original applications

Introduction
Orphan Drug Act

Since its creation in 1982, the US Food and Drug Administration's (FDA) Office of Orphan Product Development (OOPD) has been dedicated to promoting the development of products that demonstrate promise for the diagnosis and/or treatment of rare diseases or conditions.

The *Orphan Drug Act* of 1982 (*ODA*) was signed into law (Public Law 97-414)[1] on 4 January 1983 to provide tax incentives and exclusive licensing that would encourage manufacturers to develop and market drugs or biologics for diseases affecting relatively few people (fewer than 200,000 in the US). *ODA* defines an "orphan drug" as one developed for a disease or condition that occurs so infrequently in the US that there is no reasonable expectation that the costs of research, development and marketing would be recovered from sales revenues.[2] FDA's OOPD administers *ODA*'s major provisions as well as the Orphan

Drugs Grants Program, which provides funding for clinical research on rare diseases.

Prior to this legislation, private industry had little incentive to invest money in the development of treatments for small patient populations because the drugs were expected to be unprofitable. The law provides three incentives: seven-year marketing exclusivity to sponsors of approved orphan products; a tax credit of 50% of the cost of human clinical testing; and research grants for clinical testing of new therapies to treat rare diseases. Exclusive marketing rights limit competition by preventing other companies from marketing the generic version of the drug. Even in cases where there is modification to the parent drug, the law still requires the new entity to prove clinical superiority.

The original *ODA* required a potential sponsor to establish a lack of commercial viability. *ODA* expanded the definition of "orphan drugs" to include biological products, antibiotics, medical devices and medical foods.[3] It also was amended to clarify the term "rare disease or condition" as any disease or condition in the US that affected:

- fewer than 200,000 people (for vaccines and blood products, the figure of 200,000 or fewer applies to patients receiving the product annually)
- more than 200,000 people and offering no reasonable expectation that the costs of development and distribution of the drug will be recovered from sales[4]

As amended, the standard for orphan designation changed from profitability to prevalence. The requirement to show lack of economic viability applies only when prevalence exceeds 200,000. Only one drug has been approved for orphan status under the second criteria. Manufacturers rarely attempt to prove compliance with the second set of criteria because regulation requires FDA to verify unprofitability and examine all relevant financial and sales records. Patient population is determined by the total population with clinical symptoms, rather than those who would actually be eligible for use of the drug.[5]

ODA further states that an orphan medical device is one treating "any disease or condition that occurs so infrequently in the US that there is no reasonable expectation that a medical device for such disease or condition will be developed without the assistance" of grants and contracts from OOPD. A similar statement regarding medical foods and biologics is included.

ODA also created an Orphan Products Board within the Department of Health and Human Services (DHHS) to determine policy on orphan product development and to coordinate federal efforts and private sector activities.

In order to pursue the option of obtaining an orphan drug designation, the sponsor company must first seek FDA agreement that the drug qualifies for orphan designation. If the disease prevalence requirement of 200,000 persons is fulfilled, the sponsor must prove the clinical utility of the drug to uniquely treat the rare disease. Otherwise, the company may find itself competing with a similar drug that also has earned orphan designation. In these types of situations, the two drugs in question must be shown to be distinct; otherwise, a New Drug Application (NDA) will be granted only to one.

The impact of *ODA* has been far-reaching. In the 25 years following *ODA*, FDA has approved 366 drugs for rare diseases that otherwise would not have been incentivized to provide treatment options for those patients. Approximately 7,000 rare diseases have been identified. A subcategory, ultra-orphan drugs, has recently been recognized to treat diseases affecting fewer than 10,000 patients in the US.

Potential Orphan Classification Categories

Among categories that can potentially qualify for orphan classification are:

- rare diseases (small markets)
- single administration (vaccines and diagnostics that have small market potential and high liability risk)
- Third World or developing nations
- drug abuse treatment

Conditions for Orphan Status

To be eligible for orphan status, a product must:

- have a sponsor (i.e., a company, individual, scientific institution or government agency)
- not have been approved previously under an NDA, Biologic License Application (BLA) or Premarket Approval (PMA) application for the disease or condition for which orphan status is requested
- not be the subject of a marketing application submitted prior to the filing of an orphan status request

Orphan Drug Application Process

The sponsor first submits a request for orphan designation of the product for a specified rare disease or condition to OOPD. The request should include:

- description of the rare disease or condition
- description of the product
- summary of the product's indicated use(s)
- documentation supporting the assertion that potential drug users number fewer than 200,000 in the US

Once a drug has been granted orphan designation, FDA will collaborate with OOPD for any *Prescription Drug User Fee Act* (*PDUFA*) meetings with the sponsor. FDA's requirements for the drug development pathway resulting in NDA approval for orphan drugs (or applications for other products) are the same as for other drugs. *ODA* Section 525 provides for formal protocol assistance when requested by the sponsors of drugs for rare diseases or conditions. The formal review of a request for protocol assistance is the direct responsibility of the Center for Drug Evaluation and Research (CDER) or the Center for Biologic Evaluation and Research (CBER), whichever has jurisdiction for review of the product. OOPD is responsible for ensuring that the request qualifies for consideration under Section 525 of the *Federal Food, Drug, and Cosmetic Act* (*FD&C Act*).

FDA utilizes these meetings to guide the sponsor in the appropriate direction to ensure that studies are properly designed and executed to meet regulatory requirements. Under the tax-credit provision, no credit is allowed for clinical testing conducted outside the US, unless there is an insufficient patient population available for testing within the US.

FDA, through OOPD, funds the development of qualifying orphan products through its clinical study grants program. Eligibility for grant funding is extended to drugs, medical devices and medical foods for which there is no reasonable expectation of development without such assistance. An orphan designation for a drug does not guarantee a research grant will be awarded. Grant applications, submitted using the Request for Application (RFA) form are reviewed by panels of outside experts and funded by priority score. The grant program is very competitive and only about 30% of the applicants receive awards each year. Any organization, whether domestic or foreign, public or private, or profit or nonprofit, is eligible to apply for the grants. Small businesses are encouraged to apply as well. Although rare, large pharmaceutical companies have qualified for some grants.

Applications are first reviewed by the OOPD program staff for relevance and responsiveness to the RFA. Responsive applications are reviewed and evaluated for scientific and technical merit by an ad hoc panel of experts. A national advisory council conducts a second review for concurrence with the recommendations made by the initial review group. Rank ordered priority scores determine final awards.

OOPD plans to further facilitate orphan drugs by:[6]

- developing a simplified application based entirely on the prevalence requirement and rationale of the proposed product (Is there reason to believe this is a promising drug that can be expected to be effective against the proposed rare disease or condition?)
- working to revise current regulations and ways of dividing patients with a specific disease or disorder into credible subsets acceptable to OOPD (What is the acceptable medical rationale for a particular disease?)
- addressing study design for small clinical trials, which are appropriate for small patient populations
- informing policymakers of the grant program's success ($14 million awarded per year); greater awareness might lead to an increase in the grant budget, which has not changed in recent years

Regulatory and Financial Incentives for Orphan Drugs

When a drug to treat a rare disease or condition is granted orphan designation, the sponsor may be eligible for the following incentives:

- regulatory assistance and guidance from FDA in the design of an overall drug development plan
- 50% federal tax credit for expenses incurred in conducting clinical research (tax credits may be applied to prior year or applied over as many as 20 years to future taxes)
- research grants from OOPD to support clinical studies for developing orphan drugs
- waiver of *PDUFA* fees for orphan drugs

Orphan Drug Designation Holder Annual Reports (21 CFR 316.30)

Within 14 months after the date on which a drug was designated as an orphan product and annually thereafter until marketing approval, the sponsor of a designated drug shall submit a brief progress report (21 CFR 316.30) to OOPD that includes:

- short account of drug development progress, including a review of preclinical and clinical studies initiated, ongoing and completed and a short summary of the status or results of such studies
- description of the coming year's investigational plan, as well as any anticipated difficulties in development, testing and marketing
- brief discussion of any changes that may affect the product's orphan drug status (For example, sponsors of products nearing the end of the approval process should discuss any disparity between the probable marketing indication and the designated indication as related to the need for an amendment to the orphan drug designation pursuant to 21 CFR 316.26.)

As of April 2011, approximately 1,141 drugs had been granted orphan drug status. Of these, 366 drugs had received marketing approval. OOPD acts as an ombudsman to FDA review divisions, typically giving orphan drugs fast-track review. OOPD also implements the orphan product grants program and announces fund availability in the *Federal Register.*

A sponsor may request orphan drug designation at any time in the drug development process prior to submitting a marketing application for the drug product. There has been a misconception that if a drug is granted orphan status, the drug development path need not be the same as the one followed for any other therapeutic agent. The only actual difference arises from the fact that it would be difficult find the same number of subjects as required for a non-orphan drug; therefore, the clinical trial size could be smaller, which is an issue requiring negotiation with FDA. The request for designation of an approved drug product for an unapproved use may be timed without considering whether the drug has been approved previously for an orphan drug indication. Thus, a number of orphan drugs have more than one designation. In fact, as of April 2011, 2,346 designations had been granted for the 1,141 drugs mentioned above. They include:

- different indications for the same drug sponsored by the same company
- identical or different drugs sponsored by different companies

For example, Interferon has six designations for cancer or viral infections, and Interferon Alfa-2b has 10. Similarly, there may be multiple designations for the same orphan indication.

Until recently, FDA decided on a case-by-case basis

whether two drugs were different for the purposes of marketing exclusivity. A case involving a human growth hormone and a slight variation of the same product resulted in regulations promulgated in 1992 that use structural similarity to create a presumption of "sameness" between two drugs.[7] Macromolecular drugs are the same if there is only a slight difference in amino acid sequence. Micromolecular drugs are the same if the "active moiety" is identical. However, if "clinical superiority" is demonstrated, uniqueness is presumed.

Common Mistakes in Defining Subsets

Depending upon the type of rare condition or disease being used as a basis for orphan status, sponsors or applicants requesting orphan status for their drug(s) tend to make the following common mistakes in attempting to meet the requirements for orphan designation.

- dividing a subset of patients with a common disease condition, which is not medically plausible
- orphan requests with words such as severe, refractory, metastatic, late-stage, acute or chronic, which may raise questions on subset issues
- request for an already approved drug on the basis of a major contribution to the patient
- using incidence instead of prevalence for a disease condition
- inadequate scientific rationale

Multiple Applications for the Same Orphan Indication

Once a drug has been granted orphan status, that status cannot be requested for the same drug by another sponsor for the same indication. However, it is possible that more than one sponsor may receive orphan drug designation for the same rare disease or condition. For each new or different drug intended for the same or a different indication, sponsors must file a complete request for the designation.

Increase in Population and Its Impact on Orphan Status of a Drug

In general, if orphan drug status was granted for the treatment of a disease or condition estimated to affect fewer than 200,000 people in the US, the status of the drug application holds. This can be illustrated by multiple sclerosis (MS). Although MS is no longer considered a rare disease because its prevalence is now known to exceed 250,000 in the US, orphan drug regulations regarding marketing exclusivity still apply to the beta-interferons, since they were granted orphan drug status for the treatment of MS at a time when the disease was estimated to affect fewer than 200,000 in the US.

Public Knowledge of Orphan Designations

When a drug receives orphan status, the only information available from FDA is the drug's chemical name, trade name, date of designation, orphan designation, sponsor name and address and marketing exclusivity date (typically the date of NDA or BLA approval). None of the scientific rationale used to define a medically plausible subset of patients is revealed.

Pharmacogenomics, Disease Stratification and Potential Orphan Status

The use of genetic profiling techniques could benefit drug development and clinical testing, as this would allow subjects to be included in or excluded from certain clinical trials. Screening subjects with pharmacogenomic approaches could potentially indicate whether the drug is effective, ineffective or unsuitable for an individual. This methodology also opens the door to include subjects selectively in a clinical trial, provided they are screened for a known genetic diversity or genetic composition. This process is called patient stratification, and could make clinical trials smaller, faster and more cost-effective. When a pharmacogenomic approach is effective, it has the potential to reduce overall drug development costs. The consequences of disease stratification could create a much smaller market for an individual drug that may reach "orphan" levels. As the field expands and the understanding of disease stratification deepens, it may be possible that the patient population for a certain disease can be stratified into a smaller subset reaching orphan levels, based upon genetic variants.

ODA has been very successful, resulting in new drugs for more than 200 rare diseases, and FDA is actively encouraging drug companies to pursue pharmacogenomic approaches to more of the 7,000 remaining rare diseases identified by NIH.[8] However, from a regulatory perspective, pharmacogenomics could drastically change disease classification schemes and basic assumptions about what constitutes a rare disease.[9,10] It is possible that diverse rare diseases may turn out to share molecular genetic disease processes that are amenable to the same drug. Additional indications for the drug that are driven by a common set of genes likely will be found. At some point, understanding these mechanisms could lead to a redefinition of rare disease.[11]

Exclusivity and Patents

Another amendment to the act changed the exclusivity provision and made orphan status available to both patentable and unpatentable drugs.[12] The 1985 amendment extended exclusivity to orphan drugs having either of two characteristics:

1. no use or product patent issued
2. no use patent issued and an expired product patent

The biotechnology industry, where it has been known for some products to take as long as four to six years to receive patent approval, while the approval of others are delayed by legal challenges, has benefited from the exclusivity provision. Biotech drugs with orphan status may use the seven-year exclusivity provision as a surrogate patent. The *Food and Drug Administration Modernization Act* of 1997 (*FDAMA*)[13] extended exclusivity to an additional six months for orphan drugs for a pediatric indication.

There are, however, important differences between patent protection and *ODA*'s seven-year exclusivity provision. The seven years of marketing exclusivity for patented products run concurrently with any outstanding patent. Further, the protected use is only for the rare disease approved. Patent protection is broader; a product patent covers an active ingredient and all its uses. A second company cannot receive approval for any use of the active ingredient until the patent has expired. Use patents and process patents similarly provide broad protection. Exclusivity differs from patent protection, which gives the patent holder exclusive rights, regardless of whether patent rights are exercised. Under the exclusivity provisions, during the seven-year period that begins with the product's approval, a second company can receive approval to market the product for a common disease or some other rare one (provided the patent has expired).[14] The sponsor may grant other manufacturers or distributors the privilege of marketing the orphan product; however, a written request for the privilege must be submitted to FDA. A firm can lose its research and development investment while studying an orphan product because a second firm attains market approval first. To minimize these risks, companies may file cross-licensing agreements or shared exclusivity for the same or different indications. If a sponsor fails to make adequate quantities of the orphan product available, it may lose exclusivity. The sponsor also may relinquish orphan drug status, as with the AIDS drug didanosine (DDI).

Postapproval Conditions

Once an orphan product is on the market, there are no constraints against a physician prescribing it to treat other diseases. However, a sponsor may advertise the product only for those rare indications approved by FDA.[15] Under this mechanism, the drug may have a market much broader than expected for orphan drug status. It is possible for an orphan drug to achieve "blockbuster" status without losing orphan drug status. Also, the seven-year market exclusivity immunizes the sponsor from market competition and provides no price controls. Finally, a company can divide a projected market of more than 200,000 patients into several subsets and attempt to achieve orphan approval for each indication. FDA does scrutinize orphan drug applications for evidence of "arbitrary subsets" (medically implausible) and can issue penalties, including revocation of orphan

drug status. Although many legislative attempts have tried to close *ODA* loopholes (e.g., by capping profits), none has become law.

Orphan drug development is a focus of organizations such as the National Organization of Rare Disorders (NORD), a grassroots cooperative of more than 100 non-profit agencies,[16] and the Pharmaceutical Research and Manufacturers of America's (PhRMA) Commission on Drugs for Rare Diseases, which seeks promising orphan candidates to bring to the attention of potential sponsors.

Orphan Drugs Globally

The impact of the *Orphan Drug Act* on the international stage has been significant. Japan adopted an orphan drug system in 1993 (offering 10 years of market exclusivity), followed by Australia in 1998 (which offers five years of market exclusivity). The most recent entrant in the orphan drug arena is the EU.

European Union (EU)

In 2000, the EU passed its first legislation specifically for orphan drugs, Regulation (EC) 141/2000 of the European Parliament and the Council on orphan medicinal products.[17,18]

Under the EU *Orphan Medicinal Product Regulation*, a rare disease is defined as affecting no more than five in 10,000 people. The legislation offers protocol assistance, 10 years of market exclusivity and full or partial tax credit.[19,20]

However, unlike the US, the product must requalify as an orphan product at the time of submission of the marketing application in order to qualify for this benefit. The legislation is overseen by the European Medicines Agency (EMA), which has the authority to award orphan status and also approves drugs for marketing. However, each Member State has responsibility for making the drug available and dealing with reimbursement issues.

The EMA's Committee for Orphan Medicinal Products examines all applications for orphan designation and advises the European Commission on the establishment and development of policies on orphan medicinal products in the EU, as well as drawing up detailed guidelines and working internationally on matters relating to orphan medicinal products.

Unified US-EU Application

Due to their relatively small numbers, patients with a rare disease are often distributed around the world, which requires a global regulatory strategy. The introduction of a joint US-EU orphan drug application is the first step in simplifying the procedure. FDA and EMA are working together on other orphan development initiatives, possibly one for therapeutics for tropical diseases.[21]

Due to this globalization, a sponsor may wish to submit an application for orphan designation in both the EU and the US. In such cases, the sponsor may apply for orphan designation of the same product for the same use in both jurisdictions by using the "Common EMA/FDA Application form for Orphan Medicinal Product Designation." However, when submitting to FDA, the application must comply with the format defined by FDA regulations even when using this form.

Humanitarian Device Exemptions
History

Although the *Orphan Drug Act* does not specifically mention medical devices, the *Safe Medical Devices Act* of 1990 (*SMDA*) does include orphan medical devices. In 1996, FDA promulgated a final rule describing the orphan devices process that subsequently was codified in 21 CFR 814, Subpart H.13.[22] OOPD is responsible for granting orphan designation to devices known as humanitarian use devices (HUDs), which must meet the following criteria:

- device treats or diagnoses a disease in fewer than 4,000 patients per year in the US
- no comparable FDA-approved therapy exists for the proposed indication
- evidence is provided that the applicant could not otherwise bring the device to market

Incentives to manufacturers for developing HUDs are identical to those for developing orphan drugs.

Process

The Humanitarian Device Exemption (HDE) process[23,24] involves two steps:

1. The applicant must request and obtain HUD designation from OOPD. The application's required contents are outlined in 21 CFR 814.102. Among other requirements, the application must precisely define the proposed indication for use. If the applicant proposes using the device for a limited subset of a larger group of patients suffering from a more common disease or condition, the application must contain evidence that the subset is medically plausible and justify the proposed limitation. The application also must document, with appended authoritative references, that the rare disease affects fewer than 4,000 individuals per year in the US. OOPD has 45 days to consider the HUD request and render an approval, disapproval or request for more information.
2. Once the applicant receives HUD designation, it must submit an HDE application to the Office of Device Evaluation (ODE) at the Center for Devices and Radiological Health (CDRH). Contents of the HDE application are set forth in 21 CFR 814.104. The purpose of the application is to assist ODE reviewers in understanding why the device deserves the HDE. One major difference between a Premarket

Approval Application (PMA) and one for an HDE is that the HDE is exempt from the PMA effectiveness requirements, unless specifically requested by FDA. Otherwise, effectiveness would be required under Sections 514 and 515 of the *FD&C Act*. However, the application must contain an explanation of probable device benefits and demonstrate that those probable benefits outweigh the risk of injury or illness from use. If the intended price of the device is more than $250, the HDE application must include verification that the amount charged does not exceed the costs of research, development, fabrication and distribution per either of two statements:

- report by a certified public accountant
- attestation by a responsible individual of the applicant organization

FDA makes a threshold determination as to whether the HDE application is sufficiently complete to permit substantive review. The agency can refuse to file for any of four reasons:

1. application is incomplete
2. comparable device already is available to treat or diagnose the disease or condition
3. application contains an untrue statement or omits material information
4. HDE lacks a statement of certification or disclosure, or both, as required by 21 CFR 54

ODE has 75 days to review the application and send the applicant an approval order, an approvable letter, a nonapprovable letter or an order denying approval.

Labeling

HDE labeling requirements match those for PMA-approved devices in 21 CFR 814.20(b)(10). In addition, the labeling of an approved HDE device must bear the following statement: "Humanitarian Device. Authorized by Federal law for use in the treatment [or diagnosis] of [specify disease or condition]. The effectiveness of this device for this use has not been demonstrated."

Distribution

The HDE holder is responsible for ensuring that an HUD is administered only at hospitals or institutions that have an Institutional Review Board (IRB) constituted and acting in accordance with 21 CFR 56. The initial use of the HUD must be approved by the IRB and the IRB must provide continuing oversight of the use of the HUD. The IRB does not have to review and approve each individual use of the HUD. Instead, the IRB may approve the use of the device in general for groups of patients meeting certain criteria or for devices under a treatment protocol. The IRB may specify limitations on the use of the device based on any criterion it deems appropriate. Unless the data are intended for use in a clinical investigation, informed consent is not required because an HDE provides temporary marketing approval and does not constitute research or an investigation.

Additional Indication(s)

Once an HUD is approved, the applicant may seek different indications for use by requesting and obtaining HUD designation and filing a new, original HDE for the new indication. The new, original HDE may incorporate by reference any information or data previously submitted to the agency under the previous HDE.

Quality System

An approved HDE is subject to the same Quality System Regulations (QSR) in 21 CFR 820 and postapproval requirements as a PMA-approved product. The latter may include the following:

- restriction of the device's sale, use and distribution (prescription only)
- Phase 4 studies to evaluate the device's safety, effectiveness and reliability for its intended use; in the HDE-approval order, FDA states the study conditions, which include:
  - o a reason or purpose
  - o number of patients to be evaluated
  - o reports required
- prominent display in the labeling (and advertising/promotional materials) of warnings, hazards or precautions important for safe and effective device use, including any patient information
- inclusion of identification codes on the device or its labeling
- records pertaining to patient tracing if such information is necessary to protect public health
- maintenance of records for specified periods of time and record organization and indexing into identifiable files to enable FDA to determine whether there is reasonable assurance of the device's safety or effectiveness
- periodic reports in accordance with the HDE approval order, contents of which are described in 21 CFR 814.126(b)(1)
- batch testing of the device
- Medical Device Reports (MDRs) submitted to FDA in compliance with 21 CFR 803 (also should be submitted to the IRB of record)
- records of the facility names and addresses to which the HUD has been shipped and all correspondence with reviewing IRBs

Revocation

Once FDA approves a PMA or clears a 510(k) for treating (or diagnosing) the same disease or condition, the HDE can be revoked.

Misbranding

The HDE holder cannot promote the device for any patient population other than the target population for the indicated HDE use. Promotion to groups other than the target population constitutes misbranding. In addition, an HDE holder cannot imply that its device is effective for the indicated use because there is no requirement to submit clinical effectiveness data in the HDE. Through April 2011, 51 devices had been approved under the HDE program.

Summary

- Regulatory agencies throughout the world attempt to encourage orphan product and humanitarian device sponsors through incentives, exclusivities and special postapproval conditions.
- Patients with rare diseases/conditions or infrequent need for treatment may benefit from using orphan products or humanitarian devices.

References

1. *Orphan Drug Act*, Public Law 97-414, 4 January 1983.
2. Ibid.
3. *Orphan Drug Amendments* of 1988, Public Law 100-290, 18 April 1988.
4. *Health Promotion and Disease Prevention Amendments* of 1984, Public Law No. 98–551, 30 October 1984).
5. Op cit 1.
6. Tankosic T. "Orphan Drug Development: commercial strategies flourish." *SCRIP* "Drug Market Developments," 2008; 19(5)
7. *Orphan Drug Amendments* of 1985, Public Law 99-91, 99, 15 August 1985.
8. The Office of Rare Diseases at the NIH maintains a list of rare diseases and conditions on its website.
9. Maher PD and Haffner M. "Orphan Drug Designation and Pharmacogenomics: Options and Opportunities." *BioDrugs*, 20, no. 2 (2006): pp. 71–79.
10. Shah J. "Economic and regulatory considerations in pharmacogenomics for drug licensing and healthcare." *Nature Biotechnology*, 21, no. 7 (July 2003): pp. 747–753.
11. Tucker L. "Pharmacogenomics: A Primer for Policymakers" National Health Policy Forum, Background Paper, 28 January 2008.
12. Op cit 7.

13. *Food and Drug Administration Modernization Act* of 1997.
14. Op cit 7.
15. 21 CFR 312.2.
16. Myers AS. "Orphan Drugs: The Current Situation in the United States, Europe and Asia." *Drug Information Journal* 31 (1997): 101–104.
17. Regulation (EC) 141/2000 of the European Parliament and of the Council of 16 December 1999 on orphan medicinal products. *Official Journal of the European Communities* (22 January 2000): 1–5.
18. Commission Regulation (EC) 847/2000 of 27 April 2000 laying down the provisions for implementation of the criteria for designation of a medicinal product as an orphan medicinal product and definitions of the concepts "similar medicinal product' and 'clinical superiority," *Official Journal of the European Communities* (28 April 2000): 5.
19. *SCRIP* "Drug Market Developments," 2008; 19(5).
20. 21 CFR 814, Subpart H.
21. Op cit 19.
22. Op cit 20.
23. FDA. "Final Rule: Medical Devices; Humanitarian Use of Devices," *Federal Register* 61 (1996): 33232.
24. FDA. "Final Rule: Medical Devices; Humanitarian Use of Devices," *Federal Register* 63 (1998): 59217–59222.

Reading List

Carter MJ and Bennett AR. "Developments in Orphan Drugs." *Food, Drug, Cosmetic Law Journal* 44 (1989): 627–632.

Clissold DB. "Prescription for the Orphan Drug Act: The Impact of the FDA's 1992 Regulations and the Latest Congressional Proposals for Reform," *Food and Drug Law Journal* 50 (1995): 125–147.

Finke MJ. "Orphan Products and the Pharmaceutical Industry." *Clinical Research Practices and Drug Regulatory Affairs* (1983): 19–25.

Grossman DB. "The Orphan Drug Act: Adoption or Foster Care." *Food, Drug, Cosmetic Law Journal* 39 (1984): 128–132.

Henkel J. "Orphan Products: New Hope for People With Rare Disorders," *FDA Consumer* (18 June 1994): 17–20.

Levitt JA and Kelsey JV. "The Orphan Drug Regulations and Related Issues," *Food and Drug Law Journal* 48 (1993): 526–530.

Shah J. "Economic and regulatory considerations in pharmacogenomics for drug licensing and healthcare". 2003 Nature Publishing Group, http://www.nature.com/naturebiotechnology

Shulman SR et. al. "Implementation of the Orphan Drug Act: 1983–1991," *Food and Drug Law Journal* 47 (1992): 363–401.

Tucker L. "Pharmacogenomics: A Primer for Policymakers." National Health Policy Forum, Background Paper, 28 January 2008.

Blood and
Blood Products

By Sue Sutton-Jones

Objectives

- Understand FDA strategies to protect the blood supply
- Understand compliance regulations for blood and blood products
- Understand requirements for a biologics license
- Learn about biological product deviation reporting

Laws, Regulations and Guidelines Covered in This Chapter

- *Public Health Service Act* of 1944 (*PHS Act*), Section 351
- *Federal Food, Drug and Cosmetic Act* of 1938 (*FD&C Act*)
- 21 CFR 201.25 Bar code label requirements
- 21 CFR 211.100 Written procedures; deviations
- 21 CFR 601 Licensing requirements
- 21 CFR 606 Current Good Manufacturing Practice for blood and blood components
- 21 CFR 607 Establishment registration and product listing for manufacturers of human blood and blood products
- 21 CFR 610 General biologics products standards
- 21 CFR 640 Additional standards for human blood and blood products
- 21 CFR 803 Medical device reporting
- 21 CFR 820 Quality system regulation

Introduction

The US Food and Drug Administration (FDA) is responsible for ensuring the safety of the US blood supply. This responsibility includes regulation of the collection of both blood and blood components, such as clotting factors used for transfusion or manufacture of drugs. FDA's authority for the review and approval of blood products resides in Section 351 of the *Public Health Service Act of 1944* (*PHS Act*) and the regulation of these products resides under the *Federal Food, Drug, and Cosmetic Act* of 1938 (*FD&C Act*). The Center for Biologics Evaluation and Research (CBER) is the center within FDA that is responsible for the regulation of blood and blood products. CBER develops and enforces quality standards, performs inspection of blood establishments and monitors reports of deviations and adverse events.

Advisory Committees

There are three Advisory Committees related to blood and blood products. CBER manages the Blood Products Advisory Committee and Transmissible Spongiform Encephalopathies Advisory Committee. The Blood Products Advisory Committee advises the commissioner in discharging his or her responsibilities as they relate to helping ensure safe and effective biological products and related medical devices, and, as required, any other product for which FDA has regulatory responsibility.[1] The Transmissible Spongiform Encephalopathies Advisory Committee[2] advises the commissioner in discharging responsibilities as they relate to helping to ensure safe and effective products. This committee specifically focuses on the safety of products that may be at risk for transmission of spongiform encephalopathies having an impact on the public health. The third committee, the Advisory Committee on Blood Safety and Availability, is overseen by the Department of Health and Human Services (DHHS). This committee provides advice to the secretary and assistant secretary for health regarding research initiatives on diseases involving blood and blood products, and for issuing and enforcing regulations concerning the collection, preparation and distribution of these products, and regulations related to the transmission of communicable diseases.[3]

FDA Strategies for the Safety of Blood and Blood Products

HIV infection resulting from blood transfusion has been documented repeatedly since the first case report in late 1982. In the US, almost all cases are due to blood transfused before March 1985, when HIV antibody testing became available to screen donated blood.[4] Since that time, FDA has focused on ensuring the safety of blood and blood products by advocating the use of new technologies, standards, guidelines and strategies to minimize the risk of consumer exposure to unsafe products. Blood donors are required to answer risk-based questions geared to eliminate the potential for individuals from donating unsafe blood. These questions identify behaviors, transmittable disease states or exposure to certain geographic areas for periods of time that may indicate the donor is unsuitable. By regulation, unsuitable donors may be excluded from blood donations permanently or for a specified period. Further, all donated blood is tested for seven infectious diseases to help prevent unsuitable blood from being administered to patients.

In 1997, FDA initiated the Blood Action Plan.[5] The plan was approved by DHHS in 1998 and ensures coordination between CBER and FDA's Office of Regulatory Affairs (ORA), Office of Chief Counsel and Office of Policy, and the Centers for Disease Control (CDC), the National Institutes of Health (NIH) and the Centers for Medicare and Medicaid Services (CMS). The intent is to leverage scientific and regulatory information and actions to further elevate the safety of blood and blood products. The program focuses on improvement in seven areas:

1. updating blood regulations
2. reinventing blood regulations
3. emerging infectious diseases
4. ensuring compliance of plasma fractionation establishments
5. notification and lookback
6. FDA response to emergencies and Class I recalls affecting blood safety
7. monitoring and increasing the blood supply

Through this collaborative program, new or revised

standards, guidance documents and compliance programs are put into place. These documents can be found electronically at www.fda.gov/BiologicsBloodVaccines/GuidanceComplianceRegulatoryInformation/Guidances/Blood/default.htm.

FDA's "Five Layer Approach"

The efforts of FDA to improve and promote the safety of blood and blood products through the Blood Action Plan, leveraging technology and science, has resulted in a key systematic program. This program has a "five layer" approach to ensure the safety of the blood supply and products derived from blood or blood components. These five layers create a seamless safety system from the initial collection of blood at the donor center all the way through to distribution and use of a blood product.

1. Donor Screening

The first layer begins with donor screening. Potential donors must answer questions about their health and risk factors. Transmission of HIV and other blood-borne viruses can occur during transfusion of blood components (e.g., whole blood, packed red cells, fresh-frozen plasma, cryoprecipitate and platelets) derived from the blood of an infected individual. Depending upon the production process used, blood products derived from pooled plasma can also transmit HIV and other viruses, but recombinant clotting factors cannot. Donor screening establishes a donor's eligibility to donate blood and blood components by documenting that the individual is free of any diseases transmissible by blood transfusion. This process must be done on the day of the donation (21 CFR 640.3(a) and 640.63(a)).

After completing the questionnaire at the donation site, the potential donor is interviewed by a trained healthcare professional about his medical history and given a physical examination. Donors may be temporarily deferred from donating blood for what may seem to be minor illnesses, such as a fever, cold, cough or sore throat, or if they are taking certain drugs. These precautions are necessary to prevent any unintentional transmission of a disease. Once the donor has recovered and has no symptoms of the minor illness, he may donate. Permanent exclusion from donating is covered by a specific guidance citing risk factors such as human immunodeficiency virus (HIV) infection, male homosexual activity since 1977, or a history of intravenous drug use or viral hepatitis. Individuals who respond "yes" to any questions about such risk factors are not allowed to donate blood for injectable use. In certain circumstances, to avoid being singled out as a transmission risk in the volunteer setting, a volunteer donor may be allowed to donate blood and indicate by a bar code that the unit should not be used.

2. Donor Testing

The second layer ensuring blood supply safety is testing of each unit of blood collected. Each unit or bag of donor blood must be tested for hepatitis B, hepatitis C, syphilis, HIV 1 and 2, or human T-lymphotropic virus (HTLV) Types I and II. Any donor who is positive for one of the seven diagnostic tests above will be placed on a deferred donor list and the unit collected will be destroyed. In some situations, such as donation of platelets, testing for CMV (cytomegalovirus) may be performed; however, this test is not routine for all blood collections.

3. Donor Lists

The third layer of control is the requirement that all blood donation establishments keep a current list of deferred donors and check donor names against that list each time a person offers to donate blood. Any person whose name appears on the list may not donate. These lists are shared among blood donation establishments to ensure that an individual who has been identified as a risk for transmission of infectious disease cannot avoid detection by going to another establishment.

4. Quarantine of Untested Blood

Blood products collected must be appropriately stored and are not released for use until all testing has been completed and the information has been checked for accuracy. Whenever a repeat donor has a repeatedly reactive screening test for HBsAg, anti-HBc, anti-HCV or anti-HTLV-I, blood establishments should promptly, within 72 hours if possible, identify and quarantine within-date blood and blood components in inventory from prior collections, extending back five years. For a test that is repeatedly reactive and there is a record available of the donor's last negative test results from a licensed screening test, the quarantine of prior collections should only extend back to 12 months before such a test. In addition, blood establishments should promptly request consignees of such products to immediately quarantine all previously distributed products extending back five years or 12 months before the donor's last negative test results from licensed serological tests. Quarantined units should be destroyed or appropriately labeled either as, 1) "biohazard" and "Not for use for transfusion or further manufacturing into injectable products," in the case of products originating from donors who subsequently test repeatedly reactive for HBsAg or anti-HCV, or as, 2) "biohazard" and "Not for use for transfusion," in the case of products originating from donors who subsequently test repeatedly reactive for anti-HBc or anti-HTLV-I.

5. Deviations and Nonconformances

Lastly, blood establishments must investigate any deviations where the safeguards cited in items 1–4 were ineffective, and must correct the system deficiencies that allowed the failure to occur. Licensed establishments must report to FDA any manufacturing problems, errors or accidents that may affect the safety, purity or potency of their distributed finished products using a Biological Product Deviation Report or BPDR. On 7 November 2000, FDA published a final rule to amend the requirements for reporting errors and accidents during the manufacture of products. The rule amended the regulation at 21 CFR 600.14 for licensed biological products, and added a requirement at 21 CFR 606.171 applicable to all manufacturers of blood and blood components. The amended regulation at 21 CFR 600.14 and the new regulation at 21 CFR 606.171 require the reporting of any event associated with manufacturing, to include testing, processing, packing, labeling or storage, or with the holding or distribution of a licensed biological product or a blood or a blood component, in which the safety, purity, or potency of a distributed product may be affected. A manufacturer is required to report to CBER's Office of Compliance and Biologics Quality (OCBQ) as soon as possible, but not to exceed 45 calendar days from the date of discovery of information reasonably suggesting a reportable event has occurred. To facilitate reporting, FDA has developed a standardized reporting format that may be used for electronic or hard copy submissions. Directions for completing and mailing the forms are provided by CBER and can be accessed at www.fda.gov/downloads/AboutFDA/ ReportsManualsForms/Forms/UCM061463.pdf.

CBER's Direct Recall Classification (DRC) program provides blood and plasma establishments the opportunity to electronically report recall-related information directly to CBER. The standardized reporting established for the submission of electronic Biological Product Deviation Reports (eBPDRs) has been expanded to include the collection of Additional Information (AI) necessary for recall classification purposes. Electronically submitted eBPDRs that represent a potential recall situation and contain 18 or fewer components are candidates for DRC. Currently, for recall classification purposes, eBPDRs that contain more than 18 components require collection of recall documentation through the local district office. Healthcare professionals and consumers may voluntarily report adverse events through the FDA MedWatch program or through the FDA Consumer Complaint Coordinator in their geographic area.

"Lookback" Procedures

"Practices for Blood and Blood Components; Notification of Consignees Receiving Blood and Blood Components at Increased Risk for Transmitting HIV Infection," published in the *Federal Register* of 30 June 1993 (58 FR 34962) establishes the requirement for "lookback" procedures for all blood and blood products within a 90-day implementation timeframe. The short implementation phase emphasizes the importance of being able to address post-donation information and donors whose status may change over time. Analogous procedures related to donor screening for HIV antigen and to post-donation information on increased risk of Creutzfeldt- Jacob Disease (CJD) were recommended in three memoranda issued on 8 August 1995, entitled "Recommendations for Donor Screening with a Licensed Test for HIV-1 Antigen," "Disposition of Products Derived from Donors Diagnosed with, or at Known High Risk for, Creutzfeldt-Jakob Disease" and "Precautionary Measures to Further Reduce the Possible Risk of Transmission of Creutzfeldt-Jakob Disease by Blood and Blood Products." As a result, all licensed and registered blood establishments must implement lookback procedures and are audited by FDA to ensure that they are functional at each inspection. Under a lookback procedure, blood establishments retrieve and quarantine units previously collected from a donor who originally tested negative for HIV or another infectious disease, but subsequently tested positive at a later donation. As part of the investigation, the blood establishment will conduct additional testing on a current sample of the donor's blood to confirm the positive result. If the results are confirmed, previously donated units from that individual cannot be used in transfusions or manufacture of injectable products, and anyone receiving such units must be notified. Further guidance for lookback procedures may be found on the CBER website, *Guidance for Industry: "Lookback" for Hepatitis C Virus (HCV): Product Quarantine, Consignee Notification, Further Testing, Product Disposition, and Notification of Transfusion Recipients Based on Donor Test Results Indicating Infection with HCV* and Memorandum to All Registered Blood and Plasma Establishments: "Recommendations for the Quarantine and Disposition of Units from Prior Collections from Donors with Repeatedly Reactive Screening Tests for Hepatitis B Virus (HBV), Hepatitis C Virus (HCV) and Human T-Lymphotropic Virus Type I (HTLV-I)," 19 July 1996.

Notification Process for Transfusion Related Fatalities and Donation Related Deaths

21 CFR 606.170(b) requires that facilities notify CBER's OCBQ as soon as possible after confirming a complication of blood collection or transfusion to be fatal. The collecting facility is to report donor fatalities, and the compatibility testing facility is to report recipient fatalities. The regulation also requires the reporting facility to submit a report of the investigation within seven days after the fatality. In addition, 21 CFR 640.73 requires notification by telephone as soon as possible if a source plasma donor has a fatal reaction which, in any way, may be associated with plasmapheresis.

Software Used to Control the Collection Process in Blood Banks

Blood establishment computer software used to manage

donor registries, record testing of blood and storing of donor records and other data that enable lookback procedures and accurate donor lists is regulated by FDA as a device and is subject to a 510(k). Facilities that manufacture and distribute these software products are subject to the device provisions of the *FD&C Act* and FDA's current Good Manufacturing Practice (CGMP) regulations for devices at 21CFR 820, including establishment registration, product listing, premarket notification or approval, and MDR regulations at 21 CFR 803. As part of the clearance process, all blood establishment computer systems will be evaluated for evidence of validation (21 CFR 606.160; 211.68(b)) that computer programs, especially those dealing with processing, labeling and distribution of blood and blood components, consistently perform as required and within pre-established limits. Blood establishment computer systems and hardware are considered by FDA to be a major concern because a failure or latent flaw could directly result in death or serious injury to the patient and, therefore, require comprehensive information to be validated and filed prior to use. In addition to GMP requirements, blood establishment computer software must also protect the confidentiality of sensitive medical information about the donor from external and internal inquiries. Changes to the software and database should only be made by authorized person(s) and traceable to the time and person making the change so that the integrity and reproducibility of data are assured. A high level of data integrity must be established and demonstrated (21 CFR 211.68(b)).

FDA has taken this rigorous approach in regulating blood banking software to further enhance the seamless approach to blood safety and quality discussed earlier.

Blood Establishment Registration (BER)

All owners or operators of establishments that manufacture blood products are required to register with FDA, pursuant to Section 510 of the *FD&C Act*, unless they are exempt under 21 CFR 607.65. A list of every blood product manufactured, prepared or processed for commercial distribution must be submitted with the registration documentation. Products must be registered and listed within five days of beginning operation, and annually between November 15 and December 31. Blood product listings must be updated in June and December each year. Form FDA 2830, Blood Establishment Registration and Product Listing, is used to submit registration and product listing information to the agency.

Section 351(a) of the *PHS Act*, as amended 21 November 1997 (the *Food and Drug Administration Modernization Act* (*FDAMA*); Public Law 105-115), mandates in part that no person shall introduce or deliver for introduction into interstate commerce any biological product unless a biologics license is in effect for that product. In the past, both an establishment license (one per legal entity) and product license (one for each approved product) have been issued. However, as of 19 February 1998 (effective date of *FDAMA*), biologics license certificates will be issued for all new biological products and when existing licenses are reissued.

Barcode Labeling for Blood and Blood Products

The requirement for barcodes on certain products is another step in assuring blood safety by preventing mistakes in the handling of blood products. The intent of FDA's barcode rule is to reduce medication errors, including transfusion errors in the hospital setting. The regulation requiring barcode labeling that is machine readable for blood and blood components intended for transfusion is 21 CFR 606.121(c)(13). This requirement applies to all blood establishments that manufacture, process, repack or relabel blood and blood components, including hospital transfusion services that pool or aliquot blood components. FDA also requires that specific human drug and biological product labels contain a barcode consisting of, at a minimum, the National Drug Code (NDC) number. This regulation can be found in 21 CFR 201.25.

Inspection of Blood Establishments

FDA began conducting inspections of establishments that manufacture blood or blood products for human use in 1972 under Section 351 of the *PHS Act*. The purpose of the inspections is to "ensure that blood establishments manufacture biological products that are safe, pure, potent and have the quality they represent and the establishment manufactures them according to Current Good Manufacturing Practice (CGMP) for Blood and Blood Component regulations and applicable standards."

In 1997, FDA established Team Biologics, a group of specialized investigators who conduct routine and CGMP follow-up inspections of manufacturers of biologic products regulated by CBER. The Team Biologics Operation Group, made up of senior managers from ORA and CBER, provides guidance and support for Team Biologics and supplies a forum for setting policy and discussing regulatory issues.

The inspection strategy takes a system-based approach, identifying five elements in blood establishment operations required to achieve the five layers of protection for the blood supply:

- Quality Assurance System—various planned activities providing confidence that all procedures/processes that influence product manufacture and overall quality are monitored to ensure they are working as expected (21 CFR 211.100 and 606.100)
- Donor (Suitability) Eligibility System—the system that protects donor safety, determines a donor's suitability for blood collection (including donor deferral from history screening and/or testing), notifies donors of unsuitability for donation and, where acceptable to FDA, permits donor re-entry (21 CFR610.40, 610.41, 640.63, 640.65)
- Product Testing System—the system(s) that tests for communicable diseases, blood grouping and typing, and cross-matches blood for transfusion by direct testing or electronically (21 CFR 606.40)
- Quarantine/Inventory Management System—the system(s) pertaining to product storage, distribution and retrieval, quarantine and distribution (release for use or destruction) (21 CFR 606.60)
- Production and Processing System—process controls in the manufacture of specific blood and blood components and equipment quality control, calibration and maintenance (21 CFR 606.160)

The inspection of each element should review:
- the accuracy, availability and appropriateness of procedures
- the adequacy of qualifications, training and number of personnel for the operations
- the appropriateness of the facility for the operations and the adequacy of its maintenance
- equipment maintenance to ensure it will perform as intended
- record maintenance to ensure traceability of steps and that a complete history of work performed is provided

Routine inspections are required by statute and generally occur biennially. They may be conducted at two levels:
- Level 1—a comprehensive review of all elements employed at the establishment
- Level 2—a review of the quality assurance system plus two others; eligibility is based upon favorable inspectional history, recent Level 1 inspection and no evidence of unfavorable trends in monitoring data (recalls, deviation reports, fatality reports, etc.)

Summary
- FDA is responsible for ensuring the safety of the US blood supply and regulates the collection of blood and blood components such as clotting factors used for transfusion or manufacture of drugs.
- FDA's authority for the review and approval of blood products resides in Section 351 of the *PHS Act* and the regulation of these products resides under the *FD&C Act*.
- All owners or operators of establishments that manufacture blood products are required to register with FDA, pursuant to section 510 of the *FD&C Act*, unless they are exempt under 21 CFR 607.65.

- FDA has a "five layer" approach to assuring the safety of the blood supply and products derived from blood or blood components. These five layers overlap from the initial collection of blood at the donor center all the way though to the distributor of a blood product.
- All licensed and registered blood establishments must implement lookback procedures.
- FDA regulates blood establishment computer software as medical devices.

References

1. Blood Products Advisory Committee Charter, www.fda.gov/AdvisoryCommittees/ CommitteesMeetingMaterials/ BloodVaccinesandOtherBiologics/ BloodProductsAdvisoryCommittee/ucm121602. htm. Accessed 29 April 2011.
2. Transmissible Spongiform Encephalopathies Advisory Committee Charter, www.fda.gov/ AdvisoryCommittees/Committees MeetingMaterials/BloodVaccinesandOther BiologicsTransmissibleSpongiform EncephalopathiesAdvisoryCommittee/ucm129558. htm. Accessed 29 April 2011.
3. Advisory Committee on Blood Safety and Availability, www.hhs.gov/ash/bloodsafety/ advisorycommittee/charter/charter_acbsa.pdf. Accessed 17 May 2011.
4. Peterman TA, Jaffe HW, Feorino PM, Getchell JP, Warfield DT, Haverkos HW, Stoneburner RL, Curran JW. Transfusion-associated acquired immunodeficiency syndrome in the United States. *JAMA*. 1985 Nov 22–29;254(20):2913–7.
5. CBER Blood Action Plan. FDA website. http:// www.hhs.gov/ash/bloodsafety/miscellaneous/blood_ action_plan.pdf. Accessed 29 April 2011.

Recommended Reading

21 CFR 600 - 680

Guideline for Quality Assurance in Blood Establishments (July 1995).

Compliance Program Manual 7342.001 "Inspection of Licensed and Unlicensed Blood Banks, Brokers, Reference Laboratories, and Contractors" & 7342.002 "Inspection of Source Plasma Establishments."

Guidance for Industry: Implementation of Acceptable Full-Length Donor History Questionnaire and Accompanying Materials for Use in Screening Donors of Blood and Blood Components (October 2006).

FDA memorandum, "Revised Recommendations for the Prevention of Human Immunodeficiency Virus (HIV) Transmission by Blood and Blood Products" (23 April 1992). Available at www. fda.gov/downloads/BiologicsBloodVaccines/ GuidanceComplianceRegulatoryInformation/ OtherRecommendationsforManufacturers/ MemorandumtoBloodEstablishments/UCM062834. pdf. Accessed 29 April 2011.

FDA memorandum, "Revised Guideline for the Collection of Platelets, Pheresis" (7 October 1988). Available at www.fda. gov/downloads/BiologicsBloodVaccines/ GuidanceComplianceRegulatoryInformation/ OtherRecommendationsforManufacturers/ MemorandumtoBloodEstablishments/UCM063003. pdf. Accessed 29 April 2011.

Guidance for Industry: Changes to an Approved Application: Biological Products: Human Blood and Blood Components Intended for Transfusion or for Further Manufacture (July 2001). Available at www.fda.gov/BiologicsBloodVaccines/ GuidanceComplianceRegulatoryInformation/ Guidances/Blood/ucm076729.htm. Accessed 29 April 2011.

FDA Correspondence, Letter to Blood Establishment Computer Software Manufacturers (31 March 1994). Available at www.fda.gov/ downloads/BiologicsBloodVaccines/ GuidanceComplianceRegulatoryInformation/ OtherRecommendationsforManufacturers/ MemorandumtoBloodEstablishments/UCM062804. pdf. Accessed 29 April 2011.

FDA, *General Principles of Software Validation; Final Guidance for Industry and FDA Staff* (January 2002). Available at www.fda.gov/ MedicalDevices/DeviceRegulationandGuidance/ GuidanceDocuments/ucm085281.htm. Accessed 29 April 2011.

Guidance for Industry and FDA Staff: Guidance for the Content of Premarket Submissions for Software Contained in Medical Devices (11 May2005). http://www.fda.gov/ MedicalDevices/DeviceRegulationandGuidance/ GuidanceDocuments/ucm089543.htm. Accessed 29 April 2011.

Reviewer Guidance for a Premarket Notification Submission for Blood Establishment Computer Software (13 January 1997). http://www. fda.gov/downloads/BiologicsBloodVaccines/ GuidanceComplianceRegulatoryInformation/ OtherRecommendationsforManufacturers/ MemorandumtoBloodEstablishments/UCM062208. pdf. Accessed 29 April 2011.

Memorandum to All Registered Blood Establishments— Requirements for Computerization of Blood Establishments (8 September 1989). http://www. fda.gov/downloads/BiologicsBloodVaccines/

GuidanceComplianceRegulatoryInformation/
OtherRecommendationsforManufacturers/
MemorandumtoBloodEstablishments/UCM062883.
pdf. Accessed 29 April 2011.

Memorandum to All Registered Blood
Establishments - Recommendations for
Implementation of Computerization in Blood
Establishments (6 April 1988). http://www.
fda.gov/downloads/BiologicsBloodVaccines/
GuidanceComplianceRegulatoryInformation/
OtherRecommendationsforManufacturers/
MemorandumtoBloodEstablishments/UCM063007.
pdf. Accessed 29 April 2011.

*Guidance for Industry—Process Validation: General
Principles and Practices* (January 2011).
http://www.fda.gov/downloads/Drugs/
GuidanceComplianceRegulatoryInformation/
Guidances/UCM070336.pdf. Accessed 29 April
2011.

*Inspection Guide: Computerized Systems in Drug
Establishments* (February 1983). http://www.fda.gov/
ICECI/Inspections/InspectionGuides/ucm074869.
htm. Accessed 29 April 2011.

Chapter 24

Human Cell and Tissue Products

By Martha Wells, MPH, RAC

Objectives

- Review the history of human tissue regulations
- Explain the legal basis for human tissue regulation under the *Public Health Service Act*
- Identify the differences between 21 CFR 1270 and 21 CFR 1271
- Differentiate between tissue-related products that are regulated by FDA and those that are not
- Identify those factors that allow regulation of a cell or tissue without premarket approval
- Understand the key concepts of the tissue regulations
- Identify new policies for streamlined licensure of cord blood products regulated as biological products

Laws, Regulations and Guidances Covered in this Chapter

- *Public Health Service Act*, 42 USC 264
- *Federal Food, Drug, and Cosmetic Act* of 1938
- 21 CFR Part 1270 Human Tissue Intended for Transplantation
- 21 CFR Part 1271 Human Cells, Tissues, and Cellular and Tissue-Based Products
- *Guidance for Industry: Regulation of Human Cells, Tissues, and Cellular and Tissue-Based Products (HCT/Ps)—Small Entity Compliance Guide (August 2007)*
- *Guidance for Industry: Eligibility Determination for Donors of Human Cells, Tissues, and Cellular and Tissue-Based Products (HCT/PS) (August 2007)*
- *Final Guidance for Industry: Minimally Manipulated, Unrelated Allogeneic Placental/Umbilical Cord Blood Intended for Hematopoietic Reconstitution for Specified Indications (October 2009)*

History and Background of Human Cell and Tissue Regulation

In the early 1990s, the US Centers for Disease Control and Prevention (CDC) reported that human immunodeficiency virus (HIV) had been transmitted through transplantation of human tissue. Information was also reported that suggested potentially unsafe tissue was being imported into the US for transplantation into humans. Prompted by reports that potentially unsafe bone was being imported, the commissioner of food and drugs ordered an investigation, the results of which identified an immediate need to protect the public health from the transmission of HIV and Hepatitis B and C through transplantation of unsuitable tissue. Concerns that disease transmission could occur, coupled with information derived from these investigations, prompted the US Food and Drug Administration (FDA) to publish an interim final rule in December 1993 that specifically required testing for certain communicable diseases and screening of donors, and recordkeeping for certain human tissues intended for transplantation. This regulation, in Title 21 of the Code of Federal Regulations (CFR) Part 1270,[1] only applied to musculoskeletal, ocular and skin products from non-living human donors. A final rule was issued in July 1997.

21 CFR 1270

For 21 CFR 1270, FDA chose to regulate tissues under the legal authority of Section 361 of the *Public*

Health Service Act (*PHS Act*).[2] This section authorizes the surgeon general, with the approval of the secretary of the Department of Health and Human Services (DHHS), to make and enforce such regulations as judged necessary to prevent the introduction, transmission or spread of communicable diseases from foreign countries into the US or from state to state. Tissues and cells regulated only under the authority of Section 361 do not require premarket approval. Applicable regulations apply to these products regardless of intra- or interstate distribution.

21 CFR 1271

In 1997, FDA announced its plans for a more comprehensive, risk-based approach for regulation of human cells, tissues and cellular and tissue-based products (HCT/Ps).[3] The goals of FDA's new regulatory framework for cells and tissues were to:

- prevent unwitting use of contaminated tissues with the potential for transmitting infectious disease
- prevent improper handling or processing that might contaminate or damage tissues
- ensure that clinical safety and effectiveness are demonstrated for cells and tissues that are highly processed, used for purposes other than replacement or combined with non-tissue components, or that have systemic effects

Since that time, the agency has proposed and finalized three rules to implement this proposed approach. These requirements were also promulgated under Section 361 of the *PHS Act* and are codified as 21 CFR 1271.[4] They became effective in whole for cells and tissues recovered on or after 25 May 2005. General guidance has been published for establishments regulated under the new requirements (**Table 25-1**).[5]

Scope of Oversight

Human cells or tissues intended for implantation, transplantation, infusion or transfer into a human recipient are regulated as HCT/Ps. FDA's Center for Biologics Evaluation and Research (CBER) regulates HCT/Ps under 21 CFR 1270 and 1271.

CBER does not regulate the transplantation of vascularized human organ transplants such as kidney, liver, heart, lung or pancreas. The Health Resources Services Administration (HRSA) oversees the transplantation of vascularized human organs. HRSA is a separate agency within DHHS.

The following are considered HCT/Ps for purposes of FDA regulation:

- bone (including demineralized bone)
- ligaments
- tendons
- fascia

- cartilage
- ocular tissue (corneas and sclera)
- skin
- arteries and veins
- pericardium
- amniotic membrane
- dura mater
- heart valves
- hematopoietic stem/progenitor cells derived from peripheral and cord blood
- semen, oocytes and embryos

These are examples of articles that are not considered HCT/Ps:

- vascularized human organs for transplantation (HRSA)
- whole blood or blood components or blood derivative products (subject to 21 CFR 607 or 207)
- secreted or extracted human products such as milk, collagen and cell factors (however, semen is an HCT/P)
- minimally manipulated bone marrow for homologous use and not combined with another article (HRSA)
- products used in the manufacture of an HCT/P (ancillary products)
- cells, tissues and organs derived from animals other than humans (xenotransplantation)
- in vitro diagnostic products (defined in 21 CFR 809.3(a))
- blood vessels recovered with organs for use in organ transplantation (HRSA)

General Provisions (21 CFR 1271, Subpart A)

The criteria that form the foundation of FDA's tiered, risk-based approach to regulating HCT/Ps are found in 21 CFR 1271.10(a). HCT/Ps that meet all of these criteria are subject only to regulation under section 361 of the *PHS Act* and to the regulations in Part 1271. No premarket approval is required and compliance is determined at FDA inspection. These four criteria are:

- minimal manipulation
- intended for homologous use
- not combined with another article
- no systemic effect and not dependent on metabolic activity of living cells except if for autologous use, use in a first-degree or second-degree blood relative or for reproductive use

Important definitions for understanding 21 CFR 1271.10 include:

- "autologous use"—use in the individual from whom the cells or tissue were recovered

Table 25-1. 21 CFR 1271 at a Glance: Effective 25 May 2005

Tissue Rule	Issues Addressed
Establishment Registration and Listing	Applicability: types and uses of products that will be regulated by these rules; requirements for registering and listing HCT/Ps
Donor Eligibility	Requirements for donor screening and testing for relevant communicable disease agents and diseases
Current Good Tissue Practices (CGTP)	Manufacturing to ensure that HCT/Ps do not contain communicable disease agents; reporting; labeling and compliance/inspections

- "allogeneic use"—use in a first- or second-degree blood relative, including parents, children, siblings, aunts, uncles, nieces, nephews, first cousins, grandparents and grandchildren (important for hematopoietic stem cell therapies)
- "minimal manipulation"—for structural tissue, processing that does not alter the original relevant characteristics of the tissue relating to the tissue's utility for reconstruction, repair or replacement; for cells or nonstructural tissues, processing that does not alter the relevant biological characteristics of the cells or tissues
- "homologous use"—repair, reconstruction, replacement or supplementation of a recipient's cells or tissues with an HCT/P that performs the same basic function or functions in the recipient as in the donor

HCT/Ps that do not meet all four of the criteria in 21 CFR 1271.10(a) are regulated as drugs, devices and/or biological products under Section 351 of the *PHS Act* and the *Federal Food, Drug, and Cosmetic Act*. Thus, these HCT/Ps are subject to the regulations specific to drugs, biological products or medical devices, in addition to applicable sections of 21 CFR 1271. In other words, the 21 CFR 1271 requirements supplement the Good Manufacturing Practice (GMP) requirements for HCT/Ps regulated as biological products and the Quality Systems Regulation (QSR) requirements for HCT/Ps regulated as medical devices.

Examples of HCT/Ps that would be regulated under Section 351 are:
- autologous chondrocytes expanded *in vitro* for repair of cartilage defects
- allogeneic hematopoietic stem/progenitor cells, cord blood
- genetically modified cell therapy

Registration and Listing (21 CFR 1271, Subpart B)

Since 2001, FDA requires any establishment that manufactures HCT/Ps to register and submit a list of every HCT/P it manufactures within five days of beginning operation, and to re-register annually (see **Figure 25-1**).

All foreign establishments exporting HCT/Ps to the US must also register and list. For HCT/Ps, manufacture is defined as any or all steps in the recovery, processing, storage, labeling or distribution of any human cell or tissue, and the screening or testing of the cell or tissue donor. Establishment registration does not mean that an establishment is in compliance with all requirements. Compliance is determined at inspection. As of 2011, more than 2,500 establishments are registered with FDA. There are certain exceptions from registration in 21 CFR 1271.15. For example, establishments that use HCT/Ps solely for nonclinical scientific or educational purposes are not required to register and list.

Donor Eligibility (21 CFR 1271, Subpart C)

A donor eligibility determination based on donor screening and testing for relevant communicable disease agents and disease (RCDADs) is required for all donors of HCT/Ps, with some exceptions. Examples of donors not requiring donor eligibility determinations include autologous donors and sexually intimate donors of reproductive cells and tissues. HCT/Ps must not be administered until the donor has been determined to be eligible, with some exceptions.

Unless exempt, all donors must be tested for these RCDADs:
- HIV, type 1 and 2
- hepatitis B and C viruses
- *Treponema pallidum*

Donors of leukocyte-rich HCT/Ps such as hematopoietic stem/progenitor cells and semen must also be tested for cytomegalovirus and human t-lymphotropic virus, types I and II. In addition, reproductive donors must be tested for the sexually transmitted agents *Chlamydia trachomatis* and *Neisseria gonorrhea*.

Donors must be screened by reviewing their relevant medical records for risk factors for and clinical evidence of the RCDADs listed above and for communicable disease risks associated with xenotransplantation (live cells, tissue or organs from a nonhuman animal source) and human transmissible spongiform encephalopathy including Creutzfeldt-Jakob disease. In addition, they must

Figure 25-1. Form FDA 3356

DEPARTMENT OF HEALTH AND HUMAN SERVICES
FOOD AND DRUG ADMINISTRATION

ESTABLISHMENT REGISTRATION AND LISTING FOR HUMAN CELLS, TISSUES, AND CELLULAR AND TISSUE-BASED PRODUCTS (HCT/Ps)

(See reverse side for instructions)

See Instructions for OMB Statement. FORM APPROVED: OMB No. 0910-0543. Expiration Date: 8/31/10

1. REGISTRATION NUMBER (Field Establishment Identifier)

FEI

2. REASON FOR SUBMISSION
a. ☐ INITIAL REGISTRATION/LISTING
b. ☐ ANNUAL REGISTRATION/LISTING
c. ☐ CHANGE IN INFORMATION
d. ☐ INACTIVE

VALIDATION – FOR FDA USE ONLY

PART I – ESTABLISHMENT INFORMATION

3. OTHER FDA REGISTRATIONS
a. BLOOD FDA 2830   NO.
b. DEVICE FDA 2891   NO.
c. DRUG FDA 2656   NO.

4. PHYSICAL LOCATION *(Include legal name, number and street, city, state, country, and post office code.)*

a. PHONE:
b. ☐ SATELLITE RECOVERY ESTABLISHMENT (MANUFACTURING ESTABLISHMENT FEI NO. ____)
c. ☐ TESTING FOR MICRO-ORGANISMS ONLY

5. ENTER CORRECTIONS TO ITEM 4

6. MAILING ADDRESS OF REPORTING OFFICIAL *(Include institution name if applicable, number and street, city, state, country, and post office code.)*

a. PHONE:

7. ENTER CORRECTIONS TO ITEM 6

8. U.S. AGENT
a. E-MAIL ADDRESS:
b. PHONE:

9. REPORTING OFFICIAL'S SIGNATURE
a. TYPED NAME:
b. E-MAIL ADDRESS:
c. TITLE: d. DATE:

PART II – HCT / P INFORMATION

10. ESTABLISHMENT FUNCTIONS AND TYPES OF HCT / Ps

Types of HCT / Ps	Establishment Functions									11. HCT / Ps DESCRIBED IN 21 CFR 1271.10	12. HCT / Ps REGULATED AS MEDICAL DEVICES	13. HCT / Ps REGULATED AS DRUGS OR BIOLOGICAL DRUGS	14. PROPRIETARY NAMES
	Recover	Screen	Test	Package	Process	Store	Label	Distribute					
a. Bone													
b. Cartilage													
c. Cornea													
d. Dura Mater													
e. Embryo ☐ SIP ☐ Directed ☐ Anonymous													
f. Fascia													
g. Heart Valve													
h. Ligament													
i. Oocyte ☐ SIP ☐ Directed ☐ Anonymous													
j. Pericardium													
k. Peripheral Blood Stem Cells ☐ Autologous ☐ Family Related ☐ Allogeneic													
l. Sclera													
m. Semen ☐ SIP ☐ Directed ☐ Anonymous													
n. Skin													
o. Somatic Cell Therapy Products ☐ Autologous ☐ Family Related ☐ Allogeneic													
p. Tendon													
q. Umbilical Cord Blood Stem Cells ☐ Autologous ☐ Family Related ☐ Allogeneic													
r. Vascular Graft													
s.													
t.													
u.													
v.													

FORM FDA 3356 (4/08)

PSC Graphics (301) 443-1090   EF

Page 1 of 2

INSTRUCTIONS FOR COMPLETING FORM 3356: ESTABLISHMENT REGISTRATION AND LISTING FOR HUMAN CELLS, TISSUES, AND CELLULAR AND TISSUE-BASED PRODUCTS (HCT/Ps)

Completion of Form FDA 3356 is required under 21 CFR Part 1271, 207.20 and 807.20 for all establishments engaged in the recovery, processing, storage, labeling, packaging, or distribution of any HCT/P, or the screening or testing of a cell or tissue donor. After we receive your form, we will update our records and send a validated form to the reporting official.

PART I. ESTABLISHMENT INFORMATION

NOTE: You are required to register and list your HCT/Ps by submitting this form if you recover, process, store, label, package, or distribute any HCT/P, or screen or test the HCT/P donor unless one of the following exceptions applies. You are not required to submit this form if:

a. You use HCT/Ps solely for nonclinical scientific or educational purposes,

b. You remove and then implant HCT/Ps solely for autologous use during the same surgical procedure,

c. You are a carrier who accepts, receives, carries, or delivers HCT/Ps in the usual course of business as a carrier,

d. You only receive or store HCT/Ps solely for implantation, transplantation, infusion, or transfer within your facility,

e. You only recover reproductive cells or tissue and immediately transfer them into a sexually intimate partner of the cell or tissue donor, or

f. You are an individual person who works under contract, agreement, or other arrangement with or for a registered establishment and only recover and send HCT/Ps to the registered establishment.

Item 3. OTHER FDA REGISTRATIONS – Provide the registration number if your establishment is already registered with FDA as a Blood, Medical Device or Drug establishment. Your establishment will not be given a new registration number and you are not required to fill in items 4 to 8 of Part I. Item 9 must be filled out and signed on all forms. If you choose not to complete, Items 4 to 8 of Part I, you still must complete and sign Item 9. Then proceed to Part II and provide product information.

Item 4. PHYSICAL LOCATION – Provide the legal name, street address including the postal code of the actual location and

a. Telephone number.

b. Indicate (with an X) if you are a satellite recovery establishment that supports recovery personnel in the field by providing temporary storage for recovered HCT/Ps for shipment to your parent manufacturing establishment, but do not perform any other activities or manufacturing steps. Provide the FEI NO. of your parent manufacturing establishment.

c. Indicate (with an X) if you are an establishment that performs testing of HCT/Ps for micro-organisms if that is the only HCT/P processing function that you perform.

Item 6. MAILING ADDRESS OF THE REPORTING OFFICIAL – Provide the reporting official's mailing address including the postal code if it is different from the actual location of the establishment.

Items 8. U.S. AGENT – Non-U.S. establishments only. Provide your U.S. agent name, institution name if applicable, street address, e-mail address, and telephone number. United States agent means a person residing or maintaining a place of business in the United States whom a foreign establishment designates as its agent.

Item 9. REPORTING OFFICIAL'S SIGNATURE – The reporting official as listed in Item 6 is the person appointed by the owner or operator to register the from and answer all the correspondence and inquiries relative thereto. The dated signature by the reporting official affirms that all information contained on the form is true and accurate, to the best of his or her knowledge.

PART II. HCT/P INFORMATION (If item 2.c is checked, only indicate the information being changed.)

Item 10. ESTABLISHMENT FUNCTIONS AND TYPES OF HCT/Ps – Indicate (with an X) the activity (ies) performed by the registered establishment in conjunction with the type of HCT/P that the registered establishment manufactures. Test and screen refer to the donor, not the HCT/P. For reproductive HCT/Ps, indicate whether the HCT/Ps are from sexually intimate partners (SIP), directed, or anonymous. For hematopoietic stem/progenitor cells and somatic cells, indicate whether the HCT/Ps are autologous, family related, or allogeneic. Family related means allogeneic use in a first degree or second degree relative.

Item 11. LISTING FOR HCT/Ps DESCRIBED IN 21 CFR 1271.10 – To list HCT/Ps that are described in 21 CFR 1271.10 (a) indicate (with an X) each HCT/P that fulfills all of the following criteria:

a. The HCT/P is minimally manipulated,

b. The HCT/P is intended for homologous use only, as reflected by the labeling, advertising, or other indications of the manufacturer's objective intent,

c. The manufacture of the HCT/P does not involve the combination of the cell or tissue component with a drug or a device, except for a sterilizing, preserving, or storage agent, if the addition of the agent does not raise new clinical safety concerns with respect to the HCT/P, and either

d. The HCT/P does not have a systemic effect and is not dependent upon the metabolic activity of living cells for its primary function, or the HCT/P has a systemic effect or is dependent upon the metabolic activity of living cells for its primary function, and (i) is for autologous use, (ii) is for allogeneic use in a first-degree or second-degree blood relative, or (iii) is for reproductive use.

If your HCT/P type is not preprinted on the form, list it on lines s-v.

Item 12. HCT/P LISTING FOR MEDICAL DEVICES – Indicate (with an X) each HCT/P that is regulated as a medical device under the Federal Food, Drug, and Cosmetic Act.

Item 13. HCT/P LISTING FOR DRUGS OR BIOLOGICAL DRUGS – Indicate (with an X) each HCT/P that is regulated as a drug or biological drug under the Federal Food, Drug, and Cosmetic Act and/or section 351 of the Public Health Service Act.

NOTE: For items 11, 12, and 13 indicate changes to HCT/P listing such as discontinuance (indicate with a D), or resumption (indicate with an R) of a HCT/P into commercial distribution in June and December or at the time the change occurs as directed under 21 CFR Part 1271.21. Dates of HCT/P discontinuance / resumption should be provided on an additional page.

Item 14. PROPRIETARY NAMES – Indicate any applicable proprietary names used for the HCT/Ps listed, such as a trademark.

NOTE: If necessary add an additional page to complete Items 11, 12, 13, or 14.

After completion, return the form to:

Food and Drug Administration
Center for Biologics Evaluation and Research (HFM-775)
1401 Rockville Pike, Rockville, MD 20852-1448
ATTENTION: Tissue Establishment Registration Coordinator
FAX No. (301) 827-3844

Public reporting burden for this collection of information is estimated to average .75 hour per response, including the time for reviewing instructions, searching existing data sources, gathering and maintaining the data needed, and completing and reviewing the collection of information. Send comments regarding this burden estimate or any other aspect of this collection of information, including suggestions for reducing this burden to:
Department of Health and Human Services
Food and Drug Administration
Office of Chief Information Officer (HFA-250)
5600 Fishers Lane
Rockville, MD 20857

An agency may not conduct or sponsor, and a person is not required to respond to, a collection of information unless it displays a currently valid OMB control number.

FORM FDA 3356 (4/08)

be screened for other RCDADs such as West Nile virus, sepsis and vaccinia (recent smallpox vaccination). Relevant medical records are a collection of documents that includes a current donor medical history interview; a current report of the physical assessment of a cadaveric donor or the physical examination of a living donor; and other available records. FDA has provided detailed guidance concerning its current thinking regarding donor testing and screening.[6]

Current Good Tissue Practices, Reporting and Labeling (21 CFR 1271, Subparts D and E)

These current Good Tissue Practices (CGTPs) requirements address the methods, facilities and controls used for manufacturing HCT/Ps to prevent the introduction, transmission and spread of communicable disease. Communicable diseases include, but are not limited to, those transmitted by viruses, bacteria, fungi, parasites and transmissible spongiform encephalopathy agents. The donor eligibility requirements discussed above are also considered to be CGTPs. These requirements are applicable to the manufacture of Section 361 HCT/Ps and, to some extent, to HCT/Ps regulated as biological products and medical devices. They address all aspects of manufacture from recovery to distribution with the focus on establishing a comprehensive quality program to oversee such manufacture. The quality program must be designed to prevent, detect and correct deficiencies that may lead to an increased risk of introduction, transmission or spread of communicable diseases.

The 21 CFR 1271 requirements for reporting and labeling currently only apply to nonreproductive HCT/Ps regulated under Section 361 of the *PHS Act*. Other HCT/Ps must follow other applicable requirements when regulated as biological products or medical devices. Adverse reactions involving a communicable disease must be reported to FDA if they are fatal, life-threatening, result in permanent impairment or damage, or necessitate medical or surgical intervention, including hospitalization. As required for other FDA adverse event reports, HCT/P adverse reaction reports are submitted to FDA's MedWatch system.[7,8] In addition, establishments that distribute HCT/Ps are required to report certain deviations in manufacturing. The labeling requirements focus on information that must appear on the HCT/P label, including a distinct identification code and a description of the type of HCT/P. Other requirements address information that may accompany the HCT/P or appear on the label, such as the name and address of the establishment that determined release criteria and made the HCT/P available for distribution.

Inspection and Enforcement (21 CFR 1271, Subpart F)

This subpart only applies to HCT/Ps regulated under Section 361 of the *PHS Act*. For example, general inspectional provisions are described for notification, frequency and copying of records. What distinguishes these Part 1271 provisions from the inspection and enforcement requirements for other FDA-regulated products is that compliance actions are focused on providing protection against risks of communicable disease transmission. FDA has provided its investigators with detailed descriptions of how to conduct HCT/P inspections and address HCT/P importation.[9,10,11]

2009 Completed Policy Development: Streamlined Regulation of Cord Blood Products

More recently, FDA has developed a streamlined approach to licensure of hematopoietic progenitor cells derived from cord blood (HPC-C) for allogeneic use. Though some cord blood products for autologous and family-related use are regulated only under the new requirements in 21 CFR 1271 and Section 361 of the *PHS Act*, those intended for allogeneic unrelated recipients are considered biological products (**Table 25-2**). FDA delayed implementation of requirements for submission of Biological License Applications (BLAs) and Investigational New Drug Applications (INDs) for these HCT/Ps and published two guidances (one for BLAs and one for INDs) on 20 October 2009,[12,13] announcing that manufacturers must now have these applications approved by 20 October 2011. The BLAs required for the specified indications listed in the BLA guidance will be streamlined in that they will not require that each establishment demonstrate clinical efficacy, but can rely on clinical data that was submitted to FDA for review in a public docket. In addition, FDA has updated a *Compliance Program Guidance for Biological Products*[14] to include HPC-C compliance issues to assist investigators with both pre-licensure and annual investigations.

FDA has not yet completed its policy for another HCT/P, hematopoietic progenitor cells derived from peripheral blood. Because these are also life-saving therapies where access to the best human leukocyte antigen (HLA) match for a patient is crucial, FDA is being very careful to develop guidance that will ensure product safety and efficacy but will not impede patient care.

Summary

- FDA has developed and implemented comprehensive risk-based regulations that apply to a wide range of HCT/Ps:
  - the level and type of regulation is commensurate with the risk posed by the product characteristic
  - like products are treated alike
  - FDA exercises regulatory oversight only to the degree appropriate to protect the public health

Table 25-2. FDA Regulation of Minimally Manipulated Cord Blood Products

Origin and Use of Cord Blood	Applicable FDA Requirements	Premarket Application Required
Autologous	21 CFR 1271 (exempt from donor eligibility requirements)	No, if 1271.10 criteria met
Allogeneic: first or second degree blood relative	21 CFR 1271 (donor eligibility required)	No, if 1271.10 criteria met
Allogeneic: unrelated	Parts of 1271, 201, 211, 600, 610	Yes, IND and/or BLA

- These requirements are broad and focus on ensuring that HCT/Ps are neither contaminated nor capable of transmitting communicable diseases.
- Unlike many other FDA-regulated products, most HCT/Ps are not required to undergo premarket review and approval before distribution.
- For certain HCT/Ps (Section 361 HCT/Ps), the new regulations comprise the sole regulatory requirements.
- FDA has completed policy development for streamlined licensure for allogeneic cord blood and is still developing policy for peripheral blood stem cell products.
- For HCT/Ps regulated as drugs, devices and/or biological products, the new tissue regulations supplement other requirements (GMP/QSR).
- All establishments that perform a manufacturing function must register and list with FDA.

References

1. 21 CFR 1270. Available at www.access.gpo.gov/nara/cfr/waisidx_08/21cfr1270_08.html. Accessed 29 April 2011.
2. *Public Health Service Act.* Available at http://www.fda.gov/RegulatoryInformation/Legislation/ucm148717.htm. Accessed 29 April 2011.
3. "A Proposed Approach to the Regulation of Cellular and Tissue-Based Products." 62 *FR* 9721 (4 March 1997).
4. 21 CFR 1271. Available at www.access.gpo.gov/nara/cfr/waisidx_08/21cfr1271_08.html. Accessed 29 April 2011.
5. *Guidance for Industry: Regulation of Human Cells, Tissue, and Cellular and Tissue-Based Products (HCT/Ps) Small Entity Compliance Guide* (August 2007). Available at www.fda.gov/BiologicsBloodVaccines/GuidanceComplianceRegulatoryInformation/Guidances/Tissue/ucm073366.htm. Accessed 29 April 2011.
6. *Guidance for Industry: Eligibility Determination for Donors of Human Cells, Tissue, and Cellular and Tissue-Based Products (HCT/Ps)* (August 2007). Available at www.fda.gov/BiologicsBloodVaccines/GuidanceComplianceRegulatoryInformation/Guidances/CellularandGeneTherapy/ucm072929.

htm. Accessed 29 April 2011.
7. *Guidance for Industry: MedWatch Form FDA 3500A: Mandatory Reporting of Adverse Reactions Related to Human Cells, Tissue, and Cellular and Tissue-Based Products (HCT/Ps)* (November 2005). Available at www.fda.gov/BiologicsBloodVaccines/GuidanceComplianceRegulatoryInformation/Guidances/Tissue/ucm074000.htm. Accessed 29 April 2011.
8. SOPP 8508—*Procedures for Handling Adverse Reaction Reports Related to "361" Human Cells, Tissues, and Cellular and Tissue Based Products* (March 2008). Available at www.fda.gov/BiologicsBloodVaccines/GuidanceComplianceRegulatoryInformation/ProceduresSOPPs/ucm073048.htm. Accessed 29 April 2011.
9. "Compliance Program 7341.002A: Inspection of Tissue Establishments" (covers human tissue recovered before 25 May 2005). Available at www.fda.gov/BiologicsBloodVaccines/GuidanceComplianceRegulatoryInformation/ComplianceActivities/Enforcement/CompliancePrograms/ucm095218.htm. Accessed 29 April 2011.
10. "Compliance Program 7341.002: Inspection of Human Cells, Tissues, and Cellular and Tissue-Based Products (HCT/Ps)" (covers human tissue recovered after 25 May 2005). Available at www.fda.gov/biologicsbloodvaccines/guidancecomplianceregulatoryinformation/complianceactivities/enforcement/complianceprograms/ucm095207.htm. Accessed 29 April 2011.
11. "Compliance Program 7342.007 Addendum: Imported Human Cells, Tissues, and Cellular and Tissue-based Products (HCT/Ps)." Available at www.fda.gov/downloads/BiologicsBloodVaccines/GuidanceComplianceRegulatoryInformation/ComplianceActivities/Enforcement/CompliancePrograms/ucm095253.pdf. Accessed 29 April 2011.
12. *Final Guidance for Industry: Minimally Manipulated, Unrelated Allogeneic Placental/Umbilical Cord Blood Intended for Hematopoietic Reconstitution for*

Specified Indications (October 2009). Available at www.fda.gov/downloads/BiologicsBloodVaccines/GuidanceComplianceRegulatoryInformation/Guidances/Blood/UCM187144.pdf. Accessed 29 April 2011.

13. *Draft Guidance for Industry and FDA Staff: IND Applications for Minimally Manipulated, Unrelated Allogeneic Placental/Umbilical Cord Blood Intended for Hematopoietic Reconstitution for Specified Indications* (October 2009). Available at www.fda.gov/downloads/BiologicsBloodVaccines/GuidanceComplianceRegulatoryInformation/Guidances/Blood/UCM187146.pdf. Accessed 29 April 2011.

14. *Compliance Program Guidance Manual 7345.848: Inspection of Biological Drug Products* (October 2010). Available at www.fda.gov/BiologicsBloodVaccines/GuidanceComplianceRegulatoryInformation/ComplianceActivities/Enforcement/CompliancePrograms/ucm095393.htm. Accessed 29 April 2011.

Reading List

FDA CBER tissue website, http://www.fda.gov/BiologicsBloodVaccines/TissueTissueProducts/default.htm. Accessed 29 April 2011.

"Keeping Human Tissue Transplants Safe," *FDA Consumer Magazine*, May-June 2005 (http://findarticles.com/p/articles/mi_m1370/is_3_39/ai_n16419504/?tag=mantle_skin;content). Accessed 29 April 2011.

Consumer Frequently Asked Questions, 2007 FDA, CBER website (www.fda.gov/BiologicsBloodVaccines/TissueTissueProducts/QuestionsaboutTissues/ucm101559.htm). Accessed 29 April 2011.

Frequently asked Questions about Tissue Transplants from the Centers for Disease Control and Prevention Website. AATB website. (www.aatb.org/Frequently-Asked-Questions-about-Tissue-Transplants-from-the-Centers-for-Disease-Control-and-Prevention-CDC)

Prebula R. "Current Good Tissue Practices; The Core Requirements when Donating Human Tissue," *FDLI Update*, November/December 2007

Shapiro JK and Wesloloski BJ. "FDA's Regulatory Scheme for Human Tissue, A Brief Overview," *FDLI Update*, November/December 2007

Weber DJ. "Understanding and Implementing Good Tissue Practices (GTPs)," *Regulatory Focus*, July 2008, 13(7):18–28.

Weber DJ. "Navigating FDA Regulations for Human Cells and Tissue," *BioProcessing International*, 2(8): 22-26, 2004

Wells MA. "Overview of FDA Regulation of Human Cellular and Tissue-Based Products," *Food and Drug Law Journal*, 52, 401-408, 1997

Wells MA and Lazarus EF. "FDA Streamlines Licensure approach for Certain Cord Blood Products," *Regulatory Focus*, April 2010, 15(4):36–39.

Regulations Pertaining to Pediatrics

By Susan Hamann, MS, MT(ASCP), RAC

Objectives

◆ Understand the regulations pertaining specifically to pediatric healthcare products
◆ Outline the changes in regulations
◆ Review the requirements of the *Pediatric Medical Safety and Improvement Act* and the changes mandated in *FDAAA*
◆ Review the requirements of the *Pediatric Research Equity Act* (*PREA*) and the changes mandated in *FDAAA*
◆ Review the requirements of the *Best Pharmaceuticals for Children Act* (*BPCA*) and the changes mandated in *FDAAA*

Laws, Regulations and Guidelines covered in this chapter

◆ *Guidance for Industry: General Considerations for the Clinical Evaluation of Drugs in Infants and Children* (1977)
◆ American Academy of Pediatrics Guidelines for the Ethical Study of Drugs in Infants and Children (1977)
◆ *Orphan Drug Act* of 1983
◆ American Academy of Pediatrics Guidelines for the Ethical Conduct of Studies to Evaluate Drugs in Pediatric Populations (1995)
◆ *Guidance for Industry: The Content and Format of Pediatric Use Section* (May 1996)
◆ *Food and Drug Administration Modernization Act* of 1997
◆ *Best Pharmaceuticals for Children Act of 2002*
◆ *Pediatric Research Equity Act* of 2003
◆ *Food and Drug Administration Amendments Act* of 2007
◆ *Pediatric Medical Device Safety and Improvement Act* of 2007

Introduction

Children are not small adults. Their bodies do not necessarily respond to drugs as might be expected by adjusting the dose for a smaller person. There have been instances where children have died or suffered serious injury as a result of taking drugs that have been shown to be safe in adults. Children also have medical needs that must be considered when medical devices are used. Medical devices that function properly in adults may have different results in children. Therefore, there is a need to evaluate medical devices in children to account for differences in growth, metabolism and activity levels.

A number of steps have been taken to provide additional information on pediatric treatments (see History of Pediatric Initiatives, below). However, two major advancements took place in the mid-1990s.

"Up to 1994 most drugs (75–80%) were not labeled as either safe or effective for infants and children and off label use was the norm for these therapeutic orphans. There was little awareness among practitioners that prescribing for children was not evidence-based."[1] The Eunice Kennedy Shriver National Institute of Child Health and Human Development (NICHD) established the Pediatric Pharmacology Research Unit (PPRU) Network in 1994. This organization was formed to respond to the need for appropriate drug therapy studies in pediatric patients.

Reasons for possible gaps in the pediatric knowledge base include:

• ethical concerns in enrolling pediatric patients in studies

- limited populations for certain diseases
- technical difficulties in conducting pediatric trials
- belief that dosing could be determined by weight-based calculations
- lack of accepted endpoints and validated pediatric assessment tools
- limited marketing potential compared to adults

Since the inception of the PPRU Network, researchers have conducted a variety of drug studies, including pharmacokinetic studies, pharmacodynamic studies and studies of trial design.

In 1997, a major change occurred when the US Food and Drug Administration (FDA) issued new regulatory approaches that expanded and created systems to encourage development of medical and surgical devices for pediatric patients; to ensure that drugs that are or will be prescribed for children are tested for safety and effectiveness in children; and to review study designs to ensure that pediatric patients are protected and that these studies result in data that are medically and ethically appropriate for pediatric therapeutics.

History of Pediatric Initiatives

- 1972—Former FDA Commissioner Charles Edwards states at the annual meeting of the American Academy of Pediatrics (AAP) that most prescription products used in children are given empirically.
- 1973—The National Academy of Sciences issues a report calling for innovative investigative programs to provide information on the use of pharmacologic agents in the pediatric population.
- 1974—AAP issues a report commissioned by FDA on the evaluation of drugs to be used in the treatment of pregnant women, infants and children.
- 1975—Professor John Wilson of the Department of Pediatrics at LSU Medical Center publishes a survey of prescription drug package inserts noting that 78% of package inserts state the product had either not been studied in infants and children or had no pediatric statement.[2]
- 1977—Publication of three documents related to pediatric research:
  o FDA publishes *Guidance for Industry: General Considerations for the Clinical Evaluation of Drugs in Infants and Children.*
  o National Commission on Pediatric Research issues *General Considerations for the Clinical Evaluation of Drugs in Infants and Children.*
  o AAP issues *Guidelines for the Ethical Study of Drugs in Infants and Children.*
- 1979—FDA publishes a regulation adding a pediatric use subsection to the precautions section of the approved product package insert.
- 1983—The *Orphan Drug Act* establishes the precedent of incentives, provided by the federal government, to develop new therapeutics for underserved populations.
- 1994—FDA revises pediatric use regulation to allow extrapolation of adult efficacy data if the disease course in adults and children is similar.
- 1994— NICHD establishes the first national network for pediatric pharmacology.
- 1995—AAP revises *Guidelines for the Ethical Conduct of Studies to Evaluate Drugs in Pediatric Populations.*
- 1996—FDA issues *Guidance for Industry: The Content and Format of Pediatric Use Section.*
- 1996—The National Institutes of Health (NIH) initiates a policy of requiring NIH-funded clinical research to address applicability to pediatric populations.
- 1997—The *Food and Drug Administration Modernization Act* (*FDAMA*) establishes an incentive program for pediatric studies for medicinal products. Incentives, such as six months' additional patent exclusivity, may be permitted after FDA issues a Written Request for relevant pediatric studies to the product sponsor. The incentive is granted after a review confirms the study has been conducted in accordance with the FDA agreement. The program is limited to chemical moieties and excludes biological products and some antibiotics.
- 1998—FDA publishes a regulation ("Pediatric Rule") mandating pediatric studies when the disease or condition is similar in adults and children, and if either widespread use is anticipated or the product is a therapeutic advance.
- 2002—The Federal Court in the District of Columbia invalidates the 1998 Pediatric Rule, holding that FDA overstepped its authority in requiring pediatric testing unless the manufacturer can show that it is highly unlikely the drug will be used in pediatric populations.
- 2002—The *Best Pharmaceuticals for Children Act* (*BPCA*) renews the pediatric incentive program and establishes a program for the study of off-patent products through the NICHD.
- 2003—The *Pediatric Research Equity Act* (*PREA*) establishes the mandates of the 1998 Pediatric Rule as law for drugs and biological products, excluding products with Orphan Drug designation. (See the section on *PREA* below for details.)
- 2006—FDA, under the incentive programs defined in the *BPCA*, revises product package inserts for 118 products with new pediatric information.
- 2007—As of the end of the first quarter of the

calendar year, FDA:

- o had issued 340 Written Requests for pediatric studies since the incentive program began
- o had granted an incentive for pediatric studies to 136 products for 129 active chemical moieties of 149 determinations (91% favorable determination rate)
- o had revised product package inserts for 55 products under *PREA*

- 2007—The *Food and Drug Administration Amendments Act* (*FDAAA*) becomes law and renews, with modification, *PREA* and *BPCA* and introduces the *Pediatric Medical Device Safety and Improvement Act.* In general, the pediatric population includes patients' age "birth to 16 years, including age groups often called neonates, infants, children and adolescents."[3] Each of these is reviewed below in detail.

Pediatric Medical Device Safety and Improvement Act

FDAAA contains the provisions for the *Pediatric Medical Device Safety and Improvement Act* in Title III.[4]

Section 302—Tracking Pediatric Device Approvals

This section specifies that device protocols and applications must include an evaluation that describes any pediatric subpopulations suffering from the disease or condition the device is intended to treat, diagnose or cure, and the number of affected pediatric patients, if readily available. If the course of the disease or condition and the effects of the device are sufficiently similar in adult and pediatric patients, FDA has the specific authority to conclude that adult data may be used to support a determination of a reasonable assurance of effectiveness in pediatric populations, as appropriate. A study may not be needed in each pediatric subpopulation if data from one subpopulation can be extrapolated to another subpopulation. This section requires that FDA provide an annual report to Congress containing information pertaining specifically to pediatric usage of devices, allowing tracking of the number and types of devices approved specifically for children or for conditions that occur in children, as well as the timelines for completing premarket approvals and humanitarian device exemptions.

Section 303—Modification to Humanitarian Device Exemption

This section modified the *Food, Drug, and Cosmetic Act* of 1938 (*FD&C Act*), Section 520, to allow exemptions from the requirements for demonstrating effectiveness for treatment or diagnosis of diseases or conditions that affect fewer than 4,000 individuals. It also allows sponsors to make a profit on devices approved under the humanitarian

device exemption (HDE) that are specifically designed to meet a pediatric need. This exemption from the usual HDE requirements is conditional, based upon appropriate labeling for use in the pediatric population and approval of HDE after passage of *FDAAA*, and sets a limit on the number of devices that can be distributed annually (i.e., the annual distribution number (ADN)). The device distributor is obligated to notify FDA if the number of devices distributed during any calendar year exceeds the ADN. Adverse event reports are to be reviewed and evaluated by the FDA Pediatric Advisory Committee and reported to Congress. This section also defines pediatric populations as under the age of 21; subpopulations are defined in **Table 26-1**. Additional subpopulations may also be defined.

Section 304—Encouraging Pediatric Medical Device Research

This section requires the NIH director to designate an office to serve as a contact point to identify and access funding for pediatric medical device research. It directs NIH, FDA and the Agency for Healthcare Research and Quality (AHRQ) to submit a plan to expand pediatric medical device research. The plan must include a survey of pediatric healthcare providers to assess unmet pediatric medical device needs and provide a research agenda for improving pediatric medical device development and FDA clearance or approval of pediatric medical devices, and for evaluating the short- and long-term safety and effectiveness of those devices.

Section 305—Demonstration Grants for Improving Pediatric Device Availability

Demonstration grants for nonprofit consortia were established by this section to facilitate the development, production, approval and distribution of pediatric devices. This section requires the consortia to coordinate with NIH to identify research issues that require further study and with FDA to facilitate pediatric medical device approval. These funds aim to encourage innovation and connect qualified individuals with potential manufacturers; mentor and manage pediatric device projects from concept through development and marketing; assess the scientific and medical merit of medical device projects; and provide other assistance and advice consistent with the purposes of this section.

Table 26-1. Definition of Pediatric Subpopulations

Pediatric Subpopulation	Approximate Age Range
newborn	birth to 1 month of age
infant	1 month to 2 years of age
child	2 to 12 years of age
adolescent	12-21 years of age

Section 306—Amendments to Office of Pediatric Therapeutics and Pediatric Advisory Committee

FDA's Pediatric Advisory Committee has the authority to monitor medical devices and make recommendations for improving their availability and safety.

Section 307—Postmarket Surveillance

For Class II or Class III devices that are expected to have significant pediatric usage, FDA may require a manufacturer to conduct postmarket surveillance. FDA may require a prospective surveillance period of more than 36 months for these devices as a condition of approval. Dispute resolution may be requested by a manufacturer.

Premarket Assessment of Pediatric Medical Devices

FDA assesses device safety and effectiveness in the pediatric population using the same regulatory basis, scientific approaches and processes as those for adult medical devices. However, special consideration is given to devices meant for use in pediatric patients.

The agency does not believe that clinical data are always necessary to demonstrate safety and effectiveness for all devices intended for pediatric populations. A number of factors will be used to determine the need for clinical data, including the nature of the device, the device's adult use history, whether known factors can be extrapolated to the pediatric population and the underlying disease or condition being treated. Well-designed bench and animal testing may be considered sufficient in some cases.

If a device is modified to meet the needs of a pediatric population, the manufacturer must conduct a risk analysis of the changes and develop methods to adequately address or mitigate the identified risks.

FDA may require clinical testing in the following circumstances:

- Supporting information from sources such as pre-clinical bench or animal testing, literature or adult clinical trials is inadequate to establish safety and effectiveness for the pediatric indication.
- Adult data are inadequate to predict pediatric risks and adverse events.
- Pediatric data are needed for validation of device design modifications.
- Pediatric data are needed to develop an age-appropriate treatment regimen.

When minors are involved in research, the regulations require the assent of the child and the permission of the parent(s) rather than the consent of the subject.

Indications for use should be supported by appropriate data for the targeted populations and subpopulations.

Contraindications, warnings and precautions for devices intended for pediatric use should clearly address the risks associated with the pediatric subject's age, size and maturity, and alert the user to specific hazards associated with the use of the device in the target population.

The manufacturer should make a concerted effort to obtain and report the frequency of device-related adverse events according to the various subgroups in which the device will be used.

Any instructions for use provided specifically for the pediatric patient should be age appropriate with respect to written language and other visual and auditory tools. The labeling must be satisfactory for all pediatric subgroups.

Pediatric Research Equity Act (PREA)

PREA originally became law on 3 December 2003. It requires pediatric studies of certain drugs and biological products unless waived or deferred. It does not apply to drugs with orphan designation. The "Pediatric Mandate" is included in the *PREA* law.

A pediatric assessment is required for applications with new ingredients, new indications, new dosage forms, new dosing regimens or new routes of administration. The assessment must contain sufficient data to adequately assess the drug or biological product's safety and effectiveness and to support dosing and administration for each relevant pediatric subpopulation.

Pediatric studies should have minimal risk, or have the prospect of direct benefit with greater than minimal risk, or have no prospect of direct benefit but, with a minor increase over minimal risk, be likely to yield generalized knowledge about the subject's disorder or condition. The types of data submitted under *PREA* will depend upon the nature of the application, what is known about the product in pediatric populations and the underlying disease or condition being treated. *PREA* does not require applicants to conduct separate safety and effectiveness studies in pediatric patients in every case.

For a course of disease or effect similar to adults, effectiveness can be extrapolated from adequate and well-controlled studies in adults, when supplemented with other information (e.g., safety, pharmacokinetics and pharmacodynamics). Extrapolation from one age group to another is permitted, where appropriate.

FDA may grant a deferral when the drug or biologic is ready for approval in adults or when additional safety and effectiveness data are determined to be necessary. The deferral is tracked as a Phase 4 or postmarketing commitment.

A full waiver is granted when the condition does not occur in the pediatric population or the required studies are impossible or highly impractical. A waiver may also be granted when strong evidence suggests that the drug or biologic would be ineffective or unsafe in children. If the drug or biologic does not represent a meaningful therapeutic benefit over existing therapies and is not likely to be used in a substantial number of pediatric patients, a full waiver may also be granted. FDA has used 50,000[5] patients as representing a "substantial number."

A partial waiver may be granted for an age subset of the pediatric population using the same conditions and criteria that apply for a full waiver. A partial waiver may also be granted if reasonable attempts to produce a pediatric formulation for a particular subset of the pediatric population have failed. An update[6] in *PREA* 2007 requires the sponsor to submit documentation to FDA explaining why a pediatric formulation cannot be developed. Labeling should include information that states that a full or partial waiver has been granted because there is evidence that the drug or biologic would be ineffective or unsafe.

If a waiver is granted, FDA will make the application for the waiver publically available.

For marketed drugs and biological products, FDA can require study data after providing notice to the sponsor of the approved application and providing an opportunity for a written response and a meeting. This situation may occur if the drug or biologic is used for a substantial number of pediatric patients for the labeled indication and in the absence of adequate labeling that could pose significant risks to pediatric population. Additional studies may also be required if there is reason to believe that the drug or biologic would represent a meaningful therapeutic benefit over existing therapies and the absence of adequate studies could pose significant risks to pediatric patients. Waiver and deferral criteria are the same as those for new drugs and biologics.

A pediatric plan is a statement of intent that outlines the applicant's planned pediatric studies. It should also indicate whether the applicant plans to request a waiver or deferral and the basis for the request. FDA encourages applicants to discuss the pediatric plan at pre-Investigational New Drug (pre-IND) application meetings, especially for products intended for life-threatening or severely debilitating diseases. For products that are not intended for treating life-threatening or severely debilitating diseases, applicants may submit and discuss the pediatric plan no later than the End-of-Phase 2 meeting.

PREA 2007 now requires that the sponsor's Annual Report document study status, reasons for lack of progress and plans for completing studies in a timely fashion. The Annual Report will become publically available on the FDA website.

FDAAA contains the *PREA* provisions in Title IV, which includes a number of changes to the original *PREA*. The updates include:[7]

- requires an annual review from an applicant that has received a deferral
- makes annual deferral reviews public
- requires manufacturers that have tried but have

been unsuccessful in producing a pediatric formulation to submit to FDA the reasons why the formulation cannot be developed

- changes the criteria for applying *PREA* to already marketed drugs; new language allows FDA to use a "benefit" standard as opposed to a "risk" standard
- shortens the "request and response" period for the holder to an expedited 30-day review of private funding before referral to *PREA*
- requires an FDA internal committee to review study plans and assessments as well as deferrals and waivers
- requires FDA to track the number and type of studies completed, as well as labeling changes and other data resulting from *PREA*
- modifies the *BPCA* dispute resolution process and applies it to *PREA*; the modified language reduces the overall time period for resolving disputes over labeling and removes the provision requiring labeling to be the only remaining open issue before referral for resolution
- requires FDA to make medical, statistical and clinical pharmacology reviews publically available
- requires sponsors to provide physicians and other healthcare providers with new pediatric labeling information
- requires reporting of adverse events for drugs studied under *PREA* and provides for review by the Pediatric Advisory Committee
- requests the Institute of Medicine to review past study requests issued by FDA and make recommendations to the agency for future requests
- continues linkage of *PREA* to the expiration of *BPCA* on 1 October 2012
- establishes a coordinated internal review committee to *BPCA* and *PREA*
- requires the Government Accountability Office to produce a report on the results of *BPCA* and *PREA* with recommendation for improving the programs

Best Pharmaceuticals for Children Act (BPCA)

The *Best Pharmaceuticals for Children Act* of 2002 followed the 1998 Pediatric Rule, which was invalidated in 2002 by the federal court in the District of Columbia.

FDAAA in 2007 increased the authority and effectiveness of *BPCA*.

To initiate the process defined in *BPCA*, FDA issues a Written Request to holders of approved applications. The sponsor may also submit a proposed pediatric study request, which may generate a formal Written Request by FDA. The Written Request is a legal document requesting that the sponsor conduct studies in the pediatric population. The Written Request specifies the indication, population, type of studies, safety parameters, longer-term follow-up and timeframe for completion and response.

The criteria for issuing a Written Response include:

- serious or life-threatening condition
- frequency of disease/condition
- whether there are other therapeutic options available
- how often the drug is used or expected to be used in the pediatric population
- whether adequate safety data are available to move into the pediatric population (based on animal studies and adult experience)
- whether there is an appropriate and acceptable benefit compared to the risks

There are defined processes for both on- and off-patent drugs.

- On-patent process—The sponsor has 180 days to respond to FDA's Written Request for an on-patent drug. The manufacturer can agree to conduct studies or decline the request. If it agrees, the potential incentive is six months of exclusivity added to and covering the same scope as any exclusivity currently covering the product. There is a specific time when this exclusivity can be requested and a formal procedure for granting it, which is discussed below. If the sponsor declines, FDA may publicize the fact that the sponsor has declined the Written Request. If the drug is not developed by the current supplier, referral is made to the Foundation for the NIH for possible funding of studies by grant mechanism.

- The formal mechanism to allow the additional six months of exclusivity is a three-step process. It starts with the Written Request by FDA to the sponsor. After completing the studies or otherwise complying with the Written Request, the sponsor replies with a report that addresses the information requested and makes a claim for the six months' exclusivity. FDA then takes action based upon an evaluation of the report. The study results do not need to be positive or lead to a change in the label in order for the exclusivity to be granted.

- Off-patent process—NIH, in consultation with FDA, develops a list of pediatric therapeutic needs. FDA issues Written Requests based upon a priority list to all current suppliers. The suppliers have 30 days to respond to the Written Request. This is a right of first refusal. If all current suppliers decline, NIH will issue a request for proposals to perform studies under contract using a special fund. Study reports are submitted to FDA for evaluation and inclusion in product labeling.

Dissemination of Information

FDA can publicize the fact that the innovator of a drug with exclusivity has declined a Written Request. Study reports in response to Written Requests are published in the FDA dockets, as are the reviews of the study reports and recommended label changes. Summaries of clinical and pharmacology submissions are published in the dockets and in the *Federal Register*.

BCPA Dispute Resolution

If FDA recommends label changes and the supplier does not accept the recommendations, the issue is referred to the Pediatric Subcommittee for advice. If the Pediatric Subcommittee recommends label changes and the supplier declines, FDA may declare the product misbranded.

Major Provisions of BPCA

BPCA renewed the pediatric incentive program and established a program for the study of off-patent products through NICHD.

Provisions included in the 2007 update established procedures to ensure proper pediatric labeling and adverse event reporting and tracking, and created the requirement for the pediatric plan for the availability of investigational drugs or INDs. Reports are required to be submitted by the Institute of Medicine on pediatric study practices; by the General Accounting Office on the enrollment of minority children and pediatric exclusivity; and by FDA on patient access to new cancer therapeutics.

FDAAA contains the provisions for *BPCA* in Title V. The updates include:[8]

- allows FDA to request preclinical studies as part of a Written Request
- requires pediatric studies under *BPCA* to be submitted and exclusivity awarded nine months before the expiration of the patent
- allows FDA to issue one study request for more than one use of a drug, and to issue one study request to capture both on- and off-label uses
- requires a manufacturer that declines a Written Request, on the basis that it was unable to produce a pediatric formulation, to submit to FDA the reasons why the formulation cannot be developed
- requires manufacturers to submit all postmarket adverse events as part of the exclusivity application or supplement
- lengthens the time FDA has to review submitted studies from 90 to 180 days
- shortens the "request and response" period for the holder to an expedited 30-day review of private funding before referral to *PREA*
- requires FDA to make study requests public after the drug has been granted the additional exclusivity

- requires prominent public disclosure when a manufacturer creates a pediatric formulation and fails to market it
- requires an internal FDA committee to review Written Requests prior to issuance
- provides authority for internal committee review of studies submitted in response to Written Requests
- requires FDA to track the number and type of studies completed, as well as labeling changes and other data resulting from *BPCA*
- applies dispute resolution to all drugs that are issued study requests, not just those granted exclusivity; sets a time for referral to the Pediatric Advisory Committee if the sponsor does not make the requested label change
- grants FDA explicit authority to indicate on a label when a product has been studied in children
- requires FDA to make the actual medical, statistical and clinical pharmacology review (not summaries) publicly available
- requires sponsors that have been granted exclusivity to provide physicians and other healthcare providers with any new pediatric labeling information
- provides for Pediatric Advisory Committee review of all adverse events for one year following the awarding of exclusivity
- requires FDA to determine if a drug should be studied under *PREA* if a study is declined by a manufacturer; if applicable, FDA will report why it did not use *PREA*
- allows only 30 days to determine whether private donations are available to completely fund all studies in a declined Written Request before referral to *PREA*
- provides for review by the Institute of Medicine of past Written Requests issued by FDA to make recommendations to FDA for future requests and to make recommendations of incentives to encourage the study of biologics in children
- grants NIH expanded authority to examine needs in pediatric therapeutics, including drugs

The *Patient Protection and Affordable Care Act* of 2010 expanded *BPCA* to include biologics.[9]

Summary

Pediatric initiatives are catalysts for increased activity in pediatric clinical research. Full safety and efficacy studies are not always necessary to obtain exclusivity. If FDA agrees with the premise that the medication's pathophysiology and mode of action are similar in adults and in one or more pediatric age groups, efficacy data may be extrapolated from adult studies to support the application. Prospective studies are required to confirm the types of evidence needed to support extrapolation to pediatric patients.

New programs and incentives have been developed to expedite the development of new therapies for pediatric populations. Since 1998, FDA has issued 333 Written Requests for pediatric studies,[10] and there have been 404 revised product inserts (368 with new pediatric studies)[11] under *PREA*.

References

1. National Institutes of Health. http://nih.gov/grants/guide/rfa-files/RFA-HD-08-021.html. Accessed 2 May 2011.
2. Curry JI, Lander TD and Stringer MD. Review article: "Erythromycin as a prokinetic agent in infants and children." *Aliment Pharmacol Ther* 2001:15:595-603.
3. 21 CFR 201.57 (f)(9).
4. American Academy of Pediatrics. www.aap.org/advocacy/washing/Therapeutics/docs/devicesidexside.pdf. Accessed 2 May 2011.
5. Government Accountability Office www.gao.gov/new.items/d01705t.pdf. Accessed 2 May 2011.
6. *Food and Drug Amendments Act* of 2007 Section 505(b)(2)(d)(2)(A)(i)IIii.
7. American Academy of Pediatrics www.aap.org/advocacy/washing/Therapeutics/docs/bpcapreasidexside.pdf. Accessed 2 May 2011.
8. Ibid.
9. *Patient Protection and Affordable Care Act* of 2010. www.fda.gov/downloads/Drugs/GuidanceComplianceRegulatoryInformation/UCM216146.pdf. Accessed 2 May 2011.
10. Written Requests Issued. FDA website. http://www.fda.gov/Drugs/DevelopmentApprovalProcess/DevelopmentResources/ucm050002.htm. Accessed 5 May 2011.
11. Pediatric Labeling Changes through February 25, 2011. FDA website. www.fda.gov/downloads/ScienceResearch/SpecialTopics/PediatricTherapeuticsResearch/UCM163159.pdf. Accessed 5 May 2011.

Recommended Reading

Guidance for Industry and FDA Staff: Premarket Assessment of Pediatric Medical Devices (May 2004). Available at www.fda.gov/downloads/MedicalDevices/DeviceRegulationsandGuidance/GuidanceDocuments/UCM089742.htm. Accessed 2 May 2011.

Guidance for HDE Holders, Institutional Review Boards (IRBs), Clinical Investigators, and FDA Staff: Humanitarian Device Exemption (HDE) Regulation: Questions and Answers (July 2010). Available at www.fda.gov/MedicalDevices/DeviceRegulationandGuidance/

GuidanceDocuments/ucm110194.htm. Accessed 2 May 2011.

"Improving Access to Safe Drugs and Medical Devices for Children." American Academy of Pediatrics. Available at www.aap.org/advocacy/washing/Therapeutics/. Accessed 2 May 2011.

"Improvements Made in the 2007 Reauthorization of the Best Pharmaceuticals for Children Act (BPCA) and the Pediatric Research Equity Act (PREA).: American Academy of Pediatrics (September 2007). Available at www.aap.org/advocacy/washing/Therapeutics/docs/bpcapreaonepage.pdf. Accessed 2 May 2011.

"Best Pharmaceuticals for Children Act; Pediatric Research Equity Act—2007 REAUTHORIZATION Improvements to Existing Law." American Academy of Pediatrics (September 2007). Available at www.aap.org/advocacy/washing/Therapeutics/docs/bpcapreasidexside.pdf. Accessed 2 May 2011.

"Summary of Innovations in the Pediatric Medical Device Safety and Improvement Act of 2007." American Academy of Pediatrics. Available at www.aap.org/advocacy/washing/Therapeutics/docs/deviceonepage.pdf. Accessed 2 May 2011.

NIH. Pediatric Pharmacology and Therapeutics Research Consortium (PPTRC) (U54). Available at http://grants.nih.gov/grants/guide/rfa-files/RFA-HD-08-021.html. Accessed 2 May 2011.

FDA. Developing Products for Rare Diseases & Conditions. Available at www.fda.gov/ForIndustry/DevelopingProductsforRareDiseasesConditions/default.htm. Accessed 2 May 2011.

FDA. *Draft Guidance for Industry: How to Comply with the Pediatric Research Equity Act* (September 2005). Available at www.fda.gov/downloads/Drugs/GuidanceComplianceRegulatoryInformation/Guidances/ucm079756.pdf. Accessed 2 May 2011.

FDA. *Guidance for Sponsors, Industry, Researchers, Investigators, and Food and Drug Administration Staff: Certifications To Accompany Drug, Biological Product, and Device Applications/Submissions: Compliance with Section 402(j) of The Public Health Service Act, Added By Title VIII of The Food and Drug Administration Amendments Act of 2007* (January 2009). Available at www.fda.gov/RegulatoryInformation/Guidances/ucm125335.htm. Accessed 2 May 2011.

FDA. *Guidance for Industry: Development of Preventive HIV Vaccines for Use in Pediatric Populations* (June 2009). Available at www.fda.gov/BiologicsBloodVaccines/GuidanceComplianceRegulatoryInformation/Guidances/Vaccines/ucm074819.htm. Accessed 2 May 2011.

Grylack L. "Pediatric Drug Development: Focus on US Regulatory Issues." *Regulatory Focus*, Vol. 13, No. 3, March 2008, pp 26–31.

Klimek J. "US Pediatric Developments." *Regulatory Focus*, Vol. 13, No. 3, March 2008, pp 32–35.

Swit MA. "FDAAA—An Abbreviation in Search of Understanding: A Review of Selected Drugs and Biologics Provisions of the Food and Drug Administration Amendments Act of 2007." *Regulatory Focus*, Vol. 13, No. 2, February 2008, pp 26–33.

Hirschfeld S. NIH. "Pediatric Medical Device Sagety and Improvement Act of 2007." Private communication.

Hirschfeld S. NIH. "Federal Pediatric Initiatives." Private communication.

Tassinari MS *Pediatric Regulations in the US and Europe* November 2010 Available at www.fda.gov/downloads/AdvisoryCommittees/CommitteesMeetingMaterials/Drugs/OncologicDrugsAdvisoryCommittee/UCM236390.pdf. Accessed 2 May 2011.

American Academy of Pediatrics website, http://aap.org. Accessed 2 May 2011.

US Food and Drug Administration Pediatric Drug Development webpage, www.fda.gov/Drugs/DevelopmentApprovalProcess/DevelopmentResources/UCM049867.htm. Accessed 2 May 2011.

US Food and Drug Administration Pediatric Therapeutics webpage, www.fda.gov/ScienceResearch/SpecialTopics/PediatricTherapeuticsResearch/default.htm. Accessed 2 May 2011.

Dietary Supplements and Homeopathic Products

By Maruthi Prasad Palthur and Evelyn Cadman

Objectives

- Develop a broad understanding of the regulation of dietary supplements
- Understand claims permitted for dietary supplements
- Understand basic current Good Manufacturing Practice regulations (CGMPs) for dietary supplements
- Understand the basic regulatory requirements for adverse event reporting
- Develop a broad understanding of the regulation of homeopathic drug products

Laws, Regulations and Guidelines Covered in This Chapter

- *Dietary Supplement Health Education Act* of 1994 (*DSHEA*)
- 21 CFR 101.36 Nutrition labeling of dietary supplements
- 21 CFR 101.93 Structure/function claims
- 21 CFR 111 Current Good Manufacturing Practice in manufacturing, packaging, labeling, or holding operations for dietary supplements
- 21 CFR 190.6 Requirement for premarket notification of new dietary ingredients
- *Public Health Security and Bioterrorism Preparedness and Response Act* of 2002 (Public Law 107-188). 107th Congress
- 21 CFR 110.310. Prior notice of imported food under the Public Health Security and Bioterrorism Preparedness and Response Act of 2002
- *Guidance for Industry: A Dietary Supplement Labeling Guide* (April 2005)
- 21 CFR 190.6 New dietary ingredient notifications
- *Draft Guidance for Industry: Questions and Answers Regarding Adverse Event Reporting and Recordkeeping for Dietary Supplements as Required by the Dietary Supplement and Nonprescription Drug Consumer Protection Act* (October 2007)
- *Guidance for Industry: Substantiation for Dietary Supplement Claims Made Under Section 403(r) (6) of the Federal Food, Drug, and Cosmetic Act* (January 2009)
- "Claims That Can Be Made for Conventional Foods and Dietary Supplements" (September 2003)
- FTC, *Dietary Supplements: An Advertising Guide for Industry*
- *Guidance for Industry: Evidence-Based Review System for the Scientific Evaluation of Health Claims* (January 2009)
- *Guidance for Industry: Iron-Containing Supplements and Drugs: Label Warning Statements Small Entity Compliance Guide* (October 2003)
- *Guidance for Industry: Notification of a Health Claim or Nutrient Content Claim Based on an Authoritative Statement of a Scientific Body* (June 2998)
- *Guidance for Industry: Evidence-Based Review System for the Scientific Evaluation of Health Claims* (January 2009)
- *Guidance for Industry: Food Labeling; Nutrient Content Claims; Definition for "High Potency" and Definition for "Antioxidant" for Use in Nutrient Content Claims for Dietary Supplements and Conventional Foods; Small Entity Compliance Guide* (July 2008)
- *Guidance for Industry: Statement of Identity, Nutrition Labeling, and Ingredient Labeling of Dietary Supplements; Small*

Entity Compliance Guide (January 1999)
- *Guidance for Industry: Structure/Function Claims, Small Entity Compliance Guide* (January 2002)
- *Guidance for Industry: Evidence-Based Ranking System for Scientific Data* (January 2009)
- *Guidance for Industry: Interim Procedures for Qualified Health Claims in the Labeling of Conventional Human Food and Human Dietary Supplements* (July 2003)
- *Guidance for Industry: Prior Notice of Imported Food Questions and Answers* (Edition 2) (May 2004)
- *Guidance for Industry: Questions and Answers Regarding Establishment and Maintenance of Records (Edition 4); Final Guidance* (September 2006)
- *Draft Guidance for Industry: Questions and Answers Regarding Adverse Event Reporting and Recordkeeping for Dietary Supplements as Required by the Dietary Supplement and Nonprescription Drug Consumer Protection Act* (October 2007)
- *Draft Guidance for Industry: Questions and Answers Regarding the Labeling of Dietary Supplements as Required by the Dietary Supplement and Nonprescription Drug Consumer Protection Act* (Revision 1) (December 2008)
- *Guidance for Industry: Questions and Answers Regarding Food Allergens, Including the Food Allergen Labeling and Consumer Protection Act of 2004* (Edition 4) (October 2006)
- *Guidance for Industry: FDA Export Certificates* (July 2004)
- *Compliance Policy Guide, Guidance for FDA and CBP Staff. Sec. 110.310 Prior Notice of Imported Food Under the Public Health Security and Bioterrorism Preparedness and Response Act of 2002* (May 2009)
- *Guidance for Industry: Questions and Answers Regarding Registration of Food Facilities* (Edition 4) (August 2004)
- "Criteria Needed With Request For Certificate Of Free Sale For Dietary Supplement(s), Infant Formula(s), & Medical Food(s)" December 2006)
- *Guidance for Industry: FDA Export Certificates* (July 2004)
- Compliance Policy Guide 7132.15, Section 400.400 "Conditions Under Which Homeopathic Drugs May Be Marketed" (Revised March 1995)
- 21 CFR 207 Registration of producers of drugs and listing of drugs in commercial distribution
- 21 CFR 211 Current Good Manufacturing Practice for finished pharmaceuticals
- *Current Good Manufacturing Practice in Manufacturing, Packaging, Labeling, or Holding Operations for Dietary Supplements; Small Entity Compliance Guide* (December 2010)
- 21 CFR 201 Labeling
- The Homeopathic Pharmacopoeia of the United States, Guidelines For Homeopathic Drugs

Introduction

Controversies over the regulation of vitamin and mineral dietary supplement product dosages and health claims arose in the 1960s and 1970s.[1] Between 1941 and 1979, the US Food and Drug Administration (FDA) attempted to limit the dosages of dietary supplements that could be sold without a prescription, limit the claims that could be made, and require a disclaimer on supplement products stating that there was no scientific basis for the routine use of vitamins and minerals.[2,3] Litigation and eventually legislation limited FDA's ability to regulate supplements with the end result that final rules were never enacted and proposed rules were withdrawn.[4]

In November 1989, FDA first issued a warning against the use of L-tryptophan products and subsequently recalled them. There was growing evidence that linked L-tryptophan, an amino acid promoted to relieve occasional sleeplessness, among other things, to a serious but rare blood disorder, eosinophilia. In 1990, sufficient evidence had been developed to link the disorder to a product from a Tokyo firm, Showa Denko KK, which had introduced a new production method in early 1989. Unfortunately, by that time, 1,478 cases and 21 deaths due to eosinophila linked to L-tryptophan use had been reported.[5]

Concurrently, the *Nutrition Labeling Education Act* (*NLEA*) was passed in 1990, requiring FDA to regulate food labeling and include references to dietary supplements. In the early 1990s, several bills were introduced in both the House and Senate that would have impacted the dietary supplement industry. One such bill introduced in the House was the *Nutrition Advertising Coordination Act* of 1991 (HR 1662 SC2). This bill was thought to threaten the future availability of vitamins and other supplements because it defined misbranding in part as a claim that "characterizes the relationship of any nutrient … to a health-related condition."[6] The *Dietary Supplement Consumer Protection Act* of 1993 (HR 2923 IH), which was also introduced in the House, stated that a dietary supplement would be deemed unsafe unless the ingredient was "generally recognized, among experts qualified by adequate training and experience to evaluate its safety, as having been adequately shown through scientific procedures to be safe under the conditions of its intended use."[7] This provision was retroactive to products that were on the market. The legislation further stated that FDA would establish regulations stipulating the uses as well as "the maximum quantity which may be used or permitted in the dietary supplement."[8] The interpretation of this proposed legislation was that dietary supplements, which had previously been regulated as foods, would be moved into a regulatory status very similar to drugs.

While neither of these bills passed, in response to the proposed legislation, the supplement and health foods industries promoted a public letter-writing campaign that declared FDA was seeking to regulate vitamins as drugs. The campaign resulted in an estimated two million[9] letters to Congress, prompting passage of the *Dietary Supplement Health Education Act* of 1994 (*DSHEA*).[10] The first paragraph of the executive summary in the Report of the Commission on Dietary Supplement Labels, states:

> "The *Dietary Supplement Health and Education Act* (*DSHEA* or the Act) of 1994 was enacted by Congress following public debate concerning the importance of dietary supplements in leading a healthy life, the need for consumers to have current and accurate information about supplements, and controversy over the Food and Drug Administration (FDA) regulatory approach to dietary supplements. President Clinton, in signing the legislation into law on October 25, 1994, said: After several years of intense efforts, manufacturers, experts in nutrition, and legislators, acting in a conscientious alliance with consumers at the grassroots level, have moved successfully to bring common sense to the treatment of dietary supplements under regulation and law."

In *DSHEA*, Congress defined dietary supplements and dietary ingredients; required ingredient and nutrition labeling; provided for claims and nutritional support statements that can be used for dietary supplements; outlined guidelines for information that can be provided on supplement products; and gave FDA the authority to establish Good Manufacturing Practice (GMP) regulations for dietary supplements. In addition, *DSHEA* allowed the continued sale of dietary ingredients on the market as of 15 October 1994. The law also established a framework for assuring the safety of new dietary ingredients (NDIs).

Prior to 1994, vitamins, minerals and other dietary supplements were regulated as foods;[11] however, with the passage of *DSHEA*, a new class of FDA-regulated products was created. In addition, the law allowed statements of nutritional support to be made regarding dietary supplement products. The resulting dietary supplement regulations promulgated by FDA are very similar to food regulations. Like foods, dietary supplements are not subject to agency approval prior to marketing. Dietary supplement product labels must include a supplement facts box that is similar, but not identical to the nutrition facts boxes used on food products. Dietary ingredients that were not on the market as of 15 October 1994 must be the subject of NDI petitions that are similar in content to "generally regarded as safe" (GRAS) notifications used for new food additives. Additionally, most nutrient content claims, which were

established in *NLEA*, may also be used on dietary supplement products.

Definition of Dietary Ingredients and Dietary Supplements

Dietary ingredients were traditionally viewed as essential vitamins, minerals and other nutrients such as fats, carbohydrates and proteins. In 1990, *NLEA* added "herbs, or similar nutritional substances,"[12] to the definition of dietary supplement. In *DSHEA*, this definition was expanded further as Congress defined dietary supplements as

> "products (other than tobacco) intended to supplement the diet that bear or contain one or more of the following dietary ingredients:
>
> A vitamin;
> A mineral;
> An herb or other botanical;
> An amino acid;
> A dietary substance for use by man to supplement the diet by increasing the total dietary intake; or
> A concentrate, metabolite, constituent, extract, or a combination of any ingredient mentioned above.
>
> Further, dietary supplements are products intended for ingestion, are not represented for use as a conventional food or as a sole item of a meal or the diet, and are labeled as dietary supplements."[13]

The prohibition on representing dietary supplements as conventional foods was underscored by the agency's 2009 publication of a guidance document regarding liquid dietary supplements.[14] FDA noted that this guidance was issued to address the trend of marketing beverages as dietary supplements and of including ingredients in beverages and conventional foods that are not GRAS. The guidance states in part, "Liquid products that suggest through their serving size, packaging, or recommended daily intake that they are intended to be consumed in amounts that provide all or a significant part of the entire daily drinking fluid intake of an average person in the U.S., are represented as beverages. In addition, the name of a product can represent the product as a conventional food. Product or brand names that use conventional food terms such as "beverage," "drink," "water," "juice," or similar terms represent the product as a conventional food."

NDI Notifications

Dietary supplement ingredients and products are not subject to premarket approval; however, FDA must be notified prior to introducing any dietary ingredients that were not marketed in the US prior to 15 October 1994 onto the marketplace.[15] Notification must be given to the Office of Nutritional Products, Labeling and Dietary Supplements (ONPLDS) at least 75 days before introducing the NDI into interstate commerce. The notification must include:

- name and address of the manufacturer or distributor of the NDI or supplement product that contains the NDI
- NDI name, including the Latin binomial name of any herb or other botanical
- description of the products that contain the NDI along with the level of the NDI in the product; conditions of ordinary or recommended uses of the supplement
- history of use or other evidence establishing the safety of the dietary ingredient under the conditions of use, including any citation to and reprint, copy or English translation of published articles or other evidence that is the basis upon which the distributor or manufacturer has concluded that the NDI or product containing the NDI will reasonably be expected to be safe
- signature of the person designated by the manufacturer or distributor of the NDI or dietary supplement that contains the NDI

FDA will acknowledge and provide the date of receipt of the NDI notification. The date FDA provides is the filing date for the notification and the NDI may not be introduced into interstate commerce for 75 days after the filing date. FDA will put the NDI notification, with the exception of any trade secret or confidential information, "on public display" 90 days after receipt of the submission. Although the NDI may be introduced into the marketplace 75 days after filing, this does not guarantee that FDA agrees there is sufficient information to presume reasonable safety. As stated in 21 CFR 190.6 (f), "Failure of the agency to respond to a notification does not constitute a finding by the agency that the NDI or the dietary supplement that contains the NDI is safe or is not adulterated under section 402 of the act." A list of NDIs submitted between 1995 and early 2000, along with their status and links to the notifications, can be found at www.fda.gov/Food/DietarySupplements/ucm109764.htm.

Labels and Labeling

As for all other classes of FDA-regulated products, "labels" are "any display of written, printed, or graphic matter on the immediate container of any article, or any such matter affixed to any consumer commodity or affixed to or appearing upon a package containing any consumer commodity"[16] and "labeling" "includes all written, printed, or graphic matter accompanying an article at any time while such article is in interstate commerce or held for sale after shipment or delivery in interstate commerce."[17] Labeling regulations for dietary supplement products are found in 21 CFR 101.36.[18] This section frequently references 21 CFR 101.9,[19] which covers food labeling. Both food and dietary

supplement labels must include a statement of identity; a net quantity of contents statement; an ingredient list; the address of the manufacturer, packer or distributor; and a facts box that declares the nutrients present in the product.

Dietary supplement facts boxes are very similar to the nutrition facts boxes used on food labels. While both must list key nutrients when present at threshold levels defined by regulation, the order in which some of the nutrients must appear differs between foods and dietary supplements. Another key difference is that nutrition facts boxes must list certain nutrients such as fats even when they are not present in the product; for dietary supplements, so called "zero-value" nutrients must not be listed in the facts box unless claims are being made about them. Supplement facts boxes also may list the quantities of dietary ingredients such as herbs, amino acids, concentrates or metabolites (see **Figure 27-1**).

The *Food Allergen Labeling and Consumer Protection Act* of 2004 (*FALCP*) requires that foods and dietary supplements alert consumers to the presence of any of the "major" allergens.[20] Congress defined "major allergens" as the eight foods responsible for 90% of food allergies. The so-called "big 8" allergens are: milk, eggs, fish, crustacean shellfish, tree nuts, peanuts, wheat and soybeans. Allergens must be declared by their common or usual name (i.e., milk, peanuts, wheat, etc.) and may either be declared in the ingredient list or in a separate statement. The species must be listed when fish, crustacean shellfish or tree nut allergens are declared.

Claims Permitted on Dietary Supplement Products

NLEA permitted nutrient content claims such as "high in fiber" or "rich source of vitamin C" on foods and dietary supplements. The guidelines for determining whether a product is eligible to bear such claims are found in the following sections of the CFR:

- 21 CFR 101.13 Nutrient content claims—general principles.
- 21 CFR 101.54 Nutrient content claims for "good source," "high," "more," and "high potency"
- 21 CFR 101.56 Nutrient content claims for "light" or "lite"
- 21 CFR 101.60 Nutrient content claims for the calorie content of foods
- 21 CFR 101.61 Nutrient content claims for the sodium content of foods
- 21 CFR 101.62 Nutrient content claims for fat, fatty acid and cholesterol content of foods
- 21 CFR 101.65 Implied nutrient content claims and related label statements
- 21 CFR 101.67 Use of nutrient content claims for butter
- 21 CFR 101.69 Petitions for nutrient content claims

Figure 27-1. Sample Supplement Facts Boxes

Supplement Facts

Serving Size 1 cup (228g)
Servings Per Container 2

Amount Per Serving

Calories 260	Calories from Fat 120

	% Daily Value*
Total Fat 13g	20%
Saturated Fat 5g	25%
Trans Fat 2g	
Cholesterol 30mg	10%
Sodium 660mg	28%
Total Carbohydrate 31g	10%
Dietary Fiber 0g	0%
Sugars 5g	
Protein 5g	

Vitamin A 4%	•	Vitamin C 2%	
Calcium 15%	•	Iron 4%	

Supplement Facts

Serving Size: 1 capsule
Servings Per Container: 30

	Amount per serving	% Daily Value
Vitamin A	2,500 IU	50%
Vitamin C	2.3 mg	4%
Vitamin D	165 IU	41%
Vitamin E	1.6 IU	5%
Thiamin	4.8 mg	320%
Riboflavin	2.2 mg	130%
Niacin	26 mg	130%
Vitamin B6	4.2 mg	210%
Vitamin B12	2.4 mg	40%
Pantothenic acid	8.8 mg	88%
Calcium	11 mg	1%
Iron	1.6 mg	9%
Magnesium	0.2 mg	<1%
Zinc	0.2 mg	1%
Selenium	15 mcg	21%
Copper	0.04 mg	2%
Manganese	0.03 mg	2%
Molybdenum	20 mcg	27%
Potassium	0.4 mg	<1%
Cobalt	10 mcg	†
Lecithin (from soybean)	14 mg	†
Rutin	5 mg	†

Percent Daily Value are based on a 2,000 calorie diet.
† Daily value not established.

INGREDIENTS: THIAMIN HYDROCHLORIDE, THIAMIN
HYDROCHLORIDE, THIAMIN HYDROCHLORIDE, THIAMIN
HYDROCHLORIDE

In addition, *NLEA* provided for the establishment of allowable health claims. Petitions for such claims may be made for foods, supplements or related ingredients when the benefits of the ingredients have been documented in publically available scientific literature. As a result, FDA has approved allowable health claims based upon significant scientific agreement of data supporting the claims. Examples of claims include:

Calcium
Regular exercise and a healthy diet with enough calcium help teen and young adult white and Asian women maintain good bone health and may reduce their high risk of osteoporosis later in life.

Soluble Fiber
Soluble fiber from foods such as oats, as part of a diet low in saturated fat and cholesterol, may reduce the risk of heart disease. A serving of oats supplies x grams of the 3 grams of soluble fiber from oats necessary per day to have this effect.

Specific information about allowable health claims can be found in the following regulations:
- 21 CFR 101.70 Petitions for health claims
- 21 CFR 101.71 Health claims: claims not authorized

- 21 CFR 101.72 Health claims: calcium and osteoporosis
- 21 CFR 101.73 Health claims: dietary lipids and cancer
- 21 CFR 101.74 Health claims: sodium and hypertension
- 21 CFR 101.75 Health claims: dietary saturated fat and cholesterol and risk of coronary heart disease
- 21 CFR 101.76 Health claims: fiber-containing grain products, fruits and vegetables and cancer
- 21 CFR 101.77 Health claims: fruits, vegetables and grain products that contain fiber, particularly soluble fiber, and risk of coronary heart disease
- 21 CFR 101.78 Health claims: fruits and vegetables and cancer
- 21 CFR 101.79 Health claims: Folate and neural tube defects
- 21 CFR 101.80 Health claims: dietary noncariogenic carbohydrate sweeteners and dental caries
- 21 CFR 101.81 Health claims: Soluble fiber from certain foods and risk of coronary heart disease (CHD)
- 21 CFR 101.82 Health claims: Soy protein and risk of coronary heart disease (CHD)
- 21 CFR 101.83 Health claims: plant sterol/stanol esters and risk of coronary heart disease (CHD)

Provisions in the *Food and Drug Administration Modernization Act* of 1997 (*FDAMA*)[21] allow the use of claims based on current, published authoritative statements from "a scientific body of the United States with official responsibility for public health protection or research directly related to human nutrition." The law specifically notes that some such authoritative scientific bodies include the National Academy of Sciences (NAS) or any of its subdivisions, the National Institutes of Health (NIH) and the Centers for Disease Control and Prevention (CDC). *FDAMA* further provided that such claims could be made 120 days after submission of a notification of the claim. *FDAMA* claim notifications must include: the exact wording of the claim; a concise description of the basis for determining that the requirements for an authoritative statement have been satisfied; a copy of the referenced authoritative statement; and, for a health claim, "a balanced representation of the scientific literature relating to the relationship between a nutrient and a disease or health-related condition to which the claim refers," or, for a nutrient content claim, "a balanced representation of the scientific literature relating to the nutrient level to which the claim refers." FDA has issued guidance[22] but has not published specific regulations on *FDAMA* claims. Current authorized *FDAMA* claims cover:

- Choline Nutrient Content Claims
- Fluoride and the Risk of Dental Caries
- Potassium and the Risk of High Blood Pressure and Stroke
- Saturated Fat, Cholesterol and Trans Fat, and the Risk of Heart Disease
- Substitution of Saturated Fat with Unsaturated Fatty Acids and Risk of Heart Disease
- Whole Grain Foods and the Risk of Heart Disease and Certain Cancers

Yet another class of claims, "qualified health claims," has been created as a result of the court decision in *Pearson v. Shalala*. In this suit, FDA's general health claims regulations for dietary supplements and the agency's decision not to authorize health claims for four specific substance/disease relationships were challenged. A district court first ruled for FDA (14 F. Supp. 2d 10 (D.D.C. 1998)). However, on appeal, the US Court of Appeals for the DC Circuit reversed the lower court's decision (164 F.3d 650 (D.C. Cir. 1999)). The appeals court ruled that the First Amendment does not permit FDA to reject health claims that are deemed potentially misleading unless the agency also determines that no disclaimer would eliminate the potential deception. The disclaimers mentioned in the decision are what "qualify" the health claim. In general, qualified health claims are not supported by data that meet the standard of significant scientific agreement[23] required for health claims and are qualified by inclusion of a statement regarding the strength

of the data. Examples of qualified health claims include:

Omega-3 Fatty Acids
Supportive but not conclusive research shows that consumption of EPA and DHA omega-3 fatty acids may reduce the risk of coronary heart disease. One serving of [Name of the food] provides [ ] gram of EPA and DHA omega-3 fatty acids. [See nutrition information for total fat, saturated fat, and cholesterol content.]

B Vitamins
As part of a well-balanced diet that is low in saturated fat and cholesterol, Folic Acid, Vitamin B6 and Vitamin B12 may reduce the risk of vascular disease. FDA evaluated the above claim and found that, while it is known that diets low in saturated fat and cholesterol reduce the risk of heart disease and other vascular diseases, the evidence in support of the above claim is inconclusive.

Other qualified health claims cover the relationships between:
- selenium and cancer
- antioxidant vitamins and cancer
- phosphatidylserine and cognitive dysfunction and dementia
- nuts and heart disease
- walnuts and heart disease
- monounsaturated fatty acids from olive oil and coronary heart disease
- green tea and cancer
- chromium picolinate and diabetes
- calcium and colon/rectal cancer and calcium and recurrent colon/rectal polyps
- calcium and hypertension, pregnancy-induced hypertension and preeclampsia
- tomatoes and/or tomato sauce and prostate, ovarian, gastric and pancreatic cancers
- unsaturated fatty acids from canola oil and reduced risk of coronary heart disease
- corn oil and corn oil-containing products and a reduced risk of heart disease
- folic acid and neural tube birth defects[24]
- (Note that there also is a folic acid/neural tube defect health claim.)

DSHEA allowed statements of nutritional support to be made for dietary supplements. Statements of nutritional support may discuss: the benefit of the supplement in relation to a classic nutrient deficiency disease; the role of a nutrient or dietary ingredient in affecting the structure or function of the human body or its systems; the documented mechanism by which a nutrient or dietary ingredient acts to maintain the structure or function of the body; or general well-being supported from consumption of a nutrient or dietary ingredient. All such claims must be truthful, not misleading, supported by scientific data and accompanied by the following disclaimer: "This statement has not been evaluated by the Food and Drug Administration. This product is not intended to diagnose, treat, cure, or prevent any disease."[25]

If claims are made regarding nutrient deficiency diseases such as scurvy from lack of vitamin C, the prevalence of the disease in the US must be disclosed. Since such nutrient deficiency diseases are rare, most claims made about dietary supplement products discuss the manner and/or mechanism by which a dietary ingredient affects or maintains human structure or function. Since dietary supplements may not be marketed to "diagnose, treat, cure, or prevent any disease," these so-called structure/function claims may only describe how the supplement affects or maintains the normal, healthy structure or normal, healthy function of the human body and its systems.

To assist industry in crafting acceptable structure/function claims, FDA has published regulations[26] and guidance[27] that define disease and provide criteria for evaluating whether dietary supplement claims are disease claims. The definition of "disease" is listed in 21 CFR 101.93(g)(1) as "damage to an organ, part, structure, or system of the body such that it does not function properly (e.g., cardiovascular disease), or a state of health leading to such dysfunctioning (e.g., hypertension); except that diseases resulting from essential nutrient deficiencies (e.g., scurvy, pellagra) are not included in this definition." Section 101.93(g)(2) lists 10 criteria for identifying statements that are prohibited disease claims, which state explicitly or imply that a dietary supplement product:

1. has an effect on a specific disease or class of diseases
2. has an effect on the characteristic signs or symptoms of a specific disease or class of diseases, using scientific or lay terminology
3. has an effect on an abnormal condition associated with a natural state or process, if the abnormal condition is uncommon or can cause significant or permanent harm
4. has an effect on a disease or diseases through: a) the name of the product; b) a statement that the product contains an ingredient that is not listed in the definition of dietary ingredients and that has been regulated by FDA as a drug and is well known to consumers for its use or claimed use in preventing or treating a disease; c) citation of a publication or reference, if the citation refers to a disease use; d) use of the term "disease" or "diseased," except in general statements about disease prevention that do not refer explicitly or implicitly to a specific disease or class of diseases or to a specific product or ingredient; or e) use of pictures, vignettes, symbols or other means
5. belongs to a class of products that is intended to diagnose, mitigate, treat, cure or prevent a disease

6. is a substitute for a product that is a therapy for a disease
7. augments a particular therapy or drug action that is intended to diagnose, mitigate, treat, cure or prevent a disease or class of diseases
8. has a role in the body's response to a disease or to a vector of disease
9. treats, prevents or mitigates adverse events associated with a therapy for a disease, if the adverse events constitute diseases
10. otherwise suggests an effect on a disease or diseases

Dietary supplements may be marketed to affect certain conditions that are considered part of typical, everyday living due to their mild nature and infrequent occurrence. Such conditions that are not considered diseases typically resolve without requiring medical attention. They include occasional irregularity and mild stress due to everyday living and occasional sleeplessness. It is clear that these same symptoms can indicate disease if they are not mild or occasional.

In order to legally make structure/function or any other type of claim about dietary supplement products, the manufacturer must have data to substantiate the claim. FDA has published a draft guidance on dietary supplement claim substantiation.[28] The guidance refers to the FTC standard of competent and reliable scientific evidence, defined in FTC case law as "tests, analyses, research, studies, or other evidence based on the expertise of professionals in the relevant area, that has been conducted and evaluated in an objective manner by persons qualified to do so, using procedures generally accepted in the profession to yield accurate and reliable results."[29] The level of substantiating evidence sufficient for a particular claim is affected by the language and meaning of the claim, the quality of the studies and the relevance of the studies to the actual product, as well as the total body of evidence relating to the claim. The data substantiating product claims are not submitted to FDA but should be available if needed to answer any questions that may arise regarding the claim.

Third-Party Literature

Although dietary supplements may not be marketed to "diagnose, treat, cure or prevent any disease," many dietary ingredients—particularly herbs, botanicals and glandular extracts—have been used historically in traditional and folk medicine of various cultures. This body of information is difficult to use in dietary supplement promotional materials without violating regulations on allowable claims for dietary supplement products. Section 403B of *DSHEA* makes provision for the use of "third-party literature" by stating that "a publication, including an article, a chapter in a book, or an official abstract of a peer-reviewed scientific publication that appears in an article and was prepared by the author or the editors of the publication, which is reprinted in its entirety, shall not be defined as labeling when used in connection with the sale of a dietary supplement to consumers."[30]

The provision for the use of third-party literature goes on to list criteria to which the information must conform. Any articles, books or other literature used in the sale of dietary supplements must:

- be truthful and not misleading
- not promote a particular manufacturer or brand of a dietary supplement
- be displayed or presented with other such items on the same subject matter, so as to present a balanced view of the available scientific information on a dietary supplement
- be displayed physically separated from the dietary supplements
- not have appended to it any information by sticker or any other method

The act also states that these criteria "shall not apply to or restrict a retailer or wholesaler of dietary supplements in any way whatsoever in the sale of books or other publications as a part of the business of such retailer or wholesaler."[31]

Claim Submission

Dietary supplement manufacturers must notify ONPLDS of any claims or statements of nutritional support they wish to make about their products. The claims must be submitted no later than 30 days after first using the claims in the marketplace. Claims submitted to ONPLDS are reviewed, but not approved; however, FDA may send a letter objecting to the claims in response to the submission.

Supplement Advertising and the FTC

FTC is dually charged with ensuring that US consumers are protected from fraud, deception and unfair business practices and that a fair and competitive marketplace exists for businesses. The agency has investigative, enforcement and litigation authority over many areas that impact businesses and consumers daily. FTC's Division of Advertising Practices is the nation's enforcer of federal truth-in-advertising laws. Among other things, this division's law enforcement activities focus on claims for products promising health benefits including foods, drugs, medical devices and dietary supplements.

FDA works closely with FTC under a 1971 memorandum of understanding[32] governing the division of responsibilities between the two agencies. FDA has primary responsibility for claims appearing on product labeling, including packaging, inserts and other promotional materials distributed at the point of sale. FTC has primary responsibility for claims made in advertising, including print and broadcast advertisements, infomercials, websites, catalogs and similar direct marketing materials.

The most basic requirement of FTC regulations is that all advertisements must be truthful, not misleading and appropriately substantiated. FTC's advertising guide for the supplement industry[33] provides detailed examples of claims, how to identify claims and ways to determine adequate levels of substantiation.

Other Regulations

The *Public Health Security and Bioterrorism Preparedness and Response Act* of 2002[34] (*Bioterrorism Act*) amended the *FD&C Act* to require facilities that manufacture, process, hold or package food to register with FDA. FDA has stated that, according to the *FD&C Act*, dietary supplements and dietary ingredients are "food" and therefore, facilities that manufacture these products must register.[35] Registration may be submitted electronically[36] or by mail or facsimile. As detailed in 21 CFR 1.232, the following information must be included to register a dietary supplement facility:

- facility name, full address and telephone number
- parent company name, address and telephone number, if the facility is a subsidiary
- owner, operator and agent in charge names, addresses and telephone numbers; foreign facilities must also provide the name, address and telephone number of their US agent
- emergency contact telephone number; foreign facilities must also provide an emergency contact phone number for their US agent
- all trade names the facility uses
- applicable food product categories as identified in 21 CFR 170.3
- a statement in which the owner, operator or agent in charge certifies that the information submitted is true and accurate; the person submitting the registration must also provide a statement certifying that the information submitted is true and accurate if he or she is someone other than the owner, operator or agent in charge

Facility registrations must be updated within 60 days of any changes in the information submitted. Form FDA 3537 is used for both registering and updating facility registrations.

Dietary Supplement Good Manufacturing Practices

More than a decade after receiving authorization from Congress to establish current Good Manufacturing Practices (CGMPs) for dietary supplements and four years after FDA published its proposed rule,[37] the agency released its final rule,[38] 21 CFR 111 Current Good Manufacturing Practice in manufacturing, packaging, labeling, or holding operations for dietary supplements ("dietary supplement CGMP rule"). Previously, dietary supplement manufacturing and distribution were regulated under "umbrella" CGMPs established for food generally, and were not subject to individualized CGMPs. Although the general food CGMPs in 21 CFR 110 apply to a variety of food products, including dietary supplements, they do not address the unique characteristics of dietary supplements.

The dietary supplement CGMP rule in 21 CFR 111 establishes the minimum CGMPs necessary for activities related to manufacturing, packaging, labeling or holding dietary supplements to ensure product quality.

The dietary supplement CGMP rule went into effect 24 August 2007. However, FDA established the following compliance dates, which are associated with the size of the dietary supplement company in terms of full-time equivalent employees. The compliance date was 25 June 2008 for companies with more than 500 employees; June 2009 for companies with fewer than 500 employees; and June 2010 for companies with fewer than 20 employees.

The dietary supplement CGMP rule applies to all domestic and foreign establishments that manufacture, package, label or hold dietary supplements, including those involved with testing, quality control, packaging and labeling, and distribution in the US. The dietary supplement CGMP rule does not apply to retail establishments holding dietary supplements only for purposes of direct retail sale to individual consumers, although this exception does not include a retailer's warehouse or other storage facility or a warehouse or other storage facility that sells directly to individual consumers. The dietary supplement CGMP rules do not apply to dietary ingredient suppliers.

The dietary supplement CGMP rule requires:
- written procedures for personnel (Subpart B)
- cleaning the physical plant, including pest control (Subpart C)
- calibrating instruments and controls (Subpart D)
- calibrating, inspecting and checking automated, mechanical or electronic equipment (Subpart D)
- maintaining, cleaning and sanitizing equipment and utensils (Subpart D)
- quality control operations, including conducting a material review and making a disposition decision (Subpart F)
- components, packaging, labels and labeling (Subpart G)
- laboratory operations (Subpart J)
- manufacturing operations (Subpart K)
- packaging and labeling operations (Subpart L)
- holding and distributing operations (Subpart M)
- returned dietary supplements (Subpart N)
- product complaints (Subpart O)

The dietary supplement CGMP rule is divided into 16 user-friendly question and answer subparts (Subparts A–P) and was published in *Federal Register* Volume 72, No. 121 on 25 June 2007. Each subpart is presented according to its specific operations to make it easier to find the relevant production and process control requirements.

Following is the general outline of GMP concepts. The outline is not intended to be complete or all-inclusive, but does provide some key points.
- Establish minimum requirements for personnel, including rules to prevent microbial contamination from sick personnel, employee and supervisor qualifications and record retention (21 CFR 111.10, 21 CFR 111.12, 21 CFR 111.13 and 21 CFR 111.14).
- Establish minimum requirements for physical plant and grounds, equipment and utensils, design and construction, including requirements for written procedures, the use of automated, mechanical or electronic equipment, and record development, retention and maintenance (21 CFR 111.15, 21 CFR 111.16, 21 CFR 111.20, 21 CFR 111.23, 21 CFR 111.25, 21 CFR 111.27, 21 CFR 111.30 and 21 CFR 111.35).
- Require the establishment of specifications in the production and process control system that will ensure dietary supplements meet the identity, purity, strength and composition established in specifications, and are properly packaged and labeled as specified in the master manufacturing record (21 CFR 111.55, 21 CFR 111.60, 21 CFR 111.70, 21 CFR 111.75 and 21 CFR 111.77).
- Permit the use of a "certificate of analysis" from a component supplier for specifications other than the identity of a dietary ingredient in lieu of having manufacturers conduct tests or examinations on all components received (21 CFR 111.75).
- Establish minimum requirements for representative samples and reserve samples (21 CFR 111.80 and 21 CFR 111.83).
- Establish minimum requirements for quality control and require implementation of quality control operations to ensure the quality of a dietary supplement (21 CFR 111.105, 21 CFR 111.110, 21 CFR 111.113, 21 CFR 111.117 and 21 CFR 111.120).
- Require the preparation and use of a written master manufacturing record for each unique formulation of manufactured dietary supplement and for each batch size to ensure manufacturing process is performed consistently and to ensure uniformity in the finished product from batch to batch (21 CFR 111.205, 21 CFR 111.210,21 and 21 CFR 111.123)
- Require design and conduct of all manufacturing

operations of dietary supplements in accordance with adequate sanitation principles to prevent contamination of components or dietary supplements (21 CFR 111.355, 21 CFR 111.360 and 21 CFR 111.365).

- Require testing of a subset of finished product batches, basing the testing system on either a sound statistical sampling plan or testing of all finished batches (21 CFR 111.75).
- Establish minimum requirements for the batch production record (21 CFR 111.255 and 21 CFR 111.260).
- Require the establishment and use of laboratory control processes related to establishing specifications and to the selection and use of testing and examination methods (21 CFR 111.303, 21 CFR 111.310, 21 CFR 111.315, 21 CFR 111.320 and 21 CFR 111.325).
- Establish minimum requirements for packaging and labeling operations to assure the quality of the dietary supplement and that the dietary supplement is packaged and labeled as specified in the master manufacturing record (21 CFR 111.160 and 21 CFR 111.415).
- Require reserve samples of dietary supplements to be held in a manner that protects against contamination and deterioration (21 CFR 111.465).
- Require holding of components and dietary supplements under appropriate conditions of temperature, humidity and light so that the identity, purity, strength and composition of the components and dietary supplements are not affected and are protected against mix-up, contamination or deterioration (21 CFR 111.455).
- Establish minimum quality control operations required for returned dietary supplements and require identification and quarantine of returned dietary supplements until quality control personnel conduct a material review and make a disposition decision (21 CFR 111.130, 21 CFR 111.503, 21 CFR 111.510, 21 CFR 111.515, 21 CFR 111.525, 21 CFR 111.530 and 21 CFR 111.535).
- Require a qualified person to investigate any "product complaint" that involves a possible failure of a dietary supplement to meet any CGMP requirement, with oversight by quality control personnel (21 CFR 111.553 and 21 CFR 111.560).
- Establish minimum requirements for records and recordkeeping (21 CFR 111.605 and 21 CFR 111.610).
- Require records associated with the manufacture, packaging, labeling or holding of a dietary supplement to be kept for one year beyond the shelf life dating or, if shelf life dating is not used, for two

years beyond the date of distribution of the last batch of dietary supplements associated with those records (21 CFR 111.605).

FDA examined the economic implications of the dietary supplement CGMP rule as required by the *Regulatory Flexibility Act* (5 U.S.C. 601–612) and determined that the rule would have a significant economic impact on a substantial number of small entities. In compliance with Section 212 of the *Small Business Regulatory Enforcement Fairness Act* (Public Law 104–121), FDA has released a Small Entity Compliance Guide[39] (SECG), stating in plain language the requirements of the 21 CFR 111 regulations. FDA issued this SECG as Level 2 guidance consistent with the agency's good guidance practices regulation (21 CFR 10.115(c)(2)). This SECG restates, in simplified format and language, FDA's requirements for Current Good Manufacturing Practice in manufacturing, packaging, labeling, or holding operations for dietary supplements, including the requirements for a Petition to Request an Exemption from 100 Percent Identity Testing of Dietary Ingredients. In addition, the SECG includes several recommendations made by FDA in the dietary supplement CGMP rule so that the guidance in those recommendations will be readily accessible to small businesses.

On 15 December 2010, FDA took new steps aimed at keeping consumers safe from harmful products that are marketed as dietary supplements and that contain undeclared or deceptively labeled ingredients.

The new steps include:

- a letter from the FDA commissioner to the dietary supplement industry emphasizing its legal obligation and responsibilities to prevent tainted products from reaching the U.S. market[40]
- a new rapid public notification system (RSS Feed) on its website to more quickly warn consumers about these products[41]

Companies that make or distribute tainted products may receive Warning Letters and/or face enforcement actions such as product seizures, injunctions and criminal prosecution. Responsible individuals may also face criminal prosecution.

Adverse Event Reporting

On 22 December 2006, President George W. Bush signed into law the *Dietary Supplement and Nonprescription Drug Consumer Protection Act* (Pub. L. 109-462, 120 Stat. 3469). This law amends the *FD&C Act* with respect to adverse event reporting and recordkeeping for dietary supplements and nonprescription drugs marketed without an approved application.

The manufacturer, packer or distributor whose name (pursuant to section 403(e)(1) of the *FD&C Act*) appears on the label of a dietary supplement marketed in the US is required to submit to FDA all serious adverse event reports associated with use of the dietary supplement in the US. The effective date for compliance with the requirements of this law was 22 December 2007.

An "adverse event" is "any health-related event associated with the use of a dietary supplement that is adverse."

A "serious adverse event" is an adverse event that results in:

- death
- a life-threatening experience
- inpatient hospitalization
- a persistent or significant disability
- incapacity
- a congenital anomaly or birth defect
- a medical or surgical intervention, based on reasonable medical judgment, to prevent an outcome described above

The *Dietary Supplement and Nonprescription Drug Consumer Protection Act* usually refers to the entity (manufacturer, packer or distributor) that is required to submit a serious adverse event report to FDA as the "responsible person." Serious adverse event reports, as well as all follow-up reports of new medical information received within one year after the initial report, must be submitted to FDA on MedWatch Form 3500A along with a copy of the dietary supplement label and any other attachments no later than 15 business days after the report is received by the responsible person. However, voluntary reports of adverse events associated with a dietary supplement may be submitted on MedWatch Form 3500, the voluntary reporting form.

FDA requires that mandatory reports using MedWatch Form 3500A for serious adverse events associated with the use of dietary supplements be submitted in hard copy by mail only. FDA does not currently accept dietary supplement serious adverse event reports electronically or by facsimile.

The following five data elements,[42] at a minimum, are necessary for FDA to avoid duplication in its adverse event reports database and to interpret the significance of adverse events, facilitate follow-up and detect fraud:

- an identifiable injured person
- an identifiable initial reporter
- responsible person's identity and contact information (i.e., the manufacturer, packer or distributor submitting the serious adverse event report to FDA)
- a suspect dietary supplement
- a serious adverse event or fatal outcome

If a serious adverse event involves multiple dietary supplements that are manufactured, packaged or distributed by the same responsible person, the responsible person should submit only one serious adverse event report to FDA on Form 3500A. If a serious adverse event involves multiple suspect dietary supplements that were manufactured, packaged or distributed by more than one responsible person (e.g., manufacturers A and B), and if the event is reported to one of the responsible persons (manufacturer A), that responsible person (manufacturer A) should submit a serious adverse event report to FDA, identifying both its own product(s) and manufacturer B's product(s) in the Suspect Product section of Form 3500A. In such a case, manufacturer A should send manufacturer B a copy of the submitted Form 3500A, including manufacturer A's report number. Manufacturer B need not submit a separate report to FDA for the serious adverse event unless manufacturer B has information about the serious adverse event that was not provided to FDA in manufacturer A's report. If manufacturer B does have such information, it must be reported to FDA as a follow-up report of new medical information, accompanied by a copy of manufacturer A's serious adverse event report. It is not necessary for manufacturer B to submit its own separate serious adverse event report on Form 3500A.

If the serious adverse event involves a nonprescription drug product marketed without an approved application and a dietary supplement that is also manufactured, packaged or distributed by the same responsible person, and the initial reporter views each product as suspect, the responsible person should submit one report about the serious adverse event to both the Center for Drug Evaluation and Research (CDER) and the Center for Food Safety and Applied Nutrition (CFSAN). The report should include information about both suspect products in section C and should use one manufacturer report number.

There is no requirement to provide a sample of the dietary supplement to FDA with the adverse event report, and the agency does not recommend that a sample be submitted unless requested.

Instructions for completing MedWatch Form 3500A to report a serious adverse event associated with a dietary supplement can be found at www.fda.gov/Safety/MedWatch/HowToReport/DownloadForms/ucm149238.htm.

The responsible person must maintain records related to each report of a serious adverse event for six years. These records should include, at a minimum, copies of the following:

- the responsible person's serious adverse event report to FDA on MedWatch Form 3500A, with attachments
- any new medical information about the serious adverse event received by the responsible person
- any reports to FDA of new medical information related to the serious adverse event
- communications between the responsible person and

- o the initial reporter
- o any other person(s) who provided information related to the adverse event

Any new medical information received within one year of the initial report must be submitted to FDA within 15 business days of receipt.

Dietary supplements labeled on or after 22 December 2007 need to include a domestic address or domestic phone number at which the responsible person can receive reports of adverse events.[43] Products that do not include such information (such as those imported from foreign manufacturers) will be deemed "misbranded" and subject to regulatory action by FDA.

Import and Export Regulations

The *Bioterrorism Act* of 2002, Section 307, added Section 801(m) to the *FD&C Act* requiring that FDA receive prior notice for food imported or offered for import into the US. Prior notice is notification to FDA that an article of food, including animal feed or pet food, is being imported or offered for import into the US in advance of the arrival of the article of food at the US border. Section 801(m) also provides that if an article of food arrives at the port of arrival with inadequate prior notice (e.g., no prior notice, inaccurate prior notice or untimely prior notice), the food is subject to refusal of admission under Section 801(m)(1) of the act and may not be delivered to the importer, owner or consignee.

The prior notice must be submitted to FDA electronically via either the US Customs and Border Protection (Customs) Automated Broker Interface (ABI) of the Automated Commercial System (ACS) or FDA's Prior Notice System Interface (FDA PNSI).

Prior notice must be received and confirmed electronically by FDA no more than five days before arrival and, as specified by the mode of transportation below, no less than:

1. two hours before arrival by land by road
2. four hours before arrival by air or by rail
3. eight hours before arrival by water
4. the time consistent with the timeframe established for the mode of transportation for an article of food carried by or otherwise accompanying an individual if it is subject to prior notice

Instructions for submitting prior notice and information on prior notice of imported foods can be found at www.fda. gov/Food/GuidanceComplianceRegulatoryInformation/ PriorNoticeofImportedFoods/default.htm. Additional information on Customs' procedures for prior notice can be found at www.cbp.gov.

Failure to submit prior notice by a person who imports or offers for import an article of food is a prohibited act under Section 301(ee) of the act (21 U.S.C. 331(ee)) and could result in the US bringing civil, criminal and debarment actions against him or her. When it is consistent with the public protection responsibilities of the agency, and depending upon the nature of the violation, FDA gives individuals and firms an opportunity to take voluntary and prompt corrective action before initiating regulatory actions.[44] Accordingly, FDA may elect to refuse prior notices or send compliance letters to give the responsible parties warning before pursuing other regulatory actions, e.g., injunction, prosecution, etc.

The regulatory actions for violations include:

- refusal under Section 801(m) of the act for no prior notice, inaccurate prior notice or untimely prior notice
- hold under Section 801(l) of the act for importing or offering for import food from a foreign facility that is not registered under section 415 of the act
- injunction under Section 302 of the act
- prosecution under Sections 301 and 303 of the act
- debarment under Section 306 of the act
- Customs seizure and assessment of civil monetary penalties for violation of any laws enforced by Customs and Border Protection, including 19 U.S.C. 1595a(b), against any person who directs, assists financially or otherwise, or is in any way concerned in the importation of any merchandise contrary to law

The *Bioterrorism Act* requires domestic and foreign facilities that manufacture, process, pack or hold food for consumption in the US to register with FDA. In addition, the act amended Chapter VIII of the *FD&C Act* by adding Section 801(l), which requires any food for human and animal consumption from an unregistered foreign facility that is imported or offered for import to be held at the port of entry until the foreign facility has been registered.

In addition, the *Bioterrorism Act*, Section 305, added Section 415 to the *FD&C Act* to require domestic and foreign facilities that manufacture, process, pack or hold food for human or animal consumption in the US to register with FDA. Dietary supplements and dietary ingredients are regulated as foods by FDA. The *Bioterrorism Act* makes failure to register a prohibited act under Section 301 of the *FD&C Act*.

Owners, operators or agents in charge of domestic or foreign facilities that manufacture/process, pack or hold foods for human or animal consumption in the US are required to register the facility with FDA. Domestic facilities are required to register whether or not food from the facility enters interstate commerce.

Foreign facilities that manufacture, process, pack or hold food also are required to register unless food from that facility undergoes further processing (including packaging) by another foreign facility before the food is exported to the US. However, if the subsequent foreign facility performs only a minimal activity, such as putting on a label, both facilities are required to register. Foreign facilities are required to designate a US agent for purposes of the registration regulation. The US agent acts as a communications link between FDA and the foreign facility. FDA will treat representations by the US agent as those of the foreign facility, and will consider information or documents provided to the US agent equivalent to providing the information or documents to the foreign facility.

Registrants must register using Form FDA 3537. Registrations can be submitted in hardcopy format by mail, electronically via the Internet, on CD-ROM or by fax. Instructions for completing Form 3537 and additional information on registration of food facilities can be found at www.fda.gov/Food/GuidanceComplianceRegulatoryInformation/RegistrationofFoodFacilities/default.htm.

Section 801(e)(1) of the *FD&C Act* states that a food intended for export must not be deemed to be adulterated or misbranded under the act if it: (A) accords to the specifications of the foreign purchaser; (B) is not in conflict with the laws of the country to which it is intended for export; (C) is labeled on the outside of the shipping package that it is intended for export; and (D) is not sold or offered for sale in domestic commerce.[45] Dietary ingredients and dietary supplements for export are subject to Section 801(e)(1) of the act and would be subject to the notification and record-keeping requirements of 21 CFR 1.101.[46]

Currently, FDA issues the "certificate of free sale" as an export certificate for food, including dietary supplements that are legally marketed in the US.[47] The criteria needed to request a certificate of free sale for dietary supplements can be found at www.fda.gov/Food/InternationalActivities/Exports/ExportCertificates/ucm152749.htm. A certificate of free sale is only issued for products manufactured in the US.

The requirements for prior notice do not apply to dietary supplements that are imported and then exported without leaving the port of arrival until export.

Homeopathic Products

The term "homeopathy" is derived from the Greek words *homeo* (similar) and *pathos* (suffering or disease). Homeopathy is the practice of treating the syndromes and conditions constituting disease with remedies that have produced similar syndromes and conditions in healthy subjects.[48]

History of Homeopathy in Food and Drug Law

As both the chief sponsor of the *FD&C Act* and a homeopathic physician, Senator Royal Copeland of New York amended the *Food and Drugs Act* of 1906 by defining "drug" to include those homeopathic drugs listed in the *Homeopathic Pharmacopoeia of the United States* (*HPUS*).

For five decades (from 1938–88), homeopathic drugs were sold in a regulatory vacuum. FDA action was based upon institutional understanding and informal agreements between agency officials and industry members. From 1982–88, the industry, professional and consumer members of the community through the American Homeopathic Pharmacists Association worked with FDA in the development of a regulatory framework called a Compliance Policy Guide, CPG 7132.15 "Conditions under which homeopathic drugs may be marketed." CPG 7132.15 provides guidance on the regulation of over-the-counter (OTC) and prescription homeopathic drugs, and delineates those conditions under which homeopathic drugs may ordinarily be marketed in the US.

FDA does not regulate homeopathic drugs in precisely the same way as conventional or allopathic drugs; in fact, the agency treats homeopathic drugs, both prescription and OTC, quite differently. Unlike conventional drugs, homeopathic drugs are not subject to premarket approval, which involves filing a new drug application (NDA) in order to market the drug. Furthermore, unlike other OTC drugs, which are either required to be submitted for OTC review or to file an NDA, OTC homeopathic drugs are not subject to the FDA review process. Like some drug OTC products, homeopathic drugs need to comply with a monograph.

The FDA Compliance Policy Guide, CPG 7132.15 and *HPUS* form the basis for the regulation of homeopathic drugs in the US.[49]

Definition of Homeopathic Drugs

A homeopathic drug is any drug labeled as being homeopathic that is listed in *HPUS*, an addendum to it or its supplements. The potencies of homeopathic drugs are specified in terms of dilution, i.e., 1x (1/10 dilution), 2x (1/100 dilution), etc. Homeopathic drug products must contain diluents commonly used in homeopathic pharmaceuticals. Drug products containing homeopathic ingredients in combination with nonhomeopathic active ingredients are not homeopathic drug products.

Homeopathic drugs generally must meet the standards for strength, quality and purity set forth in *HPUS*. *HPUS* is declared a legal source of information on homeopathic drug products in Section 201(g)(1) of the *FD&C Act*. *HPUS* is a compilation of standards for source, composition and preparation of homeopathic drugs, which the *FD&C Act* also recognized as an official compendium. Section 201(j) of the act (21 U.S.C. §321) defines the term "official compendium" as the "official *United States Pharmacopoeia*, official *Homeopathic Pharmacopoeia of the United States*, official *National Formulary* or any supplement to them."

Introduction to the Homeopathic Pharmacopoeia Convention of the United States (HPCUS)

The Homeopathic Pharmacopoeia Convention of the United States (HPCUS) is a nongovernmental, nonprofit, scientific organization composed of experts who have appropriate training and experience, and have demonstrated additional knowledge and interest in the principles of homeopathy. HPCUS is an autonomous body that works closely with FDA and homeopathic organizations. The HPCUS board appoints a Monograph Review Committee (MRC), a Pharmacopoeia Revision Committee (PRC) and a Council on Pharmacy to assist in its ongoing responsibilities.

HPCUS is responsible for the production and constant updating of *HPUS*. *HPUS* is published as the *Homeopathic Pharmacopoeia of the United States Revision Service*. *HPUS* is "written" by a group of pharmacists, physicians and lay people who meet three to six times a year to review monographs and pharmacy procedures. The *HPUS Revision Service*, also known as the subscription service, began in December 1988. One or two revisions are published each year. Annual subscription updates are required to keep the *HPUS Revision Service* current and official.

HPUS is divided into two sections, General Pharmacy and Drug Monographs. General Pharmacy contains all official manufacturing procedures for all official homeopathic dosage forms as well as labeling guidelines and administrative information. In addition, criteria and procedures for inclusion in *HPUS* are published. *HPUS* contains approximately 1,300 individual monographs of official drug substances. Each monograph lists complete identifying data for the drug as well as specific manufacturing standards.

The *HPUS* online database is a powerful tool that provides quick access to all *HPUS* publications. The database includes the most current monograph and quality control specifications, along with real-time updates. To access the *HPUS* online database, visit www.hpus.com.

HPUS Approval Process

To be included in *HPUS*, a drug must have sufficient clinical data or "drug proving" to show efficacy. In a homeopathic drug proving, a homeopathically prepared substance is administered to healthy volunteers in order to produce the symptoms specific to that substance and thereby reveal its inherent curative powers. During a homeopathic drug proving, the goal is to provoke temporary symptoms associated with the homeopathic medication. These symptoms are then arranged to form a symptom pattern or "remedy picture" that is specific to that particular homeopathic substance and provides the basis for a better understanding of its possible effects in patients.

To be eligible for inclusion in *HPUS*, the drug must meet the first three criteria and at least one of the latter four (4, 5, 6 or 7):

1. HPCUS has determined that the drug is safe and effective.
2. The drug must be prepared according to the specifications of the General Pharmacy and relevant sections of *HPUS*.
3. The submitted documentation must be in an approved format as set forth in the relevant sections of *HPUS*.
4. The therapeutic use of a new and nonofficial homeopathic drug is established by a homeopathic drug proving and clinical verification acceptable to HPCUS.
5. The therapeutic use of the drug is established through published documentation that the substance was in use prior to 1962. This documentation must include the symptom picture, including subjective and any available objective symptoms.
6. The therapeutic use of the drug is established by at least two adequately controlled, double-blind clinical studies using the drug as the single intervention; and the study is to be accompanied by adequate statistical analysis and adequate description of the symptom picture acceptable to HPCUS, including the subjective symptoms and, where appropriate, the objective symptomatology.
7. The drug's therapeutic use is established by: data gathered from clinical experience encompassing the symptom picture and pre- and post-treatment, including subjective and any available objective symptoms; or data documented in the medical literature (all sources of medical literature may be considered on a case-by-case basis) subjected to further verification (statistical and/or other forms of verification).

Homeopathic drug provings on healthy volunteers are carried out according to Hahnemann's classical directions, and also adhere to the current regulations for conventional clinical trials

Clinical verification of all or part of the symptom picture established in a homeopathic drug proving is designed to further demonstrate a homeopathic medication's potential clinical applicability. Clinical verification may also use a variety of methodologies in a prospective or retrospective fashion. The design and sample size will vary on a case-by-case basis, depending upon what is being verified (symptom picture, keynotes or a specific clinical indication). The responsibility for scientifically sound clinical verification protocol lies with the sponsor. The study design for the clinical verification of the symptoms gathered in a drug proving should be submitted to the MRC and the PRC for review prior to beginning clinical verification. For additional information, refer to the HPCUS *Guidelines for Homeopathic Drug Provings*, HPCUS Outline for Protocols for Homeopathic Drug Provings and HPCUS *Guidelines for Clinical Verification* (www.hpus.com).

To be considered for inclusion in *HPUS*, a monograph must adhere to the specified format and must be accompanied by documentation that it meets the eligibility criteria for inclusion in *HPUS*.

A sponsor desiring to have monographs considered for inclusion in *HPUS* must submit them to the editor. If the monographs are acceptable, the editor will forward them, with any comments and accompanying documentation, to the chairman of the MRC. The MRC will perform a comprehensive review of each monograph and recommend its categorization under one of three headings: approved for publication in *HPUS*; deferred for presentation of additional data; or not approved for publication in *HPUS*.

The editor will publish a list of the monographs that the MRC has recommended for the approved category and the not-approved category, and the reasons for the action taken, in an appropriate medium such as the *Journal of the American Institute of Homeopathy*, *Homeopathy Today* or *American Homeopathy*. The editor will also forward the annotated monographs, the monograph list and any accompanying documentation to the chairman of the PRC. A minimum of 90 days, beginning on the 15th day of the month of publication of the monograph list, is permitted for receipt of comments from the general public. At the end of the 90-day period, any public comments received by the editor will be forwarded to the PRC chairman. The PRC will perform a comprehensive review of each monograph and recommend categorization under one of three headings: approved for publication in *HPUS*; deferred for presentation of additional data; or not approved for publication in *HPUS*. MRC and PRC recommendations are reviewed and acted upon by the board of directors. If acceptable, the monograph is granted final approval for inclusion in *HPUS*, and the secretary notifies the sponsor of the board's decision.

Labeling and Advertising

All homeopathic products are drugs within the meaning of the *FD&C Act* and, therefore, are subject to applicable FDA regulations for labeling, advertising and promotion. Homeopathic drug product labeling must comply with the provisions of Sections 502 and 503 of the *FD&C Act* and 21 CFR 201. The label shall contain, in prominent type, the word "HOMEOPATHIC" or "Homeopathic."

The Statement of Ingredients must appear in accordance with Section 502(e) of the *FD&C Act* and 21 CFR 201.10. Labeling must bear a statement of the quantity and amount of ingredient(s) in the product in conformance with Section 502(b) of the act, as well as 21 CFR 201.10, expressed in homeopathic terms, e.g., 1x, 2x. On each label and package, the letters "HPUS" should be appended to the name of each official drug or drugs present in the product, e.g., "Arnica Montana 3X HPUS." In addition, the following statement must appear at the end of the formula section of each label when all product(s) contained therein are official: "The letters 'HPUS' indicate that the component(s) in this product is (are) officially monographed in the *Homeopathic Pharmacopoeia of the United States*. The designation 'HPUS' is restricted (or may be appended only) to those substances (or Homeopathic Drug Products) whose monographs have been reviewed by the

Convention and have been approved for publication in the current Pharmacopoeia by the Board of Directors."

Other general labeling requirements include the manufacturer, packer or distributor's name and place of business, in conformance with Section 502(b) and 21 CFR 201.1, adequate directions for use (Section 502(f) and 21 CFR 201.5) and Established Name (Section 502(e)(3) of the *FD&C Act* and 21 CFR 201.10). The label and labeling must be in the English language as described and provided for under 21 CFR 201.15(c)(1), although it is permissible for industry to include the labeling in both English and Latin.

The label of a prescription homeopathic drug product shall bear a statement of identity (21 CFR 201.50), declaration of net quantity of contents (21 CFR 201.51), a statement of the recommended or usual dosage (21 CFR 201.55) and information described under 21 CFR 201.56 and 21 CFR 201.57. An exemption from adequate directions for use under Section 503 is applicable only to prescription drugs. All prescription homeopathic drug products must bear the prescription legend, "Caution: Federal law prohibits dispensing without prescription" (Section 503(b)(1)), and a package insert bearing complete labeling information for the homeopathic practitioner must accompany the product.

The label of OTC homeopathic drug products must comply with the principal display panel provision (21 CFR 201.62); a statement of identity (21 CFR 201.61) shall conform to the provisions for declaring net quantity of contents under 21 CFR 201.62. OTC homeopathic drugs intended for systemic absorption, unless specifically exempted, must bear a warning statement in conformance with 21 CFR 201.63(a). Other warnings, such as those for indications conforming to those in OTC drug final regulations, are required as appropriate.

Homeopathic products intended solely for self-limiting disease conditions amenable to self-diagnosis (of symptoms) and treatment may be marketed OTC. Homeopathic products offered for conditions not amenable to OTC use must be marketed as prescription products. The criteria specified in Section 503(b) of the *FD&C Act* apply to the determination of prescription status for all drug products, including homeopathic drug products. If *HPUS* specifies a distinction between nonprescription and prescription status of products that is based upon strength and is more restrictive than Section 503(b) of the act, the more stringent criteria will apply.

Any drug included in *HPUS* is considered "official" and those not included in *HPUS* would be "nonofficial." According to the understanding, any official drug can be sold without any further documentation being generated by the manufacturer. Nonofficial drugs require the manufacturer to produce a proving or sufficient clinical data for FDA to make a determination as to whether the drug was, in fact, homeopathic.

If any homeopathic drug is promoted significantly beyond the recognized or customary practice of homeopathy, the priorities and procedures concerning FDA's policy on health fraud will apply (CPG 7150.10 "Health Fraud-Factors in Considering Regulatory Action" 5 June 1987).

Good Manufacturing Practices

All firms that manufacture, prepare, propagate, compound or otherwise process homeopathic drugs must register as drug establishments in conformance with Section 510 of the *FD&C Act* and 21 CFR 207.[50]

Homeopathic drug products must be manufactured in conformance with CGMPs Section 501(a)(2)(B) of the *FD&C Act* and 21 CFR 211. However, due to the unique nature of these drug products, there are two exemptions to this requirement. First, homeopathic drugs need not have expiration dating (21 CFR 211.137). Second, FDA proposed an amendment that exempted homeopathic drug products from the requirement for laboratory determination of identity and strength of each active ingredient prior to the release and distribution of the drug on the market (21 CFR 211.165). Until there is a final ruling on this proposed testing requirement amendment, FDA has a policy of not enforcing this regulation against homeopathic drugs.

Summary

- Dietary supplements are regulated as a class of food products and may be marketed to support the normal, healthy structure or function of the human body and its systems.
- Dietary supplements are subject to GMP regulations and adverse event reporting requirements, and facilities must be registered with FDA; however, product listing and premarket approval are not required.
- Homeopathic products are a class of drug products regulated through a Compliance Policy Guide.
- Homeopathic drug products are not subject to the NDA process. They are subject to approval by the Homeopathic Pharmacopoeia Convention of the United States (HPCUS) or must conform to monographs published in the *Homeopathic Pharmacopoeia of the United States* (HPUS).
- Homeopathic drug products must comply with labeling regulations found in 21 CFR 201.

References

1. Pray WS. *A History of Nonprescription Product Regulation*, Pharmaceutical Products Press, New York (2003).
2. "Chapter II: Background on dietary supplements." Commission on Dietary Supplement Labels. Available at www.health.gov/dietsupp/ch2.htm. Accessed 3 May 2011.
3. "Vitamin and Mineral Drug Products for Over-the-Counter Human Use." *Federal Register*, Vol 44, No. 53, p. 16126 (16 March 1979).
4. Pray WS. "The FDA, Vitamins, and the Dietary Supplement Industry." *US Pharm.* 2008;33(10):10–15.
5. Op cit 1.
6. *Nutrition Advertising Coordination Act* of 1991 (HR 1662 SC2).
7. *Dietary Supplement Consumer Protection Act* of 1993 (HR 2923 IH).
8. Op cit 3.
9. Soller RW. "Regulation in the Herb Market: The Myth of the 'Unregulated Industry.'" *HerbalGram.* 2000;49:64 American Botanical Council.
10. *Dietary Supplement Health and Education Act* of 1994 (Public Law 103-417, 103rd Congress).
11. FDA information on *Dietary Supplement Health and Education Act* of 1994, 1 December 1995. Available at www.fda.gov/Food/DietarySupplements/default.htm. Accessed 3 May 2011.
12. *Nutrition Labeling Education Act* of 1990 (Public Law 101-535, 101st Congress).
13. Op cit 6.
14. *Guidance for Industry: Factors that Distinguish Liquid Dietary Supplements from Beverages, Considerations Regarding Novel Ingredients, and Labeling for Beverages and Other Conventional Foods* (December 2009). Available at www.fda.gov/food/GuidanceComplianceRegulatoryInformation/GuidanceDocuments/ucm192702.htm. Accessed 3 May 2011.
15. 21 CFR 190.6 Requirement for premarket notification.
16. 21 CFR 1.3(b).
17. 21 CFR 1.3(a).
18. 21 CFR 101.36 Nutrition labeling of dietary supplements.
19. 21 CFR 101.9 Nutrition labeling of food.
20. *Food Allergen Labeling Consumer Protection Act* of 2004 (Public law 108-282).
21. *Food and Drug Administration Modernization Act* of 1997 (*FDAMA*) (Public Law 105-115).
22. "*FDA Modernization Act of 1997 (FDAMA)* Claims." Available at www.fda.gov/Food/LabelingNutrition/LabelClaims/FDAModernizationActFDAMAClaims/default.htm. Accessed 3 May 2011.
23. 21 CFR 101.14(c).
24. "Qualified Health Claims." Available at www.fda.gov/Food/LabelingNutrition/LabelClaims/QualifiedHealthClaims/default.htm. Accessed 3 May 2011.
25. Op cit 6.

26. 21 CFR 101.93 Certain types of statements for dietary supplements.

27. *Guidance for Industry: Structure/Function Claims Small Entity Compliance Guide* (January 2002). Available at www.fda.gov/Food/GuidanceComplianceRegulatoryInformation/GuidanceDocuments/DietarySupplements/ucm103340.htm. Accessed 3 May 2011.

28. *Guidance for Industry: Substantiation for Dietary Supplement Claims Made Under Section 403(r) (6) of the Federal Food, Drug, and Cosmetic Act* (December 2008). Available at www.fda.gov/Food/GuidanceComplianceRegulatoryInformation/GuidanceDocuments/DietarySupplements/ucm073200.htm. Accessed 3 May 2011.

29. *Draft Guidance for Industry: Substantiation for Dietary Supplement Claims Made Under Section 403(r)(6) of the Federal Food, Drug, and Cosmetic Act.*

30. "Section 5 Dietary Supplement Claims, Dietary Supplement Labeling Exemptions," *Dietary Supplement Health and Education Act* of 1994 (Public Law 103-417, 103rd Congress).

31. Op cit 6.

32. Memorandum of Understanding Between Federal Trade Commission and the Food and Drug Administration, Federal Register, Vol 36, No. 180, 16 September 1971.

33. Federal Trade Commission, *Dietary Supplements: An Advertising Guide for Industry.* Available at www.ftc.gov/bcp/edu/pubs/business/adv/bus09.shtm. Accessed 3 May 2011.

34. *Public Health Security and Bioterrorism Preparedness and Response Act* of 2002 (Public law 107-188).

35. *Guidance for Industry: Questions and Answers Regarding Registration of Food Facilities* (Edition 4) (August 2004). Available at www.fda.gov/Food/GuidanceComplianceRegulatoryInformation/GuidanceDocuments/FoodDefenseandEmergencyResponse/ucm082703. Accessed 3 May 2011.

36. "Registration of Food Facilities." Available at www.fda.gov/Food/GuidanceComplianceRegulatoryInformation/RegistrationofFoodFacilities/default.htm. Accessed 3 May 2011.

37. 68 *Fed. Reg.* 12158 (13 March 2003).

38. 21 CFR Part 111 Current Good Manufacturing Practice in manufacturing, packaging, labeling, or holding operations for dietary supplements; final rule. Available at www.accessdata.fda.gov/scripts/cdrh/cfdocs/cfcfr/cfrsearch.cfm?cfrpart=111. Accessed 3 May 2011.

39. *Current Good Manufacturing Practice in Manufacturing, Packaging, Labeling, or Holding Operations for Dietary Supplements; Small Entity Compliance Guide* (December 2010). Available at www.fda.gov/Food/GuidanceComplianceRegulatoryInformation/GuidanceDocuments/SmallBusinessesSmallEntityComplianceGuides/ucm238182.htm. Accessed 3 May 2011.

40. FDA News Release: Tainted products marketed as dietary supplements potentially dangerous (15 December 2010). Available at www.fda.gov/NewsEvents/Newsroom/PressAnnouncements/2010/ucm236967.htm. Accessed 3 May 2011.

41. Tainted Products That are Marketed as Dietary Supplements RSS Feed. Available at www.fda.gov/AboutFDA/ContactFDA/StayInformed/RSSFeeds/TDS/rss.xml. Accessed 3 May 2011.

42. *Guidance for Industry: Questions and Answers Regarding Adverse Event Reporting and Recordkeeping for Dietary Supplements as Required by the Dietary Supplement and Nonprescription Drug Consumer Protection Act* (October 2007; Revised June 2009). Available at www.fda.gov/Food/GuidanceComplianceRegulatoryInformation/GuidanceDocuments/DietarySupplements/ucm171383.htm. Accessed 3 May 2011.

43. *Draft Guidance for Industry: Questions and Answers Regarding the Labeling of Dietary Supplements as Required by the Dietary Supplement and Nonprescription Drug Consumer Protection Act* (December 2007; Revised December 2008 and September 2009). Available at www.fda.gov/Food/GuidanceComplianceRegulatoryInformation/GuidanceDocuments/DietarySupplements/ucm179018.htm. Accessed 3 May 2011.

44. "Sec. 110.310 Prior Notice of Imported Food Under the *Public Health Security and Bioterrorism Preparedness and Response Act* of 2002. Compliance Policy Guide, Guidance for FDA and CBP Staff" (May 2009). Available at www.fda.gov/Food/GuidanceComplianceRegulatoryInformation/GuidanceDocuments/FoodDefenseandEmergencyResponse/ucm153055.htm. Accessed 3 May 2011.

45. *FD&C Act*, Section 801 (21 USC 381) Imports and exports. Available at www.fda.gov/RegulatoryInformation/Legislation/FederalFoodDrugandCosmeticActFDCAct/FDCActChapterVIIIImportsandExports/ucm107032.htm. Accessed 3 May 2011.

46. 21 CFR 1.101 Notification and recordkeeping.

47. FDA Export Certificates to Foreign Governments FAQs. Available at www.fda.gov/Food/InternationalActivities/Exports/ExportCertificates/default.htm. Accessed 3 May 2011.

48. Compliance Policy Guide 7132.15, Sec. 400.400, "Conditions Under Which Homeopathic Drugs May Be Marketed." Available at www.fda.gov/ICECI/ComplianceManuals/CompliancePolicyGuidanceManual/ucm074360.htm. Accessed 3 May 2011.

49. *Homeopathic Pharmacopoeia of the United States*, "The Regulation of Homepathic Medicines." Available at www.hpus.com/regulations.php. Accessed 3 May 2011.

50. "Drug Registration and Listing System." Available at www.fda.gov/Drugs/GuidanceComplianceRegulatoryInformation/DrugRegistrationandListing/default.htm. Accessed 3 May 2011.

Recommended Reading

Dietary Supplement Health Education Act of 1994 (*DSHEA*)

21 CFR Part 1: Prior Notice of Imported Food Under the Public Health Security and Bioterrorism Preparedness and Response Act of 2002. Available at www.fda.gov/Food/FoodDefense/Bioterrorism/PriorNotice/ucm106610.htm. Accessed 3 May 2011.

21 CFR 101.36 Nutrition labeling of dietary supplements

21 CFR 101.93 Structure/function claims

21 CFR 111 Current Good Manufacturing Practice in manufacturing, packaging, labeling, or holding operations for dietary supplements

21 CFR 190.6 Requirement for premarket notification of new dietary ingredients

Public Health Security and Bioterrorism Preparedness and Response Act of 2002 (Public Law 107-188, 107th Congress).

"Labeling and Nutrition: Food Labeling and Nutrition Overview." Available at www.fda.gov/Food/LabelingNutrition/default.htm. Accessed 3 May 2011.

New Dietary Ingredient in Dietary Supplements. Available at www.fda.gov/Food/DietarySupplements/ucm109764.htm. Accessed 3 May 2011.

Guidance for Industry: Substantiation for Dietary Supplement Claims Made Under Section 403(r) (6) of the Federal Food, Drug, and Cosmetic Act (December 2008). Available at www.fda.gov/Food/GuidanceComplianceRegulatoryInformation/GuidanceDocuments/DietarySupplements/ucm073200.htm. Accessed 3 May 2011.

"Claims That Can Be Made for Conventional Foods and Dietary Supplements" (September 2003). Available at www.fda.gov/Food/LabelingNutrition/LabelClaims/ucm111447.htm. Accessed 3 May 2011.

Guidance for Industry: Evidence-Based Review System for the Scientific Evaluation of Health Claims (January 2009). Available at www.fda.gov/Food/GuidanceComplianceRegulatoryInformation/GuidanceDocuments/FoodLabelingNutrition/ucm073332.htm. Accessed 3 May 2011.

Guidance for Industry: Iron-Containing Supplements and Drugs: Label Warning Statements Small Entity Compliance Guide (October 2003). Available at www.fda.gov/Food/GuidanceComplianceRegulatoryInformation/GuidanceDocuments/DietarySupplements/ucm073014.htm. Accessed 3 May 2011.

Guidance for Industry: Notification of a Health Claim or Nutrient Content Claim Based on an Authoritative Statement of a Scientific Body (June 1998). Available at www.fda.gov/Food/GuidanceComplianceRegulatoryInformation/GuidanceDocuments/FoodLabelingNutrition/ucm056975.htm. Accessed 3 May 2011

Guidance for Industry: Food Labeling; Nutrient Content Claims; Definition for "High Potency" and Definition for "Antioxidant" for Use in Nutrient Content Claims for Dietary Supplements and Conventional Foods Small Entity Compliance Guide (July 2008). Available at www.fda.gov/Food/GuidanceComplianceRegulatoryInformation/GuidanceDocuments/FoodLabelingNutrition/ucm063064.htm. Accessed 3 May 2011.

Guidance for Industry: Statement of Identity, Nutrition Labeling, and Ingredient Labeling of Dietary Supplements Small Entity Compliance Guide (January 1999). Available at www.fda.gov/Food/GuidanceComplianceRegulatoryInformation/GuidanceDocuments/DietarySupplements/ucm073168.htm. Accessed 3 May 2011.

Guidance for Industry: Structure/Function Claims Small Entity Compliance Guide (January 2002). Available at www.fda.gov/Food/GuidanceComplianceRegulatoryInformation/GuidanceDocuments/DietarySupplements/ucm103340.htm. Accessed 3 May 2011.

Guidance for Industry: Interim Procedures for Qualified Health Claims in the Labeling of Conventional Human Food and Human Dietary Supplements (July 2003). Available at www.fda.gov/Food/GuidanceComplianceRegulatoryInformation/GuidanceDocuments/FoodLabelingNutrition/ucm053832.htm. Accessed 3 May 2011.

Guidance for Industry: Prior Notice of Imported Food Questions and Answers (Edition 2) (May 2004). Available at www.fda.gov/Food/GuidanceComplianceRegulatoryInformation/GuidanceDocuments/

FoodDefenseandEmergencyResponse/ucm078911.
htm. Accessed 3 May 2011

*Guidance for Industry: Questions and Answers Regarding
Establishment and Maintenance of Records (Edition
4)* (September 2006). Available at www.fda.gov/
Food/GuidanceComplianceRegulatoryInformation/
GuidanceDocuments/
FoodDefenseandEmergencyResponse/ucm062801.
htm. Accessed 3 May 2011.

*Guidance for Industry: Questions and Answers Regarding
Adverse Event Reporting and Recordkeeping
for Dietary Supplements as Required by the
Dietary Supplement and Nonprescription Drug
Consumer Protection Act* (October 2007; Revised
June 2009). Available at www.fda.gov/Food/
GuidanceComplianceRegulatoryInformation/
GuidanceDocuments/DietarySupplements/
ucm171383.htm. Accessed 3 May 2011.

*Draft Guidance for Industry: Questions and Answers
Regarding the Labeling of Dietary Supplements
as Required by the Dietary Supplement and
Nonprescription Drug Consumer Protection Act*
(December 2007; Revised December 2008; Revised
September 2009). Available at www.fda.gov/Food/
GuidanceComplianceRegulatoryInformation/
GuidanceDocuments/DietarySupplements/
ucm179018.htm.;Accessed 3 May 2011.

*Guidance for Industry: Questions and Answers
Regarding Food Allergens, including the Food
Allergen Labeling and Consumer Protection Act
of 2004* (Edition 4); Final Guidance (October
2006). Available at www.fda.gov/Food/
GuidanceComplianceRegulatoryInformation/
GuidanceDocuments/FoodLabelingNutrition/
ucm059116.htm. Accessed 3 May 2011.

Guidance for Industry: FDA Export Certificates (July
2004) Available at www.fda.gov/downloads/
RegulatoryInformation/Guidances/ucm125822.pdf.
Accessed 3 May 2011.

HPCUS Guidelines for Homeopathic Drugs. Available at
www.hpus.com/.

Clarke JH. *A Dictionary of Practical Materia Medica.* (3
vol.). London (U.K.): The Homeopathic Publishing
Co.; 1902.

Chapter 27

Cosmetics

By Evelyn Cadman

Objectives

+ Understand the classification of cosmetics and related products
+ Understand the basic regulations covering cosmetic product sales in the US

Regulations and Guidelines for the Cosmetic Industry

+ 21 CFR 1 General enforcement regulations
+ 21 CFR 250 Section 250.250 Requirements for drugs and cosmetics—hexachlorophene
+ 21 CFR 700 Subpart A (Section 700.3) Cosmetics—General provisions
+ 21 CFR 700 Subpart B (Sections 700.11–700.35) Requirements for specific cosmetic products
+ Amendment to Section 700.27 (71 *FR* 59653) 11 October 2006
+ 21 CFR 701 Subpart A (Sections 701.1–701.9) Cosmetic labeling—General provisions
+ 21 CFR 701 Subpart B (Sections 701.10–701.19) Package form
+ 21 CFR 701 Subpart C (Sections 701.20–701.30) Labeling of specific ingredients
+ 21 CFR 710 Voluntary registration of cosmetic product establishments
+ 21 CFR 720 Voluntary filing of cosmetic product ingredient and cosmetic raw material composition statements
+ 21 CFR 740 Cosmetic product warning statements
+ Cosmetics Good Manufacturing Practice Guidelines
+ Cosmetics Labeling Manual
+ "Intercenter Agreement Between the Center for Drug Evaluation and Research and the Center for Food Safety and Applied Nutrition to Assist FDA in Implementing the Drug and Cosmetic Provisions of the Federal Food, Drug and Cosmetic Act for Products that Purport to be Cosmetics but Meet the Statutory Definition of a Drug"
+ FDA Recall Policy for Cosmetics

Introduction

Although the US Food and Drug Administration (FDA) was given responsibility for cosmetics as a result of the *Federal Food, Drug, and Cosmetic Act* of 1938 (*FD&C Act*), less-extensive regulations have been promulgated for this industry sector than for others regulated by the agency. The act defined cosmetic adulteration and misbranding and made provisions for FDA to write regulations making exemptions to compliance. The act further affected cosmetics by requiring that FDA certify color additives. No other premarket approval is required for cosmetic products or their ingredients. It is the manufacturer's responsibility to assure that its cosmetic products and ingredients are safe and properly labeled in full compliance with the law. FDA's Center for Food Safety and Applied Nutrition (CFSAN) regulates cosmetics only after they have been introduced into the marketplace. Cosmetic manufacturers may voluntarily register their facilities and product lists but there is no regulatory requirement for registration. Good Manufacturing Practices (GMPs) are encouraged but are not required by regulation.

The *FD&C Act* defines "cosmetics" as "(1) articles intended to be rubbed, poured, sprinkled, or sprayed on, introduced into, or otherwise applied to the human body or any part thereof for cleansing, beautifying, promoting attractiveness, or altering the appearance, and (2) articles intended for use as a component of any such articles; except that such term shall not include soap."[1] Interestingly, soaps are defined by regulation as articles made primarily of alkali salts of fatty acids whose detergent properties are due to the alkali-fatty acid compounds and that are labeled and sold only as soap.[2]

These definitions and, particularly, the stipulation that soaps may only be labeled and sold as soap allude to the principle that the intended use of the product determines how it is regulated. If a product to be applied to the body in some fashion is intended to do anything other than cleanse or beautify, that product is not a simple cosmetic. As such, shampoos with ingredients for treating dandruff are regulated both as cosmetics and as over-the-counter (OTC) drugs. Similarly, toothpaste with fluoride to prevent cavities is both a cosmetic and an OTC drug.

The following 13 categories of cosmetic products are listed in 21 CFR 720.4(c):

- baby products
- bath preparations
- eye makeup preparations
- fragrance preparations
- hair preparations (non-coloring)
- hair coloring preparations
- makeup preparations (not eye)
- manicuring preparations
- oral hygiene products
- personal cleanliness products
- shaving preparations
- skin care preparations (creams, lotions, powder and sprays)
- suntan preparations

Safety and Adulteration

As noted previously, FDA does not approve cosmetics or cosmetic ingredients, other than colors, prior to their introduction into the marketplace. Only after market introduction do cosmetic products come under FDA's authority. Nevertheless, Section 601 of the *FD&C Act* prohibits the introduction into interstate commerce of cosmetics that are adulterated.[3] Cosmetic products may be considered adulterated if they:

- may be injurious to users under conditions of customary use (except for hair dyes)
- are composed of a potentially harmful substance
- contain filthy, putrid or decomposed substances
- contain a non-permitted or non-certified color additive
- are manufactured or held under unsanitary conditions that may have caused them to become injurious to users or contaminated with filth
- are packaged in containers composed of harmful substances

While injurious products are not permitted, cosmetic manufacturers are not required to conduct product testing to substantiate product performance or safety. However, if safety testing has not been conducted, the following warning must be included on the product label, "WARNING: The safety of this product has not been determined." As noted in the regulation, this warning statement "does not constitute an exemption to the adulteration provisions of the Act or to any other requirement in the Act or this chapter."[4] Since cosmetic ingredients do not require prior FDA approval or certification of safety and since safety testing is not required, FDA must prove that an ingredient is harmful or unsafe under conditions of use prior to removing unsafe, adulterated products from the market.

Although FDA does not certify or approve cosmetic ingredients other than colors, the use of a few ingredients is prohibited or restricted by regulation due to safety concerns. The prohibited ingredients, listed in 21 CFR 700, are:

- bithionol
- mercury compounds
- vinyl chloride
- halogenated salicylanilides
- zirconium complexes in aerosol cosmetics
- chloroform
- methylene chloride
- chlorofluorocarbon propellants
- hexachlorophene
- methyl methacrylate monomer in nail products

Additionally, FDA restricts the use of certain materials from cattle due to concerns regarding Bovine Spongiform Encephalopathy.[5] FDA also promotes the use of safe ingredients in cosmetics by participating in the Cosmetic Ingredient Review (CIR). CIR is an industry-sponsored organization that reviews cosmetic ingredient safety and publishes its results in open, peer-reviewed literature. FDA participates in CIR in a non-voting capacity.

Cosmetic Labeling and Misbranding

The *FD&C Act* gives FDA regulatory authority over cosmetic product labeling. Federal Trade Commission (FTC) regulations authorized by the *Fair Packaging and Labeling Act* (*FPLA*) also apply to cosmetic products. The labeling regulations promulgated by FDA are found in 21 CFR 701 and 740, while those promulgated by FTC are found in 16 CFR 500.

The definition of "label" differs between the *FD&C Act* and *FPLA*. The *FD&C Act* definition is "a display of written, printed or graphic matter upon the immediate container," while *FPLA* defines the term as "written, printed or graphic matter affixed to any consumer commodity or affixed to or appearing upon a package containing any consumer commodity." However, any disparity in the definition is overcome by the *FD&C Act* requirement that any information required on the label of the immediate container shall also appear on any outer container.[6]

Taken together, the acts and regulations listed above require five basic elements on cosmetic product labels:

- statement of identity
- net quantity of contents
- ingredient list
- signature line declaring the product manufacturer or distributor's name and location
- certain warning statements

Some of these required elements must appear on the principal display panel (PDP) of the label. The PDP is the portion of the label most likely to be displayed under customary conditions of retail sale. Typically, the PDP is the front panel of the package; however, any other panel that includes the product name is considered an alternate PDP and must include any label elements required by regulation to appear on the PDP. Some cosmetics are marketed in very small or highly stylized or decorative containers. The regulation under 21 CFR 710.13 states that the PDP of cosmetics in "'boudoir-type' container[s] including decorative cosmetic containers of the 'cartridge,' 'pill box,' 'compact,' or 'pencil' variety, and those with a capacity of one-fourth ounce or less" may be affixed to the container via a tag.

Statement of Identity

A statement of identity must appear on cosmetic label PDPs. According to 21 CFR 701.11, the statement of identity shall be the common or usual name of the cosmetic; a descriptive name; a fanciful name commonly understood to identity such a cosmetic; or an illustration or vignette depicting the intended cosmetic use of the product. The categories and subcategories of cosmetic products listed in 21 CFR 720.4 may serve as appropriate statements of identity.

The statement of identity may appear anywhere on the PDP but must be generally parallel to the container. The statement must be in bold type of "a size reasonably related to the most prominent printed matter on such panel."[7]

Net Quantity of Contents Statement

The regulations stipulating the format, placement and size of the net quantity of contents (net contents) statements are found in 21 CFR 701.13. The net contents statement must accurately declare the quantity of cosmetic in the container whether in terms of weight, volume, measure, numerical count or a combination thereof. The net contents statement on aerosol products must declare the net quantity of contents expelled.

Generally, if the cosmetic is a liquid, the net contents statement must be expressed as a fluid measure such as the US fluid ounce, pint, quart, etc. Fluid measures must declare the volume at 68°F (20°C). Cosmetics that are solid, semi-solid, viscous or a mixture of solid and liquid must be declared in avoirdupois pounds and ounces. Net contents declarations for aerosol products are made in terms of weight. Net contents may additionally be stated in metric units. The term "net weight" or "net wt." must be used in conjunction with a weight statement; terms such as "net contents" or "net" may be used in a liquid statement of contents.

The net contents statement must appear on the PDP and any alternate PDPs in the lower 30% of the panel, generally parallel to the base of the package as displayed. The statement must be distinct and conspicuous, printed in boldface type that is in distinct contrast to other matter on the package. The statement must be at least one-sixteenth inch in height for PDPs smaller than five square inches and one-eighth inch for PDPs of 5 to 25 square inches.

The net contents statement must be separated from other text above or below it by a space at least equal to the height of the lettering used in the statement itself. Separation of the statement from other label items on either side must be by a space at least twice the width of the letter "N" of the text used in the contents statement.

Ingredient List

Cosmetic product ingredients must be listed on the immediate container as well as any outer container in descending order of prominence, unless the ingredients are flavors, fragrances or trade secret[8] elements. The ingredient list must be in a type size not less than one-sixteenth of an inch in height as measured on the lower-case "o" for most packages. If the total area available to bear labeling is less than 12 square inches, the ingredient list may be in type of one-thirty-second of an inch in height. The ingredient list may appear on any information panel. If there is no information panel, the ingredient list must appear on the PDP.

Ingredient Naming Conventions

Cosmetic ingredients must be indentified by established names specified in 21 CFR 701.30. If no name for an ingredient has been specified by FDA, regulations stipulate that the names used in the following references are to be used in the order listed.

- CTFA (Cosmetic, Toiletry and Fragrance Association, Inc.) *Cosmetic Ingredient Dictionary*, Second Ed., 1977
- *United States Pharmacopeia*, 19th Ed., 1975, and Second Supplement to the USP XIX and NF XIV, 1976
- *National Formulary*, 14th Ed., 1975, and Second Supplement to the USP XIX and NF XIV, 1976.)
- *Food Chemicals Codex*, 2d Ed., 1972; First Supplement, 1974, and Second Supplement, 1975
- United States Adopted Name (USAN) and the

USP dictionary of drug names, USAN 1975, 1961-1975 cumulative list

If the ingredient is not listed in any of the above sources, it should be designated by a common name generally recognizable to consumers. If the ingredient does not have a common name, it should be listed by its chemical name.

Name and Place of Business

Cosmetic labels are also required to conspicuously declare the name and place of business of the manufacturer, packer or distributor. If the name listed is not that of the manufacturer, it must be preceded by an appropriate statement such as "distributed by" or "packed by." The corporate name must be used and the business address must include the street, city, state and zip code. The street address is not required if the corporation is listed in a current city directory or telephone directory.

Warning Statements

As noted previously, labels on cosmetics whose safety has not been substantiated must include a warning noting that fact. Specific warning statements are also required on:

- cosmetics in self-pressurized containers (21 CFR 740.11)
- feminine deodorant sprays (21 CFR 740.12)
- foaming detergent bath products (21 CFR 740.17)
- coal tar hair dyes posing a risk of cancer (21 CFR 740.18)
- sun tanning preparations (21 CFR 740.19)

In addition, the label of any product that may pose a health hazard must include a warning statement, as appropriate, regarding the associated hazard. Any required warning statements must be prominent and conspicuous using bold type no less than one-sixteenth inch in height on a contrasting background.

Incomplete or improper labeling may render a cosmetic misbranded. Section 602 of the *FD&C Act* prohibits the introduction into interstate commerce of cosmetics that are misbranded.[9] Cosmetic products are considered misbranded if:

- labeling is false or misleading
- label fails to state prominently and conspicuously any required information
- container presentation or fill is misleading

Claims

By definition, cosmetics are intended to cleanse, beautify, promote attractiveness or alter appearance. Accordingly, claims about cosmetic products are restricted to stating how the product changes appearance, beautifies or cleanses, and may not discuss changes to the structure or any function of the human body. As noted previously, the intended use of a product determines how it is regulated. Intended use can be established in part by claims on the product label, labeling, advertising or promotional material, including websites. Cosmetic products marketed to change the body's structure or function or to diagnose, treat, cure or prevent disease are drugs or medical devices. A product that "improves the appearance of fine lines or wrinkles" is a cosmetic, but products that remove or physically alter wrinkles, such as injected collagen or Botox, are medical devices and drugs, respectively.

It is common today to see products that are labeled as "cruelty free" or "not tested on animals." These terms have no legal meaning and their use has not been restricted by FDA. Consequently it is unclear what meaning is intended by the companies using these claims. No matter the intended meaning, these and any other claims on cosmetic and all other consumer products must meet the basic standard of the Federal Trade Commission (FTC) that they be truthful and not misleading. FDA and FTC published a memorandum of understanding in 1971 stating that the agencies would work in tandem on cases of improper claims and advertising.[10]

GMPs

GMPs are not included in cosmetic regulations; however, compliance with GMPs can minimize the risk that products will be adulterated or misbranded. Consequently, the agency has published guidelines for the industry based on FDA's Inspection Operations Manual.[11]

Section 301 of the *FD&C Act* authorizes FDA to enter and inspect cosmetic company facilities to prevent introduction of adulterated or misbranded cosmetics into interstate commerce. Companies complying with these guidelines are less likely to encounter regulatory problems.

These guidelines are basic to all GMP procedures and cover the building, equipment, personnel, raw materials, production procedures, laboratory controls, recordkeeping, labeling and customer complaint files. In brief, the building construction and design should be adequate to permit orderly, sanitary manufacturing operations. Production, storage and handling equipment and utensils should be appropriate for the application and easy to clean and maintain. Personnel are to be properly trained and all materials used in the manufacture of the cosmetics should be stored and handled so as to prevent contamination and ensure certain identification and regulatory status. Manufacturing control procedures should be in place to ensure that the product will be properly made and match specifications and labeling. The guidelines outline procedures for examining or testing incoming raw materials to ensure identification and purity as well as retention of manufactured lots for compliance checks. Additionally, the maintenance of records is covered in the GMP guidelines. Records should be kept of all materials; batch manufacturing, processing, handling, transferring, holding and filling; and labeling and distribution of all finished products. Records of any consumer complaints should also be kept.

Cosmetics That are Also Drugs or Medical Devices

According to the definition above, shampoo used for cleansing the hair is a cosmetic. However, shampoo that includes ingredients to control dandruff and toothpaste containing fluoride for prevention of cavities are also OTC drugs and must conform to regulations for both drugs and cosmetics.[12] Similarly, contact lenses used to alter the appearance of eye color and breast implants are regulated as medical devices.[13]

When a cosmetic product is also an OTC drug, the label must have a "Drug Facts" box to declare the active drug ingredients, indications, uses, etc., as required by regulation (See "Chapter 13 Over-the-Counter Drug Products"). The cosmetic ingredients in cosmetic/OTC combination products must be declared in the inactive ingredient portion of the drug facts box. Cosmetics that are also medical devices must be the subject of Premarket Approval Application or 510(k) submissions, as appropriate, and must conform to all applicable medical device regulations.

Related Products

Some companies market products as "cosmeceuticals," a term that has no recognized regulatory status.[14] Such products may only be promoted to cleanse or beautify. However, if their labeling includes claims that they affect the structure or function of the body, these products would be regulated as drugs or devices. Aromatherapy products pose interesting regulatory questions: perfumes are regulated as cosmetics by FDA, while room deodorizers are regulated by the Consumer Product Safety Commission. If a scented product is marketed to treat or prevent a disease or otherwise affect the body's structure or function, it is regulated as a drug.[15]

Permanent and temporary tattoos as well as permanent make-up are regulated as cosmetics.[16] The pigments used are regulated as color additives and are subject to premarket approval. It is difficult to determine the contents of permanent tattoo pigments since products for professional use are exempt from labeling regulations. The resurgence in the popularity of tattoos has prompted FDA to update communications regarding the safety of tattooing.[17] It is interesting to note that even though henna is approved only for use in hair dye and not for direct application to skin, products containing henna are on the market for use in *mehndi*, the South Asian practice of skin decoration that is popular among some groups in the US. FDA has issued an import alert requiring that henna products intended for use on the skin be detained.[18]

Products that are used to cleanse or beautify animals are classified as grooming aids and are not regulated by FDA. In recent years, some grooming aids designed for animals have become popular with people.[19] Bag Balm, originally intended for use on cows' udders, became a popular hand cream, and products formulated to keep horses' hooves healthy have been used by people to strengthen fingernails. If a manufacturer markets grooming aids to humans, labeling must comply with cosmetic regulations.

Facility and Product Registration

Cosmetic companies are not subject to mandatory establishment registration or ingredient reporting but they may voluntarily register their establishments and their product compositions through FDA's Voluntary Cosmetic Registration Program (VCRP).[20,21] Data provided through the VCRP helps CIR prioritize its safety testing program. Unless noted as proprietary, information provided through VCRP may be obtained through the *Freedom of Information Act*.

Registration also enables FDA to notify cosmetics companies about potential problems with the ingredients in their products and helps the agency with inspections that may be necessary. The VCRP is not an approval program and registrants are prohibited from using participation in the VCRP as a promotional tool.[22]

Importing and Exporting Cosmetic Products

Cosmetic products imported into the US must comply with the same regulations as those produced domestically. While registration is not required, foreign cosmetic companies are encouraged to participate in the VCRP. Any companies or individuals wishing to import cosmetics or any other FDA-regulated product into the US must file an entry notice and entry bond with the US Customs Service. The Customs Service notifies FDA of the import and FDA makes a determination regarding the product's admissibility. FDA may admit the product into the US, refuse entry or examine the product for compliance, including performing laboratory testing of the ingredients.

Cosmetic products for export from the US do not have to comply with US regulations, but only with those of the importing country.[23] Some countries require certificates for imported products. FDA does issue certificates for cosmetic products intended for export; however, since cosmetics are not approved by FDA these certificates simply list the product names provided by the exporter and do not indicate agency review or approval of the product.[21] Form FDA 3613d is used for requesting cosmetics certificates.

Compliance and Enforcement

FDA carries out enforcement activities against cosmetics companies despite the fact that cosmetic manufacturing facilities are not required to register with FDA or comply with GMP regulations, and that cosmetic products are not subject to premarket review or approval.[24] Many FDA enforcement actions are carried out to ensure that cosmetic products are not adulterated or misbranded. As noted previously, FDA works with FTC to enforce cosmetics labeling regulations. In addition, CFSAN, which has regulatory responsibility for cosmetics, works with the Center for Drug Evaluation and Research (CDER) through an inter-center agreement when reviewing cosmetic products with labeling that includes drug claims.[25] Under this agreement, a product promoted as a cosmetic to enhance eyelashes was the subject of Warning Letters and finally product seizure due to the presence of a glaucoma drug.[26] Similarly, Warning Letters were issued regarding various skin care products marketed with drug claims.[27] While FDA does not have authority to recall cosmetic products, the agency can request that a company recall its products.[28] On 5 January 2009, FDA announced recall of a make-up remover due to contamination with *pseudomonas aeruginosa*.[29]

FDA has also undertaken enforcement actions against devices marketed for cosmetic use to beautify the skin and hair. Gaunitz Hair Sciences LLC was marketing a laser for hair growth,[30] while Sunetics International Corporation was marketing laser skin and hair brushes[31] and Rejuvenu International Ltd. was marketing a hair removal system.[32] None of these devices had premarket clearance and most were being promoted to change the structure or function of the body and were, therefore, unapproved medical devices. All of these companies received letters notifying them that their products were adulterated and misbranded.

Summary

- Cosmetics are products that are applied to or introduced into the body for cleansing, beautifying, promoting attractiveness or altering the appearance.
- Cosmetics are not subject to premarket approval or GMP regulations; facility registration and product listing are voluntary.
- Regulations require that cosmetic products be safe but do not require safety testing.
- Regulations prohibit the marketing of cosmetic products that are adulterated or misbranded.
- Five basic elements must appear on cosmetic product labels:
  o statement of identity
  o net quantity of contents statement
  o ingredient list
  o signature line
  o certain warning statements
- Products that alter both appearance and the structure or function of the body are regulated as drugs or medical devices.

References

1. *Federal Food, Drug, and Cosmetic Act* of 1938 (*FD&C Act*), Chapter II. FDA website. www.fda.gov/opacom/laws/fdcact/fdcact1.htm. Accessed 5 May 2011.
2. 21 CFR Part 701.20 Detergent substances, other than soap, intended for use in cleansing the body.
3. *FD&C Act*, Chapter VI.
4. 21 CFR Sec. 740.10 (c) Labeling of cosmetic products for which adequate substantiation of safety has not been obtained.
5. Bovine Spongiform Encephalopathy (BSE). FDA website. www.fda.gov/Cosmetics/ProductandIngredientSafety/PotentialContaminants/ucm136786.htm. Accessed 5 May 2011.
6. *FD&C Act*, Section 201(k).
7. 21 CFR 710.11 Identity labeling.
8. 21 CFR 720.8 Confidentiality of statements.
9. Op cit 3.
10. "Memorandum of Understanding Between Federal Trade Commission and the Food and Drug Administration," *Federal Register*, Vol 36, No. 180, 16 September 1971.
11. Cosmetic Good Manufacturing Practice Guidelines/Inspection Checklist, 12 February 1997; Updated April 24, 2008. FDA website. www.fda.gov/Cosmetics/GuidanceComplianceRegulatoryInformation/GoodManufacturingPracticeGMPGuidelinesInspectionChecklist/default.htm. Accessed 5 May 2011.
12. "Is It a Cosmetic, a Drug, or Both? (Or Is It Soap?)." FDA website. www.fda.gov/Cosmetics/GuidanceComplianceRegulatoryInformation/ucm074201.htm. Accessed 5 May 2011.
13. *Guidance for Industry, FDA Staff, Eye Care Professionals, and Consumers: Decorative, Non-corrective Contact Lenses* (November 2006). FDA website. www.fda.gov/MedicalDevices/DeviceRegulationandGuidance/GuidanceDocuments/ucm071572.htm. Accessed 5 May 2011.
14. "Cosmeceutical" (24 February 2000). FDA website. www.fda.gov/Cosmetics/ProductandIngredientSafety/ProductInformation/ucm127064.htm. Accessed 5 May 2011.
15. Aromatherapy (13 March 2000). FDA website. www.fda.gov/Cosmetics/ProductandIngredientSafety/ProductInformation/ucm127054.htm. Accessed 5 May 2011.
16. Tattoos & Permanent Makeup (Updated 23 June 2008). FDA website. www.fda.gov/Cosmetics/ProductandIngredientSafety/ProductInformation/ucm108530.htm. Accessed 5 May 2011.
17. Ibid.

18. Import Alert. Detention Without Physical Examination of Henna Based Skin Color. FDA website. www.accessdata.fda.gov/cms_ia/importalert_138.html. Accessed 5 May 2011.

19. Willman M. "Using Pet Products on People." *Los Angeles Times* (22 October 1999).

20. 21 CFR 710 Voluntary registration of cosmetic product establishments.

21. 21 CFR 720 Voluntary filing of cosmetic product ingredient and cosmetic raw material composition statements.

22. Voluntary Cosmetic Registration Program (VCRP). FDA website. www.fda.gov/Cosmetics/GuidanceComplianceRegulatoryInformation/VoluntaryCosmeticsRegistrationProgramVCRP/default.htm. Accessed 5 May 2011.

23. Cosmetics Exports. FDA website. www.fda.gov/Cosmetics/InternationalActivities/ImportsExports/CosmeticExports/default.htm. Accessed 5 May 2011.

24. Fleder J. "Cosmetics Product Enforcement" — Not an Oxymoron, *Update*, July/August 2008, Issue 5, 47–50. Food and Drug Law Institute, Washington, DC. Reprinted at www.hpm.com/pdf/FLEDER2.pdf. Accessed 5 May 2011.

25. "Intercenter Agreement Between the Center for Drug Evaluation and Research and the Center for Food Safety and Applied Nutrition to Assist FDA in Implementing the Drug and Cosmetic Provisions of the Federal Food, Drug and Cosmetic Act for Products that Purport to be Cosmetics but Meet the Statutory Definition of a Drug" (1 June 2006). FDA website. www.fda.gov/Cosmetics/GuidanceComplianceRegulatoryInformation/ComplianceEnforcement/ucm2005170.htm. Accessed 5 May 2011.

26. Approximately $2 Million of Potentially Harmful "Cosmetic" Eye Product Seized. News release 16 November 2007. FDA website. www.fda.gov/NewsEvents/Newsroom/PressAnnouncements/2007/ucm109028.htm. Accessed 5 May 2011.

27. Warning Letter (29 March 2007). FDA website. www.fda.gov/ICECI/EnforcementActions/WarningLetters/2007/ucm076343.htm. Accessed 5 May 2011.

28. Cosmetics Recall and Alerts policy (29 July 2002). FDA website. www.fda.gov/Cosmetics/ProductandIngredientSafety/RecallsAlerts/default.htm. Accessed 5 May 2011.

29. Recall—Firm Press Release. Celeste Industries Corporation Recalls All Lots of simplySmart Remove Make Up Remover (5 January 2009). FDA website. www.fda.gov/Safety/Recalls/ArchiveRecalls/2009/ucm128452.htm. Accessed 5 May 2011.

30. Warning Letter (7 August 2008). FDA website. www.fda.gov/ICECI/EnforcementActions/WarningLetters/2008/ucm1048189.htm. Accessed 5 May 2011.

31. Warning Letter (7 August 2008). FDA website. www.fda.gov/ICECI/EnforcementActions/WarningLetters/2008/ucm1048188.htm. Accessed 5 May 2011.

32. Warning Letter (16 August 2004). FDA website. www.fda.gov/ICECI/EnforcementActions/WarningLetters/2004/ucm146892.htm. Accessed 5 May 2011.

Veterinary Products

Updated by Jeff Zinza, RAC

Objective

- Identify the regulations and agencies governing veterinary products
- Develop a broad understanding of the regulation of veterinary drugs, feeds, devices and biologics

Laws, Regulations and Guidelines Covered in This Chapter

- *Federal Food, Drug, and Cosmetic Act* of 1938
- *Animal Medicinal Drug Use Clarification Act* of 1994 (*AMDUCA*)
- *Animal Drug Availability Act* of 1996 (*ADAA*)
- *Animal Drug User Fee Act* of 2003 (*ADUFA I*)
- *Animal Drug User Fee Amendments* of 2008 (*ADUFA II*)
- *Animal Generic Drug User Fee Act* of 2008 (*AGDUFA*)
- *Minor Use and Minor Species Animal Health Act* of 2004 (*MUMS*)
- *Generic Animal Drug and Patent Term Restoration Act* of 1988 (*GADPTRA*)
- *Virus-Serum-Toxin Act* of 1913 (*VSTA*)
- *Federal Insecticide, Fungicide, and Rodenticide Act* of 1972 (*FIFRA*)
- 9 CFR Subchapter E—Animals and animal products—viruses, serums, toxins, and analogous products; organisms and vectors
- 21 CFR 225–226 Current Good Manufacturing Practice for medicated feeds and Type A medicated articles
- 21 CFR 501 Animal food labeling
- 21 CFR 511 New animal drugs for investigational use
- 21 CFR 514 New animal drug applications
- 21 CFR 515 Medicated mill feed license
- 21 CFR 516 New animal drugs for minor use and minor species
- 21 CFR 530 Extralabel drug use in animals
- 21 CFR 558 New animal drugs for use in animal feeds
- *Guidance for Industry 61: FDA Approval of New Animal Drugs for Minor Uses and for Minor Species* (April 1999)
- *Guidance for Industry 82: Development of Supplemental Applications for Approved New Animal Drugs* (October 2002)
- *Draft Guidance for Industry 132: The Administrative New Animal Drug Application Process* (November 2002)
- *Guidance for Industry 170: Animal Drug User Fees and Fee Waivers and Reductions* (October 2008)
- *Guidance for Industry 173: Animal Drug Sponsor Fees under the Animal Drug User Fee Act (ADUFA)* (February 2005)
- VS Memorandum No. 800.50: Basic License Requirements and Guidelines for Submission of Materials in Support of Licensure (February 2011)
- VS Memorandum No. 800.57: Market Suspensions (September 1999)
- VS Memorandum No. 800.78: Preparation and Submission of Facilities Documents (November 2010)
- VS Memorandum No. 800.91: Categories of Inspection for Licensed Veterinary Biologics Establishments (May 1999)
- VS Memorandum 800.101: US Veterinary Biological Product Permits for Distribution and Sale (May 2002)

Introduction

Veterinary medical products are diverse, ranging from new animal drugs, vaccines, devices and diagnostic test kits to animal food additives, feed ingredients and animal grooming aids. Veterinary medical products may be used to prevent, treat or diagnose diseases in animals. They also include products that may be administered to or consumed by animals that produce food for humans, as well as those that may be consumed by pets or companion animals.

A veterinary medical product may be regulated by one of several US federal agencies, depending upon the product type and its intended use. These regulatory bodies focus on ensuring that marketed products safely and effectively relieve animal pain and suffering, sustain animal health and improve farm animal productivity without compromising public health.

FDA

The US Food and Drug Administration's (FDA) Center for Veterinary Medicine (CVM) is responsible for ensuring that animal drugs and medicated feeds are safe and effective, and that food from treated animals is safe to eat. CVM also is responsible for regulatory oversight of medical devices used in veterinary medicine. CVM's authority is derived from the *Federal Food, Drug, and Cosmetic Act* of 1938 (*FD&C Act*) and amendments.

Animal Drugs

Since 1968, the *FD&C Act* has included provisions designed to ensure that animal drugs are safe and effective for their intended uses and do not result in unsafe residues in foods. Two main processes are involved in regulating the interstate shipment of animal drug products. The Investigational New Animal Drug exemption (INAD) allows the interstate shipment of experimental drugs for testing in animals. The New Animal Drug Application (NADA) process—and its variants, the Abbreviated New Animal Drug Application (ANADA) and Administrative NADA—allow the marketing of a new animal drug.

INAD

Typically, the new animal drug approval process begins when a drug sponsor submits a request for an INAD exemption to CVM. This exemption will allow the sponsor to use, ship and label a particular unapproved drug for experimental purposes without violating the *FD&C Act*.

Once CVM grants the INAD exemption, the sponsor must:
- ensure proper and safe investigational drug packaging and labeling
- report to CVM the names and locations of investigators to whom drugs are shipped
- maintain records of all drug shipments for at least two years after delivery

- maintain all reports received from investigators for at least two years after the termination of the investigation or approval of a new animal drug application
- ensure that the new animal drug or animal feed containing a new animal drug will actually be used for tests in animals and is not used in humans
- notify CVM immediately if a safety problem is observed (periodic safety reporting is not required, except as specified in 21 CFR 514.80(b)(4))
- notify FDA or the US Department of Agriculture (USDA) prior to slaughter of food animals treated with the investigational drug
- submit a request under the INAD for categorical exclusion under 21 CFR 25.30 or 25.33 (If such exclusion is not authorized, then an environmental assessment (EA) must be submitted in accordance with 21 CFR 25.40.)

The sponsor may ask the Office of New Animal Drug Evaluation (ONADE) to review protocols for experimental work intended to support an NADA submission. Although such review is not required, it may help the sponsor obtain the necessary data.

NADA

The *FD&C Act* prohibits the introduction into interstate commerce of new animal drugs without an approved NADA. The NADA includes data demonstrating the drug's safety in the target animal and for humans who might consume products from the treated animal.

ONADE reviews the NADA to determine whether the animal drug should be approved for marketing and to evaluate the drug's effectiveness for the purposes claimed. If ONADE determines that the NADA information shows the product will be safe and effective for its intended use, it makes a recommendation to the CVM director. If the director agrees with the recommendation, the application is approved, and a notice of the approval is published in the *Federal Register*. CVM must take an appropriate action within 180 days after the filing of an NADA.

Section 512(b) of the *FD&C Act* and 21 CFR 514 describe information that must be submitted to FDA as part of an NADA. An NADA normally will be submitted to FDA in several sections or volumes:
- Identification (21 CFR 514.1(b)(1))
- Table of Contents and Summary (21 CFR 514.1(b)(2))
- Labeling (21 CFR 514.1(b)(3))—copies of each proposed label
- Components and Composition (21 CFR 514.1(b)(4))—a list of all drug product components, a statement of the drug product's composition and a complete description of antibiotic drug substances'

fermentation

- Manufacturing Methods, Facilities and Controls (21 CFR 514.1(b)(5))—a detailed description of the manufacturer, personnel, facilities/equipment, new animal drug substance synthesis, raw material controls (specifications, tests and methods), manufacturing instructions, finished product analytical controls (specifications, tests and methods), stability program, container/packaging and lot-control number system
- Samples (21 CFR 514.1(b)(6))—only if requested by CVM
- Analytical Methods for Residues (21 CFR 514.1(b)(7))—method(s) and data for determining drug residues remaining in food-producing animals
- Evidence to Establish Safety and Effectiveness (21 CFR 514.1(b)(8))—data/information to permit evaluation of the drug product's safety and effectiveness for the claim(s) in the proposed species
- Applicant's Commitments (21 CFR 514.1(b)(11)) to label and market the new animal drug under the conditions stated in the NADA
- Good Manufacturing Practice Compliance (21 CFR 514.1(b)(12)(ii))—a statement that methods, facilities, and controls described in 21 CFR 514.1(b)(5) conform to current Good Manufacturing Practice
- Good Laboratory Practice Compliance (21 CFR 514.1(b)(12)(iii))—a statement of compliance or noncompliance with Good Laboratory Practices (21 CFR 58) for each nonclinical laboratory study
- Environmental Assessment (21 CFR 514.1(b)(14))—an EA (21 CFR 25.40) containing sufficient data/information to permit evaluation of the drug product's environmental safety or a claim for a categorical exclusion from preparing an EA (21 CFR 25.33), as appropriate

  EAs focus on the use and disposal of veterinary drugs or feed additives. If CVM determines that the EA information indicates no significant environmental impact is expected, the center prepares a Finding of No Significant Impact (FONSI). In general, drugs for therapeutic use in companion animals receive a FONSI, whereas such drugs as broad-spectrum endoparasiticides in food-producing animals will require a full EA.

- Freedom of Information Summary (21 CFR 514.11)—a summary of the studies serving as the basis for drug approval; FDA will release these to the public, as requested, to comply with the *Freedom of Information Act* of 1966 (*FOIA*)

CVM must evaluate NADAs and ANADAs within 30 days of receipt to determine whether the submission meets the standards for filing, i.e., contains all required information. If CVM determines the application is not acceptable for filing, it must notify the applicant of the reason.

Like drugs intended for use in humans, new animal drugs must be produced under current Good Manufacturing Practice (CGMP) requirements. CVM's *Guidance for Industry: Drug Substance Chemistry, Manufacturing, and Controls Information* describes the drug substance information sponsors must submit to ensure continued drug substance and drug product quality (identity, strength, quality, purity and potency) in support of NADAs and ANADAs. In an effort to support global harmonization, CVM's CGMP requirements are moving into alignment with the International Cooperation on Harmonisation of Technical Requirements for Registration of Veterinary Products (VICH). The CVM guidance indicates that this chemistry, manufacturing and controls information can be presented in the format of the Common Technical Document—Quality (CTD-Q).

The NADA also must be accompanied by a user fee. The user fee system was initially put in place for animal drugs under the *Animal Drug User Fee Act* (*ADUFA*) of 2003, also known as *ADUFA I*, and is similar to those for human drugs and medical devices. Each fee category—sponsor, product, establishment and application—accounts for approximately 25% of the total fees collected. *ADUFA* was originally scheduled to set to expire on 30 September 2008, but the *Animal Drug User Fee Amendments of 2008*, also known as *ADUFA II* extended this user fee program until 2013, in addition to other enhancements. The law provides for fee waivers or reductions, upon request, when:

- the fee would present a significant barrier to innovation because of limited resources available to such person or other circumstance
- the fee to be paid under *ADUFA* will exceed the anticipated present and future costs incurred by FDA in reviewing NADAs
- the NADA or supplement is intended solely to provide for the animal drug's use in a free-choice medicated feed
- the application is submitted under the provisions of the *Minor Use or Minor Species Act* (*MUMS*) (discussed below) and intended solely to provide for a minor use or minor species indication
- the applicant is a recognized small business submitting its first animal drug application to FDA for review

Provisions are provided within *ADUFA* for the return of 75% of the user fee if the application is refused for filing.

ADUFA, as written, does not apply to ANADAs submitted under Section 512(b)(2) of the *FD&C Act*. However, the *Animal Generic Drug User Fee Act* of 2008 (*AGDUFA*) amended the *FD&C Act* and authorized FDA to collect fees to support the review of generic new animal drugs.

Each approved animal drug manufacturer must submit certain information to FDA regarding patents covering the animal drug or its method of use and the agency is required to make this information public. In addition, FDA must publicize a list of all animal drug products approved for safety and effectiveness, and must update the list monthly. This list, entitled List of FDA-Approved Animal Drug Products and known as the *Green Book*, is available online at www.fda.gov/AnimalVeterinary/Products/ApprovedAnimalDrugProducts/UCM042847.

The *Animal Drug Availability Act* of 1996 (*ADAA*) introduced several amendments to the *FD&C Act*, lending flexibility to the way CVM regulates animal drugs and medicated feeds. This law was designed to increase the number of animal drugs on the market through several means:

- amending the current definition of "substantial evidence of effectiveness," thereby permitting flexibility in the studies required to demonstrate a new animal drug's effectiveness and eliminating the requirement for field studies
- providing greater direct interaction between animal drug sponsors and FDA during the drug development process
- creating a new category of drugs—Veterinary Feed Directive Drugs—allowing new animal drug approval and use in animal feed, on a veterinarian's order, while incorporating safeguards to ensure the safe use of such drugs
- supporting "flexible labeling," permitting a range of acceptable or recommended doses to appear on animal drug product labeling rather than one optimum dose (This broadens the approval process to make available more drugs to treat minor species.)

Phased Review and Administrative NADAs

CVM does not require applicants to submit an NADA as one complete package. Instead, applicants may submit individual, completed technical sections or components to the INAD file for technical review. For instance, the applicant may submit the target animal safety, effectiveness, human food safety and labeling separately when the necessary data and information have been compiled for each. Overall NADA requirements remain the same as described above.

When each technical submission has been submitted for phased review and CVM has issued a "technical section complete" letter for each, the manufacturer submits an Administrative NADA. CVM must review and respond to this submission within 180 days, but review should be completed more quickly, as the scientific content already has been assessed.

Expedited Review

Under the CVM Expedited Review Status (ERS) program, certain products that offer important advances in animal health or in the reduction of human pathogens in food animals receive priority review. Products approved for expedited review will receive higher priority and a faster review than routine applications. For instance, an expedited NADA review generally should be completed within 90 days, rather than 180. The standards for data quality and evaluation are unchanged.

A sponsor may apply for expedited review status at the INAD or NADA stage. ONADE will review and assess the request and should reach a decision on the status within 60 days of receiving the request.

MUMS

MUMS is similar in principle to the human *Orphan Drug Act* of 1983. It provides incentives to sponsors to address the shortage of FDA-approved drugs for treating relatively rare disorders of major veterinary species (minor use) and less-common animal species (minor species) under a veterinarian's care.

MUMS defines minor species as all animals other than the major species (cattle, horses, swine, chickens, turkeys, dogs and cats). Minor species include zoo animals, ornamental fish, parrots, ferrets and guinea pigs. Some animals of agricultural importance also are considered minor species for the purposes of *MUMS*, e.g., sheep, goats, catfish and other food fish, and honeybees.

MUMS creates three major incentives:

Conditional Approvals

A sponsor of a veterinary drug for a minor use or minor species can apply for "conditional approval," which allows the sponsor to market the drug before collecting all necessary effectiveness data, but only after proving the drug is safe in accordance with the full FDA approval standard and that there is a reasonable expectation of effectiveness. The drug sponsor can keep the product on the market for up to five years, through annual renewals, while collecting the remaining required effectiveness data. This provision is managed by the ONADE, not by the Office of Minor Use & Minor Species Animal Drug Development (OMUMS).

Indexing

CVM can designate unapproved new drugs as legally marketed for a minor species. CVM may add the intended use to the Index of Legally Marketed Unapproved New Animal Drugs for Minor Species (the Index). 21 CFR 516, Subpart C, provides standards and procedures to establish an index of legally marketed unapproved new animal drugs. Under the indexing rule, CVM:

- grants investigational exemptions for indexing purposes

- determines the eligibility of new animal drugs for indexing consideration
- approves the selection of qualified expert panels to review drug safety and effectiveness data
- reviews the findings of expert panels, issues final decisions and publishes the index

Designation

Similar to *Orphan Drug Act* provisions for human drugs with limited uses, CVM may designate a drug as eligible for monetary incentives and marketing exclusivity. The manufacturer of the drug under development for a minor use or minor species is eligible for safety and effectiveness data development grants. The product is granted seven years of marketing exclusivity upon its approval or conditional approval for the minor use or minor species.

Abbreviated New Animal Drug Application (ANADA)

Products that are the same as an approved animal drug (the "pioneer" or reference product), have identical intended uses, and are demonstrated to be bioequivalent to the reference product may be approved through an ANADA. Broadly, the ANADA must contain information on the patent status of the reference product and the generic product's ingredients; labeling; bioequivalence; human food safety; chemistry, manufacturing and controls; and environmental impact.

CVM cannot approve generic versions of drugs that are still protected by patent or marketing exclusivity. Furthermore, the center will not approve ANADAs based on drugs that have been withdrawn from the market for safety or efficacy reasons.

The *Generic Animal Drug and Patent Term Restoration Act* of 1988 (*GADPTRA*) also provides for awarding of market exclusivity periods to products newly approved under NADAs, similar to the exclusivity awarded to certain newly approved drugs for human use. With *AGDUFA* of 2008, ANADAs submitted after 1 July 2008 are subject to a user fee program similar to that set forth by *ADUFA*. *AGDUFA* provides for fee waivers or reductions, upon request, when the generic drug is intended solely to provide for a minor use or minor species indication.

Compendial Requirements

The *United States Pharmacopeia* (*USP*) and *National Formulary* (*NF*) are recognized as the official US compendia for human and animal drugs under the *FD&C Act*'s adulteration and misbranding provisions (Sections 501 and 502). Since 1980, the two compendia have been published under the same cover (the *USP–NF*). Monographs for drug substances and preparations are featured in the *USP*; excipient monographs are in the *NF*.

Under *FD&C Act* requirements, ingredients, manufactured products and compounded preparations must have the strength, quality and purity specified in relevant *USP* and *NF* monographs. Monographs include the ingredient or preparation name; definition; packaging, storage and labeling requirements; and the specification. The specification is a series of analytical tests, test procedures and acceptance criteria. Certain tests and procedures require the use of official USP Reference Standards. *USP–NF* general chapters describe in detail analytical tests and procedures that are referenced in multiple monographs.

Animal Feeds, Medicated Feeds and Type A Medicated Articles

Feeds are either intended solely to meet an animal's nutritional requirements (non-medicated feeds) or as a means to orally administer drugs (medicated feeds). Animal feeds are defined under *FD&C Act* Section 201(w). CVM is responsible for both non-medicated animal feeds—including pet foods—and medicated feeds.

Animal feeds, like human foods, must be pure and wholesome, contain no harmful or deleterious substances and be truthfully labeled. Animal food labeling regulations are found in 21 CFR 501. Additionally, canned foods—including canned pet foods—must be processed in conformance with low-acid canned food regulations (21 CFR 113). Non-medicated animal feeds generally do not require FDA approval before they are marketed, provided that they are made from ingredients that are either approved food additives or are generally recognized as safe (GRAS) for their intended use. FDA is of the opinion that the *Dietary Supplement and Health Education Act* (*DSHEA*) does not apply to animal nutritional supplements and "nutraceuticals." Substances marketed as human dietary supplements fall under the pre-*DSHEA* regulatory scheme when marketed for animals; they are considered food, food additives, GRAS items or new animal drugs, depending on the intended use. However, CVM has often exercised regulatory discretion and waived food additive petitions or NADAs for such articles when they are determined not to present animal or human safety concerns.

If a food substance is intended to treat or prevent disease or to affect the body's structure or function other than as a food, it falls within the *FD&C Act*'s definition of a drug. Thus, it must be the subject of an approved NADA, similar to that described above, before it can be marketed. Under 21 CFR 558, FDA recognizes Type A Medicated Articles, Type B Medicated Feeds and Type C Medicated Feeds.

Type A Medicated Articles are mixtures of one or more drug substance(s) with suitable vehicles. They are used to facilitate active drug component dilution and admixture with animal feed before administration. The manufacture of a Type A Medicated Article requires approval by CVM of either an NADA or ANADA for the medicated article. Type A Medicated Articles are divided into two categories. Category I includes those drugs that require no withdrawal period at the lowest use level in each species for which they are approved. Category II includes those drugs that require a withdrawal period at the lowest use level for at least one species for which they are approved, or are regulated on a "no-residue" basis or with a zero tolerance because of drug residue carcinogenic concerns. A Type A Medicated Article is intended solely for use in manufacturing another Type A Medicated Article (e.g., mixing two Type A Medicated Articles containing different active pharmaceutical ingredients to manufacture a third Type A Medicated Article) or a Type B or Type C Medicated Feed. Type A Article CGMPs are found in 21 CFR 226.

A Type B Medicated Feed contains either a Type A Medicated Article or another Type B Medicated Feed, plus a substantial quantity of nutrients (not less than 25% of the total weight), and is intended solely for use in manufacturing another Type B Medicated Feed or a Type C Medicated Feed. Before being fed to animals, a Type B Medicated Feed must be substantially diluted with one or more nutrients to produce a nutritionally appropriate and medically safe Type C Medicated Feed for administration to the patient.

A Type C Medicated Feed contains an active drug component(s) and is intended either to be offered as a complete animal feed or to be fed top-dressed or offered free-choice in conjunction with other animal feed to supplement the animal's total daily ration. A Type C Medicated Feed is produced by substantially diluting a Type A Medicated Article, a Type B Medicated Feed or another Type C Medicated Feed. Medicated feed CGMPs are found in 21 CFR 225.

A feed manufacturing facility must hold a medicated feed mill license to manufacture a Type B or Type C Medicated Feed from a Category II, Type A Medicated Article. No license is required if drug use is limited to Category I drugs (all types) and Type B sources of Category II drugs. FDA routinely inspects medicated feed mills and Type A Medicated Article manufacturers.

Postapproval Reporting

Under *FD&C Act* Section 506A and 21 CFR 514.8, the holder of an approved NDA or ANADA must notify FDA about each change in each established, approved application condition beyond the variations already provided for in the application. There are four reporting categories:

- Prior Approval Supplement—CVM must approve the supplement before the change can be implemented.
- Supplement—Changes Being Effected in 30 days (CBE-30)—The manufacturer may distribute the drug made using the change 30 days after CVM receives the supplement, unless CVM notifies the manufacturer that more information or prior approval is needed.
- Supplement—Changes Being Effected (CBE)—

The manufacturer may begin distribution of the drug made using the change upon CVM's receipt of the supplement.
- Annual Report—The manufacturer may make minor changes during the year and document them in the Annual Report.

The change reporting category is based on the change's potential to adversely affect the drug product's identity, strength, quality, purity or potency, as these factors may relate to its safety or effectiveness. The sponsor must also submit a Manufacturing Changes and Stability Report (MCSR) annually.

Manufacturers must report serious, unexpected adverse drug events to CVM within 15 working days of becoming aware of the event. The manufacturer must investigate the event and submit a follow-up report. These events are reported on the Veterinary Adverse Drug Reaction, Lack of Effectiveness, Product Defect Report (Form FDA 1932).

In addition, product and manufacturing defects that may result in serious adverse drug events are to be reported to CVM within three working days of the manufacturer's becoming aware that a defect may exist. The manufacturer should first inform CVM by telecommunication and then submit a Form FDA 1932.

Manufacturers also must submit a Transmittal of Periodic Reports and Promotional Material for New Animal Drugs (Form FDA 2301) periodically, reporting postmarketing surveillance experience and other information for new animal drugs. As described in 21 CFR 14.80, this form must be submitted every six months for the first two years following NADA or ANADA approval and yearly thereafter. Form FDA 1932 also accompanies Form FDA 2301 as part of the periodic drug experience report, and is used to report adverse drug events and product/manufacturing defects. Adverse drug reactions include lack of drug effectiveness and any adverse reaction occurring in humans from exposure during manufacture, testing, handling or use.

Extralabel Use

The *Animal Medicinal Drug Use Clarification Act* of 1994 (*AMDUCA*) allows veterinarians to prescribe certain approved animal drugs for extralabel uses, and to prescribe approved human drugs for animals under certain conditions. Extralabel use refers to the use of an approved drug in a manner that is not in accordance with the approved label directions.

Under *AMDUCA*, any extralabel use must be by or on the order of a veterinarian in accordance with an appropriate medical rationale; must not result in violative residues in food-producing animals; and must be in conformance with additional restrictions in the implementing regulations in 21 CFR 530. Specific drugs identified in 21 CFR 530.41 are prohibited from extralabel use. To avoid volatile residues in food-producing animal products, veterinarians may obtain appropriate withdrawal times for drugs administered extralabel by consulting the Food Animal Residue Avoidance Databank (FARAD) at www.farad.org.

Veterinary Devices

CVM has jurisdiction over medical devices for veterinary use; however, these devices are given regulatory discretion and are not subject to the same premarket approval requirements as medical devices intended for use in humans. Further, unlike medical devices for use in humans, veterinary devices are not subject to performance standards.

Veterinary medical devices that are not safe, effective or properly labeled are deemed to be adulterated and/or misbranded under *FD&C Act* Sections 501 and 502. Thus, it is the manufacturer and/or distributor's responsibility to assure that these veterinary medical devices are safe, effective and properly labeled. Veterinary device labeling must not be false or misleading, and must bear directions for use that are adequate for each target animal group for which the device is intended. Animal devices that do not comply with the *FD&C Act* may be subject to seizure, and firms and individuals responsible for marketing these illegal devices may be subject to other penalties under the act, including fines. While the *FD&C Act* authorizes imprisonment for certain violations, it is imposed only in extremely rare cases.

Although the Quality System Regulation in 21 CFR 820 applies to human devices only, CVM recommends that veterinary device manufacturers become familiar with these regulations and be guided by them in manufacturing and assembling their devices. CVM strongly recommends that labeling be sent in for Office of Surveillance and Compliance review to avoid misbranding.

Diagnostics used in safety testing of foods derived from animals may be regulated by the Center for Food Safety and Applied Nutrition (CFSAN) under product-specific regulations and guidelines. Additionally, veterinary electronic devices that emit radiation are subject to the *Radiation Control for Health and Safety Act* of 1968—which contains various performance and safety standards—and must be registered with the Center for Devices and Radiological Health (CDRH).

Animal Grooming Aids

Cosmetic articles intended to cleanse and beautify animals are referred to as "animal grooming aids." Grooming aids formulated only to cleanse or beautify animals are not subject to federal regulation, as the *FD&C Act* definition of "cosmetic" applies only to articles for use in humans. However, CVM still is concerned with the safety of such products, and tracks complaints and adverse reactions.

If animal grooming aids are labeled with direct or implied therapeutic claims, they may fall into the definition of drugs under *FD&C Act* Section 201(g) or the definition

of new animal drugs under Section 201(v).

USDA
Veterinary Biologics

Animal biologics are subject to both the *FD&C Act* and the *Virus-Serum-Toxin Act* (*VSTA*) of 1913, as amended. Veterinary biologics, including vaccines, bacterins, antisera, diagnostic kits and certain other products of biological origin, are regulated by the Center for Veterinary Biologics (CVB) in the Animal and Plant Health Inspection Service (APHIS) of USDA.

CVB implements *VSTA* provisions to ensure that pure, safe, potent and effective veterinary biologics are available for the diagnosis, prevention and treatment of animal diseases. CVB develops or approves appropriate product release standards and procedures; issues licenses and permits; monitors and inspects products and facilities; and controls veterinary biologic field tests and batch release.

To sell or manufacture a veterinary biologic product in the US, a manufacturer must hold both a Veterinary Biologics Product License for the product and a Veterinary Biologics Establishment License for the manufacturing facility. The Veterinary Biologics Product License application must include:

- APHIS Form 2003, Application for United States Veterinary Biological Product License
- an outline of production (9 CFR 114.8–.9)
- master seed and cell reports for each microorganism and cell stock used in biological product manufacture, describing testing performed to demonstrate the purity, identity and safety of each (9 CFR 113)
- additional information regarding all master seeds used in the production of new live biological products and those created through recombinant technology (this must provide adequate data for the CVB laboratory to establish proper biocontainment requirements and conduct confirmatory testing)
- for vaccines, study protocols for host animal immunogenicity/efficacy, safety, backpassage, shed/spread, immunological interference and other relevant areas
- for diagnostic test kits, study protocols to assess diagnostic sensitivity and specificity, repeatability and reproducibility of results

Applicants also must submit such additional relevant product data and information as:

- in-process procedures and corresponding validation reports
- host animal immunogenicity/efficacy reports
- potency test development reports
- product safety reports

- stability reports
- Veterinary Biologics Production and Test Reports (APHIS Form 2008) for satisfactory pre-licensing serials (numbered lots) of product (three consecutive serials)
- labels and/or label sketches
- other data as necessary to support approval of label claims

Product samples must be selected and shipped to the CVB laboratory according to procedures described in 9 CFR 113.3.

The CVB Policy, Evaluation and Licensing unit (CVB-PEL) reviews production facility and biological product license applications and awards licenses. This unit also reviews product importation permit applications and establishes licensing, testing and permit requirements and procedures.

Laboratories within CVB-PEL conduct pre-license testing and post-license quality-control monitoring. During pre-license testing, the laboratories assay parent materials (master seeds and cells) and final product. CVB-PEL tests master seed and master cell stock purity and identity (including identity of construct and expressed antigen for genetically engineered products) whether the intended final product is live vaccine, inactivated vaccine or a diagnostic kit. Initial product serials (usually three) are tested for purity and potency to ensure quality product is reproducible and product tests are appropriate and transferable.

The *VSTA* does not require that ingredients and manufactured products conform with standards for strength, quality and purity specified in relevant *USP* and *NF* monographs. Instead, the manufacturer must test all serials in accordance with the filed outline of production prior to sale and report results to CVB's Inspection and Compliance unit (CVB-IC). Results are compared with CVB-PEL check testing. Certain serials are selected for additional CVB-PEL testing. Each satisfactory batch is released by CVB-IC for marketing.

CVB-IC conducts random confirmatory potency and purity tests of serials as an additional manufacturing quality control program check. In addition, CVB-IC may test the marketed product's safety, purity, potency or efficacy in response to consumer or manufacturer concerns. CVB also monitors reports of suspected adverse events related to veterinary biologics.

Licensed veterinary biological manufacturing facilities must meet 9 CFR 108–116 requirements relating to sterilization/pasteurization processes, packaging and labeling, records and reports and other manufacturing topics. CVB-IC conducts periodic, unannounced, in-depth inspections of all licensed facilities. Products imported from other countries must meet all US standards and foreign facilities receive inspections similar to those of domestic firms.

If CVB has reason to believe a marketed product is unsatisfactory or presents a risk to the health of animals, to the public health or to the environment, it may notify the manufacturer to stop distribution and sale of the product. If there are indications that raise questions regarding a product's purity, safety, potency or efficacy, or if there may be a problem regarding a product's preparation, testing or distribution, the manufacturer must inform CVB within three days of discovering the problem.

Similar to FDA's CVM guidance documents, CVB communicates guidance to industry through the use of Veterinary Services Memorandums and CVB Notices.

Phased Review of Product License Applications

CVB does not require applicants to submit a product license application as one complete package. Instead, applicants may submit individual, completed licensing deliverables for technical review. For instance, the applicant may submit the license application and outline of production, field safety and effectiveness reports and labeling separately when the necessary data and information have been compiled for each.

Tissue Residues

USDA's Food Safety and Inspection Service (FSIS) is responsible for inspecting meat and poultry products in slaughter and egg processing plants and establishments that further process meat and poultry products, and has primary responsibility for the wholesomeness of these products. FSIS reports detection of violative drug residues in meat and poultry to FDA's CVM for regulatory follow-up.

Environmental Protection Agency—Animal Pesticides

Pesticides administered to animals—including topical flea products, fly sprays, ear tags and insecticide dips, and pesticidal feeds—are regulated by the Environmental Protection Agency (EPA) under the *Federal Insecticide, Fungicide, and Rodenticide Act* of 1947 (*FIFRA*). According to *FIFRA*, pesticides include substances and mixtures of substances intended for preventing, destroying, repelling or mitigating any pest, if they are not considered to be new animal drugs under the *FD&C Act*. For example, articles having pesticidal qualities used to treat systemic macroinvertebrate parasite infestations are regulated as new animal drugs. Articles used to treat external macroinvertebrate parasites are regulated as pesticides.

Primary pesticide regulatory concerns are the safety of the worker who applies the product and the environmental effects caused by the product's manufacture, use and disposal. Actual product efficacy and safety are of lesser concern. Pesticide products are not required to be produced under CGMPs.

The *FD&C Act* authorizes EPA to set maximum pesticide

residue levels for foods or animal feed. Pesticide residues in foods are monitored and the tolerances enforced by FDA (fruits and vegetables, seafood) and USDA's Food Safety and Inspection Service (meat, milk, poultry, eggs and aquacultural foods).

Extralabel or unregistered pesticide use is prohibited unless EPA grants an emergency exemption.

Summary

- New animal drugs are reviewed and approved by the FDA's CVM through the submission of an NADA.
- *GADPTRA* requires that a generic animal drug product sponsor submit and receive approval of an ANADA prior to marketing.
- Animal drugs must be produced under CGMPs.
- The *VSTA* requires biological animal products and facilities to be licensed. Samples of all licensed biological products are submitted to USDA's CVB for testing and approval prior to sale.
- Veterinary medical devices are subject to regulatory discretion. While they are not subject to premarket approval requirements, it is the manufacturer's responsibility to ensure that these devices are safe, effective and properly labeled. Veterinary devices not meeting these requirements may be deemed adulterated and/or misbranded under the general provisions of *FD&C Act* Sections 501 and 502.
- Animal grooming aids with direct or implied therapeutic claims may be considered new animal drugs.
- Pesticides that are not new animal drugs are regulated by EPA.

References

Guidance for Industry 169: Drug Substance Chemistry, Manufacturing, and Controls Information. Rockville, MD: CVB;, 6 August 2010.

International Cooperation on Harmonisation of Technical Requirements for Registration of Veterinary Products (VICH). VICH Guidelines. www.vichsec. org/en/guidelines.htm. Accessed 5 May 2011.

The Common Technical Document for the Registration of Pharmaceuticals for Human Use: Quality— M4Q(R1) *(CTD-Q)*. ICH website. www.ich.org/ products/ctd.html. Accessed 5 May 2011.

Draft Guidance for Industry 132: The Administrative New Animal Drug Application Process. Rockville, MD: CVM; 6 November 2002.

Guidance for Industry 200: SECG for Designation of New Animal Drugs for Minor Uses or Minor Species. Rockville, MD: CVM; 1 September 2010.

Guidance for Industry 201: SECG for Index of Legally Marketed Unapproved New Animal Drugs for Minor Species. Rockville, MD: CVM; 1 September 2010.

Form FDA 1932, "Veterinary Adverse Drug Reaction, Lack of Effectiveness, Product Defect Report." Rockville, MD: CVM; January 2010.

Guide 1240.3135, "Animal Drug Applications Expedited Review Guideline." *CVM Program Policy and Procedures Manual*. Rockville, MD: CVM; 3 December 1997. CVM.

Guidance for Industry: *Expedited Review for New Animal Drug Applications for Human Pathogen Reduction Claims*. Rockville, MD: CVM; 6 March 2001.

Index of Legally Marketed Unapproved New Animal Drugs for Minor Species; Final Rule." *Federal Register*. 26 December 2007; 72; 69107–69131.

"Designation of New Animal Drugs for Minor Uses or Minor Species; Final Rule." *Federal Register*. 26 July 2007; 72; 41010–41022.

CVMM-50: *Information on Approval of Generic Animal Drugs*. Rockville, MD: CVM; March 1992.

Federal Register; Vol. 61; No. 78; Monday, April 22, 1996; Docket number 95N–0308—Inapplicability of the Dietary Supplement Health and Education Act to Animal Products.

Veterinary Services Memorandum No. 800.50: *Basic License Requirements and Guidelines for Submission of Materials in Support of Licensure*. Ames, IA: CVB; 9 February 2011.

Veterinary Services Memorandum No. 800.57: *Market Suspensions*. Ames, IA: CVB; 17 September 1999.

Veterinary Services Memorandum No. 800.78: *Preparation and Submission of Facilities Documents*. Ames, IA: CVB; 11 November 2010.

Veterinary Services Memorandum No. 800.91: *Categories of Inspection for Licensed Veterinary Biologics Establishments*. Ames, IA: CVB; 13 May 1999.

Veterinary Services Memorandum No. 800.101: *US Veterinary Biological Product Permits for Distribution and Sale*. Ames, IA: CVB; 28 May 2002.

Recommended Reading

Center for Veterinary Medicine. US Food and Drug Administration guidance documents. www.fda.gov/AnimalVeterinary/ GuidanceComplianceEnforcement/ GuidanceforIndustry/default.htm. Accessed 5 May 2011.

American Veterinary Medical Association. Available at: www.avma.org. Accessed 5 May 2011.

Animal Health Institute. Available at: www.ahi.org.

Generic Animal Drug Alliance. www.gadaonline.org. Accessed 5 May 2011.

Center for Veterinary Biologics Veterinary Services Memorandums. www.aphis.usda.gov/animal_ health/vet_biologics/vb_regs_and_guidance. shtml. Accessed 5 May 2011.

International Cooperation on Harmonisation of
    Technical Requirements for Registration of
    Veterinary Products. www.vichsec.org/en/guidelines.
    htm. Accessed 5 May 2011.

American Feed Industry Association. www.afia.org/afia/
    home.aspx. Accessed 5 May 2011.

"Guide for the Care and Use of Laboratory Animals."
    Washington, DC: National Research Council,
    National Academy Press; 1996.

United States Pharmacopeia. www.usp.org. Accessed 5
    May 2011.

The *Green Book,* www.fda.gov/AnimalVeterinary/
    Products/ApprovedAnimalDrugProducts/
    UCM042847 . Accessed 5 May 2011.

The Food Animal Residue Avoidance Databank
    (FARAD). www.farad.org. Accessed 5 May 2011.

Food Products

Updated by Evelyn Cadman

Objectives

- Provide an overview of requirements for marketing an FDA-regulated food in the US
- Understand the basics of food labeling requirements and voluntary elements
- Develop a broad understanding of the mechanisms available for use of new ingredients and color additives in compliance with regulatory requirements
- Explain food adulteration standards and major sanitation programs, including GMP and HACCP
- Describe administrative requirements for food facilities, such as facility registration, prior notice, recordkeeping and reporting of reportable foods

Statutes, Regulations and Guidelines Covered in this Chapter

- *Federal Food, Drug, and Cosmetic Act* of 1938, as amended (codified at 21 U.S.C. §301 *et al*)
- Section 321 Definitions
- Section 331 Prohibited Acts
- Sections 341–350f Food
- Section 374 Inspection
- Section 379e Color Additives
- *Food Allergen Labeling and Consumer Protection Act* of 2004 (P.L. 108-282)
- *Public Health Security and Bioterrorism Preparedness and Response Act* of 2002 (P.L. 107-188)
- *Food and Drug Administration Modernization Act* of 1997 (P.L. 105-115)
- *Food Safety Modernization Act* of 2011 (Public Law 111-353)
- *Dietary Supplement Health Education Act* of 1994 (P.L. 103-417)
- *Nutrition Labeling and Education Act* of 1990 (P.L. 101-535)
- *Orphan Drug Act* of 1983, § 5 (P.L. 97-414)
- *Tariff Act* of 1930 (codified at 19 U.S.C. 1304)
- 9 CFR 317 Meat labeling, marking devices and containers
- 21 CFR 1 General enforcement regulations
- 21 CFR 7 Enforcement policy
- 21 CFR 70–82 Color additives
- 21 CFR 100–190 Food for human consumption
- FDA's Biotechnology Policy of 1992
- *Guidance for Industry: Regulation of Genetically Engineered Animals Containing Heritable Recombinant DNA Constructs* (January 2009)
- USDA's "A Guide to Federal Food Labeling Requirements for Meat and Poultry Products" (August 2007)
- *Food Action Defect Levels Handbook*

Introduction

The US Food and Drug Administration (FDA) is the federal agency charged with regulation of most food and food-related products. FDA derives its authority to regulate foods primarily from the *Federal Food, Drug, and Cosmetic Act* of 1938 (*FD&C Act*), as amended.[1] The *FD&C Act* defines "food" broadly to mean

> (1) articles used for food or drink for man or other animals, (2) chewing gum, and (3) articles used for components of any such article.[2]

As a result of this broad definition, FDA's regulation of food covers not just conventional human food, but also any individual component of food, ingredients, pet food and animal feed. Under the *Dietary Supplement Health Education Act* of 1994 (*DSHEA*),[3] dietary supplements are also regulated under the general umbrella of "foods," although they are subject to a number of labeling and ingredient requirements specific to dietary supplements. Regulation of dietary supplements is discussed in more detail in Chapter 27.

FDA implements the *FD&C Act* and establishes regulations to prevent food from adulteration, ensuring that foods are safe, wholesome and sanitary. FDA also regulates the misbranding of food labels and labeling, ensuring that products are honestly, accurately and informatively represented to the public. Within FDA, food regulation is managed by the Center for Food Safety and Applied Nutrition (CFSAN).

Although FDA regulates most foods, it does not regulate all foods. The US Department of Agriculture (USDA) has jurisdiction over meat, poultry and commercially processed egg products, as well as combination products (e.g., meat stew, pizza with meat toppings), depending upon the meat or poultry content. Within USDA, the Food Safety and Inspection Service (FSIS) is responsible for the inspection, safety and labeling of these products. Further, though FDA regulates bottled water, the US Environmental Protection Agency (EPA) regulates tap water, and the US Alcohol and Tobacco Tax and Trade Bureau (TTB) regulates most alcohol products.

FDA also does not regulate all aspects of food products. For example, although FDA regulates food labeling, the agency works with the Federal Trade Commission (FTC) to regulate food advertising, with the FTC taking the lead on most enforcement actions.[4] Fruits, vegetables and other plants are regulated by USDA's Animal and Plant Health Inspection Service (APHIS) to prevent the introduction of plant diseases and pests into the US. The Agricultural Marketing Service (AMS) of USDA administers the National Organic Program, which develops, implements and administers national standards for organic agricultural products and accredits the certifying agents who inspect organic operations.

Moreover, FDA works jointly with numerous federal, state and local agencies to regulate various aspects of foods and specific food categories. For example, FDA works cooperatively with states and with other agencies, such as the Centers for Disease Control (CDC), to address outbreaks of food-borne illness. The following provides more detail on some of the agencies and other jurisdictions that are responsible for some aspect of food regulation or that work cooperatively with FDA on food matters:

- States are the primary regulators for restaurants, farms and retail establishments, including grocery stores. States work cooperatively with FDA to regulate milk and shellfish, and are also involved in the regulation of weights and measures.
- FTC works with FDA to regulate all advertising, ensuring that advertisements are truthful and not misleading for consumers. Within FTC, the Bureau of Consumer Protection has a mandate to protect consumers against unfair, deceptive or fraudulent practices.
- EPA establishes pesticide tolerances (acceptable residues) for food and animal feed, while FDA enforces compliance with pesticide tolerances. EPA also establishes maximum contaminant levels in public drinking water.
- TTB, formerly the Bureau of Alcohol, Tobacco, and Firearms, enforces labeling and other regulatory requirements for beer, wine and distilled spirits.
- US Customs and Border Protection (CBP) works with FDA to regulate imported food (and other FDA-related imported products).

Food Ingredients and Packaging (Food Additives)

Unlike its regulation of drugs or medical devices, FDA has very limited authority to regulate food before it goes on the market. One significant exception is the regulation of food and color additives, which must be approved by FDA as safe for intended uses prior to marketing. The term "food additive" includes not just ingredients intentionally added to the food, but also any substance used in the production process that could reasonably end up in the food, including packaging that could leach onto food and even lubricants used on machinery that touches food during processing.

FDA approval of a new food additive must be by issuance of a regulation. For this reason, it can be important to determine whether a substance falls within any of the several exemptions from the definition of a food additive.

What is a Food Additive?

Stripping out the exclusions, the general definition of a food additive is broad:

"Any substance the intended use of which results or may

reasonably be expected to result, directly or indirectly, in its becoming a component or otherwise affecting the characteristics of any food...."[5]

The definition requires two key determinations. What is the intended use of the substance? When used as intended, can the substance be reasonably expected to end up in the food or affect the food in any way?

Substances such as cleaning solvents used on food processing machinery or packaging materials may be food additives if they could "reasonably be expected" to end up in the food in any amount or otherwise affect the food. The definition specifically states that "any substance intended for use in processing, manufacturing, packing, processing, preparing, treating, packaging, transporting or holding food" and "any source of radiation intended for any such use" can be a food additive.[6]

Regulations approving uses of direct food additives—that is, direct addition of a substance to food—can be found in 21 CFR 172 and 173. Regulations approving food additives that may indirectly become a component of food can be found at 21 CFR 175–178. Regulations approving the use of radiation on food can be found at 21 CFR 179.

What is Not a Food Additive?

The *FD&C Act* specifically excludes the following types of substances from the definition of food additive:

- any substance that is generally recognized as safe (GRAS) for its intended uses by scientific experts qualified to evaluate its safety
- pesticide chemical residues
- pesticides
- color additives
- new animal drugs
- new dietary ingredients (i.e., ingredients for use in dietary supplements)
- Prior Sanction: any substance approved or sanctioned for use prior to 6 September 1958 under the *FD&C Act*, the *Federal Meat Inspection Act* of 1906 or the *Poultry Products Inspection Act* of 1957[7]

Any substance that falls within any of these seven exclusions need not be approved as a food additive prior to use, though it may be subject to other regulations, depending upon the type of substance. For example, pesticides are approved for use by EPA[8] and color additives must be approved by FDA under the color additive approval process in a different section of the *FD&C Act*.[9]

Most of the exclusions from the definition of food additive apply to defined categories of substances—a substance either is or is not an approved pesticide or color additive, and if not, it may be a food additive. The exclusion for GRAS substances, however, is more fluid; it depends upon the evidence available supporting the safety of the intended use of the substance. Because a GRAS substance need not be approved by regulation prior to use in food, determining whether a substance is GRAS or is a food additive is important in developing new food products.

How is a Food Additive Approved?

A food additive is deemed unsafe, and cannot be used in food, unless FDA has issued a regulation setting out the conditions under which the food additive can be used safely.[10] For a food additive to be deemed "safe," FDA must determine that under the intended conditions of use, the additive presents a "reasonable certainty of no harm."

Once a substance is determined to be a food additive, it must be approved through the food additive process unless it falls in one of two limited categories: a food contact substance or a food additive intended solely for investigational use. The exception for investigational use is rarely used and requires FDA to issue a regulation allowing the exception.[11] The food contact substance notification process is discussed in more detail below.

Any person may petition FDA to issue a regulation approving a food additive for a particular use. A food additive petition must include:

- the chemical identity and composition of the food additive
- the conditions of the additive's proposed uses
- data concerning the physical or technical effect the additive is intended to produce and the quantity of the additive required to produce such effect
- methods for determining the quantity of the additive in food
- full reports of investigations made with respect to the additive's safe use[12]

FDA may also request information on the production methods used for the additive and samples of the additive, its components or the food on which it will be used.

FDA must publish a notice in the *Federal Register* within 30 days of receiving a complete food additive petition. FDA then has 90 days (which may be extended to no more than 180 days) from the filing of the petition to publish a regulation approving the use of the food additive or issue an order denying the petition.[13] Any person adversely affected by the approval or denial of a food additive petition may file objections within 30 days after publication of the order approving or denying the petition.[14] FDA must respond to the objections, including any request for a public meeting, "as soon as practicable."

FDA cannot approve a food additive petition if a fair evaluation of the data fails to establish that the proposed use of the additive will be safe, or if the data show that the proposed use of the food additive would promote consumer deception or otherwise result in adulteration or misbranding of food.[15] FDA has significant discretion to use its scientific judgment in evaluating the data to determine whether the use of a food additive is safe. For example, in determining safety, the agency may consider the probable level of consumption of the additive, the cumulative effect of the additive in the diet and other safety factors recognized by experts to be appropriate.

FDA has no discretion, however, if it determines that a food additive induces cancer. The so-called Delaney Clause in Section 409(c) of the *FD&C Act* states that FDA cannot approve the use of any food additive as safe if the food additive: (1) is found to induce cancer in man or animals when ingested; or (2) is found, by appropriate tests, to induce cancer in man or animals by methods other than ingestion.[16]

The Delaney Clause applies whenever FDA determines any risk exists that the additive may induce cancer, regardless of how small the risk.[17] Only two limited exceptions from the application of the Delaney Clause have been recognized. Courts have held that the Delaney Clause does not apply where a constituent of a food or color additive is deemed to be a carcinogen, unless the food or color additive itself is determined to induce cancer.[18] The Delaney Clause also does not apply to certain food additives intended for use as ingredients of feed for animals raised for food production.[19]

Food additive approvals apply to the additive generally, and are not intended to be proprietary to a particular product. The food additive regulation will specify the conditions of use, which may include limits on the amounts of the additive, the types of foods in which the additive can be used or even labeling requirements for the use of the additive.

Food Contact Substance Notifications

The *FD&C Act* was amended in 1997 to allow food-contact substances approved for use on food to go through a notification process rather than requiring FDA to issue a regulation.[20] A "food-contact substance" is any substance used as a component of materials used in manufacturing, packing, packaging, transporting or holding food that is not intended to have a technical effect in the food. This definition includes such substances as paper, plastics, adhesives and coatings used in food containers or packaging. It also includes antimicrobials and colors used in packaging.

Anyone may submit a food contact notification to FDA. The agency has 120 days to review the notification. FDA may issue an objection or nonacceptance letter during the 120 days if it has safety concerns about the proposed use of the food-contact substance. Before issuing an objection or nonacceptance letter, the agency typically contacts notifiers to request more information or to permit the notifier to withdraw the notification. If FDA does not issue an objection or nonacceptance letter within 120 days, the food-contact notification becomes effective on the 120-day date.

At that point, FDA sends a letter to the notifier confirming the effective date. Approvals under the food-contact notification process are proprietary—that is, they extend only to the specific proprietary substance and use in the notification, not to other identical substances. During the 120-day review period, the information submitted in the notification cannot be publicly disclosed by FDA. Similarly, FDA cannot disclose information related to a notification that is withdrawn prior to the end of the 120-day review period.

GRAS Substances

As described above, any substance generally recognized as safe for its intended uses by scientific experts qualified to evaluate its safety is not a food additive and, therefore, does not have to be approved through the food additive process prior to use. Substances used in food prior to 1958 can also be deemed GRAS based upon their common use in food, rather than requiring consensus on the scientific data,[21] but this basis for GRAS determination is rarely used anymore.

The *FD&C Act* does not set out how FDA is to determine whether a substance is GRAS. Moreover, the *FD&C Act* does not require that FDA approve a substance as GRAS prior to its use in food, so the agency only has authority to challenge whether a substance is, in fact, GRAS after it is used in food. As a result, a person may self-determine the GRAS status of a substance and use it in food. Many food manufacturers, however, will require suppliers to provide support for the assertion that a substance is GRAS to avoid the risk of FDA challenging the GRAS status of the substance after the product is on the market.

To help those seeking to determine whether a substance is GRAS, FDA issued *Guidance for Industry: Frequently Asked Questions About GRAS* in December 2004, discussing how the agency evaluates whether a substance is GRAS. The agency has also published regulations in 21 CFR 182–186 affirming the GRAS status of certain substances. Due to limited resources, FDA rarely issues such regulations. Instead, FDA has implemented a voluntary GRAS notification process to provide manufacturers with some support for the assertion that a substance is GRAS.

FDA has taken the position that for a substance to be GRAS (other than substances used in food prior to 1958), the scientific data and information supporting its safe use must be of the same quantity and quality as needed for approval of a food additive petition, must be widely available, and there must be consensus among experts that the data establish the safe use of the substance. GRAS determinations cannot be based on private, proprietary data.

Under the GRAS notification program, FDA will review claims that a substance is GRAS. GRAS notifications should include a description of the substance (including chemical identity and properties), applicable conditions of use and the basis for the GRAS determination, including discussion of the scientific information supporting the safe use of the product and information supporting consensus of experts as to the safe use. FDA will typically consult with the notifier during its review of the notification. FDA does not approve GRAS notifications. However, at the conclusion of its review, FDA may issue a letter indicating the agency does not question the basis for the GRAS determination. Alternatively, the agency may issue a letter concluding that it does not believe the notification provides a sufficient basis for a GRAS determination. Because the GRAS notification process is voluntary, FDA is not bound by any timeline in completing its review, but seeks to complete its review within 180 days.

Color Additives

A "color additive" is defined as any dye, pigment or other substance that can impart color to a food, drug or cosmetic, or to the human body, except that the term does not include any substance that FDA determines is intended solely for a use other than coloring.[22] All color additives (except cosmetic hair dyes[23]) are subject to premarket approval.[24] Unlike food additives, there is no GRAS exemption from the definition of color additives.

FDA issues regulations listing color additives that have been approved as safe for their intended uses.[25] FDA's review of color additive petitions is similar to the review of food additive petitions. The petitioner must submit data demonstrating the safety and suitability of the new color additive for its intended uses. As is the case for food additives, there is a Delaney Clause for color additives that prohibits FDA from determining that a color additive is safe for any use that will result in ingestion of the additive if it is found by FDA to induce cancer when ingested by man or animals or, if it is found by appropriate tests to induce cancer in man or animals through a method other than ingestion.

As a condition of use, some approved color additives are required to be certified by batch by FDA before they can be sold. Certification is generally required by FDA when the composition of the additive needs to be controlled to protect public health. Synthetic organic dyes, lakes[26] and pigments must be batch certified, whereas color additives derived from plant or mineral sources are generally exempt from batch certification.

As with food additives, the approved conditions of use for certain color additives may extend to labeling requirements. In addition, regulations governing labeling of color additives in foods can be found in 21 CFR 101.22.

Biotechnology and Genetically Modified Organisms

Biotechnology refers to the techniques used by scientists to modify the genetic material of microorganisms, plants or animals in order to achieve a desired trait. Common use of the terms "biotechnology" and "genetically engineered"

in the US is limited to foods produced using recombinant DNA, or gene splicing.

FDA's Biotechnology Policy, published in 1992, is limited to foods derived from new plant varieties. FDA recommends that those developing a bioengineered food consult with the agency during development to discuss relevant safety, nutritional or other regulatory issues. FDA also recommends that developers submit a scientific and regulatory assessment of the food for review by the agency. FDA has proposed a rule that would require developers to submit such an assessment to FDA 120 days before a bioengineered food is marketed. The rule has not been finalized, so no requirement to this effect is currently in place. Bioengineered plants may also be subject to regulation by USDA's APHIS.

In January 2009, FDA issued *Guidance for Industry: Regulation of Genetically Engineered Animals Containing Heritable Recombinant DNA Constructs*. In the guidance, FDA takes the position that a recombinant DNA (rDNA) construct that is in a genetically engineered (GE) animal and is intended to affect the animal's structure or function meets the definition of an animal drug, and is subject to premarket approval requirements. The guidance further states that developers of GE animals must demonstrate that the construct is safe for the health of the GE animals and, if they are food animals, that the construct and products of the construct are safe for human consumption.

Misbranding: Food Labeling and Claims

Under Section 403(a) of the *FD&C Act*, a food is misbranded if its label or labeling is false or misleading in any particular, if it is offered for sale under the name of another food, or if it is an imitation of another food without proper labeling.[27] A "label" is defined to include any "written, printed, or graphic matter upon the immediate container of any article."[28] "Labeling" is broader, and includes "all labels and other written, printed, or graphic matter (1) upon any article or any of its containers or wrappers, or (2) accompanying such article."[29] Labeling has been interpreted by FDA and the courts to include flyers, brochures and displays that are proximate to the product in a store. FDA has further interpreted labeling to include information on a website from which a product can be purchased, and even information on websites reachable through links on a website where the product can be purchased.

The *FD&C Act* prohibits misbranded foods from being introduced, delivered or received in interstate commerce.[30] FDA has authority to take action against a product if the label or labeling fails to identify "material facts."[31] Everything on a product's label or labeling must be truthful and cannot be misleading.

FDA regulates labeling for all foods, except those within USDA's jurisdiction (meat, poultry and cracked egg products). There is no label preapproval required by FDA;

however, the agency has promulgated extensive regulations governing food labeling. The labeling rules governing foods regulated by USDA are similar to FDA's requirements; however, label preapproval is required for products within USDA's jurisdiction.

There are two primary areas of food labeling regulation: required elements and voluntary claims. All food labels must contain certain uniform elements to provide meaningful information to consumers in a manner that allows for easy comparison between products. Many products also bear voluntary claims promoting the benefits or usefulness of the products as they relate to either nutrition or health.

Mandatory Labeling Elements

The *FD&C Act* establishes requirements for numerous statements that must appear on a food product's label. Food labeling is required for most packaged foods, such as breads, cereals, canned and frozen foods, snacks, desserts and drinks. Labeling requirements are very specific, often requiring near-exact placement in a mandated size on a specific component of a certain label.

Food labels must contain five primary elements (unless subject to limited exemptions):

- statement of identity
- net quantity of contents
- nutrition facts
- ingredient statement
- manufacturer's statement

Additional labeling requirements are applicable to certain products; for instance, juice content, country of origin, use of irradiation, allergen declaration, mandated warnings and labeling of infant formulas. Certain label statements are prohibited, such as false or misleading statements or unapproved nutrient content or health claims.

The required information must appear on one of two label panels. The "principal display panel" (PDP), a product's primary label, is the "part of a label that is most likely to be displayed, presented, shown, or examined under customary conditions of display" for sale.[32] The PDP must contain the product's statement of identity and net weight. In addition, the PDP may include the ingredient statement, manufacturing statement and nutrition information. Many product labels also contain an "information panel," which is typically the "part of the label immediately contiguous and to the right of the principal display panel."[33] No intervening material is permitted between the PDP and the information panel unless the panel immediately to the right of the PDP is too small to accommodate the required information. The information panel generally includes the manufacturing statement, ingredient declaration and nutrition information.

Statement of Identity

All products must bear a product identity statement that is either a standard of identity, a common or usual name or an appropriately descriptive term or "fanciful" name.[34] Additionally, products that are deemed imitations of standardized foods must be labeled as such.

Standards of Identity

The *FD&C Act* authorizes FDA to establish standards of identity for certain foods.[35] Standards of identity define what a given food product is, its name and the ingredients that must be used, or may be used, in the manufacture of the food. Food standards ensure that consumers get what they expect when they purchase certain food products, providing predictability that a product labeled as "ice cream" is actually a frozen dairy product. Once a standard of identity is established, any food that purports to be the standardized food must comply with the standard of identity, and a food may not bear the standardized name if it does not comply with the standard. The standards of identity are codified in 21 CFR Parts 130–169.

Common or Usual Name

A standard of identity does not exist for all types of foods. To ensure consistency and predictability for consumers, the common or usual name of a product must "accurately identify or describe…the basic nature of the food or its characterizing properties or ingredients."[36] Regulations establish common or usual name requirements for particular foods, which are less rigid than standards of identity, but nonetheless must be followed when labeling these types of foods. These regulations are contained in 21 CFR 102.

Descriptive or Fanciful Name

When either a standard of identity or usual name is required for a food and the nature of the food is obvious, the statement of identity is permitted to be a descriptive term or fanciful name.[37] For example, the brand name of many soft drinks serves as their statement of identity because such names are commonly used to refer to the products.

Imitation

If a food resembles a traditional food and is a substitute for the traditional food, but is nutritionally inferior to that food, it must be labeled as an imitation.[38] A food is considered nutritionally inferior if, for example, it contains less protein or a lesser amount of any essential vitamin or mineral. Products that are not nutritionally inferior and are a substitute for and resemble another food can use a fanciful name that is not false or misleading rather than using imitation labeling, such as using the phrase "Cool Whip" to identify a product that would otherwise be called "Imitation Whipped Cream."

Net Quantity of Contents

A net quantity of contents statement, expressed in terms of weight, measure, numerical count or a combination of numerical count and weight or measure, must appear in the lower 30% of the PDP.[39] The statement must declare the package's contents in both English and metric units, typically using pounds or grams for solids and ounces or milliliters for liquids. Detailed requirements mandate the type size and placement of the statement, which must appear as a "distinct item" separated from other printed label information. This statement must be accurate, although reasonable variations from stated weight are permitted for either statistical variations occurring during production under Good Manufacturing Practices or from loss or gain of moisture during distribution. As noted earlier, state and local authorities are also very active in regulating net quantity statements.

Nutrition Labeling

Regulations established to implement the *Nutrition Labeling and Education Act* of 1990 specify detailed substantive and technical requirements for the nutrition labeling of foods.[40] The embodiment of these detailed regulations is the Nutrition Facts panel. FDA places great importance on maintaining uniformity in the presentation of information in the Nutrition Facts panel. Regulations dictate such details as font sizes, indentations, use of bolding and even the width of lines in the Nutrition Facts panel. In addition to numerous other requirements, a food's nutrition label must:

- specify the serving size (based upon reference amounts customarily consumed)
- identify nutrients that must be declared
- follow specific formatting and type size requirements

Under the regulations, certain nutrients must be declared on the Nutrition Facts panel, while other nutrients may be declared voluntarily. FDA will evaluate products to confirm whether the product contains the level of nutrients that are declared on the nutrition panel, while recognizing that there will be some inherent variability in the nutritional composition of foods.

Ingredient Statement

The ingredients added to a product must be listed in the ingredient statement in descending order of predominance by weight.[41] Ingredients that are present at less than 2% of the total are exempt from the descending order of predominance requirement. Ingredients that are formulated from multiple components may either include the names of the components they combine to create followed by a parenthetical listing of each component, or list each component in descending order in the ingredient statement without

identifying the name of the multicomponent food itself. A small number of ingredients are eligible for "and/or" labeling when the ingredient may or may not be included in the product. There are also specific regulations governing the declaration of spices, flavors and colors.

Importantly, the *Food Allergen Labeling and Consumer Protection Act* of 2004 (*FALCPA*),[42] requires manufacturers to declare in English the presence of any major food allergen, specifically egg, wheat, milk, soy, fish, shellfish, peanuts and tree nuts.[43] The presence of the allergen may be declared in the ingredient statement or through the statement "Contains: (name of the allergen)" in bold immediately after the ingredient statement. The declaration for tree nuts, seafood and shellfish must indicate the particular species, while for other allergens, manufacturers are not required to specify the species (for example, Contains: Wheat, Milk, Cashews, Cod and Clams). FDA has not regulated the use of "May Contain" statements, such as "May contain milk," or implied "may contain" statements, such as "Processed in plant that also processes peanuts;" such statements are completely voluntary.

Manufacturer's Statement

The label must contain a manufacturing statement identifying the manufacturer, packer or distributor.[44] The company's actual corporate name must appear on the label, as well as its city, state and zip code. If the company is not listed in the city or telephone directory, its street address must also appear on the label. Unless it is misleading, it is acceptable to list the principal place of business instead of the actual place of manufacture. If the name on the label is not that of the manufacturer, it should be qualified with phrases such as "distributed by," "packed for" or "imported by."

Additional Requirements Imposed by USDA

Labeling for foods regulated by USDA must contain the above requirements, plus:

- an inspection legend and establishment number (in the form of a logo that looks like a USDA mark)[45]
- special handing instructions for products that require refrigeration or freezing[46]
- safe handling instructions for products that are not considered ready-to-eat[47]

Another distinction from FDA requirements is that labels for USDA-regulated products must be preapproved by FSIS prior to use.[48]

Country of Origin Labeling

USDA and US Customs and Border Protection (CBP) regulate separate country of origin labeling (COOL) requirements that affect many food products, including most imports. The *Farm Bills* of 2002 and 2008 mandated COOL for certain products. The COOL program is administered by USDA's AMS. The rules require labeling at retail to indicate the country of origin for certain covered commodities (i.e., muscle cuts and ground beef, lamb, chicken, goat and pork; wild and farm-raised fish and shellfish; perishable agricultural commodities (specifically fresh and frozen fruits and vegetables); macadamia nuts; pecans; peanuts; and ginseng).[49] Excluded from USDA COOL requirements are "processed food items," defined as retail items derived from a covered commodity that has "undergone specific processing resulting in a change of character" or that has been "combined with at least one other covered commodity." For example, breaded fish sticks; fruit cups containing cantaloupe, watermelon and honeydew; and cured hams are all considered to be processed food items and are exempt from COOL requirements.

Almost all imported products, whether or not exempt from USDA COOL requirements, are still required to be marked with country of origin labeling under the *Tariff Act* of 1930,[50] enforced by the CBP.[51] For example, although a bag of frozen peas and carrots is considered a processed food item and thus is exempt from USDA COOL requirements, if the peas and carrots are of foreign origin, CBP requires that the product's bag or its shipping container be marked with country of origin information. CBP's COOL requirements only apply until the product reaches its ultimate purchaser in the US, which may be a business that further manufactures the goods rather than a consumer. Thus, because CBP's restrictions allow labeling on shipping containers and do not transfer upon food processing, they do not have the same impact on consumers as do USDA's requirements.

Voluntary Labeling Information

Manufacturers may choose to make claims on their food labels about the attributes or benefits of their products. FDA has comprehensive requirements regarding claims, requiring authorization prior to use of nutrient content claims, health claims and qualified health claims; and notification of health or nutrient content claims under the *Food and Drug Administration Modernization Act* of 1997 (*FDAMA*).[52] FDA also regulates structure/function claims, which do not require approval prior to use.

A product's intended use will determine whether it is subject to regulation as a food, dietary supplement or drug. Claims that are made for a product are key to determining its intended use. For example (and as explained in more detail below), a claim that a product treats or prevents a disease or abnormal health condition subjects it to regulation as a drug, while the claim that a product "maintains healthy cholesterol for people with normal cholesterol" is a permissible structure/function claim for a food. Because most drugs cannot be marketed until they have received premarket approval under the *FD&C Act*, food companies must avoid making claims that would subject their products to regulation as new drugs.

Nutrient Content Claims

A nutrient content claim describes the level of a nutrient using terms such as "free," "high" and "low," or compares the level of a nutrient in a food to that of another food, using terms such as "more," "reduced" and "lite."[53] For example, the statements "zero calorie" and "high in fiber" are nutrient content claims. Under the *FD&C Act*, a food is deemed misbranded if it bears a nutrient content claim unless FDA has issued a regulation authorizing the claim and the claim is made in a manner consistent with the regulation.[54] Nutrient content claims can be express or implied, and are typically based on the reference amount customarily consumed for the food at issue. There must be an established daily value for the nutrient that is the subject of the claim. Special labeling is also required for products that exceed designated "disclosure levels" for fat, saturated fat, cholesterol and sodium amounts, requiring a statement such as "See nutrition information for fat content," for a food where the level of fat exceeds the disclosure level and a nutrient content claim is made.

Health Claims

A health claim describes the relationship between a substance (food or food component) and a disease or health-related condition.[55] For example, the statement, "While many factors affect heart disease, diets low in saturated fat and cholesterol may reduce the risk of this disease" is a model health claim. Health claims are limited to claims about reducing disease risk and cannot be claims about the cure, mitigation, treatment or prevention of disease. Since only drugs may bear claims that a product cures, mitigates, treats or prevents a disease (or unapproved health claims), such claims signal that the product is intended for use as a drug.[56] FDA will regard a food product bearing such claims as violative of the *FD&C Act* as both a misbranded food and as an unapproved new drug.

As noted, foods are deemed misbranded if they bear a health claim that is not authorized by FDA. Health claims must be supported by significant scientific agreement in order to be established. Foods are ineligible for health claims if they exceed disqualifying levels of certain nutrients (total fat, saturated fat, cholesterol and sodium), which are the same as the disclosure levels for nutrient content claims. Approved health claims are listed in the regulations at 21 CFR 101.72–101.83 and include claims relating such substances and diseases as calcium/osteoporosis and sodium/hypertension.

Qualified Health Claims

For claims for which there is not significant scientific agreement supporting the claim, manufacturers can petition to make "qualified health claims." The *FD&C Act* does not provide approval of health claims with less than significant scientific agreement. As a result of court decisions striking down FDA's denial of certain health claims on First Amendment grounds, the agency established a petition process for qualified health claims.

Though not requiring significant scientific agreement, such claims must be supported by scientific evidence. FDA has issued extensive guidance on how it evaluates scientific evidence for health claims and qualified health claims. If FDA agrees that the scientific evidence supports a qualified health claim, the agency will propose claim language for which it will exercise enforcement discretion. The claim language is tailored to accurately convey the level and quality of the science supporting the claim, e.g., "Supportive but not conclusive research shows that eating 1.5 ounces per day of walnuts, as part of a low saturated fat and low cholesterol diet and not resulting in increased caloric intake, may reduce the risk of coronary heart disease. See nutrition information for fat and calorie content." These statements are often so qualified as to not be useful. For example, in response to a petition for qualified health claims regarding a relationship between consumption of green tea and a reduced risk of certain cancers, FDA permitted the following claim:

> "Two studies do not show that drinking green tea reduces the risk of breast cancer in women, but one weaker, more limited study suggests that drinking green tea may reduce this risk. Based on these studies, FDA concludes that it is highly unlikely that green tea reduces the risk of breast cancer."

FDAMA Nutrient Content and Health Claims

FDAMA provides that nutrient content and health claims can be made on the basis of statements issued by authoritative bodies such as the National Institutes of Health or the National Academy of Sciences.[57] FDA takes the position that these claims must meet the same standard of evidence (significant scientific agreement) as FDA-approved health claims. In order to make a *FDAMA*-based claim, a petition must be filed with FDA at least 120 days prior to introducing the food bearing the claim into interstate commerce. The petition must include the exact words of the claim, a copy of the authoritative government statement relied upon, and a balanced representation of the scientific literature supporting the nutrient/disease relationship. During the 120-day period, FDA may notify the person wishing to make the claim if any of the required information has not been submitted. After 120 days, the claim may be used until FDA either issues a regulation prohibiting or modifying the claim or takes enforcement action.[58]

Structure/Function Claims

Structure/function claims describe the role of substances intended to affect the normal structure or function of humans.[59] Such claims assume that a person is healthy and just wants to maintain that good health. For example, the statement "Calcium maintains strong bones" is a structure/function claim. FDA authorization is not required prior to use of structure/function claims; however, such claims cannot be false or misleading or fail to reveal any material facts. Additionally, the claims must derive from the nutritional value of the product bearing the claim. Structure/function claims may characterize the means by which substances act to maintain such structure or function (e.g., "Fiber maintains bowel regularity"), or they may describe general well-being from consumption of a nutrient or dietary ingredient.

Structure/function claims may not explicitly or implicitly link the relationship to a disease or health-related condition. For example, it is permissible to make the claim that a substance supports memory, but not to make the claim that the substance reduces memory loss. The one exception to this rule is that claims are permitted to describe a benefit related to a nutrient deficiency disease (e.g., Vitamin C and scurvy), as long as the statement also provides information about how widespread such a disease is in the US.

Dietary Guidance

Dietary guidance statements are made to assist and encourage individuals in making better food choices and establishing healthier eating patterns. For example, the statement, "Diets rich in fruits and vegetables reduce the risk of certain cancers" is an acceptable dietary guidance statement. Although a dietary guidance statement can mention a specific disease, the disease cannot be linked to a specific food or a specific substance in food. The recommendations of recognized government (e.g., US Surgeon General, National Cancer Institute) or private professional health organizations (e.g., American Heart Association) provide the basis for dietary guidance. FDA has never codified the requirements for these statements, but has addressed this issue in preambles to regulations and in guidance documents.

Medical Foods

A "medical food" is a food that is "formulated to be consumed or administered...under supervision of a physician and which is intended for the specific dietary management of a disease or condition for which distinctive nutritional requirements...are established by medical evaluation."[60] FDA has issued limited guidance on medical foods. In general, however, to be a medical food, the product must, at a minimum, be: a food for oral or tube feeding; labeled for the dietary management of a specific medical disorder, disease or condition with distinctive nutritional requirements; and must be intended for use under medical supervision.[61]

The main distinction between medical foods and other foods is in labeling. Medical foods are not subject to labeling requirements for nutrient content claims and health claims.

In other words, medical foods may bear nutrient content claims and health claims without prior FDA approval, so long as the claims are truthful and not misleading. Medical food labels must bear a statement of identity, a statement of net quantity, a manufacturer statement, a list of ingredients and allergen labeling. Nutrition labeling requirements do not apply.

Foods for Special Dietary Uses

Foods for special dietary uses are foods "for supplying particular dietary needs which exist by reason of a physical, physiological, pathological or other condition, including but not limited to the conditions of diseases, convalescence, pregnancy, lactation, allergic hypersensitivity to food, underweight, and overweight."[62] Under 21 CFR 105.3, foods containing artificial sweeteners to reduce calories or available carbohydrate, or for use by diabetics are considered foods for special dietary use. These products must bear nutrition labeling as required for conventional foods.

Adulteration: Food Sanitation and Safety

The *FD&C Act* prohibits the adulteration of food. Conditions that can cause a food to be deemed adulterated are set out in Section 402 of the *FD&C Act*.[63] A food may be deemed adulterated if it bears or contains any:

- poisonous or deleterious added substance that may render it injurious to health
- poisonous or deleterious naturally occurring substance in a quantity that would ordinarily render it injurious to health
- unapproved pesticide chemical residue
- unapproved food additive
- unapproved new animal drug
- unapproved color additive

In addition, food may be deemed adulterated if it consists of any "filthy, putrid, or decomposed substance or if it is otherwise unfit for food;" or if it has been "prepared, packed or held under insanitary conditions" whereby it may have been contaminated with filth or rendered injurious to health. The statute also lists a number of other conditions that may render a food adulterated that are less frequently raised.

A poisonous or deleterious substance is, basically, anything in food that could cause harm, whether the substance is physical (such as a shard of glass), chemical (lead) or biological (salmonella). Whether a substance in a food is an "added substance" or a naturally occurring substance will determine the standard FDA must meet to prove adulteration. Courts have essentially held that any act of man that causes the presence of the substance in the food renders the substance an "added substance." For example, the US Court of Appeals for the Fifth Circuit has affirmed that mercury in swordfish is an "added substance" where evidence established that any amount of the mercury resulted from industrial pollution.[64]

Unavoidable Poisonous or Deleterious Substances in Food

Some poisonous or deleterious substances in food are unavoidable, such as aflatoxins in peanuts. The *FD&C Act* recognizes that some such substances may be unavoidable, and the statute provides a mechanism for the agency to establish allowable tolerances for such substances.[65] However, because such tolerances must be established by resource-intensive formal rulemaking, the agency has not issued a new tolerance for decades. Instead, the agency has a procedure for establishing what it calls "regulatory limits," which set out levels at which an unavoidable added substance may render a food injurious to health.[66] Although regulatory limits can be established by notice and comment rulemaking, which is significantly easier than formal rulemaking, the agency has never set a regulatory limit. Instead, the agency has issued action levels for certain poisonous or deleterious substances. Action levels are unenforceable guidances that represent the agency's current thinking as to what level of the substance may render it injurious to health. An action level has no legal effect, so the agency must prove in any enforcement action that the level of the substance in the food may render it injurious to health—simply providing evidence that the action level was exceeded is not sufficient.

Current Good Manufacturing Practices (CGMPs)

FDA's CGMPs for the manufacturing, packing or holding of food are set out at 21 CFR 110. Failure to follow CGMPs is a determining factor in whether a food is adulterated in that it was manufactured under conditions that rendered it unfit for food[67] or whether it was prepared, packed or held under insanitary conditions whereby the food may have been contaminated with filth or rendered injurious to health.[68] The regulations set out CGMPs for personnel, buildings and facilities, equipment and production and process controls. 21 CFR 110 also provides for "defect action levels," which establish maximum allowable levels of certain types of contamination that may result despite compliance with CGMPs. For example, FDA's *Food Defect Action Level Handbook* sets out the maximum levels of insect fragments or rodent hair that may be present in wheat flour.[69] FDA also has separate CGMP regulations for bottled water in 21 CFR 129.

HACCP—Juice and Seafood Products

Whereas all USDA-regulated products (meat, poultry and processed eggs) are required to implement Hazard Analysis and Critical Control Point (HACCP) controls for the safety of their products, FDA currently requires

HACCP only for producers of juice and seafood products. FDA's HACCP regulations require producers of juice and seafood products to conduct an analysis to identify food safety hazards that are reasonably likely to occur. If the analysis concludes such hazards exist, the producer is required to implement a HACCP plan that:

- identifies the possible hazards
- lists all critical control points (CCPs) for controlling each hazard while the product is in the producer's control
- lists critical limits that must be met at each CCP to control the hazard
- lists monitoring procedures and frequency for compliance with the critical limits
- includes any corrective actions to be taken in the event of a deviation from a critical limit
- lists verification procedures for the adequacy of the HACCP plan
- establishes a recordkeeping system that documents the monitoring of compliance with the critical limits

Under HACCP regulations, records must be maintained for a minimum of one year, and two years for some products with longer shelf lives. FDA has access to review and copy all records required to be maintained by HACCP regulations.

Acidified and Low Acid Canned Foods

Stringent processing controls are established for acidified and low acid canned foods that present significant risks of contamination, such as from *Clostridium botulinum*. The requirements for the manufacture of low acid canned foods are set out in 21 CFR 113, and the requirements for acidified foods are in 21 CFR 114. In addition to the specific GMPs set out in 21 CFR 113 and 114, manufacturers of acidified and low acid canned foods must register with FDA and file with the agency the scheduled processes they intend to use to ensure product safety.[70]

Food Safety Modernization Act of 2011

On 4 January 2011, President Obama signed the *Food Safety Modernization Act* (*FSMA*) into law.[71] This law was aimed at refocusing FDA's regulatory oversight of food production from a reactive stance to a preventive role, gave the agency recall authority, and required that all food operations that were not already covered by HACCP or acidified and low acid canned food regulations establish a program of hazard analysis and risk-based preventive controls. The law also requires FDA to propose and enact regulations for ensuring the safe harvesting and handling of raw produce; increases FDA oversight of imported foods; requires FDA to increase inspections; and allows for a program of user fees for reinspections, recalls and import activities. The

law assigns FDA the task of preparing various regulations, rulemakings and guidance documents to facilitate compliance with the act.

Inspections, Recalls, and Enforcement

FDA inspections, compliance, enforcement and recalls are generally covered in other chapters of this book. Addressed here are aspects of these FDA functions particular to foods.

FDA has the authority to inspect any factory, warehouse, establishment or vehicle in which food is manufactured, processed, packed or held for introduction into interstate commerce (excluding small farms and restaurants), as well as all pertinent equipment, finished and unfinished materials, containers and labeling therein.[72] FDA also may inspect and copy records relating to the manufacture, processing, packing, distribution, receipt, holding or importation of food if the agency has a reasonable belief that the food is adulterated and presents a threat of serious adverse health consequences or death (in other words, if the food meets the standard for a Class I recall).[73] FDA does not have the authority to inspect or copy financial data, sales data other than shipment data, pricing data, personnel data or research data.[74]

FDA's recall authorities under 21 CFR 7 apply equally to food products as to other products. One aspect particular to foods is that failure to label the presence of a major food allergen in a food product is cause for a Class I recall. As noted above, *FSMA* gave FDA the authority to require food product recalls. This authority comes into effect if a food product is deemed to present "a reasonable probability that an article of food (other than infant formula) is adulterated under section 402 or misbranded under section 403(w) and the use of or exposure to such article will cause serious adverse health consequences or death to humans or animals" and if the manufacturer will not voluntarily recall the product.

FDA may take enforcement action to seize or enjoin the continued distribution of adulterated or misbranded food. In addition, the agency can charge each violation as a misdemeanor subject to imprisonment of not more than one year and a fine of up to $1,000. If the violation was committed with the intent to defraud or mislead, FDA can charge a criminal felony, with penalties of up to three years in prison and a fine of up to $10,000.

The Reportable Food Registry

In 2007, Congress amended the *FD&C Act* to provide for a Reportable Food Registry. Under the requirements, an owner, operator or agent in charge of a registered food facility who determines that an article of food (other than infant formula or pet food or feed) that has been in the facility meets the standard for a Class I recall (reasonable probability of serious adverse health consequences or death) is required to file a report with the registry with 24 hours of the determination. The only exception to the reporting requirement is if the adulteration originated in the facility, was detected prior to transfer of the food to any other person and was corrected or the food destroyed. The report must be filed electronically through FDA's MedWatchPlus portal and must provide certain information regarding the food and the adulteration, including contact information for the immediate previous source of the food and the immediate subsequent recipient in the supply chain. FDA may then require notification of the identified persons in the supply chain. The Reportable Food Registry requirements were effective as of 8 September 2009.

Food Defense

The *Public Health Security and Bioterrorism Preparedness and Response Act* of 2002 (*Bioterrorism Act*)[75] amended the *FD&C Act* to provide several new authorities for FDA to protect against the possibility of an attack on the food system or other food safety emergency. Provisions of the *Bioterrorism Act* include facility registration, prior notice of imports and administrative detention authority.

Facility Registration

All food facilities must be registered with FDA. A "food facility" subject to the registration requirement is any facility engaged in manufacturing, processing, packing or holding food for consumption in the US.[76] The requirement extends to foreign facilities that are the last foreign facilities to engage in manufacturing or packaging of food to be imported to the US, provided such processing is more than *de minimis*.[77] The requirement does not apply to farms, retail food establishments (such as supermarkets), restaurants, fishing vessels or facilities regulated exclusively by USDA.[78]

The registration must provide, among other information, the types of food manufactured, packed or held at the facility and emergency contact information. FDA issues each facility a unique registration number.[79] Failure to register is a prohibited act under the *FD&C Act*. The information provided with each registration is exempt from public disclosure under the *Freedom of Information Act*. Congress is currently considering requiring a fee of $500 for each facility registration, as well as re-registration of each facility on an annual basis.

Prior Notice of Imported Food

Notice must be given to FDA prior to the import of any food into the US, except meat, poultry and egg products regulated by USDA; food imported for export; and foods imported for personal use only.[80] The amount of prior notice required depends upon how the food is being imported: two hours if by road, four hours if by rail, four hours if by air and eight hours if by water.[81] Prior notice

must be submitted electronically through links on FDA's website, www.fda.gov. Food submitted without prior notice may be refused for import.[82]

Administrative Detention

FDA has the authority, upon issuance of a detention order, to detain any article of food found during an inspection, examination or investigation to present a threat of serious adverse health consequences or death.[83] The detention may not exceed 20 calendar days, but up to 10 more days may be authorized if necessary to institute a seizure or injunction action.[84] Any person who can claim the detained food can appeal a detention order challenging the determination that the food presents a threat.[85]

Summary

- FDA regulates most foods. Exceptions include meat, poultry and processed egg products, which are regulated by USDA, and tap water and alcohol, which are regulated by EPA and TTB, respectively. FDA also does not regulate all aspects of food; for example, it regulates food labeling and FTC regulates food advertising. EPA sets pesticide tolerances, and FDA enforces them. FDA primarily regulates food processing and manufacturing, whereas states are the primary regulators of restaurants, farms and retail establishments.

- Under the *FD&C Act*, FDA's regulatory authority over foods can be divided into two major categories: adulteration of food and misbranding of food labels and labeling.

- Food may be deemed adulterated for a variety of reasons set out in the *FD&C Act*, including poisonous or deleterious substances in the food, filthy or insanitary conditions under which the food was produced, or use of unapproved food additives in the food. FDA has set out CGMPs for sanitation in the production of food. The production of seafood and juice products is regulated through HACCP principles set out by regulation.

- In general, food labeling is misbranded if it is false or misleading in any particular. FDA's food labeling regulations set out detailed requirements governing mandatory labeling, such as ingredient, nutrition and allergen labeling. FDA's regulations also govern how certain types of voluntary labeling, primarily claims such as structure/function claims and nutrient content claims, may be made. Nutrient content and health claims cannot be made on foods unless FDA has approved the claims.

- Food additives must be approved by regulation for specific uses prior to use. GRAS substances are exempted from the definition of food additives and, therefore, do not require premarket approval for use. FDA provides a voluntary GRAS notification program for persons seeking some assurance that the agency agrees a substance is GRAS.

- Color additives must also be premarket approved by FDA for specific uses prior to use in any FDA-regulated product. FDA requires batch approval of certain types of color additives.
- Recent food defense amendments require all food facilities to be registered with FDA. In addition, FDA must be provided with prior notice of any food imports being shipped to the US for distribution. Starting in September 2009, food facilities will also be required to report to FDA whenever the facility determines that food manufactured, processed, packed or held there presents a reasonable probability of a serious adverse health consequence or death.

References

1. The *FD&C Act* is codified at 21 U.S.C. § 301 *et al.*
2. 21 U.S.C. §321(f).
3. P.L. 103-417 (Oct. 25, 1994).
4. The distinction between "labeling" and "advertising" is discussed in more detail under Misbranding: Food Labeling and Claims. Generally, "labeling" includes the food label and all materials "accompanying" the food where sold (such as brochures, displays, or information on websites where the product can be purchased). "Advertising" is, broadly, any marketing of the product that is not labeling.
5. 21 U.S.C. §321(s).
6. Ibid.
7. Ibid.
8. See 21 U.S.C. §346a.
9. See 21 U.S.C. §379e.
10. 21 U.S.C. §348(a).
11. See 21 U.S.C. §348(j).
12. 21 U.S.C. §348(b).
13. 21 U.S.C. §348(c)(1)-(2).
14. 21 U.S.C. §348(f).
15. 21 U.S.C. §348(c)(3).
16. 21 U.S.C. §348(c)(3)(A).
17. *Les v. Reilly*, 968 F.2d 985 (9th Cir. 1992) (food additives); *Public Citizen v. Young*, 831 F.2d 1108 (D.C. Cir. 1987) (color additives).
18. See *Scott v. Food and Drug Administration*, 728 F.2d 322 (6th Cir. 1984); *Public Citizen v. Young*, 831 F.2d 1108, 1118-19 (D.C.Cir. 1987).
19. See 21 U.S.C. §348(c)(3)(A).
20. Codified at 21 U.S.C. §348(a)(3).
21. See 21 U.S.C. §321(s).
22. 21 U.S.C. §321(t).
23. See 21 U.S.C. §361(e). Cosmetics are discussed in detail in Chapter 28.
24. 21 U.S.C. §379e(a).
25. See generally 21 CFR 70–82.
26. In the context of color additives, a "lake" is a form of color additive that is extended on a substratum to make them water insoluble.
27. 21 U.S.C. §343.
28. 21 U.S.C. §321(k).
29. 21 U.S.C. §321(m).
30. *FD&C Act*, Section 331(a), (b), (c).
31. *FD&C Act*, Section 321(n).
32. 21 CFR 101.1.
33. 21 CFR 101.2(a).
34. 21 CFR 101.3.
35. *FD&C Act*, Section 401.
36. 21 CFR 102.5(a).
37. 21 CFR 101.3(b)(3).
38. 21 CFR 101.3(e).
39. 21 CFR 101.105.
40. 21 CFR 101.9.
41. 21 CFR 101.4.
42. Pub. L. No. 108-282.
43. *FALCPA* §203.
44. 21 CFR 101.5.
45. 9 CFR 317.2(c)(5).
46. 9 CFR 317.2(k).
47. 9 CFR 317.2(l).
48. 9 CFR 317.4; see also "A Guide to Federal Food Labeling Requirements for Meat and Poultry Products," FSIS, August 2007.
49. The final rule became effective on 16 March 2009 and is codified in 7 CFR 60 and 65. 74 *Fed Reg.* 2658 (15 January 2009).
50. 19 U.S.C. 1304.
51. 19 CFR 134.11
52. *FDAMA is from the Food and Drug Administration Modernization Act* of 1997, which, among other amendments, provided for health and nutrient content claims based on statements issued by authoritative government bodies, like the National Academies of Science or the National Institutes of Health.
53. 21 CFR 101.13.
54. *FD&C Act*, Sections 403(r)(1)(A) and 403(r)(2).
55. 21 CFR 101.14.
56. 21 U.S.C. §321(g).
57. 21 U.S.C. §343(r)(3)(C).
58. 21 U.S.C. §343(r)(3)(D).
59. 21 CFR 101.93.
60. *Orphan Drug Act* §5, codified at 21 U.S.C. 360ee(b)(3).
61. Food Labeling; Reference Daily Intakes and Daily Reference Values; Mandatory Status of Nutrition Labeling and Nutrition Content Revision proposed rule (56 *Fed. Reg.* 60366 at 60377, November 27,

1991.

62. Op cit 60.

63. 21 U.S.C. §342.

64. *United States v. Anderson Seafoods, Inc.*, 622 F.2d 157, 159-60 (5th Cir. 1980)

65. 21 U.S.C. §346.

66. 21 CFR 109.

67. 21 U.S.C. §342(a)(3).

68. 21 U.S.C. §342(a)(4).

69. Available at www.fda.gov/Food/ GuidanceComplianceRegulatoryInformation/ GuidanceDocuments/Sanitation/ucm056174.htm. Accessed 9 May 2011.

70. 21 CFR 108.25 (acidified foods) and 108.35 (low acid canned foods).

71. Public Law 111-353 (4 January 2011).

72. 21 U.S.C. §374.

73. 21 U.S.C. §350c.

74. 21 U.S.C. §374.

75. P.L. 107-188.

76. 21 U.S.C. §415.

77. 21 CFR 1.226(a).

78. 21 CFR 1.226.

79. 21 CFR 1.232.

80. 21 CFR 1.277.

81. 21 CFR 1.279.

82. 21 CFR 1.283.

83. 21 CFR 1.378.

84. 21 CFR 1.379.

85. 21 CFR 1.401.

FDA Inspection and Enforcement

By Alan Minsk and William H. Kitchens, JD

Objectives

- Understand FDA inspectional authority
- Understand prohibited acts under the *FD&C Act* and FDA's implementing regulations
- Understand FDA enforcement options and objectives

Laws, Regulations and GuidelinesCovered In This Chapter

- *Federal Food, Drug, and Cosmetic Act* of 1938
- Applicable Parts of 21 CFR

Introduction

The US Food and Drug Administration (FDA) is, first and foremost, a public health organization. Whether evaluating a product for potential marketing authorization, inspecting a manufacturing site or deciding whether to take enforcement action against a noncompliant company, FDA always focuses on protecting the consumer. This chapter reviews FDA's inspectional authority, prohibited acts and the agency's enforcement options in response to unlawful activity.

FDA Inspections
Overview of FDA's Inspectional Authority

FDA conducts inspections for many reasons, such as a directed inspection for a specific reason (e.g., notice of a complaint about a product); a routine audit to ensure company compliance with current Good Laboratory Practices (CGLPs), Good Clinical Practices (GCPs), current Good Manufacturing Practices (CGMPs) or the Quality System Regulation (QSR) requirements; a reinspection after a Warning Letter or other enforcement action; a recall effectiveness check; a preapproval inspection (PAI); or to evaluate prospective suppliers of products to US government agencies. The parameters of FDA's inspectional authority are set forth in Section 704 of the *Federal Food, Drug, and Cosmetic Act* of 1938 (*FD&C Act*), as amended.[1] FDA may enter a factory, warehouse, establishment or vehicle in which regulated products are manufactured, processed, packed or stored. The inspection is to occur at a reasonable time and in a reasonable manner, and "shall extend to all things therein (including records, files, papers, processes, controls, and facilities)" bearing on whether the products comply with the *FD&C Act* and FDA's implementing regulations. FDA is required to inspect at least once every two years but, due to limited financial and personnel resources, the agency focuses its efforts on high-risk products, new facilities not yet inspected and sites with poor compliance histories.

Before the domestic inspection may begin, FDA investigators must present their credentials and issue a properly signed and completed Form FDA 482, Notice of Inspection. Credentials consist of two identification cards held in a carrying case: one describes the authorities of the credential bearer, while the other contains the investigator's photograph and personal description. The identification card also contains a badge number and bears an expiration date. A person from the facility being inspected should carefully examine an inspector's credentials to ensure the individual is, indeed, a government official and to verify which agency is represented (e.g., federal or state, FDA, the Environmental Protection Agency (EPA), the Drug Enforcement Administration (DEA)).

FDA may conduct routine inspections without a search

warrant. However, the agency may seek to utilize a search warrant, for example, to carry out an inspection in a timely and effective manner, if a firm refuses to be inspected or if FDA anticipates that the firm will refuse inspection. A search warrant may be obtained by any federal enforcement officer or FDA criminal investigator. FDA may obtain a search warrant if it demonstrates to a federal magistrate court that there is probable cause to believe that a crime is being committed by a person who is being served the search warrant, or that there are records or other evidence at the facility that relate to the commission of a crime.

A routine inspection may cover the premises and all pertinent equipment, finished and unfinished materials, containers and labeling within an establishment or vehicle in which products are manufactured, processed, packed, held or transported. The *FD&C Act* provides broader inspector powers in the case of plants that manufacture prescription drugs, nonprescription drugs for human use, restricted devices and infant formulas. The overall scope of the inspection generally will be determined, in part, by the reason for the inspection and any deficiencies encountered during the current or prior investigation. FDA's Investigations Operations Manual (IOM) describes an inspection as a careful, critical, official examination of a facility to determine compliance with FDA rules and regulations. Evidence of violations gathered during inspections may be used to support an enforcement action in federal court.

Limitations on Inspections

While FDA may gather evidence during an inspection, there are limits as to what inspectors are entitled to review or gather. As a routine matter, FDA may not gather the following during an investigation:

- financial data
- pricing data
- personnel data (other than information regarding qualifications of technical and professional personnel performing FDA-related functions)
- sales data (other than shipment information)
- research data (other than information relating to new drugs and antibiotic drugs and subject to reporting to and inspection by FDA)

Further, FDA has no authority to require individuals to sign affidavits or attest to the accuracy of any observations or statements, although it may attempt to secure such evidence. FDA's legal authority to take photographs is not expressly cited in the law. There are two court cases FDA frequently cites to assert its authority to take photographs. One case involved EPA's aerial photography of open fields.[2] Another case involved a company that did not stop FDA from taking photographs, but later challenged the admissibility of the photographs as evidence in an enforcement action. In this case, the court held that, because no objection was made

when the photographs were taken during the inspection, there had been full consent by the company.[3] FDA believes it has the authority to take photographs, but it will typically respect a corporate policy against it. However, if the company will not allow the taking of photographs and FDA insists on them, the agency might seek court intervention. If the company decides to permit the taking of photographs after consulting with counsel, it should document that it protested and make its objection clear to FDA.

Pharmacies licensed by state law that do not manufacture, prepare, propagate, compound or process drugs and/or medical devices are exempt from FDA inspections. In addition, FDA's authority to inspect is limited to sites within the US. However, FDA, with US Customs and Border Protection, can detain products that appear to be noncompliant, and the agency may delay product approval if data are generated or products are manufactured at a foreign site it has not inspected. Therefore, foreign companies or sites typically do not object to FDA inspections. Moreover, FDA has recently opened posts in certain countries to expedite foreign inspections.

Types of Inspections

Inspections may be comprehensive, abbreviated, directed or conducted for the purpose of preapproval. A comprehensive inspection covers all aspects of a facility's FDA-regulated products and processes. This may include coverage of all major areas of a company's quality system in accordance with the QSR for medical devices or CGMPs for pharmaceuticals. An abbreviated inspection is performed on a specific area or at a depth described in the inspection assignment or compliance program. It may include coverage of one product or a specific aspect of the company's operations, such as complaints received by FDA or a limited number of subsystems/systems for QSR and GMP inspections. A directed inspection is usually in response to a product failure or contamination and is focused on the conditions that led to the violation.

Preapproval inspections (PAIs) cover the product preapproval process for all three FDA centers: the Center for Devices and Radiological Health (CDRH), the Center for Drug Evaluation and Research (CDER) and the Center for Biologics Evaluation and Research (CBER). There are two primary components of a PAI:

- a rigorous, scientific review of required data by the applicable center's review division to ensure the product's safety and effectiveness; the application content and process vary by center
- comprehensive compliance evaluation of production facilities to ensure that the company is capable of manufacturing the product in accordance with information submitted in the application and quality-related standards

FDA Procedures to Inspection

Investigators use the IOM as a guide when conducting investigations. It describes what evidence an investigator may obtain during an investigation and what issues should be investigated. There are many other guidance documents and materials available on FDA's website (www.fda.gov) to assist investigators in conducting inspections. These include but are not limited to:

- Compliance Policy Guides (CPG)
- Compliance Program Guidance Manuals (CPGM)
- FDA/Office of Regulatory Affairs (ORA) Guide to International Inspections and Travel
- Inspector's Technical Guide
- Regulatory Procedures Manual (RPM)

Systems Approach to Investigations

The systems approach was developed by FDA to effectively ensure products are manufactured in compliance with CGMP and QSR requirements while saving agency resources during inspections by streamlining the inspection process. The systems approach is based on the idea that a system is out of control if the product's quality, identity, strength and purity resulting from that system cannot be assured adequately. Documented CGMP deficiencies demonstrate that a system is not in a state of control. Thus, under the systems approach, FDA focuses on seven quality subsystems:

- management responsibility
- design control
- corrective and preventive action (CAPA)
- production and process controls (P&PC)
- records/document change controls
- material controls
- facilities and equipment controls (F&EC)

A deficiency in any one of these areas acts as a red flag to FDA that a company is not operating under a state of control. If a company cannot handle big issues, it is unlikely that it has addressed more specific, implementing measures.

Discussions With Management

When an inspection has concluded, the investigator will discuss, both verbally and in writing, the observations believed to be deficiencies, citing the appropriate regulation for each deficiency. Written observations are documented on a Form FDA 483 (FDA 483), Inspectional Observations. In some cases, an FDA 483 will not be issued.

Form FDA 483

At the conclusion of an FDA inspection, an FDA 483 may be issued to company management. It contains observations made by the investigator during the inspection that represent potential violations of the law or regulations. FDA 483s are not mentioned in the law and are not considered a final agency action. FDA 483s are available for review under the *Freedom of Information Act* (*FOIA*), although they may be redacted to protect confidential information.

At the conclusion of an inspection, if an FDA 483 is presented, the FDA investigator will explain the observations and solicit responses from the company. This is an important time for the company to identify any perceived errors that may appear on the form, to seek clarification and to indicate any corrective actions it plans to take. If the investigator has made an error, a correction will be made. Once the FDA 483 is issued and the investigator has left the facility, no changes may be made to the form.

A company generally responds to the agency regarding corrective action it plans to take and FDA has recently increased pressure on manufacturers to respond within 15 days of a facility inspection. The agency will accept responses after the 15-day mark, but has noted it may not take those late responses into consideration before issuing a Warning Letter. The FDA 483 response should show that the company is working in good faith to address FDA's observations, explain what has been implemented and provide a reasonable timeframe for other corrections. If the observations are serious and if the corrective action plan is going to take months to complete, a company should consider committing to submit periodic status updates to FDA until the company has met the action plan outlined in the response.

Most companies assume that an effective response to an FDA 483 will prevent the agency from pursuing other enforcement actions, such as issuing a Warning Letter. FDA is not required to issue an FDA 483 before proceeding to a Warning Letter; the particular facts of a case will dictate the agency's course of action. If FDA issues a Warning Letter, it is typically because the agency has expressed its concerns previously and does not believe the company intends to resolve the issues. FDA might also consider the deficiencies so important and basic to quality control that it wants to signal to senior management that it expects these fundamental observations to be addressed expeditiously. Unlike the procedure used for issuing an FDA 483, before a Warning Letter is issued, several groups within FDA review the issues and company responses, so the decision to send a Warning Letter is not taken lightly and is a collective one. FDA publicizes and posts Warning Letters on its website. While most companies consider a Warning Letter to be a wake-up call and take appropriate action at this point, FDA will consider court action, such as product seizure or injunctive relief (discussed later), if the violations persist. FDA is not required to issue a Warning Letter before proceeding to court.

Voluntary Corrections

FDA is more likely to consider a company's voluntary plan of compliance when the violations are not sufficiently serious or significant enough to warrant other enforcement action. Voluntary plans can take several forms. They may include the company's commitment to make corrections according to a defined timeframe. FDA frequently will offer suggestions or comments, particularly when discussing proposed timeframes. FDA rarely provides any commitments other than those implied by the recognition of the plan as an alternative to enforcement action. FDA also makes clear that its comments or suggestions are not binding and do not reflect endorsement or assurance that the company's efforts will be successful. FDA will normally not engage in any discussions of this type if it has already decided to pursue other enforcement action.

Establishment Inspection Report (EIR)

An EIR is a narrative report, prepared by the investigator after the inspection is completed, that describes the investigator's inspectional findings. The EIR will include the reason for the inspection; the dates, classification and findings of the previous inspection; the scope of the inspection; the type of inspection (e.g., comprehensive or directed); and a brief description of products, processes or systems covered during the inspection.

Inspection reports describe and discuss each objectionable condition or practice cited on the FDA 483. The reports also include samples, photographs and documents collected during the inspection that support the deficiencies observed. These documents are attached as exhibits to the EIR. The EIR and all supporting documents serve as evidence for any regulatory/compliance action FDA may consider against a company. EIRs, after redaction of sensitive information, can be disclosed under *FOIA*, although there are notable exceptions. For example, if FDA is considering taking enforcement action, it may delay disclosure of the EIR.

Possible Outcomes

At the end of all inspections and following completion of the EIR, FDA will classify the inspection using one of three primary classifications:
1. NAI—No Action Indicated
2. VAI—Voluntary Action Indicated
3. OAI—Official Action Indicated

These classifications are assigned in accordance with inspectional findings and agency policy. FDA will not take further action on investigations classified as VAI unless the company cannot achieve compliance. Appropriate enforcement actions and dates for the next inspection will be recommended for the OAI designation.

Enforcement
Section 301 Prohibited Acts

The commission of a prohibited act, as defined by

the *FD&C Act*, gives FDA the authority to exercise its enforcement remedies of seizure, injunction, civil penalties, criminal prosecution or import or export restrictions, to name a few.[4] For purposes of this chapter, the enforcement provisions apply to pharmaceuticals and medical devices, but FDA's enforcement authority reaches other product categories, such as food, color additives, cosmetics and biologics. Prohibited acts under Section 301 of the *FD&C Act* include, but are not limited to, the following:

- introducing or delivering an adulterated or misbranded product into interstate commerce
- adulterating or misbranding a product while it is in interstate commerce
- receiving an adulterated or misbranded product in interstate commerce or delivering it for pay or otherwise
- refusing to permit FDA entry or inspection
- manufacturing a product that is adulterated or misbranded
- failing to register or list drugs or devices with FDA
- altering, mutilating, destroying, obliterating or removing the labeling of, or doing of any act with respect to, a product held for sale after shipment in interstate commerce that results in such product being adulterated or misbranded

The most common violations cited by FDA in the inspectional context are adulteration and misbranding. Adulteration typically focuses on quality-related deficiencies, and misbranding includes, but is not limited to, false or misleading labeling or other information (e.g., advertising and promotion). The sale or promotion of an unapproved new drug is a separate violation.[5] While other chapters define "adulteration" and "misbranding" in more detail, a drug, device or biologic is considered adulterated if, among other things:

- It consists of a filthy, putrid or decomposed substance or has been produced under unsanitary conditions whereby it may have been so contaminated.
- It has not been manufactured in compliance with Good Manufacturing Practices.
- Its container is composed of any poisonous or deleterious substance which may render the contents injurious to health.
- Its strength, quality or purity differs from an official compendium or that which it purports or is represented to possess.
- It is a Class III medical device and does not have an approved Premarket Approval Application and is not otherwise exempt.
- It is a banned device.

A product is misbranded if, among other things:
- Its labeling is false or misleading.
- Its label fails to include the manufacturer, packer

or distributor's name and place of business, and an accurate statement of the quantity of contents.

- It is a drug and its label does not contain the established name of the drug and the established name and quantity or the proportion of each active ingredient.
- Its label fails to bear adequate directions for use and such warnings as are necessary for the protection of users.
- It is dangerous to health when used in the dosage or manner recommended by the labeling.
- It is not listed with FDA or is manufactured in a facility not registered with FDA.
- It is a device for which notification was not provided as required by section 510(k) of the *FD&C Act*.

Separately, for those products defined as biologics (e.g., serums, toxins, blood products), FDA has enforcement authority under the *Public Health Service Act*. For example, FDA may suspend or revoke product licensure for unlawful activities.[6]

US Code Title 18

The intentional submission of certain false declarations or statements to a federal government agency such as FDA is a prohibited act under Sections 301 (w) and (x) of the *FD&C Act* and is a violation of Section 1001 of Title 18 of the US Code and may subject a person to possible criminal sanctions. Under 18 USC §1001, anyone who makes a materially false, fictitious or fraudulent statement to the US government is subject to criminal penalties. Specifically, a false statement is made when a person knowingly and willfully: falsifies, conceals or covers up by any trick, scheme or device a material fact; makes any materially false, fictitious or fraudulent statement or representations; or makes or uses any false writing or document, knowing the same to contain any materially false, fictitious or fraudulent statement or entry. A person who makes any such statement, "shall be fined, imprisoned not more than five years."[7]

Enforcement Discretion

FDA has broad enforcement discretion in deciding whether to use its power and resources to pursue, investigate or penalize specific activities. The US Supreme Court has held that FDA has wide prosecutorial discretion to decide whether to exercise its discretionary powers in individual cases and that this discretion is unreviewable.[8] However, apart from the language in Section 309 of the *FD&C Act*, which states that FDA is not required to pursue minor violations when it believes "that public interest will be adequately served by a suitable written notice or warning," there is no statutory provision dictating how FDA is to use its resources to remedy all the violations that are reported to or discovered by the agency. FDA has the authority to

publicize the actions it takes and, in certain circumstances, to seek civil monetary penalties and other administrative sanctions. For example, civil penalties may be sought for violations relating to the sale or trade of drug samples, for violations of postmarketing drug safety provisions and for offenses relating to clinical trials.

Debarment

Under the *Generic Drug Enforcement Act* of 1992, FDA may debar an individual or company convicted of certain types of felonies. The statute also imposes sanctions of debarment of individuals from the pharmaceutical industry, debarment of corporations from the drug approval process, and withdrawal and suspension of product approvals for certain prohibited conduct. The practical effect is that the individual or firm can no longer provide services in any capacity to a company that has approved drug product applications, unless FDA decides otherwise (21 U.S.C. §355a–335c). The act also authorizes FDA to impose civil penalties for fraud relating to generic drug approval applications.

Enforcement Jurisdiction

FDA's authority to apply its resources to enforce compliance with the *FD&C Act* is directly related to movement or possible movement of an article in interstate commerce. Section 201(b) of the *FD&C Act* defines interstate commerce as: commerce between any state or territory and any place outside thereof, and commerce within the District of Columbia or within any other territory not organized with a legislative body. Thus, any product that is not manufactured in any "state" or "territory" as defined in the *FD&C Act* and not distributed to the US is not subject to FDA's jurisdiction. "Territory" is defined as any territory or possession of the US, including the District of Columbia, and excluding the Commonwealth of Puerto Rico and the Panama Canal Zone. A product that is manufactured in another country and distributed in interstate commerce is also subject to FDA's jurisdiction, but if the product is not distributed in the US, it cannot be seized or subjected to a request for injunctive relief. No provision of the *FD&C Act* or any regulation promulgated under the authority of the act is applicable to regulated products that do not enter into US interstate commerce. Finished products that have been shipped in interstate commerce or have been manufactured using components that have been shipped in interstate commerce are subject to FDA jurisdiction.

FDA may initiate enforcement action if it establishes certain elements of proof. It must establish jurisdiction, interstate commerce, violation and responsibility. To satisfy the jurisdictional element, the product must be subject to the provisions of the *FD&C Act* (e.g., it meets the law's definition of a drug or medical device). The interstate commerce element is satisfied if the product or any of its components is shipped across state lines, within the limitations described above. In 1997, Congress amended the *FD&C Act* so that FDA no longer has the initial burden to demonstrate a connection to interstate commerce (21 U.S.C. 379a). The violation element is satisfied if the product is adulterated, misbranded or otherwise in violation of the act (e.g., unapproved new drug). Finally, enforcement actions directed at individuals or companies must also establish responsibility for the violation.

Penalties
FDA's Administrative Sanctions (separate from judicial actions)

When a problem arises with a product regulated by FDA, the agency can take a number of actions to protect the public health. It is important to note that a risk to the public health is not the only requirement for FDA to act; a violative act is punishable. Normally, the agency works with the manufacturer to correct the problem voluntarily. If that fails, FDA may utilize administrative or judicial enforcement tools. FDA may initiate administrative enforcement outside the court system and without the involvement of the Department of Justice (DOJ). This enforcement may be specifically authorized by a statute or developed by the agency under broad statutory authority. FDA uses the following administrative sanctions:

- recalls
  - voluntary
  - mandatory (only applicable to medical devices, infant formulas and food when there is a reasonable probability that the food is adulterated or misbranded and the use of or exposure to the food will cause serious adverse health consequences or death)
- administrative detentions
- Application Integrity Policy
- device ban or repair, replacement or notification requirements
- import detention
- debarment
- clinical investigator disqualification
- license suspension or revocation
- product approval suspension, withdrawal or delay
- restitution and disgorgement
- civil money penalties
- Notice(s) of Violations
  - inspectional findings (Form FDA 483)
  - meetings
- compliance correspondence
  - Warning Letters
  - Untitled Letters (frequently used for advertising or promotional violations)
- publicity

When the agency uses administrative means to achieve enforcement, the process generally starts from an FDA field office or a center at FDA headquarters. Most administrative actions identified above require center concurrence and approval and, in some cases, consultation with FDA's Office of Chief Counsel.

Judicial Actions

The agency will generally attempt to achieve compliance through administrative means. However, in certain instances, FDA will pursue judicial actions. In pursuing judicial action, FDA may use the judicial tools of seizure, injunction or criminal prosecution. It is noteworthy that FDA, with the assistance of the Department of Justice, may bring an enforcement action; the law does not allow an individual to bring a private cause of action to enforce the *FD&C Act*.

Seizures

Seizure actions are authorized by Section 304 of the *FD&C Act*.[9] A product in violation of the *FD&C Act* is subject to seizure, a civil action providing for government "arrest" of the goods. A seizure action is against the products that are alleged to be in violation of the *FD&C Act* rather than against a company or individual. Thus, a seizure is a civil action that is intended to remove adulterated or misbranded goods from interstate commerce and accessibility to consumers. Seizure actions can occur at a company's own facilities or wherever the product is located. Seizure actions are published in FDA's Enforcement Report on its website.

FDA can initiate, through DOJ, three types of seizure actions against an industry participant: lot, multiple and mass.[10] Lot seizures generally involve one (or more) lot of product in one location that is or has become adulterated or misbranded during interstate commerce. Multiple seizures involve more than one action to arrest goods located in different jurisdictions where the goods are adulterated or lack required approval. Multiple seizures may be filed against allegedly misbranded product when it has been the subject of a prior court judgment, presents a danger to health, or contains a fraudulent or materially misleading label that may injure a purchaser. Mass seizures involve a warehouse full of products usually manufactured at one location and deemed adulterated or misbranded. FDA can accomplish injunctive-type relief through a mass seizure on the basis that the scope of the violations render every article in the facility adulterated.

The seizure process is normally triggered by the collection of a sample found to be in violation of the law. FDA requests the appropriate US Attorney's office to file a Complaint for Forfeiture in the jurisdiction where the goods to be seized are located. If the US Attorney files the complaint, a judge or magistrate signs an order for arrest for the goods and the US Marshals Service executes the warrant. Once the warrant is served by a US marshal, the goods fall under the custody of the federal government. A return is usually made to the court by the US marshal indicating the success of the seizure, including the quantity seized and its location. Anyone having an interest in the goods must file a claim within specified timeframes.

A claimant may appear and propose that the goods be reconditioned to bring them into compliance. If FDA agrees to the method of reconditioning, the court issues a Decree of Condemnation permitting reconditioning under the supervision of FDA after a bond is posted. Alternatively, the claimant can file an answer denying the allegations and seek a court trial to contest the government's assertion that the goods are in violation of the law. To argue against the seizure, the claimant must prove the product is not adulterated or misbranded. To support its case, FDA normally produces evidence gathered through facility inspections. If no claim is filed, however, the US Attorney will file a motion for a Default Decree of Condemnation and Forfeiture, ultimately resulting in the destruction of the goods by the US Marshals Service.

No prior judicial finding that a violation of the *FD&C Act* has occurred is necessary prior to the institution of a seizure action. Once a seizure action is instituted by the government, it is well established that the affected company's remedy is to contest the seizure action by the filing of a claim and answer; no separate suit seeking to enjoin the seizure action can be brought.

Injunctions

Injunctions are authorized by Section 302 of the *FD&C Act* and are utilized to enjoin conduct (i.e., proactively do something or refrain from doing something) where there is a likelihood that violations will continue or recur. FDA initiates three types of injunctions:

1. temporary restraining order
2. preliminary
3. permanent[11]

FDA seeks an injunction in two circumstances: when there have been chronic violations and efforts by the agency to obtain voluntary compliance have been unsuccessful; or when immediate court intervention is needed to address an imminent public health hazard. In the latter situation, FDA will seek a temporary restraining order. Unlike injunction proceedings brought by private litigants, FDA does not have to prove in an injunction action that there will be "irreparable injury," but merely that the violative conduct is likely to continue.[12]

When the agency's efforts to obtain correction of violative conduct over a period of time have failed, DOJ will file a Complaint for Injunction asking the court to restrain further violations and allow FDA oversight and control of the company's conduct. A Complaint for Preliminary Injunction may be sought to enjoin the company until a hearing and/or trial can be held on a Complaint for Permanent Injunction. Because most injunctions require the company to suspend all or most of its operations, judges have tended to encourage FDA and the company to agree on a plan to correct the problems. Companies also generally prefer a negotiated settlement rather than a protracted and public legal battle. Thus, FDA's inclination has been to negotiate a Consent Decree of Permanent Injunction with the company and then file it simultaneously with an abbreviated Complaint for Permanent Injunction.

Consent decrees of permanent injunctions, once granted, continue in perpetuity unless one party or the other petitions the court to vacate the injunction. Commonly, a company negotiates a sunset provision for dissolution of the injunction conditioned upon the company meeting all of the consent's provisions.

Criminal Prosecution
The Decision to Prosecute

FDA does not prosecute its own criminal cases. Rather, DOJ must bring the criminal case to court. FDA, however, does recommend cases to DOJ for criminal prosecution. Generally, FDA decides to recommend criminal prosecution in cases where there are: gross violations that evidence management's disregard for compliance with the *FD&C Act*; obvious and continuing violations where management has not exercised appropriate care; life-threatening violations or those where injuries already have occurred; and deliberate attempts to circumvent the law, such as the submission of false information to the agency.[13] Once FDA has decided to seek criminal prosecution against a corporation or an individual, it proceeds through DOJ to obtain a criminal information or an indictment, depending upon whether the criminal or misdemeanor or felony charge is involved. Recently, FDA has stated its intent to target more executives with misdemeanor prosecutions when their companies have violated the *FD&C Act*. FDA has legal authority to bring these criminal cases under a 36-year-old Supreme Court precedent.[14]

FDA has established the Office of Criminal Investigations (OCI), which conducts the majority of criminal investigations related to the *FD&C Act*. OCI obtains and executes search warrants and arrest warrants, conducts physical surveillance, obtains and serves grand jury subpoenas, and obtains and reviews telephone toll records, bank records and other materials to support a case against an individual, company or conspiracy.

Standard of Liability Under the FD&C Act

The *FD&C Act* is a "strict liability" criminal misdemeanor statute. People who commit prohibited acts can be criminally convicted notwithstanding their intent (or lack thereof) to commit a crime. Thus, the fact that a corporate officer has no direct involvement in the conditions that give rise to a criminal violation does not excuse that officer from liability. Case law makes it clear that an individual in a position of responsibility may face personal criminal accountability if he or she fails to seek out and remedy violations when they occur or implement measures that ensure violations will not occur.[15] Evidence that the individual played a role in or had knowledge of the violation is not necessary. Before pursuing criminal actions against individuals, FDA normally considers many factors, including the individual's position and authority within the company; whether a violation is likely to have harmed the public; the obviousness of the violation; whether a violation reflects a pattern of illegal behavior; and whether the proposed prosecution is a prudent use of agency resources.

Guaranty Clause

Sections 303(c)(2) and (3) of the *FD&C Act* provide a safe harbor from criminal prosecution under the general criminal penalty provisions of Section 303(a)(1). A guaranty received by a corporation, individual or employee of a corporation that states the articles delivered by the guarantor are not adulterated or misbranded within the meaning of the *FD&C Act*, and (as applicable) that they are not unapproved food additives, color additives, drugs or Class III devices subject to an approval requirement, protects the recipient of the guaranty from criminal liability. Guaranties may be limited to a specific shipment or may be general and continuing.[16]

In its enforcement regulations covering guaranties, FDA provides that a "guaranty…will expire when, after the covered products are shipped or delivered by the guarantor, the products become adulterated or misbranded, or become unapproved products" under the *FD&C Act*.[17] Thus, the original guarantor's guaranty will not serve as a "safe harbor" if the products covered by the guaranty are subsequently adulterated, misbranded or become a violative, unapproved product.

Furnishing a false guaranty is a separate prohibited act under the *FD&C Act* and can result in criminal liability. Under the *FD&C Act*, however, a company that receives a guaranty and then, in good faith, provides a subsequent guaranty premised on the original guarantor's representations, is not guilty of a prohibited act.

Section 305 Hearings

In most cases, the person against whom criminal proceedings are being contemplated will be given an opportunity to present his or her views with regard to such criminal proceedings. This is usually done in the form of a Section 305 hearing.[18] FDA is instructed by Section 305 of the *FD&C Act* to hold a hearing to give the target company or individual(s) opportunities to present views orally or in writing before any violation is reported by the secretary to

any US Attorney for institution of a criminal proceeding. A 305 hearing will not be provided, however, if the agency has reason to believe that the opportunity for a hearing may result:

- in the alteration or destruction of evidence; or
- in the prospective defendant's fleeing to avoid prosecution; or
- if a grand jury investigation of a possible felony prosecution is planned[19]

The Section 305 hearing is held pursuant to a formal notice. The hearing is usually an informal meeting, often held in an FDA district office, and its purpose is to provide a party an opportunity to furnish information that will dissuade FDA from making a criminal referral to DOJ.

Other Federal and State Regulatory Agencies

FDA primarily takes the initiative for enforcing unlawful activities relating to product manufacture, safety and quality-related issues or labeling and promotion.[20] However, there are other regulatory agencies that have the authority to take action. For example, the Consumer Product Safety Commission regulates child-resistant packaging for certain types of FDA-regulated products. The Securities and Exchange Commission can take action for misleading investor-related materials (e.g., press releases or financial statements) involving products sold by publicly traded companies. Customs and Border Protection can sample, detain or refuse imports and exports. The Federal Trade Commission regulates over-the-counter drug, food, cosmetic and most medical device advertising to ensure promotional claims are truthful, substantiated and fair.

In addition to enforcement by federal agencies, state regulatory agencies may choose to take enforcement action, typically to ensure compliance with state consumer protection laws.

Summary

FDA has broad authority to inspect establishments and facilities under its jurisdiction to protect the public health. However, the reach and scope of the inspection power is not unlimited, and firms should make their employees aware of these limitations through training and internal standard operating procedures. FDA's primary purpose in conducting inspections is to determine whether regulated products have been manufactured, packed and held under conditions that may result in such products being adulterated or misbranded, or whether products lacking required FDA approval are being distributed and sold. There are various types of FDA inspections, ranging from a comprehensive review of manufacturing controls and practices to a targeted review of a specific practice in the facility. The agency's approaches during an inspection will depend upon the scope of the inspection and the circumstances presented. Likewise, whether the agency will take administrative action or institute legal proceedings following an inspection will depend upon what FDA discovers during the inspection.

The agency has broad discretion to decide what enforcement action it will take against companies, individuals and products that violate the law, and, as a general rule, FDA attempts to choose the enforcement tool that is commensurate with the unlawful conduct. These options range from administrative sanctions, such as a Warning Letter, to a seizure, injunction or criminal prosecution in federal court with the approval and assistance of DOJ. Nevertheless, FDA prefers companies to comply voluntarily and take proactive steps to ensure regulatory compliance.

References

1. 21 U.S.C. §374.
2. *Dow Chemical v. U.S.*, 476 U.S. 227 (1986).
3. *U.S. v. Acri Wholesale Grocery Co.*, 409 F. Supp. 529 (S.D. Iowa 1976).
4. 21 U.S.C. §331 et seq.
5. 21 U.S.C. §355(a).
6. 42 U.S.C. §262.
7. 18 U.S.C. §1001.
8. *Heckler v. Chaney*, 470 U.S. 821 (*1985*).
9. 21 U.S.C. §334.
10. Parker FR. *FDA Administrative Enforcement Manual* (2005).
11. 21 U.S.C. §332.
12. Parker FR. *FDA Administrative Enforcement Manual* (2005).
13. Fine SD. "The Philosophy of Enforcement." 31 *FOOD DRUG COSM. L.J.* 324 (1976).
14. *United States v. Park*, 421 U.S. 650 (1975).
15. Ibid.
16. 21 U.S.C. §333(c)(2)–(3); 21 CFR 7.13(a)(2).
17. 21 CFR 7.13.
18. 21 U.S.C. §335. FDA, *Regulatory Procedures Manual*, Part 6: Judicial Action, Chapter 6-5 (March 2008). Available at www.fda.gov/ICECI/ ComplianceManuals/RegulatoryProceduresManual/ default.htm.
19. 21 CFR 7.84(a)(2)–(3).
20. Recently, FDA initiated a "Bad Ad Program" that encourages healthcare providers to report potential false and misleading prescription drug advertising and promotion.

Chapter 31

Healthcare Fraud and Abuse Compliance

Updated by Jennifer D. Burgar

Objectives

- Introduce and explain state and federal laws directed at preventing waste, fraud and various other abuses by life sciences firms
- Provide examples of circumstances that might trigger concerns under these laws
- Identify consequences of a violation of these laws

Laws, Regulations and Guidelines Covered in This Chapter

- *Federal Food, Drug, and Cosmetic Act* of 1938
- *Guidance for Industry: Good Reprint Practices for the Distribution of Medical Journal Articles and Medical or Scientific Reference Publications on Unapproved New Uses of Approved Drugs and Approved or Cleared Medical Devices* (January 2009)
- *False Claims Act* of 1863
- Federal and State Anti-Kickback Laws
- Federal and State Physician Self-Referral Laws (*Stark Law*)
- The Pharmaceutical Research and Manufacturers of America Code on Interactions with Healthcare Professionals
- Price Reporting Laws
- Medicaid Drug Program
  - o Federal Upper Limit
  - o Public Health Service Program
  - o Federal Government Ceiling Price
  - o Medicare Part B
  - o Medicare Part D
- State Sales and Marketing Compliance Laws
- *Physician Payment Sunshine Act* of 2009

Introduction

Life sciences firms selling items that are ultimately utilized in the healthcare industry are subject to laws directed at preventing waste, fraud and various other abuses. Any company that provides goods or services reimbursed under Medicare, Medicaid or any other federal healthcare program may be subject to civil or criminal penalties under federal laws including the *Medicare and Medicaid Patient Protection Act* of 1987 (*Federal Anti-Kickback Statute*), the *Stark Law*, the *False Claims Act* and various US Food and Drug Administration (FDA) regulations. Companies that provide goods or services reimbursed by state healthcare programs, or even by individuals or private payors, may find themselves subject to similar, but usually not identical, state statutes. This chapter introduces several key risk areas for pharmaceutical and device manufacturers, with the aim of identifying illustrative, but not exhaustive, fact patterns that may, if not properly managed, lead to allegations of fraud, waste or abuse.

Off-Label Promotion

FDA seeks to ensure the safety and efficacy of most drugs and devices. This means that most drugs and devices must be approved or cleared by FDA prior to promotion or marketing. As part of this process, FDA approves or clears drugs and devices for certain uses or indications. The agency generally prohibits manufacturers of new drugs or medical devices from promoting or marketing products for any use that FDA has not approved or cleared. According to FDA, an approved new drug that is marketed for an unapproved use is an unapproved new drug with respect to that use. Specifically, an approved drug or device or an uncleared device that is marketed for an unapproved use is considered to be misbranded. If the manufacturer promotes a drug or device for any unapproved/uncleared indication, it is commonly called "off-label promotion" and may violate both FDA laws and the *False Claims Act.*

FDA recognizes that off-label use can be appropriate and valuable to patient care, and thus the statutes allow for off-label use by physicians as part of the professional practice of medicine. In fact, drugs and devices are commonly used for off-label indications with good results. Also, FDA understands that there must be some room for free exchange of educational and scientific information in order to advance the cause of science and healthcare. For example, in FDA's *Guidance for Industry: Good Reprint Practices for the Distribution of Medical Journal Articles and Medical or Scientific Reference Publications on Unapproved New Uses of Approved Drugs and Approved or Cleared Medical Devices* (January 2009), the agency allows dissemination of certain scientific information by manufacturers, with constraints designed to ensure that these exchanges are not used as subterfuges for off-label promotion. Most companies have special processes and procedures that must be followed when disseminating off-label information to ensure adherence to FDA guidance on this point.

The *False Claims Act* may be implicated by off-label promotion. This law prohibits the filing of a false or fraudulent claim to be reimbursed by the government. The law expands to encompass companies that "cause" the filing of such a claim. Because the general rule is that Medicare and Medicaid will provide reimbursement for a drug or device only when it is prescribed for an approved use, when a company markets a drug or device for an unapproved use, the government may argue that such marketing "caused" a healthcare professional to file a claim with Medicare or Medicaid for an off-label use. The *False Claims Act* has steep per-claim civil monetary penalties and treble damages, meaning that a low-valued claim can quickly result in significant fines.

The federal government takes an aggressive stance regarding the enforcement of off-label promotion and has obtained some significant judgments against manufacturers for off-label promotion. These cases tend to emanate from sales and marketing practices designed to sell products to healthcare providers for off-label uses. For example, in January 2009, the Department of Justice (DOJ) accepted a guilty plea from Eli Lilly and Co. and fined the company $515 million. This fine was in addition to a civil settlement of approximately $800 million. This billion plus dollars of criminal and civil settlements resulted from a claim that Eli Lilly was promoting its drug Zyprexa for the treatment of dementia, Alzheimer's, depression, anxiety, sleep problems and behavioral symptoms such as agitation, aggression and hostility, despite the fact that the drug was approved only for the treatment of psychotic disorders and bipolar disorder. Similarly, in April 2009, Nichols Institute Diagnostics, a subsidiary of Quest Diagnostics Inc., pled guilty to a felony misbranding charge in violation of the *Food, Drug, and Cosmetic Act* of 1938 (*FD&C Act*) and agreed to pay a criminal fine of $40 million as part of a $302 million global settlement with the federal government. In its guilty plea, Nichols Institute Diagnostics admitted that, over approximately a six-year period beginning in May 2000, it marketed a misbranded test. The misbranding claim was premised on the allegation that Nichols Institute Diagnostics distributed marketing materials describing the Advantage Intact PTH Assay as having "excellent correlation" to another assay—despite the fact that Nichols Institute Diagnostics was aware that the Advantage Intact PTH Assay was not consistently providing equivalent results.

In addition to monetary relief, FDA may seek an injunction to prohibit companies from manufacturing and distributing unapproved drugs. For example, in April 2009, FDA announced that it was barring Neilgen Pharmaceuticals Inc., its parent company Advent Pharmaceuticals Inc. and two of its officers from manufacturing and distributing any unapproved, adulterated or misbranded drugs. According to FDA, the unapproved drugs (primarily prescription cough and cold products) manufactured by Neilgen and Advent had not undergone the agency's drug approval process. Accordingly, the companies failed to establish the drugs' safety and effectiveness and FDA had not reviewed the adequacy and accuracy of the directions for use and related label warnings. As part of the consent decree with FDA, Neilgen and Advent were ordered to destroy their existing drug supply and were expressly prohibited from commercially manufacturing and distributing any new drugs without the agency's approval. The companies were also required to consult with outside experts who could provide guidance regarding appropriate compliance standards and to obtain written authorization from FDA before resuming operations. They face the prospect of steep financial penalties for any future violations. While the failure to obtain FDA approval makes this an extreme case, the enforcement action demonstrates the significant business disruption that can result from violations of FDA regulatory requirements.

It is also important to note that claims of off-label promotion are not levied exclusively against manufacturers. For example, in 2006, DOJ charged a psychiatrist with conspiring with the manufacturer of a drug called Xyrem to promote the drug for off-label uses. According to the indictment, the manufacturer of Xyrem, Orphan Medical Inc., paid the psychiatrist thousands of dollars for promoting Xyrem for off-label uses at various speaking engagements. As a result, both the company and the physician were charged. Orphan Medical paid $20 million to settle civil and criminal charges, and in 2008, the physician pled guilty to misbranding.

Kickbacks

Patients rely on their physicians to recommend the best treatments, drugs and devices. Indeed, patients cannot obtain prescription medical products and services without a referral or order from a medical professional. Thus, the physician-patient relationship is regarded as a special, fiduciary relationship in which the physician is obliged to act with the best interest of the patient as the motivating concern. Remunerative relationships (such as consulting arrangements) between manufacturers and physicians who make referrals for or order the manufacturers' products can create an apparent or real conflict of interest, thereby potentially tainting referral decisions.

This is the underlying concern of the federal *Anti-Kickback Statute*. Generally, the statute prohibits intentionally soliciting, offering or receiving any remuneration (including any kickback, bribe, discount or rebate) in return for referring an individual to a person for the furnishing of any item or service for which payment may be made under a federal or a federally-funded state healthcare program such as Medicare or Medicaid. For example, the *Anti-Kickback Statute* would prohibit the provision of remuneration to a physician to induce or reward the physician for writing prescriptions for a particular product. The mandatory penalties for violations of this statute are severe, and a party guilty of violating the *Anti-Kickback Statute* is guilty of a felony and may be subject to a prison term of up to five years. In addition, a party that has violated the statute is excluded from participation in Medicare, Medicaid and other federal healthcare programs; for life sciences companies, this means that Medicare and Medicaid will no longer provide reimbursement for the company's products.

The application of the *Anti-Kickback Statute* is complex. Many common situations involving remuneration between manufacturers and referral sources can be structured to comply with the statute. For example, there is a "safe harbor" to the *Anti-Kickback Statute* that can protect arrangements with consultants, speakers and advisory board members providing services to companies. It is important that all remunerative relationships (i.e., transfers of value through compensation or otherwise) between manufacturers and

their customers and others in a position to generate business for the manufacturer be properly vetted for compliance with the *Anti-Kickback Statute*.

There are many examples of investigations and prosecutions under the *Anti-Kickback Statute*. These actions typically arise from cases where a device or pharmaceutical manufacturer gives something, such as excessive compensation, to a physician or another person in a position to recommend its product, and it appears that the reason behind the transfer was to induce the recipient to recommend or order the manufacturer's product. Notably, it is not unusual to see a prosecution involving allegations that a company made improper payments to a physician to induce the physician to prescribe products for off-label uses, thereby violating both the prohibition against off-label promotion and the *Anti-Kickback Statute*.

These cases often involve payments to physicians, but can also involve payments to other parties in a position to promote the manufacturer's product. For example, one fairly recent prosecution involved a large pharmacy benefit manager, Medco. The government alleged that Medco violated the *Anti-Kickback Statute* by soliciting and accepting payments from pharmaceutical companies for favorable formulary placement, and by paying kickbacks to induce health plans to award Medco contracts to provide mail order pharmacy benefits for the plans' beneficiaries.

Many states have adopted their own versions of the *Anti-Kickback Statute*. These statutes may also affect arrangements involving items or services that are not covered under a governmental program. Also, these state laws may implicate slightly different behavior than is implicated by the federal statute. The existence of these state anti-kickback statutes means that remunerative relationships with referral sources must be scrutinized for compliance with both state and federal law.

Physician-Self-Referrals

Historically, physicians have branched out from the practice of medicine to provide ancillary services to their patients, such as laboratory tests, pharmaceuticals, durable medical equipment, imaging and lithotripsy. Some physicians may own interests in hospitals or other facilities to which they refer patients, or in device companies producing products used by their patients. While this practice seems like a natural evolution—and is beneficial to the extent that it increases accessibility or quality or spurs innovation—it also has the potential for creating a conflict of interest. The financial interest provides the physician with an incentive to direct patients to purchase services or products from an entity in which he or she has an interest, despite the fact that these products or devices may not be the best or cheapest available to the patient. The conflict of interest may also provide an incentive toward over-utilization.

The *Stark Law* (named for its primary sponsor, US

Representative Pete Stark of California) and its associated regulations address this concern by prohibiting physician self-referrals for certain "designated health services" reimbursed by Medicare or Medicaid, except in certain specified circumstances. As with the *Anti-Kickback Statute*, many states have adopted their own variant of the *Stark Law* and prohibit self-referrals in the same or similar circumstances as prohibited by the federal law. Of course, not all these arrangements will be problematic; rather they may fall under one of numerous statutory or regulatory exceptions. However, all of these arrangements require careful attention.

Of particular interest to device manufacturers is the question of whether the *Stark Law* should apply to prohibit physician-owned companies (POCs) that produce medical devices from selling those devices to hospitals and other facilities for ultimate use by the physician-owner's patients. The Centers for Medicare & Medicaid Services (CMS) is currently considering how to properly regulate POCs, and has recently solicited comments from the public on this issue. The ultimate decision could impact manufacturers that enter into arrangements with POCs.

The PhRMA Code and the AdvaMed Code

In addition to laws that govern manufacturers' conduct, trade organizations have also adopted voluntary codes of ethics. The Pharmaceutical Research and Manufacturers of America (PhRMA) adopted a voluntary marketing code to govern the pharmaceutical industry's relationships with physicians and other healthcare professionals. The PhRMA Code on Interactions with Healthcare Professionals (the PhRMA Code) originally took effect in 2002 and was revised and made more stringent in 2009. Similarly, the Advanced Medical Technology Association (AdvaMed) issued its Code of Ethics on Interactions with Health Care Professionals (the AdvaMed Code) in 2005 and revised it in 2009 to coincide with the PhRMA Code revisions.

Both the PhRMA Code and the AdvaMed Code have established standards for manufacturers' interactions with healthcare professionals. For example, the codes discuss gifts, entertainment, the use of consultants, support of third-party conferences and grants. The codes have been unofficially "blessed" by the government agency charged with interpreting and investigating possible violations of the *Anti-Kickback Statute*, meaning that a company that demonstrates compliance with the codes may be spared in an *Anti-Kickback Statute* investigation. Finally, as discussed at the end of this chapter, a number of states have enacted laws that require or recommend compliance with the codes.

Bad Reimbursement Advice

Manufacturers of complex or innovative products often provide reimbursement advice to their customers. Liability can arise from advice that is faulty or perceived as promoting over-utilization. For example, in *United States v. Augustine Medical Inc.*, the government alleged that a manufacturer directed its customers to bill Medicare in a manner that obscured the true nature of its product, because it believed that if Medicare knew exactly what product was being billed, Medicare would reimburse for the product at a less-favorable rate. Augustine Medical and various individuals associated with the company faced criminal and civil enforcement actions. The company eventually settled all claims against it. However, certain Augustine Medical executives pled guilty to criminal charges related to withholding facts used to determine rights to Medicare payments, and each received probation and incurred a significant fine. Companies should take care to provide only objective and accurate reimbursement information and remind customers about their own duty to confirm reimbursement policies before submitting claims so as to avoid a similar investigation.

Price Reporting Fraud

Pharmaceutical manufacturers report drug prices under a number of different programs using several different methodologies (e.g., Average Manufacturer Price, Best Price, Average Sales Price, Average Wholesale Price and Wholesale Acquisition Cost). Additionally, sponsors of programs operating under Medicare Part D are required to report all price concessions obtained from manufacturers to CMS (e.g., rebates or discounts). Allegations that a pharmaceutical manufacturer defrauded Medicare or Medicaid (or another government program) are often premised on the alleged inaccuracy of the various pricing reports. Charges of misconduct can arise in connection with, for example, inaccurate reporting or characterization of discounts or rebates. Allegations of "marketing the spread"—where manufacturers report their Average Wholesale Price to Medicare as "x" but sell to physicians at "x-y," thereby yielding a windfall gain to physicians—have been prosecuted aggressively. Similarly, causes of action based on concealment of Best Price (where manufacturers do not report certain discounts to the states in connection with their Best Price reporting obligations under Medicaid) have also been popular theories for prosecution.

Beyond ensuring the integrity of data generated and submitted for government reimbursement purposes, accurate compliance with the various price reporting programs requires attention to periodic filing and reporting requirements. The key federal programs to which pharmaceutical manufacturers may need to submit price reporting data include the Medicaid Drug Program, Federal Upper Limit (applicable to multiple source drugs under Medicaid), Public Health Service Program, Federal Government Ceiling Price (applicable only to single source and innovator multiple source drugs), Medicare Part B and Medicare Part D (outpatient drug program).

State Laws Relating to Sales and Marketing

A number of state legislatures have sought new approaches to contain healthcare costs, track interactions between manufacturers and healthcare practitioners and generally reduce healthcare fraud. These approaches include laws requiring the reporting of marketing activities and expenditures and regulating interactions between manufacturers and healthcare professionals. As of April 2011, there were nine states with such laws: California, Connecticut, District of Columbia, Maine, Massachusetts, Minnesota, Nevada, West Virginia and Vermont. For the most part, these laws are triggered when the manufacturer interacts with a healthcare professional that is licensed in that state, such that the laws must be considered if a manufacturer interacts with a healthcare professional licensed by one of those states at a national conference (e.g., may wish to invite a physician licensed in Maine to attend a dinner after a conference in another state) or may engage a healthcare professional licensed in one of the states to serve on an advisory board or speaker's bureau.

The following is a summary of the laws of those nine states. Companies are cautioned to monitor these laws for revisions and to watch for the promulgation of new laws by other states.

California

Pharmaceutical and device manufacturers are required to adopt a Comprehensive Compliance Program (CCP). The CCP must include a specific dollar limit on "gifts, promotional materials, or items or activities" the manufacturer gives or provides to "medical or healthcare professionals." The manufacturer must declare annually in writing that it is in compliance with the provisions of the law and its CCP. The CCP and annual written declaration must be available on the company's website and through a toll-free number. Although the California law does not provide for specific penalties, violators of the law may face civil enforcement actions under other state laws.

Connecticut

Pharmaceutical and device manufacturers were required to implement, at a minimum, the PhRMA Code on or before 1 January 2011. Manufacturers are also required to adopt a comprehensive compliance program that contains all of the requirements prescribed in the PhRMA or AdvaMed Codes as such codes were in effect on 1 January 2010. The Commissioner of Consumer Protection may impose a civil penalty of not more than $5,000 for any violation of the compliance law.

District of Columbia

Any person engaged in the practice of pharmaceutical detailing in DC must obtain and maintain a license with the District's Board of Pharmacy and must agree to adhere to a code of ethics promulgated by the DC city council, which includes compliance with the PhRMA Code.

Maine

Drug manufacturers must report the value, nature, purpose and recipient (persons/entities licensed to provide healthcare in the state) of expenses associated with educational or information programs. Specifically, manufacturers must report: support for continuing medical education and charitable grants; printing design and product costs for patient education materials; consulting fees, speakers bureaus and market research; and expenses for food, entertainment and gifts, that are greater than $25. A civil penalty of $1,000 may be imposed for failure to report and for each false report or omission of required information.

Massachusetts

Drug and device manufacturers must adopt a code of conduct that complies with the requirements of the Massachusetts regulations. The code of conduct must address a number of areas, including Massachusetts' strict rules on the provision of meals to customers. Under the law, manufacturers may provide modest meals as an occasional business courtesy in connection with informational presentations of scientific, educational or business information, but only if those meals are provided in the customer's office or a hospital setting. A manufacturer must establish a program that provides for regular training of appropriate employees, including sales and marketing staff, on the marketing code of conduct. A manufacturer must adopt policies and procedures for investigating noncompliance with the regulations, taking corrective action, and reporting instances of noncompliance to appropriate state authorities. Upon request, a manufacturer must provide a copy of the marketing code of conduct, training program and policies, as well as a certification that the company is in compliance with the law to the Department of Public Health (DPH). Further, a manufacturer must disclose annually the value, nature, purpose and recipient of any fee, payment, subsidy or other economic benefit with a value of $50 or more provided directly or through its agents to a covered recipient in connection with its sales and marketing activities. A fine of not more than $5,000 per transaction, occurrence or event may be imposed for failure to comply with the law.

Minnesota

Minnesota has a gift-ban law applicable to drug manufacturers. Under the law, a drug manufacturer is prohibited from giving "any gift of value" to a healthcare professional. The following are not gifts under Minnesota law: (1) free samples and publications and educational materials; (2) items with a total combined retail value of not more than $50 per year; (3) salaries/benefits to employees; (4) payments to a conference sponsor or for other educational programs; (5) reasonable honoraria/expenses for faculty; and (6) compensation for substantial professional or consulting services. Notably, only items 4–6 are required to be disclosed annually (i.e., payments to a conference sponsor, reasonable honoraria/expenses and compensation for substantial professional or consulting services). Minnesota's gift ban law does not address penalties for failure to comply with the law.

Nevada

Under Nevada's law, drug and device manufacturers are required to adopt a written marketing code of conduct and develop a program to provide regular training to appropriate employees. A copy of the code of conduct must be provided to the Nevada Board of Pharmacy. Note that if a company uses, without modification, the PhRMA Code as its marketing code of conduct, it is permitted to so indicate on its submission to the Board of Pharmacy in lieu of submitting its marketing code of conduct. In addition, a manufacturer must adopt policies for investigating instances of noncompliance with the marketing code of conduct and must conduct an annual audit to monitor compliance with the code of conduct and certify annually to the Board of Pharmacy that an audit has been completed. Notably, Nevada's compliance law does not address penalties for failure to comply with the law.

West Virginia

Drug manufacturers must report the total number of prescribers by dollar amount categories to whom the company provides gifts, grants or payments of any kind in excess of $100 for the purpose of advertising prescription drugs. West Virginia's disclosure law does not address penalties for failure to comply with the law.

Vermont

Vermont prohibits drug and device manufacturers from offering or giving any gift to persons authorized to prescribe or recommend drugs or devices, their employees, agents or contractors and certain healthcare entities (e.g., hospitals, nursing homes). A gift is defined as anything of value provided to a healthcare provider for free or any payment, food, entertainment, travel, subscription, advance, service or anything else of value provided to a healthcare provider unless: (1) it is an allowable expenditure as defined by the law; or (2) the healthcare provider reimburses the cost at fair market value. A manufacturer must annually disclose to the Vermont Office of the Attorney General the value, nature, purpose and recipient of any allowable expenditure made to Vermont healthcare providers as well as any academic institution and any professional or patient organization representing or serving healthcare professionals or patients. Anything of value provided by a manufacturer to a healthcare professional that is not an "allowable expenditure" or otherwise exempt from the gift ban may subject the manufacturer to a civil penalty of up to $10,000 per violation. In addition, Vermont's Attorney General may seek injunctive relief, costs and attorney's fees. Violators of the disclosure rules are also subject to civil penalties of up to $10,000 per violation.

The Physician Payment Sunshine Act

On 23 March 2010, President Obama signed into law H.R. 3590, the *Patient Protection and Affordable Care Act*, commonly known as "Health Reform." A section of that law known as the *Physician Payment Sunshine Act* requires drug and device manufacturers to make an annual public disclosure of certain payments or other transfers of value to a physician or a teaching hospital.

By 1 October 2011, the entity charged with collecting such reports, the Department of Health and Human Services, is required to establish procedures for submitting information and making public disclosure. The first annual reports, covering the 2012 calendar year, are due 31 March 2013. The information will be made available on an Internet website, in a searchable format, no later than 30 September 2013.

Under the law, the transfer of anything with a value greater than $10 must be reported (or if the aggregate amount for the calendar year exceeds $100). However, there are a number of exemptions to this reporting obligation. For example, gifts of educational materials that directly benefit patients or are intended for patient use need not be reported. Failure to report is subject to significant civil monetary penalties ranging from $1,000 to $100,000 per transfer that is not disclosed.

Notably, the sunshine law preempts state reporting requirements that are duplicative in their requirements to make reports. However, any additional and more-stringent reporting requirements that states may choose to impose are not preempted.

The details of the federal sunshine law are not yet known, as (at the time of publication) the implementing regulations have not yet been published. Companies are cautioned to follow developments in this area.

Summary

Life sciences firms selling items that are ultimately utilized in the healthcare industry are subject to laws directed at preventing waste, fraud and various other abuses. While there is a multitude of scenarios under which a life sciences company can find itself in trouble, attention should be focused on avoiding activities that are common enforcement targets, including: engaging in off-label promotion; giving illegal kickbacks; involvement in prohibited physician self-referrals; distributing misleading reimbursement advice; failing to comply with price reporting obligations;

and failing to adhere to state sales and marketing laws. This chapter is designed to increase awareness of these risk areas, so you can help your company to avoid them.

Regulatory Information Resources in Review

By Diane R. Whitworth, MLS

Objectives

- Become familiar with print and electronic information resources relevant to the regulatory healthcare industry
- Understand how to access and retrieve publicly available, Internet-based government agency and association resources to support the regulatory intelligence process
- Recognize the value of industry associations to expand professional knowledge and develop regulatory core competencies
- Learn how to access selected Web 2.0 tools (blogs and social networks) to increase professional effectiveness

Laws, Regulations and Guidelines Covered in This Chapter

- *Federal Register (FR)* and Code of Federal Regulations (CFR)

Introduction

Regulatory professionals have significantly improved their productivity, effectiveness and expertise in the workplace through access to the ever-increasing array of Internet-based regulatory information resources. The ease with which regulatory information may now be obtained is profound compared to the days when the only way to acquire this documentation was via telephone, fax or mail. This chapter provides a detailed review of a broad range of electronic industry, government and association resources available to regulatory professionals. The value of each of these tools in supporting product substantiation, regulatory review analysis, strategic planning and increasing professional knowledge will be assessed.

Print and Electronic Publications

Print and electronic information resources play an essential role in a regulatory professional's ability to gain, maintain and advance knowledge and understanding of various healthcare industry product sectors. The regulatory profession is characterized by repeated job changes among professionals as well as by frequent mergers among the pharmaceutical, medical device and biologics companies themselves. For example, it is not uncommon for a regulatory professional's career to begin in the pharmaceutical industry and transition into the device area due to a job change, lateral move into another division within a company or perhaps to a work assignment in an area that requires an understanding of combination products. There are many and varied reasons why a professional may require additional regulatory information. Fortunately, print and electronic tools to fulfill this requirement are increasingly abundant.

Book Publishers

A number of publishers specialize in print and electronic publications focused on healthcare regulatory topics. This section reviews industry, government, association and standards publishers that target the regulatory healthcare profession and explains how regulatory professionals can retrieve the most relevant resources using the publisher's online catalogs. Because regulatory affairs is an interdisciplinary profession, publishers that primarily concentrate on scientific research and development (R&D), law, medicine, business or government, or possibly all of the above, may also feature publications focused specifically on the regulatory aspects of these subjects.

CRC Online Press, John Wiley & Sons, Lippincott Williams & Wilkins/Wolters Kluwer Health, Majors.com and Springer are major publishing firms that provide broad subject coverage and also feature a significant number of publications directed at the regulatory profession.

The CRC Online Press website contains numerous regulatory books within the general category of pharmaceutical science. Users can locate these publications within the following subcategories: biotechnology/biopharmaceutical; cleaning and sterilization; clinical trials; computer software; drug delivery and development; drug discovery; laboratory; manufacturing and engineering; medical devices; quality assurance; regulations and standards; and training and validation. Similarly, John Wiley & Sons produces regulatory publications on drug submissions, clinical trials, drug safety evaluation, pharmaceutical manufacturing regulations, quality and preclinical development.

Lippincott Williams & Wilkins, a division of Wolters Kluwer Health, also produces several publications on drug development, clinical trials and pharmaceuticals. Majors. com's publications focus on regulatory compliance; quality assurance; risk management; the *Health Insurance Portability and Accountability Act* (*HIPAA*); coding and reimbursement; administrative law and regulatory practice; pharmaceutical research; medical devices; biotechnology; chemistry, manufacturing and controls compliance; laboratory auditing; validation; and clinical research. Springer, by comparison, covers regulatory and toxicology issues such as pharmaceutical safety evaluation in its pharmaceutical science area.

The following keywords are effective for searching these online catalogs:
- regulatory
- regulatory affairs
- regulatory healthcare
- pharmaceutical
- biotechnology
- medical device
- pharmacology

Other industry publishers concentrate on specific regulatory areas such as quality assurance and standards. For example, the American Society for Quality (ASQ Press) publishes books, standards and training materials relating to quality issues, and the Bureau of National Affairs (BNA) concentrates on the legal aspects of regulatory affairs. Selected topics covered by BNA publications include pharmaceutical, biotechnology and health law, intellectual property and patent law.

In the same manner, the United States Pharmacopeia (USP), an official public standards-setting authority for prescription, over-the-counter (OTC) medicines and US-manufactured healthcare products, develops documentary and quality reference standards. Its key publications

include the *US Pharmacopeia–National Formulary* (*USP–NF*) and the *Food Chemical Codex*. *USP–NF* monographs contain standards and procedures that are enforceable by the US Food and Drug Administration (FDA). The *USP–NF* contains public pharmacopeial standards for medicines, dosage forms, drug substances, excipients, medical devices and dietary supplements.[1]

Another valuable standards resource for regulatory professionals is IEEE, formerly the Institute of Electrical and Electronics Engineers, which develops and publishes conference proceedings, training materials, standards and publications central to regulatory research. It is the leading global professional association for the advancement of technology and the authority on biomedical engineering and medical devices.

The International Organization for Standardization (ISO), similarly, is a key nongovernmental standards-producing organization, consisting of a network of national standards institutes representing 159 countries and a coordinating Central Secretariat in Geneva, Switzerland. ISO's catalog comprises more than 175,000 published international standards.

The American Society of Testing and Materials (ASTM) is an additional example of a standards organization that produces Special Technical Publications, compilations, manuals, monographs, journals and handbooks on regulatory topics.

Standards publications focused on healthcare regulatory issues may be found through a search of the following terms:
- biological
- biotechnology
- clinical
- pharmaceutical
- medical device
- medical instrumentation
- quality management
- regulatory

Several industry publishers specialize in publications that focus entirely or largely on regulatory and compliance issues. Barnett International is one such company; it publishes regularly updated reference manuals, industry compendiums and job aids to assist regulatory professionals in complying with federal regulations. It also prepares regulatory industry executive analyses, question and answer guides on regulatory topics and a study site training series for regulatory professionals. FDAnews is another publisher that prepares reference tools specifically aimed at the pharmaceutical, biologics and medical device regulatory industry. Its products include the Code of Federal Regulations (CFR) compilations, an adverse event compliance series and publications on biologics, biosimilars and combination drug products. Similarly, GMP Publications targets the regulatory industry through its

CFR pocket guides and Good Clinical Practice and Good Manufacturing Practice handbooks.

The Government Printing Office (GPO), serves as the country's official online bookstore for US government publications. GPO is the primary resource for gathering, cataloging, producing, providing, authenticating and preserving published information in all its forms for the executive, legislative and judicial branches of the federal government.[2] Publications pertaining to regulatory healthcare topics may be accessed by searching with the keywords "FDA" or the "Food and Drug Administration" and "DHHS" or "Department of Health and Human Services" combined with more specific terms such as "pharmaceutical," "clinical" or "drug industry." GPO Access operates within the GPO to provide free electronic access to legislative resources including Congressional bills, the *Congressional Record*, public and private law, the US Code; executive sources such as the CFR, the *FR* and presidential materials; and judicial sources including the Supreme Court, trial and appellate court cases, opinions, oral arguments and decisions.

Another type of publication of particular value to regulatory professionals is the market research report. Piribo, which brands itself as "online business intelligence for the BioPharma Industry,"[3] specializes in this type of resource. The UK-based publisher prepares detailed and costly global market research reports, handbooks, strategic analysis profiles and regulatory overviews. Report subject categories range from biotechnology, drug delivery and medical devices to prescription drugs, regulatory policy and pricing and reimbursement. Urch Publishing, like Piribo, is a UK-based publisher of market intelligence reports covering the global pharmaceutical and healthcare industry. Urch covers topics including chemicals, drug discovery/R&D, generics, pharmaceutical industry trends, pricing and reimbursement, regulatory, sales and marketing and therapeutics.

Thompson Publishing, by comparison, dedicates an entire product line to food and drug regulatory materials. Thompson's products are primarily subscription-based and are available in print or electronically. These products generally consist of two-volume manuals containing regularly updated newsletters, an archive and special reports, in conjunction with access to additional online resources. Topics covered include Good Clinical Practice, FDA advertising and promotion, FDA enforcement and medical device regulation. Aspen Publishers, another division of the aforementioned Wolters/Kluwer, also publishes a complete line of food, drug and medical device publications. It provides detailed coverage of the FDA approval process and expert guidance on generic drugs. The majority of Aspen's manuals are loose-leaf formatted and subscribers automatically receive documentation updates, supplements and/or new editions.

Many associations, such as the Regulatory Affairs Professionals Society (RAPS) and the Food and Drug Law Institute (FDLI), publish materials intended for regulatory professionals that are available in their online bookstores. This book is a key example of one such product produced by RAPS. In addition, RAPS publishes regulatory affairs certification (RAC) preparatory materials for the US, Canadian, EU and General Scope exams; self-assessment exams for each certification; and books on topics key to the development of regulatory professionals. Also included in RAPS' bookstore are third-party publications of interest to regulatory professionals. FDLI, similarly, markets its own publications as well as third-party products addressing regulatory and legal topics.

Free Industry Resources (Electronic Newsletters (e-Newsletters)

In addition to books, reports and standards, a number of industry resources are available to regulatory professionals to monitor current events and advance their knowledge of healthcare product regulation. This section reviews both free and fee-based sources. However, the free publications will be discussed in greater detail as there are several valuable free sources of which regulatory professionals may not be aware. The fee-based resources, by comparison, tend to encompass the more widely recognized monthly journals and association publications made available as a membership benefit. The sources reviewed in this section cover a range of drug, device and biologics regulatory publications. Although not comprehensive, they may give regulatory professionals a solid basis for further independent research.

Many publishers produce multiple newsletters aimed at different healthcare product sectors. For example, FDAnews publishes the following free e-newsletters: *FDAnews Device Daily Bulletin, FDAnews Drug Daily Bulletin* and *The QMN Weekly Bulletin. FDAnews Device Daily Bulletin* monitors FDA regulatory, legislative and business news developments as well as selected international news affecting the medical device industry. *FDAnews Drug Daily Bulletin* provides parallel coverage for the pharmaceutical industry. *The QMN Weekly Bulletin* covers current quality management news, regulatory developments and inspection trends. The summaries provided by these publications offer brief but valuable perspectives on current regulatory management issues for drugs, devices and quality. A link to the full-text article is listed below each summary; some of the cited sources require subscriptions to fee-based publications. These links afford regulatory professionals an opportunity to obtain further information on a particular subject as well as learn about new resources.

SmartBrief, an independent e-newsletter publisher, produces 25 industry-specific daily newsletters that are available free of charge by subscription. This company partners with trade associations and professional societies to publish its newsletters. *AdvaMed SmartBrief* is issued in conjunction with the Advanced Medical Technology Association (AdvaMed) and targets medical device, diagnostic product and health information system professionals. *BIO SmartBrief*, produced in cooperation with the Biotechnology Industry Organization (BIO), focuses on biotechnology industry professionals, and *FDLI SmartBrief* works with FDLI to reach food and drug industry professionals. The summaries in all three publications are based on original information from news organizations and are repackaged by SmartBrief's editorial staff. Each newsletter typically covers top stories: healthcare in transition; hot topics; business and market trends; science and health or science and health policy; emerging technologies; and product-specific and association-specific news. Regulatory professionals can use these publications to track current regulatory developments in time-saving compilations and obtain valuable competitive intelligence.

In a similar manner, VertMarkets has established 68 online community marketplaces for eight industry groups to connect buyers and suppliers. For each of its online industry communities, VertMarkets produces free bi-weekly email bulletins that provide not only product offerings, but also industry updates and the latest news to its members. The newsletters directed to regulatory professionals fall into the life sciences category and include the *Bioresearch Online Newsletter, Drug Discovery Online Newsletter, Laboratory Network Community Newsletter, Medical Device Online Community Newsletter* and *Pharmaceutical Online Newsletter*. Typical content includes top news stories, featured articles, featured downloads and a product showcase.

FierceMarkets is a digital media company that also specializes in supporting business-to-business marketing in the life sciences, healthcare, IT, telecom and finance industries through its e-newsletters, websites, webinars and live events. *FiercePharma* is a daily e-newsletter focused on pharmaceutical company news and market development of FDA-approved products. Regulatory professionals can stay informed and save time by reviewing these types of industry-specific publications. Categories included in *FiercePharma* are: pharmaceutical company news and reports; FDA rulings; regulations; recalls and warnings; drug launches and safety; pharmaceutical sales; and marketing news and activities of key industry professionals. *FierceBiotech* is another daily e-newsletter in the FierceMarkets' digital product family. It concentrates on drug discovery and clinical trials news as well as the latest biotechnology trends, breakthroughs and FDA approval updates. *FierceBioResearcher* reports on biotechnology research news, information and tools, with a special focus on the science of drug discovery. *FierceVaccines, FierceHealthcare* and *FierceSarbox* are the company's other three e-newsletters within the healthcare division.

F-D-C Reports, an Elsevier subsidiary, is a newsletter publisher that has been serving the healthcare product industry since 1939. Although the majority of its publications are fee-based, it does offer a complimentary subscription to a few of its weekly e-newsletters. The first of these is *Biopharma Today*, formerly *FDA Legislative Watch*. This e-newsletter covers current FDA reform initiatives specifically pertaining to the biomedical industry. The second is *Medical Devices Today*, which provides strategy, regulation, innovation and investment coverage from *The Gray Sheet, Medtech Insight, IN VIVO, Start-Up, The Silver Sheet* and *Strategic Transactions*. The articles cover drug and business development, finance, strategy, regulation and reimbursement. Summaries and reprints are excerpted from recognized publications including F-D-C Reports' *The Pink Sheet, The Gold Sheet, Pharmaceuticals Approval Monthly* and *PharmAsia News* and Elsevier Business Intelligence's *Start-Up* and *The RPM Report*.

A few other free electronic resources worth briefly mentioning are *Pharma Marketing News*, the *Pharmaceutical Technology Newsletter* and *PharmaFocus*. VirSci Corporation's *Pharma Marketing News* is a monthly newsletter for pharmaceutical and marketing professionals designed to keep subscribers informed about industry trends and innovations. It also offers a professional network for career advancement. Frequently covered topics include: physician marketing; sales and education; regulatory compliance; patient education; and direct-to-consumer advertising and marketing.

Pharma Technology Newsletter is produced by a UK-based company, SPG Media. The newsletter is dedicated to pharmaceutical professionals working with technology. Subscribers have access to the latest developments in global industry projects, company profiles, industry events and a recruitment section that provides career information and the latest job vacancies. *PharmaFocus* is also published in the UK, but unlike *Pharma Technology Newsletter*, its primary focus is on news affecting the pharmaceutical industry and the UK's National Health Service. This publication is a bit more exclusive in that it is only sent free of charge to selected permanent employees of companies that manufacture ethical and OTC pharmaceuticals and biotechnology companies. The complete version of the latest issue, however, is accessible on the website.

Three additional pharmaceutical industry-oriented e-newsletters published by Canon Communications Pharmaceutical Media Group are *PharmaLive, Therapeutics Daily* and *Daily Advantage*. Subscriptions to all three are free of charge if users register with the Pharmalive.com website. These newsletters are another great source of industry intelligence, providing summaries of industry events and trends affecting pharmaceutical and clinical professionals, accompanied by a link to the full text and related articles. Information is categorized by business and therapeutic area, and the news and information focus on clinical research, product marketing and pharmaceutical business. The therapeutic product areas covered in *Therapeutics Daily* include cardiovascular, oncology, pain and inflammation, central nervous system and infectious disease.

Several regulatory consulting firms also produce free newsletters to support their clients and the professional regulatory community. DRW Research & Information Services LLC, an independent regulatory research consulting firm, produces a free monthly e-newsletter, *DRW Monthly*, which covers a broad range of global healthcare regulatory topics. Each month is dedicated to reviewing medical device, biologics or pharmaceutical global regulatory developments. Donawa Consulting, a regulatory consultant based in Italy, also produces a quarterly publication. The *Donawa Consulting Newsletter* provides an overview of international medical device, quality system and clinical regulatory developments.

Clinical monitoring news is another area covered in a free weekly e-newsletter entitled *BioPharm Insight Clinical Newsletter*. Infinata, the publisher, is also the developer of BioPharm Insight, a commercial, fee-based database discussed later in this chapter. The newsletter covers the latest information on clinical enrollments, clinical results, drug approvals, drug licensing and medical devices. An additional free electronic resource providing current news for the clinical research community is the Association for Clinical Research Professionals' (ACRP) biweekly e-newsletter, *ACRP Wire*.

The medical device industry also receives excellent web coverage through a number of free publications. *Medical Device & Diagnostic Industry (MD&DI)* is one of 13 magazines published by Canon Communications that focus on the medical technology industry. *MD&DI* is a monthly magazine written exclusively for original equipment manufacturers of medical devices and in vitro diagnostic products. For more than 25 years, it has supported the industry's efforts to comply with regulations, keep up-to-date on current events, improve manufacturing and design processes and understand market demand. *Medical Device Link* is a Canon publication available free of charge with membership in MedicalDeviceLink.com. Once a member, the user can sign up for all of Canon Communications' publications. *Medical Device Link* is a bi-weekly email newsletter that reports on top industry headlines and important FDA announcements and features articles from several of the publisher's medical device trade publications.

Fee-Based Industry Resources

The list of fee-based regulatory publications is long and varied, ranging from industry newsletters and peer-reviewed journals to association magazines. Key publishers in the regulatory sphere include Canon Communications, Dickinson, F-D-C Reports, PJB Publishers and Thompson Publishing.

The previously mentioned Canon Communications Pharmaceutical Media Group also publishes two fee-based magazines: *Med Ad News* and *R&D Directions*. *Med Ad News* is an established resource for competitive business intelligence and marketing strategy information. *R&D Directions* provides extensive coverage of pharmaceutical product development and insight into successful R&D strategies. Canon also publishes special reports on biotechnology; company analysis; drug delivery and development; healthcare sales and marketing; pipeline data; strategic issues and therapeutic areas.

Dickinson's FDAReview is a monthly newsletter published by Ferdic Inc. that provides in-depth analyses of the medical device and drug industries as well as FDA inspection and enforcement activities including *Freedom of Information Act (FOIA)* daily logs and Warning Letter summaries. *FDAUpdate* is a weekly fax document containing *FR* updates pertaining to FDA rules and regulations; newly released Warning Letters; weekly filed citizen petitions; Advisory Committee proceedings and calendar; and late-breaking FDA and pharmaceutical product news. Free items also available on Dickinson's interactive website, *FDAWebview*, include FDA Warning Letters, *FR* notices and an FDA calendar.

In addition to the free e-newsletters published by FDAnews, this company distributes 10 fee-based subscription newsletters. The publications are: *Clinical Trials Advisor, Devices & Diagnostics Letter, Drug GMP Report, Drug Industry Daily, Generic Line, International Medical Device Regulatory Monitor, International Pharmaceutical Regulatory Monitor, The Food & Drug Letter, The GMP Letter* and *Washington Drug Letter*. As mentioned above, F-D-C Reports publishes newsletters designed to clarify developments affecting US healthcare product and services marketing and regulation for industry executives, policymakers and analysts. Newsletters published by F-D-C Reports include: *The Pink Sheet/The Pink Sheet DAILY, Pharmaceutical Approvals Monthly, The Gold Sheet* and *PharmAsia News* in the pharmaceuticals and biotechnology category; *The Silver Sheet* and *The Gray Sheet* in the medical devices and diagnostics category; *The Tan Sheet* and *The Rose Sheet* in the consumer products category; and *Health News Daily* in the health policy and biomedical research category.

Another well-recognized, fee-based publisher is Informa Healthcare, which is one of the largest publishers of business information for the pharmaceutical, biotechnology, medical devices and diagnostics industries. Its two key regulatory publications are *Regulatory Affairs Journal (RAJ) Pharma* and *Regulatory Affairs Journal (RAJ) Devices*. *RAJ Pharma* has served as a key source of global news, commentaries and analyses of regulation in the pharmaceutical and biotechnology industries since 1990. Pharmaceutical regulatory intelligence on worldwide rules governing the development, launch and postmarket surveillance of medicines and combination products is provided. Areas of coverage include: regulatory agencies and legislation; application requirements and guidelines; R&D; patents and intellectual property; international harmonization; pediatric legislation; pharmacovigilance; pharmacoeconomics; and drug safety. Since 1995, *RAJ Devices* has also reported on current worldwide news and provided analyses of worldwide medical device regulatory affairs. Some unique areas of focus include: trade and environmental issues; healthcare systems and their impact on regulation and marketing; vigilance; and approval requirements and guidelines. Informa Healthcare also produces a broad range of fee-based industry news sources (e.g., *Scrip World Pharmaceutical News*); business and market research reports; R&D analytical tools and databases (e.g., Pharmaprojects and TrialTrove); contact directories (e.g., Scrip Directory); and research journals (e.g., *Clinical Research & Regulatory Affairs, Drug Development and Industrial Pharmacy*).

Elsevier Business Intelligence distributes several e-newsletters that monitor business information and intelligence trends, technologies and companies in the medical device, diagnostics and biotech industry. The company's fee-based newsletters include *Medtech Insight, IN VIVO: The Business and Medicine Report, START-UP: Emerging Medical Ventures* and *The RPM Report. Medtech Insight* is particularly useful to regulatory professionals for its clinical and industry perspectives on products, procedures and technologies shaping the global medical technology market. *IN VIVO* provides in-depth analyses of marketing, R&D, regulatory and finance strategies in the biopharmaceutical, medical technology and diagnostics industries. *START-UP* examines new product and leading-edge company and investment trends in the pharmaceutical, biotechnology, medical device and in vitro diagnostics industries. *The RPM Report* is a useful business resource for the biopharmaceutical regulatory professional. Its primary focus is on FDA, the Centers for Medicare and Medicaid Services (CMS) and public sector issues. Global Regulatory Press' *Journal of Medical Device Regulation* is yet another important resource for medical device regulatory professionals. This is a quarterly publication currently only available in electronic format. Regulatory professionals can monitor global regulatory developments through legislative changes summarized in each issue and obtain guidance from review articles analyzing current medical device regulatory and compliance issues.

Fee-Based Association Resources

The majority of association publications are free with membership but require nonmembers to pay an annual subscription fee. RAPS is one example of an association that publishes a monthly magazine, *Regulatory Focus,* that is only available to its members. This magazine focuses on current regulatory issues affecting the drug, medical device and biological healthcare product sectors. Another member-based resource that RAPS offers is a weekly email newsletter, *RAPS Weekly Update.* Similarly, The Organisation for Professionals in Regulatory Affairs (TOPRA) publishes a member-only international journal, *Regulatory Rapporteur,* that provides current news and analyses on regulatory and legislative topics. In addition, TOPRA issues a quarterly member newsletter, *In Touch,* which serves as an association news digest covering member and organizational activities. FDLI publishes a quarterly magazine, the *Food and Drug Law Journal,* which is also available free to members and by subscription to the public. The journal features articles on food, drug, cosmetic, medical device and healthcare technology industry regulation and legislation, implications of proposed regulations, policy trends and analyses of court decisions in food and drug law. Its member-only resource, *Update,* is issued bimonthly and contains the latest association and industry news, viewpoints on industry-specific trends, FDA agency developments and articles on various regulatory topics.

In a similar manner, the Drug Information Association (DIA) publishes *DIA Today,* a member newsletter covering current industry activities, as well as the *Drug Information Journal,* a monthly scholarly, international, multidisciplinary, peer-reviewed publication. The Parenteral Drug Association (PDA) has a membership publication entitled *PDA Letter* that is comparable to the ones produced by the other organizations. It reports on science, technology, quality, regulatory affairs, association news and updates relevant to the PDA community. The *PDA Journal of Pharmaceutical Science and Technology* is a bimonthly publication that contains peer-reviewed scientific and technical papers covering the pharmaceutical and biotech industries. The journal is distributed as a member benefit and is also available by subscription. *PDA Technical Reports* are global consensus documents addressing a range of topics relating to pharmaceutical production, validation and quality assurance. Expert task forces prepare the reports, which are then reviewed by technical forums and ultimately evaluated and approved by an advisory board and the PDA board of directors. *PDA Technical Bulletins* are short, scientific position papers responding to issues raised during worldwide regulatory inspections. These board-reviewed and approved papers address a single issue in one or two pages and can be used to support an industry response to a regulatory concern.

Within the biologics/biotechnology sphere, BIO supports professionals engaged in R&D of new healthcare technology, biotechnology and related fields through its advocacy, business development and communications services. Its member-only publication, *BIO News,* is published six times a year and reports on organizational activities, professional perspectives on industry issues and member activities. The Society for Biomaterials is another biologics-focused organization that promotes progress in biomedical materials R&D. The society also publishes member-only resources to foster an understanding of current industry and regulatory developments among regulatory professionals. Members are afforded free access to its official news magazine, *Biomaterials Forum*, which is available by subscription to nonmembers as well. The forum reports on current biomaterials community activities and includes book reviews, technical briefs and professional services information. The *Journal for Biomedical Materials Research* is the official journal of the society and is a peer-reviewed publication provided free to members. It features clinical studies and research reports on a range of topics including the preparation, performance and development of new biomaterials. *Applied Materials* is published as Part B of the journal. It contains peer-reviewed articles on device development; implant retrieval and analysis; manufacturing; regulation of devices; liability and legal issues; standards; reviews of devices; and clinical applications. Nonmembers may subscribe directly by contacting John Wiley & Sons.

In the medical device and technology field, AdvaMed is a lobbying/advocacy organization that supports the industry's goals of advancing global healthcare and increasing patient access to medical technology. AdvaMed also promotes policies that encourage high ethical standards, rapid product approvals, appropriate reimbursement and international market access. Its members-only publications include three alerts: the *Member Advisory Program (MAP) Alerts* to follow the latest payment policy changes; the *Technology and Regulatory News Alert* to stay informed about key FDA regulatory developments; and the *International News Alert* to monitor global medical technology sales and operations developments. By comparison, the Medical Device Manufacturers Association (MDMA) represents the interests of smaller, innovative medical technology companies through its advocacy and educational services. Its member-only publications include the *Weekly MDMA Update*, the *Monthly Member Services Newsletter* and the *MDMA Q Review*. The latter is a quarterly e-newsletter for the entrepreneurial medical device community that covers updates on legislative and regulatory developments, association news and members-only programs and events.

Two key associations in the clinical research area are the aforementioned ACRP and the Society of Clinical Research Associates (SoCRA). In addition to its free biweekly e-newsletter, ACRP publishes a bimonthly journal, *The Monitor*, featuring peer-reviewed articles, association news and a guide to certification preparation courses and exams available only to members. SoCRA, like ACRP, is dedicated to the continuing education and development of its members and publishes the *SoCRA Research Journal*, a members-only quarterly publication that contains scientific and professional articles; society news and events; and professional opportunities and services. Selected articles from past issues of the journal are available to the public on SoCRA's website.

Online Commercial and Government Databases
Commercial Databases—Regulatory Intelligence

A number of commercial, fee-based databases are available to support the regulatory professional's legislative tracking and regulatory analysis responsibilities. These tools are extremely valuable when used in conjunction with other sources of regulatory expertise, from networking with colleagues to contacting consultants and/or directly communicating with government agency authorities.

Tarius Regulatory Database, a fee-based subscription database service owned by the Danish publishing company, The Schultz Group, is included among these database providers. The Tarius database enables regulatory and quality professionals to stay informed about the latest legislative developments worldwide and to interpret regulations and guidelines applicable to global healthcare products. Tarius offers two types of products: customized regulatory and quality databases and predefined base modules on drugs and devices. The customized database solution prescreens data from multiple global government and legislative websites according to searches defined by a particular company or individual. The predefined drug and device modules, by comparison, contain continuously updated reference documents compiled from US and EU regulatory authorities and key international regulatory bodies. As part of its database subscription service, Tarius also offers users a complimentary daily electronic summary of published *FR* proposed rules, notices and regulations pertaining to CFR Titles 9, 21 and 40 relevant to drugs, biologics and devices. Other users may pay a nominal fee to subscribe.

Liquent's IDRAC is another fee-based global intelligence database of regulatory, legal and scientific information accessed by professionals who develop and register human drug and biologics products. As is true of Tarius, IDRAC frequently updates its documents and provides expert analyses on key regulatory topics for more than 60 countries. The database also provides excellent coverage of FDA Advisory Committee activities through its AdComm Bulletins, summaries of new pharmaceutical legislation and summary bases of approvals (SBAs). In addition, subscribers can choose to receive the *IDRAC Weekly Alert*, covering current global regulatory developments, or customize an email alert with saved queries structured to meet their own information preferences.

Wolters Kluwer's MediRegs is also a provider of healthcare research products and software solutions for regulatory professionals. Its healthcare compliance software and risk management solutions product, ComplyTrack Suite, enables risk and compliance professionals to restructure their compliance programs and risk management initiatives to achieve greater efficiency. Revenue Cycle Solutions software targets coding and reimbursement healthcare professionals while the Life Science Regulatory Solutions online portal supports regulatory compliance professionals in the pharmaceutical, device and food industries. US and European database resources include regulatory publications, policy manuals, guidance documents, commission reports and automatic updates from domestic and international regulatory bodies.

MediRegs' US-focused regulatory resources include the Pharmaceutical Regulation Suite and the Device Regulation Library. The Pharmaceutical Regulation Suite provides access to enforcement materials; Establishment Inspection Reports (EIRs), 483s and Warning Letters dating back to the 1970s; SBAs dating back to 1964; US Code and public law legislation; the CFR; the *FR* back to 1991; FDA and NIH manuals and guidelines; and *FOIA* logs. The Device Regulation Library also affords regulatory professionals access to enforcement materials and EIRs, 483s and Warning Letters, as well as establishment registration and product listings, premarket approval (PMA) summaries back to 1945 and FDA product safety information.

Founded in 1975, FOI Services Inc., is an additional source for *FOIA* documents. The FOI online library contains more than 150,000 FDA-related documents including: New Drug Application and Abbreviated New Drug Application approval letters; drug reviews; drug and biologics SBAs; dissolution reviews; device and biologics premarket notifications; 510(k)s; PMAs; device Summaries of Safety and Effectiveness; EIRs; 483s; company/FDA inspection correspondence; Warning Letters; Advisory Committee minutes; guidance manuals; internal FDA meetings; color and food additive petitions; and veterinary FOI summaries. *FOIA* documents may also be identified using the online commercial database, DIOGENES— FDA Regulatory Information Online. Available through the database vendor, The DIALOG Corporation, this resource provides data from FDA's Enforcement Reports, 510(k)s, PMAs, medical device reports (MDRs) and the new drug list. Clients can request documents not already available in FOI's library. This fee-based FDA document service offers an excellent path for professionals seeking essential competitive regulatory intelligence while wishing to be discreet about their research.

Commercial Databases—Business Intelligence

In addition to the regulatory intelligence tools available to support regulatory professionals' surveillance, analysis and strategic planning responsibilities, numerous commercial business intelligence databases may now be obtained to increase their understanding of industry competition. Originally, these resources were only accessible to professional information searchers, but now the databases are specifically designed for users without prior search experience.

It is currently possible to independently access these invaluable resources through company database subscriptions.

Infinata's BioPharm Insight, briefly mentioned earlier in the chapter, is a fee-based online database that provides global biotechnology and pharmaceutical industry competitive intelligence. This resource covers the entire drug product lifecycle from discovery and development through the drug approval stages, as well as licensing deals, pharmaceutical sales/projections, management contacts and medical devices. BioPharm Insight partners with Pharmawire journalists, a part of the Financial Times Group, to report on key items including drug pipelines; patent expirations and litigation issues; licensing pipelines; and merger and acquisition pipelines. The BioPharm Insight database consists of Pharmawire Intelligence, the Clinical Trials Network, drug profiles, drug forecasts and drug licensing deals. The BioPharm Devices database, in turn, affords users detailed coverage of the medical device pipeline. Each company profile contains a review of the organization and its markets; product forecasts and launches; manufacturing facilities; and key management contacts. Profiles of devices currently in distribution are also included in the database, as well as clinical trial and Investigational Device Exemption daily updates. And lastly, BioPharm Outsource is a database containing detailed profiles of contract service providers for the pharmaceutical and biotechnology industry.

Another pharmaceutical industry competitive intelligence resource is eKnowledgebase, an interactive online pharmaceutical database. eKnowledgebase is produced by Canon Communications Pharmaceutical Media Group, the publisher of the publications *MedAdNews*, *R&D Directions* and *Trend Reports*. This fee-based database provides extensive company coverage as well as pipeline information for each stage of a drug's development. eKnowledgebase is updated daily and contains more than 26,000 compounds in development and drugs currently on the market. A user can choose to subscribe to the entire eKnowledgebase database, or purchase either the Pipeline portion to search drugs in development or the Brands portion to search drugs on the market.

Informa Healthcare's Pharmaprojects database also serves as a valuable source of pharmaceutical intelligence. This tool tracks more than 36,500 drugs in active development with a drug, company and therapy profile for each. The drug profile contains product data including therapies and indications by phase; originator and licensees; chemical data and structure; clinical trials; pharmacologies; country information; licensing opportunities and more. The company profile consists of addresses; subsidiaries; overview of operations; financial results; joint ventures and agreements; a licensing contact; and a direct link to the corporate website. The therapy profile is comprised of incidence, prevalence and market data; trends and forthcoming events; pharmacological strategies in progress; and links to related websites. Pharmaprojects enables drug regulatory professionals to analyze competitor performance, review R&D pipeline data to assess trends, and evaluate potential business partnerships. Data sources include the companies themselves, Pharmaprojects' sister publication, *Scrip World Pharmaceutical News* and interviews with company personnel who attend global conferences.

Another Informa Healthcare product that contributes to the wealth of available pharmaceutical intelligence database resources is Pipeline. This database consists of all the novel drugs and formulations developed since 1980. These drugs are tracked throughout their product lifecycle and are kept in the database even if they fail at any stage. What makes Pipeline unique is that it not only affords web-based access to an unlimited number of employees under one site license, but also includes free, unlimited research support from expert analysts and free training. Regulatory professionals can use this global drug resource to monitor competitors' R&D programs, discover new competitors, evaluate the competitive landscape for a specific drug, benchmark product performance, and identify potential collaborators.

Elsevier's PharmaPendium database, by comparison, provides drug safety data on FDA-approved drugs. This online resource affords researchers searchable access using the *Medical Dictionary for Regulatory Activities* search terminology. It also incorporates animal and human study data from FDA's Adverse Events Reporting System (AERS); drug monographs from *Mosby's Drug Consult; Meyler's Side Effect of Drugs*; preclinical, clinical and postmarket data from FDA approval packages/SBAs; Registry for Toxic Effects of Chemical Substances toxicity data; and metabolite data for approved drugs. Regulatory professionals can use this database to obtain pharmacovigilance data to evaluate the full scope of projected risks early in the drug development process.

While the pharmaceutical intelligence databases discussed earlier focus on drug pipelines and R&D data, Life Science Analytics' MedTRACK concentrates on worldwide private and public biomedical company intelligence data. MedTRACK's key areas of focus are company profiles and financials, product data, R&D spending, patents, corporate deals, venture financing, industry statistics and epidemiology.

Clinical trial surveillance information is also accessible through Citeline's TrialTrove. This database contains a comprehensive repository of global ongoing clinical trials information. Clinical and regulatory professionals have access to competitive trial information organized by 90 disease groups through analyst monitoring of more than 12,000 data sources. As is true of the Pipeline database product, TrialTrove offers users a research support service with direct access to Citeline analysts for no extra charge.

Government Databases—Legislative and Regulatory Tracking

An integral component of a regulatory professional's work is to stay informed about the latest regulatory and legislative developments. The resources reviewed in this section highlight noteworthy governmental and nongovernmental database tools to support these monitoring and surveillance responsibilities. GPO Access, discussed at the beginning of this chapter, operates within the GPO to provide electronic access to legislative reference tools. The *FR*, published by the Office of the Federal Register, National Archives and Records Administration, serves as the official daily publication for rules, proposed rules, executive orders, presidential documents and federal agency and organization notices. The *FR* volume for 2011 is Volume 76 and it may be searched separately or in conjunction with prior years dating back to 1994, Volume 59. Users may also sign up for a free daily email containing the *FR* table of contents. The CFR codifies the general and permanent rules published in the *FR*. The CFR is divided into 50 titles representing broad areas subject to federal regulation. Each CFR volume is updated once a year and issued quarterly. Titles are divided into chapters, usually bearing the issuing agency's name. Chapters, in turn, are subdivided into parts covering specific regulatory areas (e.g., 21 CFR 316.24 = Title 21—Food and Drugs; Part 316—Orphan Drugs; Chapter—Granting orphan-drug designation). Some CFR records on GPO Access date back to 1996; all titles are available from 1997 to the current year. Documents are available as ASCII text and PDF files.[4] In addition to the *FR* and CFR, GPO Access contains links to numerous searchable databases including Congressional bills, the *Congressional Record*, the US Code, statutes at large and public and private laws.

Unveiled in 1995, the Library of Congress' THOMAS database was created at the direction of the 104th Congress to make federal legislation publicly available. THOMAS offers a vast range of government resources including databases to search bill resolutions; bill and amendment summaries; bills across multiple Congresses; public laws searchable by number; House and Senate roll call votes; legislation by sponsor; Congressional activity databases; the *Congressional Record;* days-in-session calendars; committee reports; and treaties. GovTrack.us, an independent, nonpartisan, noncommercial and open-source website launched in September 2004, provides access to some of the same tools available on THOMAS and GPO Access. This website is an extremely useful tool for regulatory professionals who need to monitor the status of federal legislation or Congressional events. Users can subscribe to RSS feeds (commonly referred to as really simple syndication) throughout the site or use trackers to create customized feeds and receive email updates. RSS feeds are a family of Internet feed formats used to publish frequently updated

Table 33-1. Publisher Resources

Publisher	Website	Resources
AdvaMed	www.advamed.org/MemberPortal/	News Alerts (Fee-based)
American Society for Quality (ASQ Press)	http://asq.org/quality-press/	Books, Standards, Training Materials & Journals
American Society of Testing and Materials (ASTM)	www.astm.org/Standard/books_journals.shtml	Books, Standards, Technical Publications, Manuals, Handbooks, Journals
Aspen Publishers	www.aspenpublishers.com	Books, Journals & Newsletters (Fee-based)
Association of Clinical Research Professionals ACRP)	www.acrpnet.org/	Newsletters (Free)
Barnett International	www.barnettinternational.com/EducationalServices/Publications.aspx	Books, Reference Manuals & Compendiums
Bureau of National Affairs (BNA)	www.bna.com/products/books.htm	Books, Directories & Handbooks
Canon Communications	www.ubmcanon.com/products/publications	Newsletters (Free)
Canon Communications Pharmaceutical Media Group	https://eforms.kmpsgroup.com/paidpub/pharmalive_signup.aspx	Newsletters (Free & Fee-based)
CRC Online Press	www.crcpress.com	Books & Journals
Donawa Consulting	www.donawa.com/	Newsletters (Free)
Drug Information Association (DIA)	www.diahome.org/en/Resources/Publications/AboutPublications	Directories, Compilations, Journals & Newsletters (Fee-based)
DRW Research & Information Services	www.drw-research.com/index.htm	Newsletters (Free)
Elsevier Business Intelligence	www.elsevierbi.com/index.html www.biopharmatoday.com/	Newsletters (Free & Fee-based)
FDAnews	www.fdanews.com/	Books, White Papers & Newsletters (Free & Fee-based)
Ferdic Inc.	www.fdareview.com/	Newsletters (Fee-based)
FierceMarkets	www.fiercemarkets.com/advertise/publications	Newsletters (Free)
Food and Drug Law Institute (FDLI)	www.fdli.org/	Books, Directories, White Papers, CDs & Journals & Newsletters (Free & Fee-based)
Global Regulatory Press	www.globalregulatorypress.com/	Newsletters (Fee-based)
GMP Publications	www.gmppublications.com/	Books, Handbooks & Manuals
Government Printing Office (GPO)	http://bookstore.gpo.gov/	Books, Handbooks, Manuals, Guides, Journals & Newsletters (Fee-based)
Infinata	http://www.biopharminsight.com/company/press.html	Newsletter (Free)
Informa Healthcare	http://informahealthcare.com/action/showPublications?display=bySubject&category=area-regulatory	Newsletters (Fee-based)
Institute for Electrical and Electronics Engineers (IEEE)	www.ieee.org/index.html	Books, Standards, Conference Proceedings & Journals

International Organization for Standardization (ISO)	www.iso.org/iso/home.htm	Standards, Handbooks, CDs & Journals
John Wiley & Sons	www.wiley.com/WileyCDA/	Books & Journals
Lippincott Williams & Wilkins	www.lww.com/	Books, Journals & Newsletters (Fee-based)
Majors.com	www.majors.com	Books
Medical Device Manufacturers Association (MDMA)	www.medicaldevices.org/	Newsletters (Fee-based)
Medtech Insight	www.medtechinsight.com	Newsletters (Fee-based)
NRI Digital	www.pharmaceutical-technology.com/reg.html	Newsletters (Free)
Parenteral Drug Association (PDA)	www.pda.org	Books, Handbooks, Technical Bulletins, CDs & Journals
Piribo	www.urchpublishing.com/publications/regulatory/index.html	Market Reports
Regulatory Affairs Professionals Society (RAPS)	www.raps.org	Books, Journals, CDs & Newsletters (Fee-based)
SmartBrief	www.smartbrief.com/index.jsp	Newsletters (Free)
Society of Clinical Research Associates (SoCRA)	www.socra.org/	Journals
Springer	www.springer.com	Books, Handbooks & Journals
Thompson Publishers	www.thompson.com/public/library.jsp?cat=FOODDRUG	Books, Reports, CDs & Newsletters (Fee-based)
The Organisation for Professionals in Regulatory Affairs (TOPRA)	www.topra.org/TOPRA-Publishing	Newsletters (Fee-based)
Tradepub.com	http://thefreesite.tradepub.com/category/healthcare-and-medical/1205/	Newsletters (Free)
United States Pharmacopeia (USP)	www.usp.org	Books, Compendiums, & Standards
VirSci Corporation	www.virsci.com/pharmamarketing.html	Newsletters (Free)
Note! Website URLs are current at time of publication.		

works—such as blog entries, news headlines, audio and video—in a standardized format.[5]

Government Databases—Federal Agency Resources

In addition to the legislative and regulatory tracking databases discussed previously, many federal agencies have built their own specialized databases to monitor specific regulatory issues and provide public access to biomedical, clinical and other useful government resources. This section focuses primarily on the databases created within FDA's centers. The Center for Drug Evaluation and Research (CDER) and the Center for Devices and Radiological Health (CDRH) have developed the largest number of database systems, with some overlap between CDER and the Center for Biologics Evaluation and Research (CBER). The Center

for Veterinary Medicine (CVM) and the Center for Food Safety and Applied Nutrition (CFSAN) have also developed some unique databases. Due to chapter length constraints, however, this summary will review only selected center databases. A comprehensive list of all the agency's databases and corresponding website addresses is provided in **Table 33-1**.

CDER and CBER share the responsibility for reviewing postmarket safety reports submitted to the Adverse Event Reporting System (AERS), a database containing voluntarily submitted reports on approved drugs or therapeutic biologics products. CBER's other database systems include one for storing incoming Biological Product Deviation Reports and a Vaccine Adverse Event Reporting System (VAERS). Like the AERS database, VAERS is based on a cooperative agency program between CBER and the Centers for Disease Control (CDC) to address vaccine safety.

Two of CDER's most heavily searched databases focus on drug product approvals: the Approved Drug Products with Therapeutic Equivalence Evaluations (*Orange Book*) database, which lists drugs approved on the basis of safety and effectiveness, and the Drugs@FDA database, a searchable catalog of brand-name and generic prescription and OTC human drugs and biological therapeutic products approved since 1939. Drug manufacturing firms are required to register their sites with Drugs@FDA within five days of commercial distribution and re-register annually at the Drug Firm Annual Registration Status database. The National Drug Code Directory is a database of marketed prescription drugs listed by universal product identifiers. CDER's two clinically oriented databases are the Bioresearch Monitoring Information System, which identifies personnel engaged in Investigational New Drug (IND) studies, and the Clinical Investigator Inspection List, which contains data relevant to IND studies gathered by clinical investigator inspections.

CDRH has built and maintains more than 17 databases to monitor medical device and radiological products. Its 510(k) Premarket Notification (PMN) database, which contains releasable 510(k)s, and its Premarket Approval (PMA) database, which provides manufacturer premarket approval status, are critical tools for device regulatory professionals. CDRH has also developed two adverse event reporting systems similar to CDER's AERS database: the MAUDE (Manufacturer and User Facility Device Experience) database and the Medical Device Reporting (MDR) (formerly CDRH's Device Experience Network) database. MAUDE presents voluntarily submitted user facility medical device adverse event reports since 1991, distributor reports since 1993 and manufacturer reports since 1996. MDR data consist of reports on devices that may have malfunctioned or caused a death or serious injury from 1984–96, when it was replaced by MAUDE. Other noteworthy CDRH databases include the Advisory Committee/Panel Meetings database containing both information about upcoming meetings and historical information with links to summaries and/or transcripts of recent past meetings; the *Clinical Laboratory Improvement Amendments* (*CLIA*) database, which represents commercially marketed FDA- and CDC-categorized in vitro diagnostic test systems; and the Establishment Registration database, which comprises domestic establishments engaged in the manufacture, preparation, propagation, compounding, assembly or processing of medical devices intended for human use and commercial distribution. CVM's Animal Drugs@FDA is comparable to CDER's Drugs@FDA and CDRH's 510(k) and PMA databases. This database allows users to search for approved animal drug products, suitability petitions, sponsors, the *Green Book*, CFR, *FR*, patents and exclusivity. In addition, FDA maintains its own Warning Letter database through its FOI office. The Warning Letter collection covers documents issued from November 1996 to the present. The database can be searched by company, subject, issuing office or date.

In addition to the regulatory information available through FDA's databases, regulatory professionals requiring biomedical research can access PubMed, the National Library of Medicine's (NLM) biomedical database, which includes more than 18 million citations from MEDLINE and other life science journals dating back to 1948.[6] NLM also produces TOXNET, the toxicology data network, which consists of databases on toxicology, hazardous chemicals, environmental health and toxic releases. For molecular biology information, NLM's National Center for Biotechnology Information (NCBI) offers a comprehensive resource. Established in 1988, NCBI has created numerous public databases covering genetic sequencing and molecular processes affecting human health and disease, and has developed software tools for analyzing genome data. Lastly, the National Institutes of Health's (NIH) ClinicalTrials.gov site contains current information to identify federally and privately supported clinical trials for a range of diseases and conditions. The database includes 104,582 trials sponsored by NIH, other federal agencies and private industry conducted in all 50 states and 165 countries.[7]

A few additional recommended federal databases are the Forms Catalog and RegInfo.gov. Branded as "the US government's official hub for federal forms," the Forms Catalog contains many, though not all, of the citizen and business forms issued by federal agencies. Forms may be searched by agency, agency list or form number, and are alphabetically listed by form name or keyword. A direct link to forms published on specific agency websites is also available if the form being searched is not available through the Forms Catalog. The Office of Management and Budget (OMB) and the General Services Administration (GSA), in turn, jointly produce RegInfo.gov. This website contains a catalog searchable by government agency to locate all the regulatory reviews conducted by OMB's Office of Information and Regulatory Affairs (OIRA). It also has a catalog of the GSA's Regulatory Information Service Center's (RISC) semiannually published *Unified Agenda of Federal Regulatory and Deregulatory Actions* dating back to late 1995. The *Regulatory Plan* is part of the fall edition of the *Unified Agenda*. The *Regulatory Plan* serves as a defining statement of the administration's regulatory and deregulatory policies and priorities, while the *Unified Agenda* provides information about regulations that the government is considering or reviewing. RISC is responsible for gathering and publishing information on federal regulations through the semiannual *Unified Agenda of Federal Regulatory and Deregulatory Actions* and the annual *Regulatory Plan*, both required by Executive Order 12866, "Regulatory Planning and Review." The same executive order mandates that OIRA review federal regulations and information collections. OIRA also develops and oversees the implementation of government-wide policies on information technology, information quality, privacy and statistics.[8]

Reginfo.gov also provides links to several other government resources that will be briefly mentioned in this section. The first is USA.gov, the government's official portal to federal agency websites and information. This website is the product of an interagency initiative administered by the GAO's Office of Citizen Services and Communications. It provides a centralized database to locate information on US local, state and federal government agency websites. Regulations.gov is another resource that is linkable from Reginfo.gov's website. It is an extremely valuable tool for locating government agency regulations, rulemakings or notices, and is also useful for finding, submitting and obtaining public comments on proposed *FR* regulations. In addition, a comment can be submitted directly via the website by accessing documents that are still open for public comment. Business.gov, the US government's official website for small businesses, is the final website to be reviewed as a link from Reginfo.gov. This resource provides information on regulatory compliance and other information for small business owners. Managed as a partnership by 22 government agencies, Business.gov offers a wealth of information on regulatory compliance, legal issues surrounding running a business and registration, license and permit requirements. For example, a pharmaceutical or biotech small business can click on the industry link and find a page dedicated to providing information on complying with laws and regulations applicable to producers, distributors and marketers of human and veterinary drugs, medicines, biologics, medical devices and equipment and controlled substances.

Government Resources Related to Healthcare Product Regulation

The previous section reviewed federal agency databases useful for legislative tracking and healthcare product approval review and reporting. This section features government agency websites that offer additional healthcare product regulatory information.

US Government Agencies

In addition to FDA's wealth of databases, the agency, to its credit, provides users with many handy navigational tools to obtain information from its website. Upon launching the agency's homepage, users are introduced to numerous ways to access information, from using the search box highlighted in blue at the top of the page to browsing the A–Z Index listed directly below. Moreover, users can select one of the broad subject categories (food, drugs, medical devices, biologics/blood/vaccines, animal/veterinary, cosmetics, radiation-emitting products and tobacco products) listed on the left-hand side of the page to be directed to an agency center or office. Within each

of these links, additional navigational tools are provided to locate information. CDER's homepage offers the latest news and events, featured links, quick links to frequently searched topics including emergency preparedness; drug approvals and databases; drug safety and availability; development and approval process; guidance, compliance and regulatory information; science and research; and resources for consumers. CBER offers similar choices through its links to current news, key center categories, hot topics, general CBER information, useful government sites, a search box and the CBER alphabetical topic index. CDRH provides links to products and medical procedures; medical device safety; device advice; device regulation and guidance; science and research; resources for consumers; and highlighted news and events. CFSAN supplies links to featured news and events; links to cosmetics labeling and labeling claims; guidance, compliance and regulatory information; international activities; product and ingredient safety; and resources for consumers. CVM also presents featured news and events along with links to key topics related to the center including the development and approval process; guidance, compliance and enforcement; products; resources for consumers; safety and health; and science and research. Tobacco Products is the final main category listed on FDA's homepage, and the office's website follows a format comparable to the previously described centers. In addition to current news and events, the Tobacco Products webpage includes links to guidance, compliance and regulatory information; labeling; information on protecting kids from tobacco; and resources for consumers.

A few other particularly helpful resources within the FDA website are the Regulatory Information and the Office of Combination Products (OCP) pages. The Regulatory Information page covers key legislation; rules and regulations, guidances, docket management and freedom of information. The freedom of information page contains links to frequently asked questions; how to make a *Freedom of Information Act (FOIA)* request; *FOIA* fees; online payments; an electronic reading room; annual reports; the *Privacy Act;* reference materials; and contacts and links to other *FOIA* requester centers within the US Department of Health and Human Services (DHHS). The OCP website plays a role in all of the centers in which combination products are reviewed. Its links are designed to assist users in defining their own products. Consequently, the links include classification and jurisdictional information; request for designation process; guidance and regulatory information; requests for comment; and meetings, conferences and workshops.

DHHS is the US federal agency whose mission is to protect the health of all US citizens and provide essential human services. The office of the secretary and its subdivisions carry out DHHS' initiatives while 11 operating agencies perform a broad range of tasks and services, from conducting research and ensuring food and drug safety to

Table 33-2. Commercial and Government Databases

	Website	Subject Coverage
Commercial		
BioPharm Insight	www.biopharminsight.com/	Drug/Biotech & Device Business & Regulatory Intelligence
e-Knowledgebase	www.pharmalive.com/content/neweKB/	Drug/Biotech Business & Regulatory Intelligence
FOI Services	www.foiservices.com	Regulatory Intelligence
IDRAC	www.idrac.com/FrontPage.aspx	Drug/Biotech Regulatory Intelligence
MediRegs	www.mediregs.com	Regulatory Intelligence
MedTRACK	www.medtrack.com/research/default.asp	Drug/Biotech Business Intelligence
Pharmaprojects	www.pharmaprojects.com	Business & Regulatory Intelligence
Pipeline	sites.informahealthcare.com/pipeline/	Drug/Biotech Business Intelligence
Tarius	www.tarius.com	Drug/Biotech & Device Regulatory Intelligence
TrialTrove	www.citeline.com/products/trialtrove/overview/	Drug/Biotech Clinical Trial Intelligence
Government		
Business.gov	www.sba.gov/	Federal Agency Information Portal for Small Businesses
Code of Federal Regulations (CFR)	www.gpoaccess.gov/cfr/index.html	Drug/Biotech & Device Regulatory & Legislative Intelligence
Forms Catalog	http://search.usa.gov/forms?locale=en&m=false	Federal Agency Form Resource
Federal Register (FR)	www.gpoaccess.gov/fr/index.html	Drug/Biotech & Device Regulatory & Legislative Intelligence
FDA Warning Letter Database	www.fda.gov/ICECI/EnforcementActions/WarningLetters/default.htm	Drug/Biologics & Device Regulatory Intelligence
FDA/CBER On-Line: Establishment Registration & Biological Product Deviation Reporting	https://www.accessdata.fda.gov/scripts/cber/CFApps/Login/Index.cfm?CFID=19739204&CFTOKEN=4b5801a44b35d755-36EF1D27-1372-5AE1-6AA44EA2CBE290EA	Biologics/Biotech Regulatory Intelligence
FDA/CBER Vaccine Adverse Event Reporting System (VAERS)	http://vaers.hhs.gov/index	Biologics/Biotech Regulatory Intelligence
FDA/CDER Adverse Event Reporting System (AERS)	www.fda.gov/Drugs/GuidanceComplianceRegulatoryInformation/Surveillance/AdverseDrugEffects/default.htm	Drug/Biologics Regulatory Intelligence
FDA/CDER Approved Drug Products with Therapeutic Equivalence Evaluations (Orange Book) Database	www.accessdata.fda.gov/scripts/cder/ob/default.cfm	Drug/Biologics Regulatory Intelligence
FDA/CDER Bioresearch Monitoring Information System (BMIS)	www.accessdata.fda.gov/scripts/cder/bmis/	Drug/Biologics Regulatory Intelligence
FDA/CDER Clinical Investigator Inspection List	www.accessdata.fda.gov/scripts/cder/cliil/	Drug Regulatory Intelligence
FDA/CDER Drug Firm Annual Registration Status Database	www.accessdata.fda.gov/scripts/cder/drls/default.cfm	Drug/Biologics Regulatory Intelligence
FDA/CDER Drugs@FDA Database	www.fda.gov/Drugs/InformationOnDrugs/ucm135821.htm	Drugs/Biologics Regulatory Intelligence

FDA/CDER National Drug Code Directory	www.accessdata.fda.gov/scripts/cder/ndc/default.cfm	Drugs Regulatory Intelligence
FDA/CDRH Advisory Meeting Materials Archive	www.accessdata.fda.gov/scripts/cdrh/cfdocs/ cfAdvisory/search.cfm	Device Regulatory Intelligence
FDA/CDRH Clinical Laboratory Improvement Amendments (CLIA) Database	www.accessdata.fda.gov/scripts/cdrh/cfdocs/cfCLIA/ clia.cfm	Device Regulatory Intelligence
FDA/CDRH MAUDE (Manufacturer and User Facility Device Experience) Database	www.accessdata.fda.gov/scripts/cdrh/cfdocs/cfMAUDE/ search.CFM	Device Regulatory Intelligence
FDA/CDRH Medical Device Reporting (MDR) Database	www.accessdata.fda.gov/scripts/cdrh/cfdocs/cfmdr/ search.CFM	Device Regulatory Intelligence
FDA/CDRH Premarket Approval (PMA) Database	www.accessdata.fda.gov/scripts/cdrh/cfdocs/cfPMA/ pma.cfm	Device Regulatory Intelligence
FDA/CVM Animal Drugs@FDA Database	www.accessdata.fda.gov/scripts/animaldrugsatfda/	Drug Regulatory Intelligence
GovTrack.us	www.govtrack.us/	Drug/Biotech & Device Regulatory & Legislative Intelligence
GPO Access	www.gpoaccess.gov	Drug/Biotech & Device Regulatory & Legislative Intelligence
NIH ClinicalTrials.gov	http://clinicaltrials.gov/	Clinical Research
NLM—PubMed	www.ncbi.nlm.nih.gov/pubmed	Biomedical research
NLM—TOXNET	http://toxnet.nlm.nih.gov/	Biomedical/Toxicological Research
OMB/GSA RegInfo.gov	www.reginfo.gov/public/	OMB Regulatory Reviews/GSA Regulatory & Deregulatory Actions
Regulations.gov	www.regulations.gov/#!home	Federal Agency Published Regulations & Public Comments
Thomas	http://thomas.loc.gov/	Drug/Biotech & Device Regulatory & Legislative Intelligence
USA.gov	www.usa.gov/	Federal Agency Information Portal

Note: Website URLs are current at time of publication.

funding grants and programs and managing health insurance. The specific operating agencies are: the Administration for Children and Families, the Administration on Aging, the Agency for Healthcare Research and Quality (AHRQ), the Agency for Toxic Substances and Disease Registry, the Center for Medicare & Medicaid Services, CDC, FDA, the Health Resources and Services Administration, the Indian Health Service, NIH and the Substance Abuse and Mental Health Services Administration. Due to chapter length limits, the DHHS operating agencies other than FDA are not discussed in detail. However, they are listed with their corresponding website addresses in **Table 33-2**.

An especially valuable feature of the DHHS website is the ability to subscribe to multiple DHHS and partnering agency publications with a single email address. Once a user selects the Email Updates envelope icon at the top of the page and enters the appropriate email address, he or she can check the boxes next to all preferred publications. These preferences will then be forwarded to the appropriate agencies within DHHS. The partnering agencies that list publications are the National Institute of Allergy and Infectious Diseases, AHRQ, CDC, FDA, Disabilityinfo. gov, the Department of Defense Military Health System,

the President's Malaria Initiative and USAID Health.

It is also worth mentioning a few other government agency websites that are helpful to professionals conducting healthcare product regulatory reviews and designing strategic product development plans. The first is the US Environmental Protection Agency, which examines the potential environmental, chemical and medical waste regulatory concerns related to developing various healthcare products. The second is the US Federal Trade Commission (FTC), which addresses issues related to enforcing appropriate business competition and monitoring anticompetitive practices. The FTC's Bureau of Consumer Protection is specifically responsible for handling fraudulent and dishonest consumer protection activities, which encompass advertising and e-commerce oversight. Advertising and consumer safety are also key priorities for healthcare product regulatory professionals. The US Consumer Product Safety Commission (CPSC) is another agency that deeply impacts a regulatory professional's product development decisions. CPSC's primary mission is to protect the public from unreasonable risks of injury or death from a broad range of consumer products. For example, its poison prevention packaging standards and testing procedures, as

Table 33-3. Agencies Associated With Healthcare Product Regulation

Agency	Website	Subject Coverage
Consumer Product Safety Commission	www.cpsc.gov/	Poisoning, Packaging, Labeling, Prescription/OTC Drug Products
Environmental Protection Agency	www.epa.gov/	Environment & Public Health, Chemicals, Air Pollutants, Medical Waste
Federal Trade Commission	www.ftc.gov/	Business Competition & Consumer Protection
Food & Drug Administration (FDA)	www.fda.gov	Food, Drugs, Medical Devices, Biologics/Blood & Vaccines, Animal & Veterinary, Cosmetics, Radiation-Emitting Products, Combination Products
CBER	www.fda.gov/BiologicsBloodVaccines/default.htm	
CDER	www.fda.gov/Drugs/default.htm	
CDRH	www.fda.gov/MedicalDevices/default.htm	
CFSAN	www.fda.gov/Food/default.htm	
CVM	www.fda.gov/AnimalVeterinary/default.htm	
OCP	www.fda.gov/CombinationProducts/default.htm	
FOIA Reading Room	www.fda.gov/RegulatoryInformation/foi/default.htm	
Information for the FDA-Regulated Industry	www.fda.gov/ForIndustry/default.htm	
Department of Health & Human Services (DHHS)	www.hhs.gov	Public Health, Food & Drug Safety, Grants & Funding, Research, Health Insurance
Administration for Children & Families	www.acf.hhs.gov/	
Administration on Aging	www.aoa.gov/	
Agency for Healthcare Research & Quality	www.ahrq.gov/	
Agency for Toxic Substances & Disease Registry	www.atsdr.cdc.gov/	
Centers for Disease Control & Prevention	www.cdc.gov/	
Centers for Medicare & Medicaid Services	www.cms.gov/	
Health Resources & Services Administration	www.hrsa.gov/	
Indian Health Service	www.ihs.gov/	
National Institutes of Health	www.nih.gov/	
Substance Abuse & Mental Health Services Administration	www.samhsa.gov/	
Global Harmonization Task Force (GHTF)	www.ghtf.org/	Medical Devices
International Conference on Harmonisation of Technical Requirements for Registration of Pharmaceuticals for Human Use	www.ich.org	Drugs & Biologics
World Health Organization (WHO)	www.who.int	Public Health, Drugs & Biologics
WHO Biologicals Program	www.who.int/biologicals/en	
WHO Essential Medicines & Pharmaceutical Policies	www.who.int/medicines/about/en/index.html	

Note: Website URLs are current at time of publication.

well as its child-resistant and senior-friendly packaging guidelines, determine how OTC and prescription drugs and physician samples must be packaged. Although a regulatory professional's decision making process is shaped by several other federal agency regulations and guidelines, this chapter will not go into detail about these governmental bodies. However, an in-depth and instructive discussion on this subject appears in a 2007 *Regulatory Focus* article by Novales-Li and Temple.[9]

Global Organizations

Although this chapter centers on US regulatory information resources, a few global organizations are too important to overlook given the critical role the US plays within each of these groups. The International Conference on Harmonisation (ICH) is one of these global bodies. ICH brings together the regulatory bodies of the EU, US and Japan and experts from the pharmaceutical industry in the three regions to discuss scientific and technical aspects of product registration.[10] The organization's safety, efficacy, quality and multidisciplinary guidelines are indispensable to pharmaceutical regulatory professionals as they evaluate proposed products to ensure regulatory compliance.

The Global Harmonization Task Force (GHTF) is another international organization in which US regulatory representatives actively participate. GHTF is a partnership between national medical device regulatory authorities and the regulated industry and is composed of five founding members: the EU, the US, Canada, Australia and Japan. Established in 1992, the organization aims to harmonize regulatory practices that will ensure the safety, effectiveness, performance and quality of medical devices, promote technological innovation and facilitate international trade.[11] These harmonized practices are incorporated and disseminated through documents developed by five GHTF study groups. Medical device regulatory professionals review these documents as they evaluate device conformity assessment, quality management systems and postmarket surveillance issues surrounding their device products.

In March 2011, GHTF announced plans to reorganize. While details are limited at the time of publication, the intent is to develop a regulator-led harmonization and collaboration group that will allow for more detailed discussion between members on the optimum ways to achieve harmonization at an operational level.

The World Health Organization (WHO) is the final intergovernmental body to be considered in this section. WHO provides leadership on health matters, shapes the health research agenda, and sets norms and standards within the United Nations. The US actively participates in WHO activities, particularly within its Essential Medicines and Pharmaceutical Policies Department, which is involved in developing, implementing and monitoring national medicines policies and guidelines. Another WHO program in which the US participates is the Biologicals Program. The goal of this program is to ensure that national regulatory authorities implement effective systems to ensure the quality and safety of blood products and in vitro diagnostic devices. **Table 33-3** lists websites for these global organizations.

Industry Associations

Print and electronic publications, online commercial and government databases and other Internet-based government agency resources unquestionably have an integral place in a regulatory professional's work. These resources enable him or her to monitor the latest news, track the status and development of laws, regulations and guidelines, and engage in effective strategic product development. It is, however, industry associations that function as indispensable educational resources for regulatory professionals themselves. The organizations mentioned earlier in the chapter, including RAPS, DIA, TOPRA, BIO, AdvaMed, FDLI and ACRP, offer a broad variety of learning opportunities to their members. Regulatory professionals can initiate or update their knowledge of the healthcare industry and fulfill core competency requirements by participating in classroom and online courses, self-paced home study, audio and web-based training and certificate programs and attending workshops and conferences. In addition to offering formal learning options, associations enable professionals to engage in networking and to exchange information with their colleagues through forums and online communities.

Web 2.0 Tools

The second generation of Internet-based services, commonly referred to as Web 2.0, has enabled Internet users to participate in more dynamic and interactive information sharing. To complement the networking benefits of industry association memberships, regulatory professionals can now connect with colleagues through blogs and social networking websites. The rapidly growing number of blogs, or weblogs, which are regularly updated journal entries designed to be read by a professional audience and represent the unique personality of the author or website,[12] is remarkable. Some of the more popular blogs worth reviewing within the regulatory healthcare sector are: FDA Law Blog (Hyman, Phelps & McNamara PC); Biotech Blog; Eye on FDA (RX for Pharma Industry Communications and Planning); Medical Device and Diagnostic Industry (MDDI) blogs including Device Talk, Biomaterials Talk and Transforming FDA; HTA Blog (Health Technology Assessment); and Pharmalive Blogs including PharmaBlogReview, MedAdNewsInsider and R&D Directions Insider. This list does not begin to scratch the surface of the widely available information for this profession; however, it is a good starting point.

Social networking sites are another widely used Web 2.0 Internet service. Regulatory professionals can participate in sites such as LinkedIn, the Quality and Safety Regulatory Network, and reg-info.com, to establish a public professional profile, search for jobs, interact with colleagues, search for other regulatory professionals, review uploaded presentations and read member interviews. LinkedIn operates the world's largest professional network on the Internet with more than 90 million members in over 200 countries and territories.[13] Joining the network is free and simply requires the user to create a profile summarizing his or her professional experience and accomplishments. The information a user chooses to make publicly available can then be searched by other professionals within the LinkedIn network and used for the purpose of meeting and collaborating with other members. Similarly, the Quality and Safety Regulatory Network supports professionals working in quality assurance, regulatory affairs and compliance in highly regulated industries. This group was established to allow professionals to share experiences and expand their network of people and ideas in quality, regulatory, safety, health, sustainability, risk and compliance for continuous improvement across multiple industries.[14] Lastly, reg-info.com is another professional group created to allow pharmaceutical professionals to share ideas and initiate a forum for anything related to regulatory intelligence and information gathering. This community also assists pharmaceutical professionals in finding regulatory intelligence information through links to key regulatory and related information sources.[15]

Summary

This chapter has reviewed a wide range of print and electronic information resources and selected social networking tools available to regulatory professionals. From this review, it is clear that the wealth of publications, databases and government, association and industry web-based tools, as well as social networking opportunities that have sprouted up in just the past few decades is truly staggering. The new challenge for regulatory professionals is to distill the essential knowledge they require from the vast storehouse of information available to perform their jobs as effectively as possible. This will call for carefully managing electronic and print subscriptions, becoming skilled in using relevant government and industry databases, making use of associations' educational resources to advance professional knowledge and, finally, using social networking tools with discipline and discrimination. In this way, regulatory professionals will be certain to reap the greatest benefit from the abundant resources available, thereby increasing their productivity, effectiveness and overall expertise.

References

1. "About USP – An Overview." US Pharmacopeia. Available at www.usp.org/aboutUSP/. Accessed 9 May 2011.
2. "About GPO Access." GPO Access. Available at www.gpoaccess.gov/about/index.html. Accessed 9 May 2011.
3. "About Us." Piribo. Available at www.piribo.com/. Accessed 9 May 2011.
4. "Code of Federal Regulations (CFR) Main Page." GPO Access. Available at www.gpoaccess.gov/cfr/index.html. Accessed 9 May 2011.
5. "RSS." Wikipedia. Available at: http://en.wikipedia.org/wiki/RSS_(file_format). Accessed 9 May 2011.
6. "PubMed." NCBI. Available at: www.ncbi.nlm.nih.gov/pubmed/. Accessed 9 May 2011.
7. "About ClinTrials.gov." ClinTrials.gov. Available at http://clinicaltrials.gov/ct2/info/about. Accessed 9 May 2011.
8. "RegInfo.gov:Where to Federal Regulatory Information." RegInfo.gov. Available at www.reginfo.gov/public/. Accessed 9 May 2011.
9. Novales-Li P, Temple L. "Non-FDA Agencies Involved in US Healthcare Regulation." *Regulatory Affairs Focus.* Vol 12. No 8, pp 8-15 (August 2007).
10. "Welcome to the official website for ICH." ICH. Available at www.ich.org. Accessed 9 May 2011.
11. "About GHTF." Global Harmonization Task Force. Available from www.ghtf.org/about/. Accessed 9 May 2011.
12. "Glossary." bytown Internet. Available at www.bytowninternet.com/glossary. Accessed 9 May 2011.
13. "About Us." LinkedIn.com. Available at http://press.linkedin.com/about. Accessed 9 May 2011.
14. "Quality and Regulatory Network." Linkedin.com. Available at www.linkedin.com/groups?gid=80327&goback=%2Econ. Accessed 9 May 2011.
15. "reg-info.com–Regulatory intelligence for pharma." Linkedin.com. Available at http://www.linkedin.com/groups?home=&gid=833547&trk=anet_ug_hm&goback=%2Econ. Accessed 9 May 2011.

Comparative Matrix of Regulations Across Product Lines

FDA Centers		
	Source	**Centers**
Devices	www.fda.gov/MedicalDevices/default.htm	• Center for Devices and Radiological Health (CDRH) • Center for Biologics Evaluation and Research (CBER) for 510(k)s that involve blood and other biologics
Drugs	www.fda.gov/Drugs/default.htm	• Center for Drug Evaluation and Research (CDER)
Biologics	www.fda.gov/BiologicsBloodVaccines/default.htm	• Center for Biologics Evaluation and Research (CBER)
Veterinary	www.fda.gov/AnimalVeterinary/default.htm	• Center for Veterinary Medicine (CVM)
Foods	www.fda.gov/Food/default.htm	• Center for Food Safety and Applied Nutrition (CFSAN)
Tobacco	www.fda.gov/TobaccoProducts/default.htm	• Center for Tobacco Products (CTP)

FDA Requirements—Authority

	Acts
Devices	• *Pure Food and Drugs Act of 1906* • *Federal Food, Drug, and Cosmetic Act of 1938 (FD&C)* • *Fair Packaging and Labeling Act of 1966* • *Medical Device Amendments of 1976* • *Safe Medical Devices Act 1990 (SMDA)* • *Medical Device Amendments of 1992* • *Food and Drug Export Reform and Enhancement Act of 1996 (FDERA)* • *Food and Drug Administration Modernization Act of 1997 (FDAMA)* • *Medical Device User Fee and Modernization Act of 2002 (MDUFMA)* • *Food and Drug Administration Amendments Act of 2007 (FDAAA)*
Drugs	• *Pure Food and Drugs Act of 1906* • *Federal Food, Drug, and Cosmetic Act of 1938 (FD&C)* • *Fair Packaging and Labeling Act* • *Durham-Humphrey Amendment of 1951* • *Kefauver-Harris Drug Amendments of 1962* • *Orphan Drug Act of 1983* • *Drug Price Competition and Patent Term Restoration Act of 1984* • *Prescription Drug User Fee Act of 1992 (PDUFA)* • *Food and Drug Administration Modernization Act of 1997 (FDAMA)* • *Pediatric Research Equity Act (PREA) of 2003* • *Food and Drug Administration Amendments Act of 2007 (FDAAA)*
Biologics	• *Biologics Control Act* (also known as the *Virus-Toxin Act*) *of 1902* • *Federal Food, Drug, and Cosmetic Act of 1938 (FD&C)* • *Public Health Service Act of 1944* • *Food and Drug Administration Modernization Act of 1997 (FDAMA)* • *The Pediatric Research Equity Act (PREA) of 2003* • *Food and Drug Administration Amendments Act of 2007 (FDAAA)* • *Biologics Price Competition and Innovation Act of 2009*

Major Guidelines

	Source	Major Guidelines
Devices	www.fda.gov/MedicalDevices/DeviceRegulationandGuidance/GuidanceDocuments/default.htm	• Blue Book Memoranda • Write It Right • Premarket Approval Application (PMA), 510(k) and Investigational Device Exemption (IDE) preparation manuals • Medical Device Quality Systems Manual
	www.fda.gov/MedicalDevices/DeviceRegulationandGuidance/default.htm	• CDRH Device Advice website
Drugs	www.fda.gov/Drugs/GuidanceComplianceRegulatoryInformation/default.htm www.fda.gov/AboutFDA/CentersOffices/cder/ucm095412.htm	• Guidance documents • Guidelines • Manual of Policies & Procedures (CDER) • Current Good Manufacturing Practices (CGMP) for Drugs: Reports, Guidances and Additional Information
	www.ich.org/products/guidelines.html	International Conference on Harmonisation (ICH) Guidelines
Biologics	www.fda.gov/BiologicsBloodVaccines/GuidanceComplianceRegulatoryInformation/default.htm	• Guidance documents • Guidelines • ICH Guidelines • SOPPs • Other Recommendations - Points to Consider (PTC)

Strategies for Working with FDA

	Source	Acts
Devices	www.fda.gov/RegulatoryInformation/foi/default.htm	· Investigate predicate device history (if applicable) · Submissions conform to guidance documents and format requirements · Early and continuing communication · Answer questions asked · Comprehensive, complete, detailed submissions · Maintain credibility at all times · Take FDA seriously: Form 483s and Warning Letters · Negotiate; don't antagonize · Stay committed to internal audit programs and corrective action · Organized agendas, presentation, time for questions · Communicate often during the review process and document the communication · Use standardized test protocols as much as possible
Drugs	www.fda.gov/RegulatoryInformation/foi/default.htm	Same as Devices · Meetings with FDA at critical development time points: Phase I, End-of-Phase 2, Pre-New Drug Application (NDA) · Special Protocol Assessments · Small business user fee waiver · Accelerated approval for drugs for fast-track diseases
Biologics	www.fda.gov/RegulatoryInformation/foi/default.htm	Same as Devices and Drugs

Product License, Listing Requirements and Establishment Registration

	Source	Forms	Product Classification
Devices	21 CFR 807 21 CFR 807 21 CFR 860	2891 2891a 2892	• Initial establishment registration • Annual registration of device establishment (• Product listing • Device Classification: Class I, Class II or Class III • Combination Products (Device/Biologic or Device/Drug) Who must register: All owners/operators of any domestic establishment engaged in the manufacture, preparation, compounding or processing of a medical device; those who initiate and develop specifications, manufacture, repackage, relabel, restore and commercially distribute a device; and initial distributors (US agents of foreign manufacturers), but not domestic distributors. All registration and listing information (Annual, Initial or Updates) must be submitted electronically unless FDA grants a waiver.
Drugs	21 CFR 207 21 CFR 300 21 CFR 320 21 CFR 328-369 21 CFR 316	2656 2656e 2657 2658	• Drug establishment registration • Annual update of drug/biologic establishment • Drug product listing • Registered establishments' Reports of Private Label Distributors • Groups within FDA: topical, oncology, etc. • Prescription Drugs • Generic Drugs • Over-the-Counter Drugs • Orphan Drugs • Combination Products (Drug/Device or Drug/Biologic) Who must register: Unless specifically exempted by law or regulation, all establishments that manufacture or process drugs in the US are required to be registered with FDA and all drugs marketed within the US, including imported drugs, are required to be listed with the agency. All registration must be submitted electronically using the SPL format, unless FDA grants a waiver.

Biologics	21 CFR 207
	21 CFR 207
	21 CFR 207
	21 CFR 601
	21 CFR 607
	
	21 CFR 1271
		2656
		2656e
		2657
		
		2830
		
		3356
			• Establishment registration
			• Annual update of drug/biologic establishment
			• Drug product listing
			• Product licensing Biologics License Application (BLA)
			• Blood and blood product establishment registration and product listings
			• Combination products (biologic/device or biologic/drug)
			Who must register:
			  o All manufacturers of biological drug products
			  o All owners and operators of human blood and blood product establishments must register their establishment annually
			  o Human cells, tissue, and cellular and tissue-based product establishments
			
			All registration must be submitted electronically using the SPL format, unless FDA grants a waiver.

Premarket Approval Submissions

	Source	Forms	Premarket Approval (PMA) Submissions
Devices	21 CFR 814	None specified	**PMA Required for:** • Any Class III device that was not on the market prior to 28 May 1976 • Pre-1976 devices after FDA "calls" for PMA
			PMA Sections: • CDRH Submission Cover Sheet (optional) • Summary of submission • Indications for usc • Device description • Description of intended existing alternative practices and procedures for device • Description of marketing history (foreign) • Summary of nonclinical and clinical data • Discussion of safety and efficacy • Device Master Record • Performance standards • Technical section • Published and unpublished reports on device • Sample of device(s) • Proposed labeling • Environmental assessment • Financial Certification of Disclosure
			PMA Approval Criteria: Substantial evidence of safety and efficacy, which includes adequate and well-controlled investigations User fees apply to original PMAs and certain types of PMA supplements. Small businesses are eligible for reduced or waived fees
			Approval Time Frames: • 45-day administrative review preliminary to "filing" of PMA • Must be reviewed (initially) within 180 days after filing PMA
			Possible Outcomes: • Approval order, approvable letter, not approvable letter, order denying approval • Summary of safety and effectiveness (S&E) written with FDA approval for public dissemination

Drugs	21 CFR 314	356h	**NDA or Abbreviated New Drug Application (ANDA) Required for:**
			• Any new drug.
			  o A new drug is any drug that was not generally recognized as safe and effective before 1938
			• An approved drug may be considered a new drug if
			  o Contains a new substance (active ingredient, excipient, carrier, coating or other component)
			  o New combination of already approved drugs
			  o Proportion of ingredients has been changed
			  o New intended use of drug
			  o Dosage, method or duration of administration or application is changed

			ANDA versus NDA: The ANDA is an abbreviated new drug submission. The ANDA submission does not include preclinical (animal) and clinical (human) data to establish safety and effectiveness.
			NDA or ANDA Sections: • Summary volume • Chemistry, manufacturing and controls • Samples, methods validation and labeling • Nonclinical pharmacology and toxicology • Human pharmacokinetics and bioavailability • Microbiology • Clinical data • Statistical section

Premarket Approval Submissions cont'd

	Source	Forms	Premarket Approval (PMA) Submissions
			• Case reports and tabulations • Patent information • Patent certification • Debarment certification • Field copy certification
			Common Technical Document Sections: • Module 1: Regional information (forms, waivers, patent information, etc.) • Module 2: Table of Contents, Introduction, Quality Overall Summary, Nonclinical Overview and Summaries, Clinical Overview and Summary • Module 3: Quality • Module 4: Nonclinical Study Reports • Module 5: Clinical Study Reports (and ISS/ISE for US submissions) User fees are applicable for both NDAs and ANDAs A fee waiver or reduction for: • The first NDA of a small business • Applications for orphan products • Applications for drugs providing a benefit to public health, or applications where the fees constitute a barrier to innovation NDA may be submitted as paper or electronically Content of label must be submitted electronically in Structured Product Label (SPL) format
			NDA Approval Criteria: Substantial evidence of safety and efficacy, based on adequate and well-controlled investigations

			Approval Time Frames:
			• Within 60 days of receipt, FDA must determine whether an NDA can be filed
			• PDUFA review goals:
			  o Priority NDA: six months
			  o Standard NDA: 10 months

			Possible Outcomes: • Approval Letter • "Complete Response" letter that states the product is: approvable or not approved • Refusal to file letter • Notification that the application is withdrawn • Summary Basis of Approval (SBA) is available to public
Biologics	21 CFR 601	356h (prev. 3439)	**BLA:** Similar to NDA, filed for all biologics
	21 CFR 601.2		The following specified categories have modified requirements: • Therapeutic DNA plasmid products • Therapeutic synthetic peptides of 40 or fewer amino acids • Monoclonal antibodies for in vivo use • Therapeutic recombinant DNA-derived products
	21 CFR 601.25		User fees are applicable
			Approval Time Frames: Same as Drugs
			Possible Outcomes: same as Drugs

Premarket Notification Submission

	Source	Premarket Notification Submission

Devices	21 CFR 807, Subpart (e)	**510(k) Premarket Notification:**
		• Pertaining to Section 510(k) of *Medical Device Amendments* (1976) to *FD&C Act*
		• Preamendment devices on the market prior to 28 May 1976 are grandfathered
		• Required for devices introduced into commercial distribution after 28 May 1976 that have been classified as Class I or Class II devices when the device is:
		  o First introduced into market (not substantially equivalent to predecessor)
		  o Already marketed but introduced for the first time by manufacturer
		  o Already marketed but has a change or modification to the device that could significantly affect safety or effectiveness of the device such as changes in design, material, chemical composition, energy source, manufacturing process
		  o Has new intended use

	21 CFR 862–892	**Exemptions From Premarket Notification:** • Almost all Class I devices, except Restricted Devices • Many Class II devices • Custom devices (devices not commercially available and created for a specific patient, physician or dentist) • Distributors of 510(k)-cleared devices with written permission of the manufacturer or 510(k) holder • Initial postamendment distribution of a pre-1976 Class III device requires a 510(k)—until FDA calls for a PMA; the 510(k) must include Class III certification and summary of safety and effectiveness
		Substantial Equivalence (SE) compares a new device to a legally marketed "predicate" device. **Requirements:** • Same technological characteristics as predicate device or • Different technological characteristics but raises no new or different questions of safety or effectiveness and • Same intended use as predicate device
		510(k) Content/Format CDRH Submission Cover Sheet (Optional): • Trade, common or classification name • Establishment registration number of submitter • Device classification
	www.fda.gov/MedicalDevices/ DeviceRegulationandGuidance/ GuidanceDocuments/default. htm	**Application Contents:** • Proposed labeling (device description, specifications, intended use, directions for use) • Substantial equivalence information (comparison to predicate device) • Data demonstrating what effect modification or new intended use has on safety and effectiveness • 510(k) summary or statement
		Data Requirements: • The need for performance data depends on complexity of device and ability to demonstrate equivalence to predicate based on use and technological • FDA may require human clinical data in a 510(k) to demonstrate SE for certain high-risk devices
		***SMDA* Provisions:** • Manufacturer must receive written SE order before commercial distribution • 510(k) must include 510(k) summary or statement • Summaries and statements are made public 30 days after SE notice
		510(k) Review: • Review begins when CDRH logs in the submission • 90-day statutory requirement for FDA review (often exceeded) • Request for additional information puts submission on hold—30 days to respond—if no response; the 510(k) is withdrawn unless an extension is requested. The 90-day clock restarts when FDA receives additional data

Premarket Notification Submission

	Source	Premarket Notification Submission
		510(k) Paradigm: · Traditional 510(k): standard filing · Special 510(k): option where device modification does not affect its intended use · Abbreviated 510(k): alternative to traditional 510(k) where a guidance document exists that provides reasonable assurance that the device's safety and effectiveness have been established
		Possible Outcomes: · SE, NSE, request additional information, withhold decision until financial disclosure statement is submitted, advise the 510 (k) is not required · SE determination implies "clearance" to market device, not "approval" of device
Drugs		No comparable mechanism
Biologics		**510(k):** some products regulated by CBER are by definition "medical devices."
		Appropriate biologic "devices" are submitted as 510(k) to CBER.
		See Devices for procedure

Reporting/Recordkeeping Requirements for PMA, NDA or BLA Submissions and Application Maintenance and Changes

	Source	Forms	Reporting/Record Keeping Requirements
Devices	21 CFR 814		• *PMA Amendment* adds information or modifies a pending application: 　○ Resets 180-day "clock" for a major addition or change; and 　○ Includes additional voluntary information or additional information requested by FDA • *PMA Supplement* is used for changes or modifications to a PMA approved device: Normal 180-day review cycle • *Special PMA Supplement—Changes Being Effected* Limited supplement changes can be made once FDA has acknowledged the submission is being processed • *Alternate PMA Supplement (30-day):* FDA will have indicated that the alternate submission would be permitted (if information is insufficient, FDA will instruct the applicant what is needed and the supplement will become a 135-day supplement) • *Periodic Reports* are updates or changes post-approval, which do not affect S&E; submitted after approval letter, in annual report or as by FDA
Drugs	21 CFR 314.60 21 CFR 314.70	356h	• *NDA Amendment* adds information or modifies a pending application 　○ Extension of up to 180-day review clock for a major amendment 　○ Minor amendments do not extend the review time • NDA Supplements submit changes to an approved NDA • Manufacturing supplements/changes are submitted as: 　○ Changes requiring prior approval 　○ Changes Being Effected (CBE) 　○ Supplements (may be made before FDA approval) or 　○ Changes via Annual Report (minor changes)
	21 CFR 314.50 (d)(5)(vi)(b) 21 CFR 314.80 21 CFR 314.81 21 CFR 314.80 (c)(2)	3500A 2252	**Reporting:** • 120-day Safety Report Amendment: Due 120 days after NDA filing • Postmarketing 15-day Alert Report: (15 calendar days) for serious and unexpected adverse event • NDA Annual Report: 　○ Due within 60 days of anniversary of date of approval; 　○ Includes distribution data, labeling, CMC changes, nonclinical data and clinical data • NDA Field Alert: Three working days for failed batches, mistaken identification, contamination, etc • Periodic Adverse Drug Experience Reports: Quarterly for three years after approval and then annually
Biologics			Same as Drugs • Amendment: Submission of additional information to an unapproved license application • Supplement: Submission of changes to an approved license application • Manufacturing Supplement: Same as drugs • Biologics Deviation Report
	21 CFR 600.80	3500A VAERS-1	**Reporting:** • 15-day Alert Report (15 calendar days) for serious and unexpected adverse events • BLA/NDA Annual Reports
			• Periodic Adverse Experience/Event Reports: Quarterly for three years after approval and then annually
			• Distribution Reports: Quantity of product distributed in US; due every six months

Requirements and Submissions for Clinical Investigations

	Source	Forms	Requirements and Submissions for Clinical Investigations

Devices	21 CFR 812
	21 CFR 50
	21 CFR 56
		3674	• Investigational Device Exemptions (IDE)
			• Informed Consent
			• Institutional Review Board (IRB) Review and Approval of Protocol and Informed Consent
			• Good Clinical Practice (GCP)
			• An IDE permits a device to be shipped in Interstate commerce for clinical investigations to determine its safety and effectiveness. The IDE regulation exempts the device from:
			  ○ Misbranding and adulteration
			  ○ Establishment registration and device listing
			  ○ 510(k)/PMA
			  ○ Performance standards
			  ○ Banned devices
			  ○ Restricted devices
			  ○ QSRs/GMPs
			  ○ Records and reports
			All clinical investigations of devices to determine safety and effectiveness require an approved IDE (from IRB, or IRB and FDA, depending upon risk).

	21 CFR 812.2(b)		**IDE Time Frame:** FDA will review and approve, approve with modification or disapprove an IDE application within 30 days of receipt. Requirements vary based on risk level. The determination of significant risk versus nonsignificant risk is made by the sponsor and approved by the IRB, but may be decided by FDA.
			Nonsignificant Risk Device Studies Require: • An abbreviated IDE • IRB approval (IDE submission to FDA is not required) • Labeling: "CAUTION-Investigational Device. Limited by Federal (or US) Law to Investigational Use" • For IVDs: "For Investigational Use Only. The performance characteristics of this product have not been established."
	21 CFR 812.2(a)		**Significant Risk Device Studies Require:** • All of the requirements above for nonsignificant risk devices • IDE application and approval from FDA • Final report to FDA and IRB
	21 CFR 812.2(c)		**Exempted Investigations:** • IVDs if for laboratory research or if for human patients, provided a legally marketed IVD is used for confirmation • Custom devices • Devices shipped for animal research • Consumer preference testing if not for determining safety or efficacy • Devices intended for veterinary use only
	21 CFR 812.40-46 21 CFR 54.4		**Sponsor Responsibilities:** • Select qualified investigators • Control distribution of devices • Monitor studies • Ensure that investigator receives IRB approval • Submit IDE to FDA (if required)
	21 CFR 812.60-66 and 21 CFR 56 21 CFR 812.100		**IRB Responsibilities:** • Review and approve studies • Review and approval of informed consent • Protect the safety and welfare of subjects • Determine if the device is either significant or nonsignificant risk
	21 CFR 812.110 21 CFR 54.4		**Investigator Responsibilities:** • Get IRB approval before study • Conduct study per agreement • Follow protocol and FDA regulations • Control and supervise device use • Obtain informed consent

Requirements and Submissions for Clinical Investigations

	Source	Forms	Requirements and Submissions for Clinical Investigations
Drugs	21 CFR 312 21 CFR 50 21 CFR 56	1571 3674	· Investigational New Drug Application (IND) · Informed Consent · IRB Review and Approval of Protocol and Informed Consent · Good Clinical Practice (GCP) An IND is submitted to FDA for notification of the intention to conduct clinical studies with a new drug or biologic and to request an exemption for shipping unapproved drug or biologic. Required for new dosage form, new route of administration, new concentrations, new sponsor or manufacturer, or new indication.
	21 CFR 310 21 CFR 320		**IND Types:** · Commercial (routine) · Physician (Sponsor-Investigator) · Treatment · Emergency
			Important IND Sections: · Introductory statement · General investigational plan · Investigator's brochure · Protocol · CMC information · Pharmacology and toxicology · Previous human experience
			IND Time Frame: Effective in 30 days from FDA receipt unless clinical hold is placed on the study.
	21 CFR 312.50–53 and 21 CFR 54.4	1572	**Sponsor Responsibilities:** · Select qualified investigators · Obtain investigator records (including Statement of Investigator Protocol Signature Page, CVs, Financial Disclosure) · Control distribution of drugs · Monitor studies · Ensure that investigator receives IRB approval · Submit IND/Protocol to FDA (if required)
	21 CFR 56.108–110		**IRB Responsibilities:** · Review and approve studies · Review and approval of informed consent · Protect the safety and welfare of subjects · Ensure risk to subjects is minimized
	21 CFR 312.60		**Investigator Responsibilities:** Same as Devices
Biologics	21 CFR 312 21 CFR 50 21 CFR 56	1571 3674	· Investigational New Drug Application (IND) · Informed Consent · IRB Review and Approval of Protocol and Informed Consent · Good Clinical Practice (GCP)
			IND Time Frame: Same as Drugs
			Sponsor Responsibilities: Same as Drugs
			IRB Responsibilities: Same as Drugs
			Investigator Responsibilities: Same as Devices

Reporting/Recordkeeping Requirements for Clinical Investigations

	Source	Forms	Requirements and Submissions for Clinical Investigations

Devices	21 CFR 812.140		**Investigator Records:**
			· Correspondence
			· Device receipt, use, disposition
			· Subject records including
			   o Informed consent
			   o Adverse device effects
			   o Device exposure date and times
			   o Protocol and other records

	21 CFR 812.140		**Sponsor Records:** · NSR/SR decision · Correspondence · Device shipment and disposition · Investigator agreements and financial disclosure · Adverse device effects · Investigator list · IRB list and other records
	21 CFR 812.150		**Investigator Reports:** · Unanticipated Adverse Device Effects (10 working days) · Withdrawal of IRB approval · Progress reports · Deviations from investigational plan · Informed consent · Final report (due to sponsor and IRB within three months of study termination or completion)
	21 CFR 812.150		**Sponsor Reports:** · Unanticipated ADE (10 working days) · Withdrawal of IRB approval · Withdrawal of FDA approval · Current Investigator list · Progress reports · Recall and device disposition · Final report (for SR, notify FDA within 30 working days of the completion or termination and submit final report to FDA and all reviewing IRBs and investigators within six months. For NSR final report to all reviewing IRBs within six months.) · Significant risk determination
	21 CFR 812.140		**Record Retention:** For two years after the latter of · Date of study completion or termination or · Date that records are no longer needed to support a 510(k), PMA or notice of completion of a PDP

Drugs	21 CFR 312.62		**Investigator Records:**
			· Correspondence
			· Investigational drug receipt, use, disposition
			· Case histories
			   o Informed consent
			   o Source documentation (case report forms and medical records)
			   o Safety reports
			   o Protocol and other records
			   o Laboratory information

Reporting/Recordkeeping Requirements for Clinical Investigations

	Source	Forms	Requirements and Submissions for Clinical Investigations
	21 CFR 312.57		**Sponsor Records:** · Correspondence · Investigational drug shipment and disposition · Investigator agreements and financial disclosure · Protocol and amendments · Clinical study report and publications · Monitoring and safety reports (serious adverse events) · Investigator list · IRB list and other records · Decoding and randomization records (if applicable)
	21CFR 312.64		**Investigator Reports:** · Progress reports (to sponsor and IRB; at least annually) · Safety reports · Final report · Financial disclosure reports

	21 CFR 312.31
	
	21 CFR 312.32
	
	21 CFR 312.33
		1571
		3674
		
		1571
		3500A
		
		1571
			Sponsor Reports:
			· IND Amendments
			  o Amendments to an IND, such as new investigator or new information, must be submitted not more than every 30 days.
			· IND Safety Reports
			  o Telephone report - 7 calendar days (either by phone or fax)
			  o Unexpected fatal or life-threatening adverse experience (AE) associated with the use of the drug
			  o Written reports - 15 calendar days
			  o Serious and unexpected AE associated with the use of the drug
			· IND Annual Reports
			  o Must be submitted within 60 days of the anniversary date of when the IND became effective

	21 CFR 312.57 21 CFR 312.62		**Record Retention:** · Sponsor: two years after NDA approval or, if no application is to be filed or if the application is not approved for such indication, 2 years after the investigation is discontinued and FDA is notified. · Investigator: same as sponsor
Biologics			**Sponsor and Investigator Records:** Same as Drugs
			Reporting: Same as Drugs
			Record Retention: Same as Drugs

Labeling Requirements

	Source	Labeling Requirements
Devices	21 CFR 801	**General Requirements:** · Name and place of business · Intended use · Adequate directions (in layman terms) · Prominence of statements · English language (exceptions: product solely distributed in Puerto Rico or territories in which English is not the predominant language)
	21 CFR 809 16 CFR 1500	**IVD Labeling:** · Proprietary and established names · Intended use · Statement of warnings or precautions · Name and place of business of manufacturer, packer or distributor. · Lot or control number · For reagents, storage instructions, ingredients, and quantity of contents · For laboratory phase IVD, not represented as effective, label must include "For Research Use Only" · For products undergoing testing prior to full commercial release, label must include "For Investigational Use Only. The performance characteristics of this product have not been established." · Directions for Use Exemption for general use laboratory reagents where the product is labeled "For Laboratory Use"
	21 CFR 801	**Exemptions from Directions for Use:** · Prescription devices require this statement on the label: "Caution: Federal Law restricts this device to the sale by or on the order of a physician" · Retail exemption (devices delivered to end user by or on order of a physician) · Devices having commonly known directions to the ordinary individual · Devices for processing, repacking, or manufacturing if the label bears the statement: "Caution: For manufacturing, processing or repacking" · In vitro diagnostic products · Devices used in teaching, research, law enforcement (nonclinical use)
	21 CFR 812.5	**IDE Labeling:** · Label must bear prominently name and place of manufacturer · Contents of package · Statement: "Caution: Investigational Device. Limited by Federal (or US) Law to Investigational Use" · No representation that device is safe and effective for its investigational use
	21 CFR 820, Subpart K	**QSR/GMP Label Requirements:** · Label integrity (maintain legibility) · Separation of operations · Label inspections (for accuracy) and release · Storage (prevent mix-ups)
Drugs	21 CFR 201–202 21 CFR 208	**General Requirements:** · Label must bear prominently name and place of manufacturer, packer or distributor · Identify the quantity and dosage · National Drug Code requested to appear on all drug labels and labeling · Adequate directions for lay persons to use · No misleading statements misrepresenting drug · Statement of all ingredients with accurate names and proportions · Claims must be supported with clinical data · Label must state "Rx Only" for approved prescription drugs · Drugs scheduled by DEA must bear classification on label · English language (exceptions: product solely distributed in Puerto Rico or territories in which English is not the predominant language)

Labeling Requirements

	Source	Labeling Requirements
	21 CFR 201.100	**Exemptions From Directions for Use:** • In the possession of a person regularly and lawfully engaged in the manufacture, transportation, storage or wholesale distribution of prescription drugs • In the possession of a retail, hospital or clinic pharmacy, or public health agency, that is regularly and lawfully engaged in dispensing prescription drugs • In the possession of a practitioner licensed by law to administer or prescribe such drugs • New drugs under IND exemption • Drugs having commonly known directions • Inactive ingredients • IVD products • Prescription chemicals and other prescription components (label must include "For prescription compounding") • Drugs for processing, repacking or manufacturing if the label bears the statement: "Caution: For manufacturing, processing or repacking" • Drugs used in teaching, research, law enforcement (nonclinical use).
	21 CFR 312.26	**IND Labeling:** Immediate package of Investigational Drug must have label "Caution—New drug limited by Federal (or US) law to Investigational Use"
	21 CFR 211, Subpart G	**GMP Label Requirements:** • Label integrity (meets specifications) • Storage (prevent label mix-ups; limited access to labels) • Separation of operations (between drug products or dosage forms) • Labeling materials (inspection) • Gang printing of labels for different drug products is prohibited • Area Inspections (prior to labeling operation) • Reconciliation of labels issued and labels used • Destruction of Labels (after batch and lot are complete or obsolete/outdated)
Biologics	21 CFR 600, 606, 610 21 CFR 208	**General Requirements:** • Proper name of the product • Name, address and license of manufacturer or distributor • Lot number and other lot identification (including expiration date and recommended individual dose) • Adequate directions for lay persons to use (Medication Guide) • Statement of all ingredients with accurate names and proportions • Label must state "Rx only" for approved prescription biologics Additional information and precautionary measures are required of labels for biologics, depending upon the product.
	21 CFR 211, Subpart G	**GMP Label Requirements:** Same as Drugs

Promotion and Advertising

	Source	Form	Promotion and Advertising
Devices	*FTC Act* Section 5, 15 US Code 45		**Advertising Regulated by Federal Trade Commission (FTC):** FTC covers nonrestricted device advertising and requires · Claim substantiation and · Ads that are fair and not misleading FDA covers restricted medical devices FDA can deem the device misbranded if advertising promotes an intended use that is inconsistent with or not included in the device labeling.
	21 CFR 820.120		**PMA:** · Labeling approved in PMA · Restricted medical devices must bear the statement "Caution: Federal law restricts this device to sale, distribution, and use by or on the order of a (indicate type of practitioner and, if applicable, required training/experience, and facilities to which the use is restricted)." · "Full disclosure" in ads (warnings, cautions, adverse effects, etc.)
Drugs	21 CFR 202		**Advertising Regulated by:** · Rx Drugs: CDER's Division of Drug Marketing, Advertising and Communications (DDMAC) · OTC Drugs: FTC Noncompliance with the advertising regulations causes the drug to be "misbranded"
	21 CFR 314.81 21 CFR 314.550	2253	**NDA:** · All advertising and promotional labeling must be filed to the NDA at the time of initial dissemination/publication. · For drugs approved for serious and life-threatening diseases under accelerated approval launch materials are reviewed by FDA prior to dissemination; after 120 days following market approval, promotional material must be submitted at least 30 days prior to dissemination. · Changes in labeling are reported in the Annual Report to an approved NDA or a supplemental NDA.
			Rx Drug Advertising · Cannot make safety or efficacy claims before product approval · Can promote that a new product is coming unless product carries a boxed warning · Cannot promote use of a product for an indication not in the labeling · Promotional items cannot suggest off-label uses · Cannot be false, misleading or lacking in fair balance · Product comparisons must be supported by substantial clinical experience · Advertising must include a brief summary of side effects, contraindications and effectiveness · Promotional labeling must include a copy of the instructions for use. · Reminder advertisements are exempt from the brief summary requirement.
Biologics	21 CFR 601.45	2253 2567	Advertising Regulated by CBER's Advertising and Promotional Labeling Staff (APLS)
	21 CFR 601.12		**BLA:** Same as Drugs
			Biologics Advertising: · Concurrent notification rather than preapproval required.

Postmarketing Adverse Experience/Event and Medical Device Reporting

	Source	Form	Postmarketing Adverse Experience/Event and Medical Device Reporting
Devices	21 CFR 803	3500A	**MDR Reportable Event:** • Information that reasonably suggests that a device may have caused or contributed to a death or serious injury, or • A malfunction has occurred that would be likely to cause or contribute to a death or serious injury if the malfunction recurred
	21 CFR 803.50–803.56	3500A	**Manufacturers and Initial Distributors Must Report Within:** • Five work days of an event that requires remedial action to prevent unreasonable risk of substantial harm to public health or after becoming aware of a reportable event for which FDA has made a written request, or • 30 calendar days after the manufacturer becomes aware of a reportable event
	21 CFR 803.30–803.33	3419	**User Facility Reporting:** • Report death to FDA and manufacturer within 10 work days • Report serious injury to manufacturer only or to FDA if manufacturer is unknown within 10 work days, and • Report annually to FDA the total number of deaths and serious injuries
			Domestic Distributor Requirements: Recordkeeping only
Drugs	21 CFR 314.80		**Serious Adverse Drug Experience (SADE):** Any adverse drug experience occurring at any dose that results any of the following outcomes: • Causes death • Threatens life • Requires or prolongs existing hospitalization • Causes persistent or significant disability or incapacity • Induces congenital anomaly/birth defect • Important medical event
			Adverse Drug Experience (ADE): Any adverse event associated with the use of a drug, whether or not drug-related including: • Use of drug in professional practice • Drug overdose • Drug abuse or withdrawal • Failure of expected pharmacological action

		3500A
		
		356h
		
		356h
			Postmarketing 15-day Alert Reports
			• Needs to be filed for ADE that is:
			   o Both serious and unexpected (not in labeling)
			   o Foreign or domestic
			• No later than 15 calendar days after initial notification
			• Sources of ADE/SADE
			   o Manufacturer
			   o Healthcare professional
			   o Consumer
			   o Distributor
			   o Foreign use
			   o Literature
			   o User facility
			• Periodic Reports: quarterly for the first three years after approval. Reports to be submitted within 30 days of the close of the reporting period.
			• Annual Reports thereafter, with the reports to be submitted within 60 days of the anniversary of the issuance of the product approval

Biologics	21 CFR 314.80, 600.80		**Adverse Experience (AE):** AE reporting is any event associated with the use of a biological product in humans, whether or not it is considered product-related including: • Use of the biological product in professional practice • Biological product overdose • Biological product abuse or withdrawal • Failure of expected pharmacological action
			Serious Adverse Drug Experience: Same as Drugs
		3500A VAERS 1	**Postmarketing 15-day Alert Reports:** Same as Drugs • Reporting requirements are the same as for drugs except that vaccine AEs are reported on Vaccine Adverse Event Reporting System (VAERS) form.

Good Manufacturing Practice (GMP)/Quality System Regulation (QSR)

	Source	GMP
Devices	21 CFR 820	**Quality System Regulation (QSR):** QSR aligns US requirements with international quality standards (EN 46001 and ISO 13485), including management responsibility and review, design controls, purchasing controls, process validation, service record keeping and review, corrective and preventative action, and statistical techniques. Eliminates the distinction for critical devices. Subparts: A. General Provisions (scope, definitions, quality system) B. Quality System Requirements (management responsibility, quality audit, personnel including consultants) C. Design Controls D. Document Controls E. Purchasing Controls F. Identification and Traceability G. Production and Process Controls (production and process controls; inspection, measuring and test equipment; process validation) H. Acceptance Activities (receiving, in-process and finished device acceptance, acceptance status) I. Nonconforming Product J. Corrective and Preventive Action K. Labeling and Packaging Control (device labeling, device packaging) L. Handling, Storage, Distribution and Installation M. Records (general requirements, Device Master Record, Device History Record, Quality System Record, complaint files) N. Servicing O. Statistical Techniques Failure to comply renders the device Adulterated
Drugs	21 CFR 210–211	**Current GMP for Finished Pharmaceuticals:** A. General Provisions (scope, definitions) B. Organization and Personnel (responsibilities of quality control unit, personnel qualifications, personnel responsibilities, consultants) C. Buildings and Facilities (design, construction, lighting, air filtration, HVAC, plumbing, sewage and refuse, washing and toilet facilities, sanitation, maintenance) D. Equipment (design, size, location, construction, cleaning and maintenance, automatic, mechanical, and electronic equipment, filters) E. Control of Components and Drug Product Containers and Closures (receipt and storage; testing and approval/rejection; use of approved components, containers, and closures; retesting rejected components, containers, and closures) F. Production and Process Controls (written procedures, deviations, change in components, yield calculation, equipment identification, sampling and testing of in-process materials and products, time limitations on production, control of microbiological contamination, reprocessing) G. Packaging and Labeling Control (materials examination and usage criteria, labeling issuance, packaging and labeling operations, tamper-resistant packaging, drug product inspection, expiration dating) H. Holding and Distribution (warehousing procedures, distribution procedures) I. Laboratory Controls (general requirements, testing and release for distribution, stability testing, special testing requirements, reserve samples, laboratory animals, penicillin contamination) J. Records and Reports (general requirements, equipment cleaning and use log, component and drug product container, closure and labeling records, master production and control records, batch production and control records, production record review, laboratory records, distribution records, complaint files) K. Returned and Salvaged Drug Products
Biologics	21 CFR 210–211	**Same as Drugs Plus Additional Requirements:**

Good Manufacturing Practice (GMP)/Quality System Regulation (QSR)

	Source	GMP
	21 CFR 600, 606, and 610	**Biological Products—Subparts:** A. General Provisions (definitions) B. Establishment Standards (personnel, physical establishment, equipment, animals and care, records, retention samples, reporting of product deviations, temperatures during shipment) C. Establishment Inspections (inspectors, time of inspection, duties of inspector) D. Reporting of Adverse Experiences (postmarket reporting of adverse experiences, distribution reports, waivers)
	21 CFR 610	**General Biological Products Standards—Subparts** A. Release Requirements (Tests prior to release required for each lot. Requests for samples and protocol, official release.) B. General Provisions (equivalent methods and processes, potency, general safety test, sterility, purity, identity, constituent materials, total solids in serums, permissible combinations, cultures C. Standards Preparations and Limits of Potency D. Mycoplasma (test for mycoplasma) E. Testing Requirements for Communicable Disease Agents F. Dating Period Limitations (date of manufacture, dating periods for licensed biologics) G. Labeling Standards (container label, package label, proper name, legible type, divided manufacturing responsibility to be shown, name of selling agent or distributor, products for export, bar code label requirements)
	21 CFR 606	**Current GMP for Blood and Blood Components—Subparts:** A. General Provisions (definitions) B. Organization and Personnel C. Plant and Facilities D. Equipment (equipment, supplies and reagents) E. Reserved F. Production and Process Controls (standard operating procedures, plateletpheresis, leukapheresis, plasmapheresis) G. Finished Product Control (labeling, general requirements, container label, instruction circular) H. Laboratory Controls (laboratory controls and compatibility testing) I. Records and Reports (records, distribution and receipt, procedures and records, adverse reaction file)

Complaint Files

	Source	Complaint Files
Devices	21 CFR 820.198	**Written Procedures Required for:** • Receiving, reviewing and evaluating complaints by a formally designated unit • Processing all complaints uniformly in a timely manner • Documenting oral complaints upon receipt • Evaluating complaints to determine whether an MDR reportable event has occurred • Considering and handling device service reports that identify a reportable MDR event immediately

		Requirements:
		• The written record shall include the following information, if known
		  ○ Name of the device
		  ○ Date complaint was received
		  ○ Any device identification and control numbers
		  ○ Name, address and phone number of complainant
		  ○ Nature and details of complaint
		  ○ Date and results of investigation
		  ○ Any corrective action taken
		  ○ Reply to complainant
		  ○ Complaints that are MDRs must be clearly identified

	21 CFR 820.180	**Complaint Retention:** All records shall be retained for a period of time equivalent to the design and expected life of the device, but in no case less than two years from the date of release for commercial distribution by the manufacturer. Complaint file must be available during GMP inspection
Drugs	21 CFR 211.198	**Written Procedures Required for:** • Handling both written and oral complaints • Review to determine whether the complaint represents a serious and unexpected adverse drug experience.

		Requirements:
		• The written record shall include the following information, if known
		  ○ Name and strength of the drug product
		  ○ Lot number
		  ○ Name of complainant
		  ○ Nature of complaint
		  ○ Reply to complainant
		  ○ Finding of an investigation or reason an investigation was not necessary

		Complaint Retention: • Written records involving a drug product shall be maintained until at least one year after the expiration date of the drug product, or one year after the date that the complaint was received, whichever is longer. Complaint file must be available during an FDA GMP inspection
Biologics		Same as Drugs

FDA Inspections

	Source	Form	FDA Inspections
Devices	*FD&C Act* Section 704 21 CFR 814.44–45		**FDA May Inspect All Companies That Manufacture, Process, Pack or Hold FDA-Regulated Products Including:** · Contract testing laboratories · Clinical study sponsors, monitors and investigator sites · IRBs · Contract Research Organizations (CRO) · Foreign companies
			Types of Inspections (routine or for cause): · GMP/QSR Compliance (routine surveillance, establishment license or preapproval) · GLP Compliance · GCP Compliance (Sponsor or investigational site)
			FDA May Not Inspect: · Sales or pricing data · Retail or hospital pharmacies regulated by state law · Financial data · Personnel files (other than qualifications) · Internal audit files
		482	**Present Credentials** **Notice of Inspection**
		483	**Inspectional Observations**
		484	**Receipt for Samples**
Drugs	*FD&C Act* Section 704		**Same as Devices**
Biologics	PHS Act Section 262 21 CFR 600.20		**Same as Devices**

Lot and Batch Release Requirements

	Source	Lot and Batch Release Requirements
Devices	21 CFR 820.80	Review and sign-off of device history record by a designated individual. Sterile devices require review of sterility test results before release
Drugs	21 CFR 211.165	Lot must comply with release specifications in compendia or as negotiated and approved by FDA during the application review and approval process.
Biologics	21 CFR 610.1	Same as Drugs

Traceability Requirements

	Source	Traceability Requirements
Devices	21 CFR 820.65 21 CFR 821	Traceability required for devices intended for surgical implant or a device to support or sustain life whose failure to perform when properly used in accordance with the instructions for use provided in the labeling can be reasonably expected to result in a significant injury. Procedures established to identify unit, lot or batch of finished devices and, where appropriate, key components with a control number that facilitates corrective action. In addition to traceability requirement, FDA has identified specific devices that require tracking, as specified in 21 CFR 821.1(a): the failure of the device would be reasonably likely to have serious adverse health consequences; or the device is intended to be implanted in the human body for more than one year; or the device is a life-sustaining or life-supporting device used outside a device user facility.
Drugs	21 CFR 211, Subpart J	All manufacturing records and QC test results, forward and backward traceability from raw materials to finished product
Biologics	21 CFR 211, Subpart J 21 CFR 600.12 21 CFR 606.160 21 CFR 1271.291	Same as Drugs Tracking of blood-derived products from collection through processing, storage and distribution Tracking of human cells, tissues and cellular and tissue-based products requires establishing and maintaining a system to track all HCT/Ps from: (i) The donor to the consignee or final disposition; and (ii) The consignee or final disposition to the donor.

Retention of Product Samples

	Source	Retention of Product Samples
Devices	21 CFR 58	No requirement for devices except where required by specific company procedures or GLP
Drugs	21 CFR 211.170	**Active Ingredient:** · Reserve sample consists of at least twice the quantity necessary for all tests required (except sterility and pyrogen testing) · Retention time depends upon the active ingredient; in general, one reserve sample from each lot shall be retained for one year after expiration date of the last lot of the drug product containing it
		Radioactive Active Ingredient: · Three months after the last lot if expiration is less than 30 days or · Six months after the last lot if expiration if more than 30 days · OTC drugs that are exempt from bearing an expiration date should be retained three years after distribution of the last lot
		Each lot of drug product must be examined once per year
Biologics	21 CFR 600.13	· At least six months after the expiration date unless a different time period is specified in additional standards · The quantity must be sufficient for examination and testing of potency · At least one final container as a final package

Import and Export Requirements

	Source	Form	Import and Export Requirements
Devices	*FDERA*	2891 and 2892 (electronic)	**Import for Domestic Distribution:** Foreign manufacturers must designate a US Agent (initial importer) who shall: • Act as official correspondent • Submit establishment registration and device listing information • Submit 510(k)s or PMAs, as applicable • Forward US complaints to manufacturer • Submit MDRs
	FD&C Act Sections 801–802		**Export:** All devices not cleared for marketing in US must: • Accord to the specifications of the purchaser • Not conflict with laws of the importing country • Be labeled for export only • Not be sold in domestic commerce • May require Certificate of Exportability (COE) or Certificate of Foreign Government (CFG) Class III devices with no PMA require FDA approval to export Alternative (Section 802) for Class III devices with no PMA does not require FDA approval to export; only require "simple notification"
			Devices Must: • Meet Quality System Regulations or European National Standard 46001 • Not be adulterated, other than lack of PMA • Not be misbranded except that device must meet labeling requirements of foreign country Simple notification of name of device and listed (Tier I) country
Drugs	21 CFR 312.110 21 CFR 314.410		**Import for Domestic Distribution:** • Imports comply with requirements if subject to IND • In US, the sponsor, a qualified investigator or a domestic agent of foreign sponsor, can be consignee • New drug may be imported if it is the subject of an approved application • Drugs not approved for marketing in the US; Same as Devices
	FDERA		**Export:** **Investigational Drug** • Exports can be done under IND but not required • Each person who received drug should be an investigator named in application
			Approved Drug: • New drug may be exported if it is the subject of an approved application • Exporter must be listed as supplier in approved application, and the drug substance intended for export meets the specifications of—and is shipped with—a copy of the labeling required for the approved drug product
Biologics	*FDERA*		Same as Drugs

FDA Enforcement Options

	Source	Form	FDA Enforcement Options
Devices	*FD&C Act* Sections 301–304 21 CFR 812.119 *Safe Medical Device Act* of 1990	483	· Withdrawal of PMA or IDE approval · Criminal actions against investigator · Disqualified investigator · Inspections · Warning Letters · Adverse publicity · Recalls (mandatory and voluntary) · Alert List · Import alert · Civil penalties · Application Integrity Policy (AIP) investigation and enforcement (third-party review of data) · Injunctions, seizures, criminal actions · Request to state agencies to take action
Drugs	*Generic Drug Enforcement Act*		Same as Devices, also: · Debarment of individuals or corporations · Dear Doctor letter
Biologics			Same as Devices and Drugs

Field Corrections and Recalls

	Source	Field Corrections and Recalls
Devices	21 CFR 7 21 CFR 806 21 CFR 810	Enforcement/Recall Policy Medical Device Corrections and Removals Medical Device Recall Authority
	21 CFR 806	**Recall:** Recall Classification: Class I, II or III (assigned by FDA) Device recalls may be either voluntary (firm initiated or at FDA request) or mandatory by FDA order Mandatory Reports of Corrections/Removals required for any firm-initiated removal/correction conducted to: · Reduce risk to health posed by a device or · Remedy a violation of the *FD&C Act* caused by a device, which may present risk to health Written report required within 10 working days of removal/correction
	21 CFR 810	**Mandatory Medical Device Recall:** Cease Distribution and Notification order is issued by FDA if the agency finds a reasonable probability that a distributed device would cause serious adverse health consequences or death. The order requires a manufacturer to · Cease distribution · Notify healthcare professionals and user facilities · Instruct professionals and user facilities to cease use of the device If after a chance for hearing and further review, FDA determines that devices in distribution pose a risk, the agency may amend the order and require a recall.
		Recall Strategy Elements Must Include: · Depth of recall · Public warning · Effectiveness checks
Drugs	21 CFR 7 21 CFR 314.81	**Same as Devices Except:** NDA Field Alert: Within three days, a field alert must be sent to FDA district office for distributed product that has contamination, change, deterioration or labeling causing mistaken identity. Recalls are voluntary and may be firm-initiated or requested by FDA. "FDA-requested" recall to begin immediately. For firm-initiated recall, notify district office and it will assign the recall to a class.
Biologics	21 CFR 7 21 CFR 600.14	**Same as Drugs Except:** Biologic Product Deviation Report: Filed within 45 calendar days concerning any event, and information relevant to the event, associated with the manufacturing, to include testing, processing, packing, labeling or storage, or with the holding or distribution, of a licensed biological product, if that event meets all the following criteria: (1) Either: (i) Represents a deviation from current good manufacturing practice, applicable regulations, applicable standards, or established specifications that may affect the safety, purity, or potency of that product; or (ii) Represents an unexpected or unforeseeable event that may affect the safety, purity, or potency of that product; and (2) Occurs in your facility or another facility under contract with you; and (3) Involves a distributed biological product.

Corrective and Preventive Action Requirements

	Source	Corrective and Preventive Action Requirements
Devices	21 CFR 820.100	Requires manufacturers to establish procedures for: · Analyzing processes, operations, audit reports, quality and service records, complaints, returned devices and other information to identify existing potential causes of nonconforming product · Investigating the cause of nonconformities · Identifying the corrective and preventive action needed to prevent recurrence of nonconforming product · Verifying and validating that the corrective and preventive action is effective · Implementing changes in methods and procedures needed to effect the corrective and preventive action · Ensuring that information related to nonconforming product and corrective and preventive action is disseminated to persons responsible for ensuring quality and preventing such problems · Submitting relevant information for management review
Drugs	21 CFR 211.22	Same as Devices Quality control unit approves or rejects all components and drug products and investigates errors or out-of- specification lots.
Biologics		Same as Devices

Misbranding

	Source	Misbranding
Devices	*FD&C Act* *FD&C Act* Section 518	**Failure to:** · File a 510(k) · Provide information as required · Have advertisements approved by FDA if required · List device · Register establishment · Comply with notification or recall order or · Comply with postmarket surveillance order **Misbranding:** · False or misleading labeling including advertising and promotional materials · Label does not contain manufacturer's name and address in required prominence · Label does not contain quantity of contents · Required wording is not prominently displayed · Label does not contain adequate directions for use · Device is dangerous to health when used as prescribed · Product does not comply with color additive provision of Act · Device does not adhere to performance standard if applicable · Failure to comply (notification, reporting, record keeping) · Impression of official approval due to registration of 510(k)
Drugs	21 CFR 201	**Misbranding** · Labeling is false or misleading · Packaged form does not bear name of manufacturer, packer or distributor · Required information does not appear or is not prominently placed · Habit-forming substance does not bear habit-forming warning · Generic established name is less than one half the size of the trade/brand name · Not listed in official compendium · Packaging is misleading · Subject to deterioration without precautions · Labeling does not bear adequate directions for use · Drug is dangerous to health when used as suggested in the accompanying labeling · Antibiotic certificate of release, if required, was not issued · False or misleading advertisements or descriptive printed materials · Manufacturer not registered or drug not listed · Packaging or labeling does not comply with the *Poison Prevention Packaging Act* · Container is misleading
Biologics		Same as Drugs

Adulteration

	Source	Adulteration

Devices		• Not manufactured under GMPs
		• Contaminated and defective product
		• Class III device for which PMA:
		  ○ is not filed
		  ○ is not approved or
		  ○ has been suspended or withdrawn
		• Marketed Class III device without a PMA before FDA down-classified the device as Class I or II
		• Banned device
		• Strength, purity or quality fall below what they are represented to be
		• Not in conformance with a performance standard.
		• Contains unsafe color additives
		• Failure to comply with approved IDE requirements

Drugs	*FD&C Act* Section 501(a)–(d)	**If the Drug:** • Consists of filthy, putrid or decomposed substance • Has been prepared, packed or held under unsanitary conditions • Methods used in, or facilities or controls used for its manufacture do not conform to GMPs or • Strength differs from or purity is less than stated in the labeling
Biologics		Same as Drugs

Glossary of Terms

30-day hold
Time period between filing a protocol under an IND and FDA approval to proceed with enrollment. Also, the time period between when a company submits an IND and when it can initiate a protocol. This time line may be extended if FDA does not agree with the proposed protocol. (See "Clinical Hold.")

120-day Safety Report
Amendment to an NDA containing a safety update due 120 days after the NDA is filed.

510(k)
- Traditional 510(k): A premarket notification submitted to FDA to demonstrate that the medical device to be marketed is as safe and effective or "substantially equivalent" to a legally marketed device. 510(k) refers to the section of the *FD&C Act* authorizing the submission of the premarket notification.
- Special 510(k): For use where device modifications neither affect the intended use nor alter its fundamental scientific technology. FDA processing time is 30 days.
- Abbreviated 510(k): A type of 510(k) submission that is supported by conformance with guidance document(s), special controls or standards.

A
AABB
American Association of Blood Banks

ACE
Adverse Clinical Event

ACRP
Association for Clinical Research Professionals

ACS
American Chemical Society

Action Letter
Official communication from FDA informing NDA/BLA sponsor of an agency decision. Includes approvable, not approvable and clinical hold.

Active Ingredient
Any drug component intended to furnish pharmacological activity or other direct effect in the diagnosis, cure, mitigation, treatment or prevention of disease, or to affect the structure or any function of the body of man or other animals.

ADE
Adverse Drug Event or Adverse Drug Experience

ADME
Absorption, Distribution, Metabolism and Excretion

ADR
Adverse Drug Reaction

ADUFA
Animal Drug User Fee Act of 2003

ADUFA II
Animal Drug User Fee Amendments of 2008

Adulterated
Product containing any filthy, putrid or decomposed substance; or prepared under unsanitary conditions; or not made according to GMPs; or containing an unsafe color additive; or does not meet the requirements of an official compendium. (*FD&C Act*, SEC. 501 [351])

AdvaMed
Advanced Medical Technology Association

Advisory Committee
Committees and panels used by FDA to obtain independent expert advice on scientific, technical and policy matters.

AE
Adverse Event

AERS
Adverse Event Reporting System

AFDO
Association of Food and Drug Officials

AGDUFA
Animal Generic Drug User Fee Act of 2008

AHRQ
Agency for Healthcare Research and Quality

AIP
Application Integrity Policy. FDA's approach to reviewing applications that may be affected by wrongful acts that raise significant questions regarding data reliability.

AMDUCA
Animal Medicinal Drug Use Clarification Act of 1994

Amendment
Additions or changes to an ANDA, NDA, BLA, PMA or PMA supplement still under review. Includes safety updates. Any updates to an IND or an IDE prior to approval are also called amendments.

AMS
Agricultural Marketing Service (USDA)

ANADA
Abbreviated New Animal Drug Application

ANDA
Abbreviated New Drug Application. Used for generic drugs.

Animal Drugs@FDA
Database that allows users to search for approved animal drug products, suitability petitions, sponsors, the *Green Book*, CFR, *FR*, patents and exclusivity.

Annual Report
An annual periodic report or progress report that must be submitted to FDA. Depending on the type of application for which the report is submitted, it may include new safety, efficacy and labeling information; preclinical and clinical investigation summaries; CMC updates; nonclinical laboratory studies; and completed unpublished clinical trials.

ANPR
Advance Notice of Proposed Rulemaking

APhA
American Pharmacists Association

APHIS
Animal and Plant Health Inspection Service

API
Active Pharmaceutical Ingredient

APLB
Advertising and Promotional Labeling Branch (CBER)

Approved
FDA designation given to drugs, biologics and medical devices that have been granted marketing approval.

AQL
Acceptable Quality Level

ASTM
American Society of Testing and Materials

ASQ
American Society for Quality (formerly ASQC)

ASR
Analyte Specific Reagents

ATF
Bureau of Alcohol, Tobacco, Firearms and Explosives

AUT
Actual Use Trials

B

BACPAC
Bulk Actives Chemical Postapproval Changes

Banned Device
Device presenting a substantial deception, unreasonable risk of injury or illness, or unreasonable direct and substantial danger to public health.

BIMO
Bioresearch Monitoring Program

BIO
Biotechnology Industry Organization

Bioequivalence
The absence of a significant difference in the rate and extent to which the active ingredient or active moiety in pharmaceutical equivalents or pharmaceutical alternatives becomes available at the site of drug action when administered at the same molar dose under similar conditions in an appropriately designed study.

Biologic
A virus, therapeutic serum, toxin, antitoxin, vaccine, blood, blood component or derivative, allergenic product, protein (except any chemically synthesized polypeptide), or analogous product, or arsphenamine or derivative of arsphenamine (or any other trivalent organic arsenic compound), applicable to the prevention, treatment, or cure of a disease or condition of human beings.

BLA
Biologics License Application

Blinded Study
Clinical trial in which the patient (single-blind) or patient and investigator (double-blind) are unaware of which treatment the patient receives. Involves use of multiple treatment groups such as other active, placebo or alternate dose groups. Sometimes referred to as "masked."

BPCA
Best Pharmaceuticals for Children Act of 2002

BPCI Act
Biologics Price Competition and Innovation Act of 2009

BPDR
Biological Product Deviation Report

C
CAP
College of American Pathologists

CAPA
Corrective and Preventive Actions

CBE-30
Changes Being Effected in 30 days. A submission to an approved application reporting changes that FDA has identified as having moderate potential to adversely affect drug product identity, strength, quality, purity and potency. The supplement must be received by FDA at least 30 days before product distribution.

CBER
Center for Biologics Evaluation and Research

CBP
US Customs and Border Protection

CDC
Centers for Disease Control and Prevention

CDER
Center for Drug Evaluation and Research

CDRH
Center for Devices and Radiological Health

CF
Consent Form. Document used to inform a potential subject of the risks and benefits of a clinical trial per the Declaration of Helsinki. Sometimes referred to as ICF (Informed Consent Form) or ICD (Informed Consent Document).

CFG
Certificate to Foreign Government. Required by certain countries to prove that an exported product can be legally marketed in the US.

CFR
Code of Federal Regulations

CFSAN
Center for Food Safety and Applied Nutrition

CGMP
Current Good Manufacturing Practice

CH
Clinical Hold

CIR
Cosmetic Ingredient Review

Class I Device
Low-risk device requiring general controls to ensure safety and effectiveness.

Class II Device
Requires general and special controls to ensure safety and effectiveness. Special controls may include mandatory performance standards, patient registries for implantable devices and postmarket surveillance. Requires 510(k), unless exempted; may require clinical trials.

Class III Device
Requires general controls, special controls and premarket approval (PMA); includes devices that are life-sustaining, life-supporting or pose significant potential for risk to patient, or are not substantially equivalent to Class I or Class II devices. PMAs almost always require clinical trials.

Clearance
Devices that receive marketing permission through the 510(k) process based upon demonstrating substantial equivalence to a preamendment device or another device reviewed under section 510(k) of the *FD&C Act.*

CLIA
Clinical Laboratory Improvement Amendments of 1988

Clinical Hold
FDA order to delay proposed clinical investigation or suspend an ongoing investigation.

Clinical Investigator
A medical researcher in charge of carrying out a clinical trial's protocol.

ClinicalTrials.gov
A registry and results database of federally and privately supported clinical trials conducted in the US and around the world. Operated by NIH.

CLSI
Clinical and Laboratory Standards Institute (formerly National Committee for Clinical Laboratory Standards)

CMC
Chemistry, Manufacturing and Controls

CME
Continuing Medical Education

CMS
Centers for Medicare & Medicaid Services

COE
Certificate of Exportability. Required by certain countries for the export of unapproved devices not sold or offered for sale in the US; issued by FDA to the exporter.

Combination Product
Defined in 21 CFR 3.2(e) as a combination of two or more different types of regulated products, i.e.,
- a drug and a device
- a device and a biological product
- a drug and a biological product
- a drug, a device and a biological product

Commercial Distribution
Any distribution of a device intended for human use, which is offered for sale but does not include: internal or interplant transfer within the same parent, subsidiary or affiliate company any device with an approved exemption for investigational use.

Complaint
Any written, electronic or oral communication alleging deficiencies related to a product's identity, quality, durability, reliability, safety, effectiveness or performance after release for distribution.

Component
Any ingredient or part intended for use in the manufacture of a drug, device, cosmetic, biologic or IVD product, including those that may not appear in the finished product.

COOL
Country of Origin Labeling. Requirements for source labeling for food products (USDA)

Cosmetic
Articles intended to be rubbed, poured, sprinkled or sprayed on, introduced into or otherwise applied to the human body or any part thereof for cleansing, beautifying, promoting attractiveness or altering appearance; and, articles intended for use as a component of any such article; except that such term shall not include soap.

CPMP
Committee for Proprietary Medicinal Products (EU)

CPSC
Consumer Product Safety Commission

CRA
Clinical Research Associate

CRADA
Cooperative Research and Development Agreement (with a government agency such as NIH and FDA)

CRC
Clinical Research Coordinator

CRF
Case Report Form. Paper or electronic document used to record data collected in a clinical trial.

Critical Path Initiative
FDA's effort to stimulate and facilitate a national effort to modernize the scientific process through which a potential human drug, biological product or medical device is transformed from a discovery or "proof of concept" into a medical product.

CRO
Contract Research Organization

CSO
Consumer Safety Officer. Often the FDA contact person for sponsors. Also known as the regulatory project manager.

CTD
Common Technical Document

CTP
Center for Tobacco Products

Custom Device
A device that:
- deviates from devices generally available
- deviates from an applicable performance standard or PMA requirement in order to comply with the order of a physician or dentist
- is not generally available in finished form for purchase or dispensing by prescription
- is not offered for commercial distribution through labeling or advertising, is intended for use by an individual patient named in the order of a physician or dentist, and is to be made in a specific form for that patient
- is intended to meet the special needs of the physician or dentist

CVB
Center for Veterinary Biologics (USDA)

CVM
Center for Veterinary Medicine (FDA)

D

D&D
Design and Development Plan

DDMAC
Division of Drug Marketing, Advertising, and Communications

DDT
Drug Development Tools

DEA
Drug Enforcement Administration

Debarment
An official action in accordance with 21 CFR 1404 to exclude a person from directly or indirectly providing services in any capacity to a firm with an approved or pending drug/device product application. A debarred corporation is prohibited from submitting or assisting in the submission of any NDA or ANDA. Equivalent to disqualification for devices requiring a PMA submission.

Declaration of Helsinki
Ethical principles for medical research involving human subjects. Trials conducted under Good Clinical Practice generally follow the Declaration of Helsinki.

DESI
Drug Efficacy Study Implementation

DFUF
Device Facility User Fee

DHF
Design History File. Describes a finished device's design.

DHHS
Department of Health and Human Services

DHR
Device History Record. Contains a device's production history.

DIA
Drug Information Association

DMC
Data Monitoring Committee

DMEPA
Division of Medication Error Prevention and Analysis (CBER)

DMF
Drug Master File. Submission to FDA that may be used to provide confidential detailed information about facilities, processes or articles used in the manufacturing, processing, packaging and storing of one or more human drugs.

DMPQ
Division of Manufacturing and Product Quality (CBER)

DMR
Device Master Record. Compilation of records containing a finished device's procedures and specifications.

DNCE
Division of Nonprescription Clinical Evaluation

DRC
Direct Recall Classification

DRLS
Drug Registration and Listing System

Drug
Any article intended for use in the diagnosis, cure, mitigation, treatment or prevention of disease in man.

Drugs@FDA
A searchable database of brand-name and generic prescription and OTC human drugs and biological therapeutic products approved since 1939.

Drug Product
A finished dosage form (e.g., tablet, capsule, solution, etc.) that contains an active drug ingredient. It is generally, but not necessarily, also associated with inactive ingredients. This includes a finished dosage form that does not contain an active ingredient but is intended to be used as a placebo.

DSMICA
Division of Small Manufacturers, International, and Consumer Assistance (CDRH)

DSHEA
Dietary Supplement Health and Education Act of 1994

DTC
Direct-to-Consumer (advertising)

E
EA
Environmental Assessment

EC
European Commission, European Community or Ethics Committee

ECO
Emergency Change Order

eCTD
Electronic Common Technical Document

eBPDR
Electronic Biological Product Deviation Reports

EFTA
European Free Trade Association

EIR
Establishment Inspection Report

EMA
European Medicines Agency (formerly European Medicines Evaluation Agency)

Emergency Use IND
FDA authorization for shipping a drug for a specific emergency use for a life-threatening or serious disease for which there is no alternative treatment.

EPA
Environmental Protection Agency

ERS
Expedited Review Status. Program for veterinary products.

Establishment Listing and Registration
In accordance with 21 CFR 807, manufacturers (both domestic and foreign) and initial distributors (importers) of medical devices must electronically register their establishments with FDA. Manufacturers must also list their devices with FDA.

Excipient
An ingredient contained in a drug formulation that is not a medicinally active constituent.

Expected Life
Time a device is expected to remain functional after being placed into service.

Expiration Date
Date printed on product label indicating the end of the product's useful life. Expiration period length is determined by stability studies and negotiated with FDA.

ETASU
Elements to Ensure Safe Use

EU
European Union has 27 Member States: Belgium, Germany, France, Italy, Luxembourg, The Netherlands, Denmark, Ireland, the United Kingdom, Greece, Spain, Portugal, Austria, Finland, Sweden, Cyprus, the Czech Republic, Estonia, Hungary, Latvia, Lithuania, Malta, Poland, Slovakia, Slovenia, Bulgaria and Romania. EU policies also apply to members of the European Free Trade Association: Iceland, Norway, Switzerland and Liechtenstein.

F

FAR
Field Alert Report

Fast Track
FDA program to facilitate the development and expedite the review of new drugs intended to treat serious or life-threatening conditions that demonstrate the potential to address unmet medical needs. Accelerated NDA review.

FCA
False Claims Act

FCC
Federal Communications Commission

FD&C Act
Federal Food, Drug, and Cosmetic Act of 1938

FDA
Food and Drug Administration

FDAAA
Food and Drug Administration Amendments Act of 2007

FDA ESG
FDA Electronic Submissions Gateway. Enables the secure submission of regulatory information for review.

FDAMA
Food and Drug Administration Modernization Act of 1997

FDERA
Food and Drug Export Reform and Enhancement Act of 1996

FDLI
Food and Drug Law Institute

FALCPA
Food Allergen Labeling and Consumer Protection Act of 2004

FMECA
Failure Mode, Effects and Critical Analysis

FOIA
Freedom of Information Act

FPLA
Fair Packaging and Labeling Act

FR
Federal Register

FSMA
Food Safety Modernization Act of 2011

FTC
Federal Trade Commission

FURLS
FDA Unified Registration and Listing System for establishment registration of medical device operators and distributors.

G

GADPTRA
Generic Animal Drug and Patent Term Restoration Act of 1988

GAO
Government Accountability Office

GCP
Good Clinical Practice. Regulations and requirements with which clinical studies must comply. These regulations apply to the manufacturers, sponsors, clinical investigators and institutional review boards.

GDEA
Generic Drug Enforcement Act of 1992

GeMCRIS
Genetic Modification Clinical Research Information System. Allows public users to access basic reports about human gene transfer trials registered with NIH and to develop specific queries based on their own information needs.

Generic Drug
Drugs manufactured and approved after the original brand name drug has lost patent protection. Sponsor files Abbreviated New Drug Application (ANDA) for marketing approval.

GGP
Good Guidance Practice

GHTF
Global Harmonization Task Force. Comprised of five founding members: EU, US, Canada, Australia and Japan. Formed to encourage convergence in regulatory practices related to ensuring the safety, effectiveness/ performance and quality of medical devices, promoting technological innovation and facilitating international trade.

GLP
Good Laboratory Practice. Regulations governing the conduct of nonclinical laboratory studies that support or are intended to support applications for research or marketing applications.

GMP
Good Manufacturing Practice (for devices, see Quality System Regulation).

GPO
Government Printing Office

GPR
General Purpose Reagents

Grandfathered
Tacit approval of drugs marketed before 1938 and devices marketed before May 1976.

GRAS(E)
Generally Recognized as Safe (and Effective)

Green Book
FDA-published listing of all animal drug products approved for safety and effectiveness. Updated monthly.

GRP
Good Review Practice

GTP
Good Tissue Practice

Guidance
Documents published by FDA to provide current interpretation of regulations.

H
HAACP
Hazard Analysis and Critical Control Point (inspection technique)

Hatch-Waxman Act
Drug Price Competition and Patent Restoration Act of 1984

HCT/P
Human Cells, Tissues and Cellular and Tissue-Based Products

HDE
Humanitarian Device Exemption

HIPAA
Health Insurance Portability and Accountability Act of 1996, also known as the Privacy Rule, established the minimum federal requirements for protecting the privacy of individually identifiable health information.

HMO
Health Maintenance Organization

Homeopathic Drug
Any drug labeled as being homeopathic listed in the *Homeopathic Pharmacopeia of the United States* (*HPUS*), an addendum to it or its supplements. The practice of homeopathy is based on the belief that disease symptoms can be cured by small doses of substances which produce similar symptoms in healthy people.

HPCUS
Homeopathic Pharmacopoeia Convention of the United States

HPUS
Homoeopathic Pharmacopoeia of the United States

HUD
Humanitarian Use Device

I
IB
Investigator's Brochure

IC (ICF) (ICD)
Informed Consent (Form) (Document)

ICH
International Conference on Harmonisation of Technical Requirements for Registration of Pharmaceuticals for Human Use (participants include Europe, Japan and US; observers include Australia and Canada).

IDE
Investigational Device Exemption

IDMC
Independent Data Monitoring Committee

Inactive Ingredient
Any drug product component other than the active ingredient, such as excipients, vehicle and binders.

INAD
Investigational New Animal Drug (application)

IND
Investigational New Drug (application)

Information Amendment
Includes most submissions under an active IND, such as new protocols, final study reports, safety reports, CMC information, etc. The initial IND ends with 000; each serial amendment receives the next consecutive number.

INN
International Nonproprietary Names

Intended Use
Objective labeled use of a device.

Investigator IND
Protocol and IND submitted by an individual investigator instead of a manufacturer. A letter of authorization allows FDA to review the sponsor's DMF or cross-reference CMC information. The investigator, not the manufacturer, is responsible for maintaining the IND.

IOM
Investigations Operations Manual

IRB
Institutional Review Board or Independent Review Board

ISO
International Organization for Standardization

IUO
Investigational Use Only

IVD
In Vitro Diagnostic

L

Label
Any display of written, printed or graphic matter on the immediate container or package of, or affixed to, any article.

Labeling
All written, printed or graphic matter accompanying an article at any time while such article is in interstate commerce or held for sale after shipment in interstate commerce; includes user manuals, brochures, advertising, etc.

LDT
Laboratory developed test

LOA
Letter of Authorization. A letter from the holder of a Drug Master File to FDA, authorizing another party to reference the DMF (also Letter of Agreement).

M

Market Withdrawal
Firm-initiated removal or correction of a device, drug or biologic product involving a minor violation of the *FD&C Act*, not subject to legal action by FDA, or which involves no violation, e.g., normal stock rotation practices, routine equipment adjustments and repairs, etc.

MAF
Device Master File. Analagous to a drug master file; submission to FDA that may be used to provide confidential detailed information about a medical device or a component used in the manufacture of a medical device to FDA in support of another party's obligation.

MAPP
Manual of Policy and Procedures

MAUDE
Manufacturer and User Facility Device Experience database. Contains reports of adverse events involving medical devices.

MDR
Medical Device Reporting

MDUFMA
Medical Device User Fee and Modernization Act of 2002

Medical Device

An instrument, apparatus, implement, machine, contrivance, implant, in vitro reagent or other similar or related article, including any component, part or accessory that is:

- recognized in the official *National Formulary* or *US Pharmacopeia*, or any supplement to them
- intended for use in diagnosis of disease or other conditions, or in cure, mitigation, treatment or prevention of disease in man or other animals intended to affect the structure or any function of the body of man or other animals, and which does not achieve its primary intended purposes through chemical action within or on the body of man or other animals, and which is not dependent upon being metabolized for the achievement of its primary intended purposes. (*FD&C Act* Section 201(h))

MedDRA

Medical Dictionary for Regulatory Activities. Global standard international medical terminology designed to supersede or replace all other terminologies used within the medical product development process including COSTART and WHO-ART.

MedSun

Medical Product Safety Network. An adverse event reporting program for healthcare professionals launched in 2002 by CDRH.

MedWatch

FDA program for voluntary and mandatory reporting of AEs and product problems. (FDA Form 3500 or 3500A)

Misbranded

Designation given to a product that is incorrectly labeled (i.e., false or misleading or fails to include information required by law). Other violations may also render a product misbranded (e.g., failure to obtain a 510(k) for a device).

MMA

Medicare Prescription Drug, Improvement and Modernization Act of 2003

Modular PMA

Allows a company to file the completed portions or modules of a PMA for an ongoing review by FDA.

MOU

Memorandum of Understanding. An agreement between FDA and another country's regulatory authority that allows mutual recognition of inspections.

MSDS

Material Safety Data Sheet

MTD

Maximum Tolerated Dose

MUMS

Minor Use and Minor Species Animal Health Act of 2004

N

NADA

New Animal Drug Application

NAF

Notice of Adverse Findings

NAFTA

North American Free Trade Agreement

NAI

No Action Indicated. Most favorable FDA postinspection classification.

NCE

New Chemical Entity

NCTR

National Center for Toxicological Research

NDA

New Drug Application

NDA Field Alert

Report filed with FDA within three working days of obtaining information on any distributed drug product that has contamination, significant chemical or physical change, deterioration, batch failure or labeling causing mistaken identity.

NDC

National Drug Code. The first five digits identify establishment and last five digits identify drug name, package size and drug type.

NDF

New Dosage Form

NF

National Formulary (incorporated into the *USP-NF*)

NIDPOE

Notice of Initiation of Disqualification Proceedings and Opportunity to Explain Letter

NIH
National Institutes of Health

NLEA
Nutrition Labeling and Education Act of 1990

NLM
National Library of Medicine

NME
New Molecular Entity

NORD
National Organization for Rare Disorders

NOV
Notice of Violation letter

NRC
National Research Council or Nuclear Regulatory Commission

NSE
Not Substantially Equivalent. Designation for device that does not qualify for 510(k) clearance; generally requires a PMA.

NSR
Nonsignificant Risk

O

OAI
Official Action Indicated. Serious FDA postinspection classification.

OC
Office of the Commissioner (FDA)

OCBQ
Office of Compliance and Biologics Quality (CBER)

OCC
Office of the Chief Counsel (FDA)

OCI
Office of Criminal Investigation (FDA)

OCP
Office of Combination Products (FDA)

OCTGT
Office of Cellular, Tissue and Gene Therapies (CBER)

ODA
Orphan Drug Act of 1983

ODE
Office of Device Evaluation (FDA)

OECD
The Organization for Economic Cooperation and Development

Office of the Chief Scientist
Includes the following offices:
- Office of Counterterrorism and Emerging Threats
- Office of Scientific Integrity
- Office of the Ombudsman
- Office of Science and Innovation
- Office of Critical Path Programs

OGD
Office of Generic Drug Products (CDER)

OIG
Office of the Inspector General (FDA)

OIRA
Office of Information and Regulatory Affairs (OMB)

OIVD
Office of In Vitro Diagnostic Device Evaluation and Safety (FDA)

OIP
Office of International Programs (FDA)

OMUMS
Office of Minor Use & Minor Species Animal Drug Development (CVM)

ONADE
Office of New Animal Drug Evaluation (CVM)

OND
Office of New Drugs (CDER)

ONPLDS
Office of Nutritional Products, Labeling and Dietary Supplements (CFSAN)

OOPD
Office of Orphan Products Development (FDA)

OPA
Office of Public Affairs (FDA)

Open Label Study
A clinical trial in which subjects and investigators are aware of the treatment received.

ORA
Office of Regulatory Affairs (FDA); oversees FDA's field organization.

Orange Book
FDA-published listing of Approved Drug Products with Therapeutic Equivalence Evaluations generally known as generics (has an orange cover).

Orphan Drug
Drugs for a disease or condition that affects fewer than 200,000 persons in the US or occurs in more than 200,000 and for which there is no reasonable expectation that drug development and manufacturing costs will be recovered from US sales.

OSB
Office of Surveillance and Biometrics (CDRH)

OSHA
Occupational Safety Health Administration

OTC
Over-the-Counter. Nonprescription drugs receive this designation.

OTC Monograph
Rules for a number of OTC drug categories.

OVRR
Office of Vaccine Research and Review (CBER)

P

PAI
Preapproval Inspection

PAS
Prior Approval Supplement or Postapproval Study

PAT
Process Analytical Technology

PCPC
Personal Care Products Council (formerly Cosmetic, Toiletry and Fragrance Association)

PD
Pharmacodynamics. Study of the reactions between drugs and living structures.

PDA
Parenteral Drug Association

PDMA
Prescription Drug Marketing Act

PDP
Product Development Protocol (for medical devices) or Principal Display Panel (for product labels)

PDUFA
Prescription Drug User Fee Act of 1992

PGx
Pharmacogenomics. The study of variations of DNA and RNA characteristics as related to drug response

Pharmacovigilance
Adverse event monitoring and reporting

PhRMA
Pharmaceutical Research and Manufacturers of America

Phase I
Initial clinical safety studies in humans. May be as few as 10 subjects, often healthy volunteers, includes PK, ADME and dose escalation studies. Usually open label.

Phase II
Well-controlled clinical trials of approximately 100–300 subjects who have the condition of interest, includes PK, dose ranging, safety and efficacy.

Phase III
Larger, well-controlled clinical trials of hundreds to thousands of subjects, including both safety and efficacy data. Generally, two well-controlled studies are needed to establish efficacy for drug products.

Phase IV
Postmarket clinical trials performed to support labeling and advertising or fulfill FDA safety requirements noted at the time of NDA approval.

PHI
Protected Health Information

PHS
Public Health Service

PI
Package Insert (approved product labeling) or Principal Investigator

PK
Pharmacokinetics. The study of the processes of ADME of chemicals and medicines.

Placebo
A drug product fashioned to look like an active drug but containing no active ingredient. Used in clinical trials to blind or mask the patient, investigator or both as to the treatment received.

PLR
Physician Labeling Rule

PMA
Premarket Approval. Marketing application required for Class III devices.

PMN
Premarket Notification. A premarket notification is also called a 510(k).

PMOA
Primary Mode of Action. The single mode of action of a combination product that provides the most important therapeutic action of the combination product; used to assign a combination product to a lead FDA center.

PMS
Postmarketing Surveillance. Ongoing monitoring of the safety of approved medical products; may include Phase IV studies and AE reporting.

PNSI
Prior Notice System Interface. Used to provide prior notice for food products entering the US.

PPACA
Patient Protection and Affordable Care Act of 2010

PPI
Patient Package Insert

PPPA
Poison Prevention Packaging Act

PREA
Pediatric Research Equity Act of 2003

Preclinical Studies
Animal studies of PK and toxicity generally performed prior to clinical studies. These studies must comply with GLP.

Priority Review
FDA review category for drugs that appear to represent an advance over available therapy. NDA or BLA receives a faster review than standard applications.

Protocol
Document describing a clinical trial's objectives, design and methods. All GLP and GCP studies must follow a protocol.

PSUR
Periodic Safety Update Report

PTC
Points to Consider. Type of guidance published by FDA, usually by CBER.

PTCC
Pharmacology/Toxicology Coordinating Committee (CDER)

***Public Health Security and Bioterrorism Preparedness and Response Act* of 2002**
Also known as *Bioterrorism Act*

PWR
Pediatric Written Request. *BPCA* authorizes FDA (in consultation with NIH) to issue a written request for the conduct of pediatric studies to holders of approved NDAs and ANDAs for drugs on the NIH list.

Q
QA
Quality Assurance

QAU
Quality Assurance Unit

QC
Quality Control

QoL
Quality of Life

QSIT
Quality System Inspection Technique

QSR
Quality System Regulation (21 CFR 820). Identifies GMPs for medical devices.

R

R&D
Research and Development

RAC
Reviewer Affairs Committee (CDER) or Regulatory
Affairs Certification

RAPS
Regulatory Affairs Professionals Society

RCT
Randomized Clinical Trial or Randomized Controlled
Trial

Recall
A firm's removal or correction of a marketed product
that FDA considers to be in violation of the laws it
administers and against which the agency would initiate
legal action, e.g., seizure. Recall does not include a
market withdrawal or a stock recovery.

Recall Classification
Assigned by FDA and applicable to firm-initiated device
recalls based upon reasonable probability and relative
degree of health hazard.
- Class I: violative device would cause serious
  adverse health consequences.
- Class II: violative device may cause temporary or
  medically reversible adverse health consequences
  or such consequences are remote.
- Class III: violative device is not likely to cause
  adverse health consequences.

Regulation
Refers to Code of Federal Regulations

REMS
Risk Evaluation and Mitigation Strategy

RFR
Reportable Food Registry. An electronic portal used to
report foods suspected of causing serious adverse health
consequences.

Restricted Device
A device restricted, by regulation, to sale, distribution
and/or use only upon the written or oral authorization of
a licensed practitioner or other conditions prescribed by
the commissioner.

RFD
Request for Designation. A written submission to
OCP requesting designation of the center with primary
jurisdiction for a combination or non-combination
product.

RFR
Request for Reconsideration. A request that OCP
reconsider an RFD determination.

RLD
Reference Listed Drug. Drug product listed in the
Approved Drug Products with Therapeutic Equivalence
Evaluations book (also known as the *Orange Book*).

Rolling NDA Submission
Allows a company to file the completed portions of an
NDA for an ongoing review by FDA. Only permitted
for drugs and biologics that have received Fast Track
designation from FDA.

RTF
Refusal to File. Letter sent by FDA when incomplete
NDA or ANDA is filed. FDA will not review the
application until complete. Letter is sent within 60 days
of submission.

RUO
Research Use Only

Rx
Prescription Use Only

S

SAE
Serious Adverse Event

SBA
Summary Basis of Approval

SC
Study Coordinator

SD
Standard Deviation

SE
Substantially Equivalent

S&E
Safety and Efficacy

Shelf Life
Maximum time a device will remain functional from the date of manufacture until it is used in patient care (See Expiration Date).

Significant Risk Device
An investigational device that:
- is intended as an implant
- is represented to be for use in supporting or sustaining human life
- is for a use of substantial importance in diagnosing, curing, mitigating, or treating disease or otherwise preventing impairment of human health and presents a potential for serious risk to the subject's health, safety or welfare

SMDA
Safe Medical Devices Act of 1990

SME
Significant Medical Event

SNDA
Supplemental New Drug Application

SoCRA
Society of Clinical Research Associates

SOP
Standard Operating Procedure

Source Documents
Original documents and records containing information captured in a clinical study. Case Report Forms are monitored against source documents. Includes office charts, laboratory results, x-rays, etc.

SPA
Special Protocol Assessment

SPL
Structured Product Label. Content of package insert in XML format.

SR
Significant Risk (device)

Sponsor
Company, person, organization or institution taking responsibility for initiating, managing or financing a clinical trial.

Standard Review (S)
FDA review category for drugs with therapeutic qualities similar to those already approved for marketing.

Subject
Clinical trial participant; may be a healthy volunteer or a patient.

Subpart E
21 CFR 312. Accelerated review for life-threatening and severely debilitating illness.

Subpart H
21 CFR 314.500. Approval based upon a surrogate endpoint or a product approved with restrictions and/or requirements for Phase IV trials.

Substantial Equivalence
Comparison of a new device to a legally marketed predicate device; substantial equivalence establishes a device is as safe and as effective as another 510(k) cleared device.

Suitability Petition
A request to FDA to submit an ANDA for a product that varies from a Reference Listed Drug in indication, strength, dosage form, route of administration, etc.

SUPAC
Scale Up and Post Approval Changes

Supplement (sNDA)
NDA submission for changes to an approved NDA, including SUPAC.

Supplement (sPMA)
PMA submission for changes to an approved PMA that affect the device's safety or effectiveness.

Surrogate Endpoint
A laboratory or physical sign that is used in trials as a substitute for a clinically meaningful endpoint that is a direct measure of how a patient feels, functions or survives and is expected to predict the effect of the therapy.

T

Target Product Profile (TPP)
A format for a summary of a drug development program described in terms of labeling concepts. A TPP can be prepared by a sponsor and then shared with the appropriate FDA review staff to facilitate communication regarding a particular drug development program.

Team Biologics
A group of specialized investigators who conduct routine and CGMP follow-up inspections of manufacturers of biological products regulated by CBER. Partnership program between ORA and CBER.

Third Party Review
Under *FDAMA*, FDA has accredited third parties that are authorized to conduct the primary review of 510(k)'s for eligible devices.

THOMAS
Public federal legislation database (Library of Congress)

TK
Toxicokinetics

TOPRA
The Organisation for Professionals in Regulatory Affairs

TPP
Target Product Profile

Treatment IND (tIND)
Allows limited use of an unapproved drug for patients with a serious or life-threatening disease.

Truthful Prescription Drug Advertising and Promotion (Bad Ad Program)
Educational outreach program to help healthcare providers recognize misleading prescription drug promotion and provide them with an easy way to report this activity to the agency.

U
UADE
Unexpected Adverse Device Effect. Any serious adverse effect on health or safety or any life-threatening problem or death caused by, or associated with, a device, if that effect, problem or death was not previously identified in nature, severity or degree of incidence in the investigational plan or application, or any other unanticipated serious problem associated with a device that relates to the rights, safety or welfare of subjects.

UDI
Unique Device Identification. Would require the label of a device to bear a unique identifier, unless an alternative location is specified by FDA or unless an exception is made for a particular device or group of devices.

Unexpected AE
An AE whose nature or severity is not described in the Investigator's Brochure (for an unapproved product) or in the package insert (for an approved product).

USAN
US Adopted Name

USANC
US Adopted Names Council

USC
US Code

USCA
US Code Annotated

USDA
US Department of Agriculture

User Fees
Fees authorized by Congress to fund various FDA activities. The fee schedule for different application types is published annually in the *Federal Register*. Initially established by the *Prescription Drug User Fee Act* and later extended to medical devices, generic drugs and animal drugs.

USP
United States Pharmacopeia

V
VA
Department of Veterans Affairs

VAERS
Vaccine Adverse Event Reporting System

VAI
Voluntary Action Indicated. Moderately serious FDA postinspection classification.

VCRP
Voluntary Cosmetic Registration Program. An FDA postmarket reporting system for use by manufacturers, packers and distributors of cosmetic products that are in commercial distribution in the US.

W
Warning Letter (WL)
Serious enforcement letter issued by FDA notifying a regulated entity of violative activity; requires immediate action within 15 days.

Warning Letter Database
Contains Warning Letters issued from November 1996
to the present. Searchable by company, subject, issuing
office or date.

Well-Characterized Biologic
A biological product whose identity, purity, impurities,
potency and quantity can be determined and controlled.

WHO
World Health Organization

Index